Graduate Texts in Mathematics 95

"Order out of chaos"
(Courtesy of Professor A. T. Fomenko of the Moscow State University)

A. N. Shiryayev

Probability

Translated by R. P. Boas

With 54 Illustrations

Springer-Verlag
New York Berlin Heidelberg Tokyo

A. N. Shiryayev
Steklov Mathematical Institute
Vavilova 42
GSP-1   117333 Moscow
U.S.S.R.

R. P. Boas (*Translator*)
Department of Mathematics
Northwestern University
Evanston, IL 60201
U.S.A.

AMS Classification: 60-01

Library of Congress Cataloging in Publication Data
Shiriāev, Al'bert Nikolaevich.
  Probability.
  (Graduate texts in mathematics; 95)
  Translation of: Veroiātnost'.
  Bibliography: p.
  Includes index.
  1. Probabilities. I. Title. II. Series.
QA273.S54413   1984   519   83-14813

Original Russian edition: *Veroiātnost'*. Moscow: Nauka, 1979.

This book is part of the Springer Series in Soviet Mathematics.

Typeset by Composition House Ltd., Salisbury, England.
Printed and bound by R. R. Donnelly & Sons, Harrisonburg, Virginia.
Printed in the United States of America.

9 8 7 6 5 4 3 2 1

ISBN 0-387-90898-6 Springer-Verlag New York Berlin Heidelberg Tokyo
ISBN 3-540-90898-6 Springer-Verlag Berlin Heidelberg New York Tokyo

Preface

This textbook is based on a three-semester course of lectures given by the author in recent years in the Mechanics–Mathematics Faculty of Moscow State University and issued, in part, in mimeographed form under the title *Probability, Statistics, Stochastic Processes, I, II* by the Moscow State University Press.

We follow tradition by devoting the first part of the course (roughly one semester) to the elementary theory of probability (Chapter I). This begins with the construction of probabilistic models with finitely many outcomes and introduces such fundamental probabilistic concepts as sample spaces, events, probability, independence, random variables, expectation, correlation, conditional probabilities, and so on.

Many probabilistic and statistical regularities are effectively illustrated even by the simplest random walk generated by Bernoulli trials. In this connection we study both classical results (law of large numbers, local and integral De Moivre and Laplace theorems) and more modern results (for example, the arc sine law).

The first chapter concludes with a discussion of dependent random variables generated by martingales and by Markov chains.

Chapters II–IV form an expanded version of the second part of the course (second semester). Here we present (Chapter II) Kolmogorov's generally accepted axiomatization of probability theory and the mathematical methods that constitute the tools of modern probability theory (σ-algebras, measures and their representations, the Lebesgue integral, random variables and random elements, characteristic functions, conditional expectation with respect to a σ-algebra, Gaussian systems, and so on). Note that two measure-theoretical results—Carathéodory's theorem on the extension of measures and the Radon–Nikodým theorem—are quoted without proof.

The third chapter is devoted to problems about weak convergence of probability distributions and the method of characteristic functions for proving limit theorems. We introduce the concepts of relative compactness and tightness of families of probability distributions, and prove (for the real line) Prohorov's theorem on the equivalence of these concepts.

The same part of the course discusses properties "with probability 1" for sequences and sums of independent random variables (Chapter IV). We give proofs of the "zero or one laws" of Kolmogorov and of Hewitt and Savage, tests for the convergence of series, and conditions for the strong law of large numbers. The law of the iterated logarithm is stated for arbitrary sequences of independent identically distributed random variables with finite second moments, and proved under the assumption that the variables have Gaussian distributions.

Finally, the third part of the book (Chapters V–VIII) is devoted to random processes with discrete parameters (random sequences). Chapters V and VI are devoted to the theory of stationary random sequences, where "stationary" is interpreted either in the strict or the wide sense. The theory of random sequences that are stationary in the strict sense is based on the ideas of ergodic theory: measure preserving transformations, ergodicity, mixing, etc. We reproduce a simple proof (by A. Garsia) of the maximal ergodic theorem; this also lets us give a simple proof of the Birkhoff–Khinchin ergodic theorem.

The discussion of sequences of random variables that are stationary in the wide sense begins with a proof of the spectral representation of the covariance fuction. Then we introduce orthogonal stochastic measures, and integrals with respect to these, and establish the spectral representation of the sequences themselves. We also discuss a number of statistical problems: estimating the covariance function and the spectral density, extrapolation, interpolation and filtering. The chapter includes material on the Kalman–Bucy filter and its generalizations.

The seventh chapter discusses the basic results of the theory of martingales and related ideas. This material has only rarely been included in traditional courses in probability theory. In the last chapter, which is devoted to Markov chains, the greatest attention is given to problems on the asymptotic behavior of Markov chains with countably many states.

Each section ends with problems of various kinds: some of them ask for proofs of statements made but not proved in the text, some consist of propositions that will be used later, some are intended to give additional information about the circle of ideas that is under discussion, and finally, some are simple exercises.

In designing the course and preparing this text, the author has used a variety of sources on probability theory. The Historical and Bibliographical Notes indicate both the historical sources of the results, and supplementary references for the material under consideration.

The numbering system and form of references is the following. Each section has its own enumeration of theorems, lemmas and formulas (with no indication of chapter or section). For a reference to a result from a different section of the same chapter, we use double numbering, with the first number indicating the number of the section (thus (2.10) means formula (10) of §2). For references to a different chapter we use triple numbering (thus formula (II.4.3) means formula (3) of §4 of Chapter II). Works listed in the References at the end of the book have the form [L n], where L is a letter and n is a numeral.

The author takes this opportunity to thank his teacher A. N. Kolmogorov, and B. V. Gnedenko and Yu. V. Prohorov, from whom he learned probability theory and under whose direction he had the opportunity of using it. For • discussions and advice, the author also thanks his colleagues in the Departments of Probability Theory and Mathematical Statistics at the Moscow State University, and his colleagues in the Section on probability theory of the Steklov Mathematical Institute of the Academy of Sciences of the U.S.S.R.

Moscow   A. N. SHIRYAYEV
Steklov Mathematical Institute

Translator's acknowledgement. I am grateful both to the author and to my colleague C. T. Ionescu Tulcea for advice about terminology.

R. P. B.

Contents

Introduction

The subject matter of probability theory is the mathematical analysis of random events, i.e. of those empirical phenomena which—under certain circumstances—can be described by saying that:

They do not have *deterministic regularity* (observations of them do not yield the same outcome) whereas at the same time;

They possess some *statistical regularity* (indicated by the statistical stability of their frequency).

We illustrate with the classical example of a "fair" toss of an "unbiased" coin. It is clearly impossible to predict with certainty the outcome of each toss. The results of successive experiments are very irregular (now "head," now "tail") and we seem to have no possibility of discovering any regularity in such experiments. However, if we carry out a large number of "independent" experiments with an "unbiased" coin we can observe a very definite statistical regularity, namely that "head" appears with a frequency that is "close" to $\frac{1}{2}$.

Statistical stability of a frequency is very likely to suggest a hypothesis about a possible quantitative estimate of the "randomness" of some event A connected with the results of the experiments. With this starting point, probability theory postulates that corresponding to an event A there is a definite number $P(A)$, called the probability of the event, whose intrinsic property is that as the number of "independent" trials (experiments) increases the frequency of event A is approximated by $P(A)$.

Applied to our example, this means that it is natural to assign the probability $\frac{1}{2}$ to the event A that consists of obtaining "head" in a toss of an "unbiased" coin.

There is no difficulty in multiplying examples in which it is very easy to obtain numerical values intuitively for the probabilities of one or another event. However, these examples are all of a similar nature and involve (so far) undefined concepts such as "fair" toss, "unbiased" coin, "independence," etc.

Having been invented to investigate the quantitative aspects of "randomness," probability theory, like every exact science, became such a science only at the point when the concept of a probabilistic model had been clearly formulated and axiomatized. In this connection it is natural for us to discuss, although only briefly, the fundamental steps in the development of probability theory.

Probability theory, as a science, originated in the middle of the seventeenth century with Pascal (1623–1662), Fermat (1601–1655) and Huygens (1629–1695). Although special calculations of probabilities in games of chance had been made earlier, in the fifteenth and sixteenth centuries, by Italian mathematicians (Cardano, Pacioli, Tartaglia, etc.), the first general methods for solving such problems were apparently given in the famous correspondence between Pascal and Fermat, begun in 1654, and in the first book on probability theory, *De Ratiociniis in Aleae Ludo* (*On Calculations in Games of Chance*), published by Huygens in 1657. It was at this time that the fundamental concept of "mathematical expectation" was developed and theorems on the addition and multiplication of probabilities were established.

The real history of probability theory begins with the work of James Bernoulli (1654–1705), *Ars Conjectandi* (*The Art of Guessing*) published in 1713, in which he proved (quite rigorously) the first limit theorem of probability theory, the law of large numbers; and of De Moivre (1667–1754), *Miscellanea Analytica Supplementum* (a rough translation might be *The Analytic Method* or *Analytic Miscellany*, 1730), in which the central limit theorem was stated and proved for the first time (for symmetric Bernoulli trials).

Bernoulli was probably the first to realize the importance of considering infinite sequences of random trials and to make a clear distinction between the probability of an event and the frequency of its realization. De Moivre deserves the credit for defining such concepts as independence, mathematical expectation, and conditional probability.

In 1812 there appeared Laplace's (1749–1827) great treatise *Théorie Analytique des Probabilitiés* (*Analytic Theory of Probability*) in which he presented his own results in probability theory as well as those of his predecessors. In particular, he generalized De Moivre's theorem to the general (unsymmetric) case of Bernoulli trials, and at the same time presented De Moivre's results in a more complete form.

Laplace's most important contribution was the application of probabilistic methods to errors of observation. He formulated the idea of considering errors of observation as the cumulative results of adding a large number of independent elementary errors. From this it followed that under rather general conditions the distribution of errors of observation must be at least approximately normal.

The work of Poisson (1781–1840) and Gauss (1777–1855) belongs to the same epoch in the development of probability theory, when the center of the stage was held by limit theorems.

In contemporary probability theory we think of Poisson in connection with the distribution and the process that bear his name. Gauss is credited with originating the theory of errors and, in particular, with creating the fundamental method of least squares.

The next important period in the development of probability theory is connected with the names of P. L. Chebyshev (1821–1894), A. A. Markov (1856–1922), and A. M. Lyapunov (1857–1918), who developed effective methods for proving limit theorems for sums of independent but arbitrarily distributed random variables.

The number of Chebyshev's publications in probability theory is not large — four in all — but it would be hard to overestimate their role in probability theory and in the development of the classical Russian school of that subject.

> "On the methodological side, the revolution brought about by Chebyshev was not only his insistence for the first time on complete rigor in the proofs of limit theorems, . . . but also, and principally, that Chebyshev always tried to obtain precise estimates for the deviations from the limiting regularities that are available for large but finite numbers of trials, in the form of inequalities that are valid unconditionally for any number of trials."

> (A. N. KOLMOGOROV [30])

Before Chebyshev the main interest in probability theory had been in the calculation of the probabilities of random events. He, however, was the first to realize clearly and exploit the full strength of the concepts of random variables and their mathematical expectations.

The leading exponent of Chebyshev's ideas was his devoted student Markov, to whom there belongs the indisputable credit of presenting his teacher's results with complete clarity. Among Markov's own significant contributions to probability theory were his pioneering investigations of limit theorems for sums of independent random variables and the creation of a new branch of probability theory, the theory of dependent random variables that form what we now call a Markov chain.

> ". . . Markov's classical course in the calculus of probability and his original papers, which are models of precision and clarity, contributed to the greatest extent to the transformation of probability theory into one of the most significant branches of mathematics and to a wide extension of the ideas and methods of Chebyshev."

> (S. N. BERNSTEIN [3])

To prove the central limit theorem of probability theory (the theorem on convergence to the normal distribution), Chebyshev and Markov used what is known as the method of moments. With more general hypotheses and a simpler method, the method of characteristic functions, the theorem was obtained by Lyapunov. The subsequent development of the theory has shown that the method of characteristic functions is a powerful analytic tool for establishing the most diverse limit theorems.

The modern period in the development of probability theory begins with its axiomatization. The first work in this direction was done by S. N. Bernstein (1880–1968), R. von Mises (1883–1953), and E. Borel (1871–1956). A. N. Kolmogorov's book *Foundations of the Theory of Probability* appeared in 1933. Here he presented the axiomatic theory that has become generally accepted and is not only applicable to all the classical branches of probability theory, but also provides a firm foundation for the development of new branches that have arisen from questions in the sciences and involve infinite–dimensional distributions.

The treatment in the present book is based on Kolmogorov's axiomatic approach. However, to prevent formalities and logical subtleties from obscuring the intuitive ideas, our exposition begins with the elementary theory of probability, whose elementariness is merely that in the corresponding probabilistic models we consider only experiments with finitely many outcomes. Thereafter we present the foundations of probability theory in their most general form.

The 1920s and '30s saw a rapid development of one of the new branches of probability theory, the theory of stochastic processes, which studies families of random variables that evolve with time. We have seen the creation of theories of Markov processes, stationary processes, martingales, and limit theorems for stochastic processes. Information theory is a recent addition.

The present book is principally concerned with stochastic processes with discrete parameters: random sequences. However, the material presented in the second chapter provides a solid foundation (particularly of a logical nature) for the study of the general theory of stochastic processes.

It was also in the 1920s and '30s that mathematical statistics became a separate mathematical discipline. In a certain sense mathematical statistics deals with inverses of the problems of probability: If the basic aim of probability theory is to calculate the probabilities of complicated events under a given probabilistic model, mathematical statistics sets itself the inverse problem: to clarify the structure of probabilistic–statistical models by means of observations of various complicated events.

Some of the problems and methods of mathematical statistics are also discussed in this book. However, all that is presented in detail here is probability theory and the theory of stochastic processes with discrete parameters.

CHAPTER I
Elementary Probability Theory

§1. Probabilistic Model of an Experiment with a Finite Number of Outcomes

1. Let us consider an experiment of which all possible results are included in a finite number of outcomes $\omega_1, \ldots, \omega_N$. We do not need to know the nature of these outcomes, only that there are a finite number N of them.

We call $\omega_1, \ldots, \omega_N$ *elementary events*, or *sample points*, and the finite set

$$\Omega = \{\omega_1, \ldots, \omega_N\},$$

the *space of elementary events* or the *sample space*.

The choice of the space of elementary events is the *first step* in formulating a probabilistic model for an experiment. Let us consider some examples of sample spaces.

EXAMPLE 1. For a single toss of a coin the sample space Ω consists of two points:

$$\Omega = \{H, T\},$$

where H = "head" and T = "tail". (We exclude possibilities like "the coin stands on edge," "the coin disappears," etc.)

EXAMPLE 2. For n tosses of a coin the sample space is

$$\Omega = \{\omega : \omega = (a_1, \ldots, a_n), a_i = H \text{ or } T\}$$

and the general number $N(\Omega)$ of outcomes is 2^n.

EXAMPLE 3. First toss a coin. If it falls "head" then toss a die (with six faces numbered 1, 2, 3, 4, 5, 6); if it falls "tail", toss the coin again. The sample space for this experiment is

$$\Omega = \{H1, H2, H3, H4, H5, H6, TH, TT\}.$$

We now consider some more complicated examples involving the selection of n balls from an urn containing M distinguishable balls.

2. EXAMPLE 4 (Sampling with replacement). This is an experiment in which after each step the selected ball is returned again. In this case each sample of n balls can be presented in the form $(a_1, \ldots, a_n)$, where a_i is the label of the ball selected at the ith step. It is clear that in sampling with replacement each a_i can have any of the M values 1, 2, ..., M. The description of the sample space depends in an essential way on whether we consider samples like, for example, (4, 1, 2, 1) and (1, 4, 2, 1) as different or the same. It is customary to distinguish two cases: *ordered* samples and *unordered* samples. In the first case samples containing the same elements, but arranged differently, are considered to be different. In the second case the order of the elements is disregarded and the two samples are considered to be the same. To emphasize which kind of sample we are considering, we use the notation $(a_1, \ldots, a_n)$ for ordered samples and $[a_1, \ldots, a_n]$ for unordered samples.

Thus for ordered samples the sample space has the form

$$\Omega = \{\omega: \omega = (a_1, \ldots, a_n), a_i = 1, \ldots, M\}$$

and the number of (different) outcomes is

$$N(\Omega) = M^n. \tag{1}$$

If, however, we consider unordered samples, then

$$\Omega = \{\omega: \omega = [a_1, \ldots, a_n], a_i = 1, \ldots, M\}.$$

Clearly the number $N(\Omega)$ of (different) unordered samples is smaller than the number of ordered samples. Let us show that in the present case

$$N(\Omega) = C^n_{M+n-1}, \tag{2}$$

where $C^l_k \equiv k!/[l!\,(k-l)!]$ is the number of combinations of l elements, taken k at a time.

We prove this by induction. Let $N(M, n)$ be the number of outcomes of interest. It is clear that when $k \leq M$ we have

$$N(k, 1) = k = C^1_k.$$

Now suppose that $N(k, n) = C_{k+n-1}^k$ for $k \leq M$; we show that this formula continues to hold when n is replaced by $n + 1$. For the unordered samples $[a_1, \ldots, a_{n+1}]$ that we are considering, we may suppose that the elements are arranged in nondecreasing order: $a_1 \leq a_2 \leq \cdots \leq a_n$. It is clear that the number of unordered samples with $a_1 = 1$ is $N(M, n)$, the number with $a_1 = 2$ is $N(M - 1, n)$, etc. Consequently

$$N(M, n + 1) = N(M, n) + N(M - 1, n) + \cdots + N(1, n)$$

$$= C_{M+n-1}^n + C_{M-1+n-1}^n + \cdots C_n^n$$

$$= (C_{M+n}^{n+1} - C_{M+n-1}^{n+1}) + (C_{M-1+n}^{n+1} - C_{M-1+n-1}^{n+1})$$

$$+ \cdots + (C_{n+1}^{n+1} - C_n^n) = C_{M+n}^{n+1};$$

here we have used the easily verified property

$$C_k^{l-1} + C_k^l = C_{k+1}^l$$

of the binomial coefficients.

EXAMPLE 5 (Sampling without replacement). Suppose that $n \leq M$ and that the selected balls are not returned. In this case we again consider two possibilities, namely ordered and unordered samples.

For ordered samples without replacement the sample space is

$$\Omega = \{\omega: \omega = (a_1, \ldots, a_n), a_k \neq a_l, k \neq l, a_i = 1, \ldots, M\},$$

and the number of elements of this set (called *permutations*) is $M(M - 1) \cdots (M - n + 1)$. We denote this by $(M)_n$ or A_M^n and call it "the number of permutations of M things, n at a time").

For unordered samples (called *combinations*) the sample space

$$\Omega = \{\omega: \omega = [a_1, \ldots, a_n], a_k \neq a_l, k \neq l, a_i = 1, \ldots, M\}$$

consists of

$$N(\Omega) = C_M^n \tag{3}$$

elements. In fact, from each unordered sample $[a_1, \ldots, a_n]$ consisting of distinct elements we can obtain $n!$ ordered samples. Consequently

$$N(\Omega) \cdot n! = (M)_n$$

and therefore

$$N(\Omega) = \frac{(M)_n}{n!} = C_M^n.$$

The results on the numbers of samples of n from an urn with M balls are presented in Table 1.

Table 1

M^n	C^n_{M+n-1}	With replacement
$(M)_n$	C^n_M	Without replacement
Ordered	Unordered	Type ╲ Sample

For the case $M = 3$ and $n = 2$, the corresponding sample spaces are displayed in Table 2.

EXAMPLE 6 (Distribution of objects in cells). We consider the structure of the sample space in the problem of placing n objects (balls, etc.) in M cells (boxes, etc.). For example, such problems arise in statistical physics in studying the distribution of n particles (which might be protons, electrons, ...) among M states (which might be energy levels).

Let the cells be numbered $1, 2, \ldots, M$, and suppose first that the objects are distinguishable (numbered $1, 2, \ldots, n$). Then a distribution of the n objects among the M cells is completely described by an ordered set $(a_1, \ldots, a_n)$, where a_i is the index of the cell containing object i. However, if the objects are indistinguishable their distribution among the M cells is completely determined by the unordered set $[a_1, \ldots, a_n]$, where a_i is the index of the cell into which an object is put at the ith step.

Comparing this situation with Examples 4 and 5, we have the following correspondences:

(ordered samples) $\leftrightarrow$ (distinguishable objects),

(unordered samples) $\leftrightarrow$ (indistinguishable objects),

Table 2

(1, 1) (1, 2) (1, 3) (2, 1) (2, 2) (2, 3) (3, 1) (3, 2) (3, 3)	[1, 1] [2, 2] [3, 3] [1, 2] [1, 3] [2, 3]	With replacement
(1, 2) (1, 3) (2, 1) (2, 3) (3, 1) (3, 2)	[1, 2] [1, 3] [2, 3]	Without replacement
Ordered	Unordered	Type ╲ Sample

by which we mean that to an instance of an ordered (unordered) sample of n balls from an urn containing M balls there corresponds (one and only one) instance of distributing n distinguishable (indistinguishable) objects among M cells.

In a similar sense we have the following correspondences:

$$(\text{sampling with replacement}) \leftrightarrow \left(\begin{array}{l}\text{a cell may receive any number}\\ \text{of objects}\end{array}\right),$$

$$(\text{sampling without replacement}) \leftrightarrow \left(\begin{array}{l}\text{a cell may receive at most}\\ \text{one object}\end{array}\right).$$

These correspondences generate others of the same kind:

$$\left(\begin{array}{l}\text{an unordered sample in}\\ \text{sampling without}\\ \text{replacement}\end{array}\right) \leftrightarrow \left(\begin{array}{l}\text{indistinguishable objects in the}\\ \text{problem of distribution among cells}\\ \text{when each cell may receive at}\\ \text{most one object}\end{array}\right)$$

etc.; so that we can use Examples 4 and 5 to describe the sample space for the problem of distributing distinguishable or indistinguishable objects among cells either with exclusion (a cell may receive at most one object) or without exclusion (a cell may receive any number of objects).

Table 3 displays the distributions of two objects among three cells. For distinguishable objects, we denote them by W (white) and B (black). For indistinguishable objects, the presence of an object in a cell is indicated by a +.

Table 3

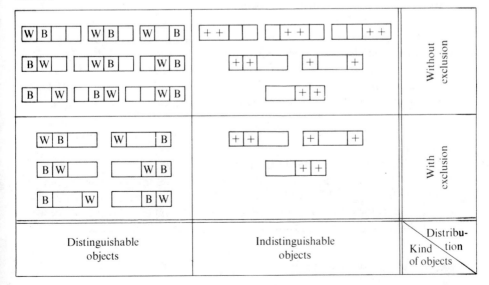

Table 4

$N(\Omega)$ in the problem of placing n objects in M cells			
Distribution ⟍ Kind of objects	Distinguishable objects	Indistinguishable objects	
Without exclusion	M^n (Maxwell–Boltzmann statistics)	C_{M+n-1}^n (Bose–Einstein statistics)	With replacement
With exclusion	$(M)_n$	C_M^n (Fermi–Dirac statistics)	Without replacement
	Ordered samples	Unordered samples	Type ⟍ Sample
	$N(\Omega)$ in the problem of choosing n balls from an urn containing M balls		

The duality that we have observed between the two problems gives us an obvious way of finding the number of outcomes in the problem of placing objects in cells. The results, which include the results in Table 1, are given in Table 4.

In statistical physics one says that distinguishable (or indistinguishable, respectively) particles that are not subject to the Pauli exclusion principle† obey Maxwell–Boltzmann statistics (or, respectively, Bose–Einstein statistics). If, however, the particles are indistinguishable and are subject to the exclusion principle, they obey Fermi–Dirac statistics (see Table 4). For example, electrons, protons and neutrons obey Fermi–Dirac statistics. Photons and pions obey Bose–Einstein statistics. Distinguishable particles that are subject to the exclusion principle do not occur in physics.

3. In addition to the concept of sample space we now need the fundamental concept of *event*.

Experimenters are ordinarily interested, not in what particular outcome occurs as the result of a trial, but in whether the outcome belongs to some subset of the set of all possible outcomes. We shall describe as *events* all subsets $A \subset \Omega$ for which, under the conditions of the experiment, it is possible to say either "the outcome $\omega \in A$" or "the outcome $\omega \notin A$."

---

† At most one particle in each cell. (Translator)

For example, let a coin be tossed three times. The sample space Ω consists of the eight points

$$\Omega = \{\text{HHH, HHT}, \ldots, \text{TTT}\}$$

and if we are able to observe (determine, measure, etc.) the results of all three tosses, we say that the set

$$A = \{\text{HHH, HHT, HTH, THH}\}$$

is the event consisting of the appearance of at least two heads. If, however, we can determine only the result of the first toss, this set A cannot be considered to be an event, since there is no way to give either a positive or negative answer to the question of whether a specific outcome ω belongs to A.

Starting from a given collection of sets that are events, we can form new events by means of statements containing the logical connectives "or," "and," and "not," which correspond in the language of set theory to the operations "union," "intersection," and "complement."

If A and B are sets, their *union*, denoted by $A \cup B$, is the set of points that belong either to A or to B:

$$A \cup B = \{\omega \in \Omega : \omega \in A \text{ or } \omega \in B\}.$$

In the language of probability theory, $A \cup B$ is the event consisting of the realization either of A or of B.

The *intersection* of A and B, denoted by $A \cap B$, or by AB, is the set of points that belong to both A and B:

$$A \cap B = \{\omega \in \Omega : \omega \in A \text{ and } \omega \in B\}.$$

The event $A \cap B$ consists of the simultaneous realization of both A and B.

For example, if $A = \{\text{HH, HT, TH}\}$ and $B = \{\text{TT, TH, HT}\}$ then

$$A \cup B = \{\text{HH, HT, TH, TT}\} \quad (= \Omega),$$

$$A \cap B = \{\text{TH, HT}\}.$$

If A is a subset of Ω, its *complement*, denoted by $\bar{A}$, is the set of points of Ω that do not belong to A.

If $B \backslash A$ denotes the *difference* of B and A (i.e. the set of points that belong to B but not to A) then $\bar{A} = \Omega \backslash A$. In the language of probability, $\bar{A}$ is the event consisting of the nonrealization of A. For example, if $A = \{\text{HH, HT, TH}\}$ then $\bar{A} = \{\text{TT}\}$, the event in which two successive tails occur.

The sets A and $\bar{A}$ have no points in common and consequently $A \cap \bar{A}$ is empty. We denote the empty set by $\varnothing$. In probability theory, $\varnothing$ is called an *impossible* event. The set Ω is naturally called the *certain* event.

When A and B are disjoint ($AB = \varnothing$), the union $A \cup B$ is called the *sum* of A and B and written $A + B$.

If we consider a collection $\mathscr{A}_0$ of sets $A \subseteq \Omega$ we may use the set-theoretic operators $\cup$, $\cap$ and $\backslash$ to form a new collection of sets from the elements of

$\mathscr{A}_0$; these sets are again events. If we adjoin the certain and impossible events Ω and $\varnothing$ we obtain a collection $\mathscr{A}$ of sets which is an *algebra*, i.e. a collection of subsets of Ω for which

(1) $\Omega \in \mathscr{A}$,
(2) if $A \in \mathscr{A}$, $B \in \mathscr{A}$, the sets $A \cup B$, $A \cap B$, $A \backslash B$ also belong to $\mathscr{A}$.

It follows from what we have said that it will be advisable to consider collections of events that form algebras. In the future we shall consider only such collections.

Here are some examples of algebras of events:

(a) $\{\Omega, \varnothing\}$, the collection consisting of Ω and the empty set (we call this the *trivial* algebra);
(b) $\{A, \bar{A}, \Omega, \varnothing\}$, the collection generated by A;
(c) $\mathscr{A} = \{A : A \subseteq \Omega\}$, the collection consisting of *all* the subsets of Ω (including the empty set $\varnothing$).

It is easy to check that all these algebras of events can be obtained from the following principle.

We say that a collection

$$\mathscr{D} = \{D_1, \ldots, D_n\}$$

of sets is a *decomposition* of Ω, and call the D_i the *atoms* of the decomposition, if the D_i are not empty, are pairwise disjoint, and their sum is Ω:

$$D_1 + \cdots + D_n = \Omega.$$

For example, if Ω consists of three points, $\Omega = \{1, 2, 3\}$, there are five different decompositions:

$$\mathscr{D}_1 = \{D_1\} \qquad \text{with} \quad D_1 = \{1, 2, 3\};$$
$$\mathscr{D}_2 = \{D_1, D_2\} \qquad \text{with} \quad D_1 = \{1, 2\}, D_2 = \{3\};$$
$$\mathscr{D}_3 = \{D_1, D_2\} \qquad \text{with} \quad D_1 = \{1, 3\}, D_2 = \{2\};$$
$$\mathscr{D}_4 = \{D_1, D_2\} \qquad \text{with} \quad D_1 = \{2, 3\}, D_2 = \{1\};$$
$$\mathscr{D}_5 = \{D_1, D_2, D_3\} \qquad \text{with} \quad D_1 = \{1\}, D_2 = \{2\}, D_3 = \{3\}.$$

(For the general number of decompositions of a finite set see Problem 2.)

If we consider all unions of the sets in $\mathscr{D}$, the resulting collection of sets, together with the empty set, forms an algebra, called the *algebra induced by* $\mathscr{D}$, and denoted by $\alpha(\mathscr{D})$. Thus the elements of $\alpha(\mathscr{D})$ consist of the empty set together with the sums of sets which are atoms of $\mathscr{D}$.

Thus if $\mathscr{D}$ is a decomposition, there is associated with it a specific algebra $\mathscr{B} = \alpha(\mathscr{D})$.

The converse is also true. Let $\mathscr{B}$ be an algebra of subsets of a finite space Ω. Then there is a unique decomposition $\mathscr{D}$ whose atoms are the elements of

$\mathscr{B}$, with $\mathscr{B} = \alpha(\mathscr{D})$. In fact, let $D \in \mathscr{B}$ and let D have the property that for every $B \in \mathscr{B}$ the set $D \cap B$ either coincides with D or is empty. Then this collection of sets D forms a decomposition $\mathscr{D}$ with the required property $\alpha(\mathscr{D}) = \mathscr{B}$. In Example (a), $\mathscr{D}$ is the trivial decomposition consisting of the single set $D_1 = \Omega$; in (b), $\mathscr{D} = \{A, \bar{A}\}$. The most fine-grained decomposition $\mathscr{D}$, which consists of the singletons $\{\omega_i\}$, $\omega_i \in \Omega$, induces the algebra in Example (c), i.e. the algebra of all subsets of Ω.

Let $\mathscr{D}_1$ and $\mathscr{D}_2$ be two decompositions. We say that $\mathscr{D}_2$ is finer than $\mathscr{D}_1$, and write $\mathscr{D}_1 \preccurlyeq \mathscr{D}_2$, if $\alpha(\mathscr{D}_1) \subseteq \alpha(\mathscr{D}_2)$.

Let us show that if Ω consists, as we assumed above, of a finite number of points $\omega_1, \ldots, \omega_N$, then the number $N(\mathscr{A})$ of sets in the collection $\mathscr{A}$ is equal to 2^N. In fact, every nonempty set $A \in \mathscr{A}$ can be represented as $A = \{\omega_{i_1}, \ldots, \omega_{i_k}\}$, where $\omega_{i_j} \in \Omega$, $1 \le k \le N$. With this set we associate the sequence of zeros and ones

$$(0, \ldots, 0, 1, 0, \ldots, 0, 1, \ldots),$$

where there are ones in the positions $i_1, \ldots, i_k$ and zeros elsewhere. Then for a given k the number of different sets A of the form $\{\omega_{i_1}, \ldots, \omega_{i_k}\}$ is the same as the number of ways in which k ones (k indistinguishable objects) can be placed in N positions (N cells). According to Table 4 (see the lower right-hand square) we see that this number is C_N^k. Hence (counting the empty set) we find that

$$N(\mathscr{A}) = 1 + C_N^1 + \cdots + C_N^N = (1 + 1)^N = 2^N.$$

4. We have now taken the first two steps in defining a probabilistic model of an experiment with a finite number of outcomes: we have selected a sample space and a collection $\mathscr{A}$ of subsets, which form an algebra and are called events. We now take the next step, to assign to each sample point (outcome) $\omega_i \in \Omega_i$, $i = 1, \ldots, N$, a *weight*. This is denoted by $p(\omega_i)$ and called the *probability* of the outcome ω_i; we assume that it has the following properties:

(a) $0 \le p(\omega_i) \le 1$ (nonnegativity),
(b) $p(\omega_1) + \cdots + p(\omega_N) = 1$ (normalization).

Starting from the given probabilities $p(\omega_i)$ of the outcomes ω_i, we define the probability $\mathsf{P}(A)$ of any event $A \in \mathscr{A}$ by

$$\mathsf{P}(A) = \sum_{\{i:\, \omega_i \in A\}} p(\omega_i). \tag{4}$$

Finally, we say that a triple

$$(\Omega, \mathscr{A}, \mathsf{P}),$$

where $\Omega = \{\omega_1, \ldots, \omega_N\}$, $\mathscr{A}$ is an algebra of subsets of Ω and

$$\mathsf{P} = \{\mathsf{P}(A); A \in \mathscr{A}\}$$

defines (or assigns) a *probabilistic model*, or a *probability space*, of experiments with a (finite) space Ω of outcomes and algebra $\mathscr{A}$ of events.

The following properties of probability follow from (4):

$$P(\varnothing) = 0, \tag{5}$$

$$P(\Omega) = 1, \tag{6}$$

$$P(A \cup B) = P(A) + P(B) - P(A \cap B). \tag{7}$$

In particular, if $A \cap B = \varnothing$, then

$$P(A + B) = P(A) + P(B) \tag{8}$$

and

$$P(\bar{A}) = 1 - P(A). \tag{9}$$

5. In constructing a probabilistic model for a specific situation, the construction of the sample space Ω and the algebra $\mathscr{A}$ of events are ordinarily not difficult. In elementary probability theory one usually takes the algebra $\mathscr{A}$ to be the algebra of *all* subsets of Ω. Any difficulty that may arise is in assigning probabilities to the sample points. In principle, the solution to this problem lies outside the domain of probability theory, and we shall not consider it in detail. We consider that our fundamental problem is not the question of how to assign probabilities, but how to calculate the probabilities of complicated events (elements of $\mathscr{A}$) from the probabilities of the sample points.

It is clear from a mathematical point of view that for finite sample spaces we can obtain all conceivable (finite) probability spaces by assigning nonnegative numbers $p_1, \ldots, p_N$, satisfying the condition $p_1 + \cdots + p_N = 1$, to the outcomes $\omega_1, \ldots, \omega_N$.

The validity of the assignments of the numbers $p_1, \ldots, p_N$ can, in specific cases, be checked to a certain extent by using the law of large numbers (which will be discussed later on). It states that in a long series of "independent" experiments, carried out under identical conditions, the frequencies with which the elementary events appear are "close" to their probabilities.

In connection with the difficulty of assigning probabilities to outcomes, we note that there are many actual situations in which for reasons of symmetry it seems reasonable to consider all conceivable outcomes as equally probable. In such cases, if the sample space consists of points $\omega_1, \ldots, \omega_N$, with $N < \infty$, we put

$$p(\omega_1) = \cdots = p(\omega_N) = 1/N,$$

and consequently

$$P(A) = N(A)/N \tag{10}$$

for every event $A \in \mathscr{A}$, where $N(A)$ is the number of sample points in A. This is called the classical method of assigning probabilities. It is clear that in this case the calculation of $P(A)$ reduces to calculating the number of outcomes belonging to A. This is usually done by combinatorial methods, so that combinatorics, applied to finite sets, plays a significant role in the calculus of probabilities.

EXAMPLE 7 (Coincidence problem). Let an urn contain M balls numbered $1, 2, \ldots, M$. We draw an ordered sample of size n with replacement. It is clear that then

$$\Omega = \{\omega : \omega = (a_1, \ldots, a_n), a_i = 1, \ldots, M\}$$

and $N(\Omega) = M^n$. Using the classical assignment of probabilities, we consider the M^n outcomes equally probable and ask for the probability of the event

$$A = \{\omega : \omega = (a_1, \ldots, a_n), a_i \neq a_j, i \neq j\},$$

i.e., the event in which there is no repetition. Clearly $N(A) = M(M - 1) \cdots (M - n + 1)$, and therefore

$$P(A) = \frac{(M)_n}{M^n} = \left(1 - \frac{1}{M}\right)\left(1 - \frac{2}{M}\right) \cdots \left(1 - \frac{n-1}{M}\right). \qquad (11)$$

This problem has the following striking interpretation. Suppose that there are n students in a class. Let us suppose that each student's birthday is on one of 365 days and that all days are equally probable. The question is, what is the probability P_n that there are at least two students in the class whose birthdays coincide? If we interpret selection of birthdays as selection of balls from an urn containing 365 balls, then by (11)

$$P_n = 1 - \frac{(365)_n}{365^n}.$$

The following table lists the values of P_n for some values of n:

n	4	16	22	23	40	64
P_n	0.016	0.284	0.476	0.507	0.891	0.997

It is interesting to note that (unexpectedly!) the size of class in which there is probability $\frac{1}{2}$ of finding at least two students with the same birthday is not very large: only 23.

EXAMPLE 8 (Prizes in a lottery). Consider a lottery that is run in the following way. There are M tickets numbered $1, 2, \ldots, M$, of which n, numbered $1, \ldots, n$, win prizes ($M \geq 2n$). You buy n tickets, and ask for the probability (P, say) of winning at least one prize.

Since the order in which the tickets are drawn plays no role in the presence or absence of winners in your purchase, we may suppose that the sample space has the form

$$\Omega = \{\omega : \omega = [a_1, \ldots, a_n], a_k \neq a_l, k \neq l, a_i = 1, \ldots, M\}.$$

By Table 1, $N(\Omega) = C_M^n$. Now let

$$A_0 = \{\omega : \omega = [a_1, \ldots, a_n], a_k \neq a_l, k \neq l, a_i = n + 1, \ldots, M\}$$

be the event that there is no winner in the set of tickets you bought. Again by Table 1, $N(A_0) = C_{M-n}^n$. Therefore

$$P(A_0) = \frac{C_{M-n}^n}{C_M^n} = \frac{(M-n)_n}{(M)_n}$$

$$= \left(1 - \frac{n}{M}\right)\left(1 - \frac{n}{M-1}\right) \cdots \left(1 - \frac{n}{M-n+1}\right)$$

and consequently

$$P = 1 - P(A_0) = 1 - \left(1 - \frac{n}{M}\right)\left(1 - \frac{n}{M-1}\right) \cdots \left(1 - \frac{n}{M-n+1}\right).$$

If $M = n^2$ and $n \to \infty$, then $P(A_0) \to e^{-1}$ and

$$P \to 1 - e^{-1} \approx 0.632.$$

The convergence is quite fast: for $n = 10$ the probability is already $P = 0.670$.

6. Problems

1. Establish the following properties of the operators $\cap$ and $\cup$:

$$A \cup B = B \cup A, \quad AB = BA \quad \text{(commutativity)},$$

$$A \cup (B \cup C) = (A \cup B) \cup C, \quad A(BC) = (AB)C \quad \text{(associativity)},$$

$$A(B \cup C) = AB \cup AC, \quad A \cup (BC) = (A \cup B)(A \cup C) \quad \text{(distributivity)},$$

$$A \cup A = A, \quad AA = A \quad \text{(idempotency)}.$$

Show also that

$$\overline{A \cup B} = \bar{A} \cap \bar{B}, \quad \overline{AB} = \bar{A} \cup \bar{B}.$$

2. Let Ω contain N elements. Show that the number $d(N)$ of different decompositions of Ω is given by the formula

$$d(N) = e^{-1} \sum_{k=0}^{\infty} \frac{k^N}{k!}. \tag{12}$$

(Hint: Show that

$$d(N) = \sum_{k=0}^{N-1} C_{N-1}^k d(k), \quad \text{where} \quad d(0) = 1,$$

and then verify that the series in (12) satisfies the same recurrence relation.)

3. For any finite collection of sets $A_1, \ldots, A_n$,

$$P(A_1 \cup \cdots \cup A_n) \leq P(A_1) + \cdots + P(A_n).$$

4. Let A and B be events. Show that $A\bar{B} \cup B\bar{A}$ is the event in which exactly one of A and B occurs. Moreover,

$$P(A\bar{B} \cup B\bar{A}) = P(A) + P(B) - 2P(AB).$$

5. Let $A_1, \ldots, A_n$ be events, and define $S_0, S_1, \ldots, S_n$ as follows: $S_0 = 1$,

$$S_r = \sum_{J_r} P(A_{k_1} \cap \cdots \cap A_{k_r}), \qquad 1 \leq r \leq n,$$

where the sum is over the unordered subsets $J_r = [k_1, \ldots, k_r]$ of $\{1, \ldots, n\}$.

Let B_m be the event in which each of the events $A_1, \ldots, A_n$ occurs exactly m times. Show that

$$P(B_m) = \sum_{r=m}^{n} (-1)^{r-m} C_r^m S_r.$$

In particular, for $m = 0$

$$P(B_0) = 1 - S_1 + S_2 - \cdots \pm S_n.$$

Show also that the probability that at least m of the events $A_1, \ldots, A_n$ occur simultaneously is

$$P(B_1) + \cdots + P(B_n) = \sum_{r=m}^{n} (-1)^{r-m} C_{r-1}^{m-1} S_r.$$

In particular, the probability that at least one of the events $A_1, \ldots, A_n$ occurs is

$$P(B_1) + \cdots + P(B_n) = S_1 - S_2 + \cdots \pm S_n.$$

§2. Some Classical Models and Distributions

1. Binomial distribution. Let a coin be tossed n times and record the results as an ordered set $(a_1, \ldots, a_n)$, where $a_i = 1$ for a head ("success") and $a_i = 0$ for a tail ("failure"). The sample space is

$$\Omega = \{\omega : \omega = (a_1, \ldots, a_n), a_i = 0, 1\}.$$

To each sample point $\omega = (a_1, \ldots, a_n)$ we assign the probability

$$p(\omega) = p^{\Sigma a_i} q^{n - \Sigma a_i},$$

where the nonnegative numbers p and q satisfy $p + q = 1$. In the first place, we verify that this assignment of the weights $p(\omega)$ is consistent. It is enough to show that $\sum_{\omega \in \Omega} p(\omega) = 1$.

We consider all outcomes $\omega = (a_1, \ldots, a_n)$ for which $\sum_i a_i = k$, where $k = 0, 1, \ldots, n$. According to Table 4 (distribution of k indistinguishable ones in n places) the number of these outcomes is C_n^k. Therefore

$$\sum_{\omega \in \Omega} p(\omega) = \sum_{k=0}^{n} C_n^k p^k q^{n-k} = (p + q)^n = 1.$$

Thus the space Ω together with the collection $\mathscr{A}$ of all its subsets and the probabilities $\mathsf{P}(A) = \sum_{\omega \in A} p(\omega)$, $A \in \mathscr{A}$, defines a probabilistic model. It is natural to call this the probabilistic model for n tosses of a coin.

In the case $n = 1$, when the sample space contains just the two points $\omega = 1$ ("success") and $\omega = 0$ ("failure"), it is natural to call $p(1) = p$ the probability of success. We shall see later that this model for n tosses of a coin can be thought of as the result of n "independent" experiments with probability p of success at each trial.

Let us consider the events

$$A_k = \{\omega: \omega = (a_1, \ldots, a_n), a_1 + \cdots + a_n = k\}, \qquad k = 0, 1, \ldots, n,$$

consisting of exactly k successes. It follows from what we said above that

$$\mathsf{P}(A_k) = C_n^k p^k q^{n-k}, \tag{1}$$

and $\sum_{k=0}^{n} \mathsf{P}(A_k) = 1$.

The set of probabilities $(\mathsf{P}(A_0), \ldots, \mathsf{P}(A_n))$ is called the *binomial distribution* (the number of successes in a sample of size n). This distribution plays an extremely important role in probability theory since it arises in the most diverse probabilistic models. We write $P_n(k) = \mathsf{P}(A_k)$, $k = 0, 1, \ldots, n$. Figure 1 shows the binomial distribution in the case $p = \frac{1}{2}$ (symmetric coin) for $n = 5, 10, 20$.

We now present a different model (in essence, equivalent to the preceding one) which describes the random walk of a "particle."

Let the particle start at the origin, and after unit time let it take a unit step upward or downward (Figure 2).

Consequently after n steps the particle can have moved at most n units up or n units down. It is clear that each path ω of the particle is completely specified by a set $(a_1, \ldots, a_n)$, where $a_i = +1$ if the particle moves up at the ith step, and $a_i = -1$ if it moves down. Let us assign to each path ω the weight $p(\omega) = p^{\nu(\omega)} q^{n-\nu(\omega)}$, where $\nu(\omega)$ is the number of $+1$'s in the sequence $\omega = (a_1, \ldots, a_n)$, i.e. $\nu(\omega) = [(a_1 + \cdots + a_n) + n]/2$, and the nonnegative numbers p and q satisfy $p + q = 1$.

Since $\sum_{\omega \in \Omega} p(\omega) = 1$, the set of probabilities $p(\omega)$ together with the space Ω of paths $\omega = (a_1, \ldots, a_n)$ and its subsets define an acceptable probabilistic model of the motion of the particle for n steps.

Let us ask the following question: What is the probability of the event A_k that after n steps the particle is at a point with ordinate k? This condition is satisfied by those paths ω for which $\nu(\omega) - (n - \nu(\omega)) = k$, i.e.

$$\nu(\omega) = \frac{n + k}{2}.$$

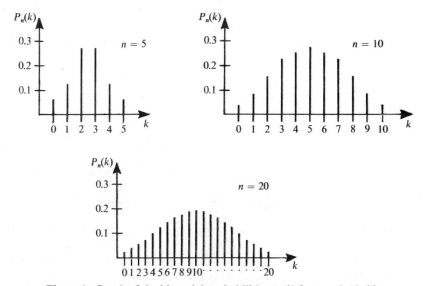

Figure 1. Graph of the binomial probabilities $P_n(k)$ for $n = 5, 10, 20$.

The number of such paths (see Table 4) is $C_n^{[n+k]/2}$, and therefore

$$P(A_k) = C_n^{[n+k]/2} p^{[n+k]/2} q^{[n-k]/2}.$$

Consequently the binomial distribution $(P(A_{-n}), \ldots, P(A_0), \ldots, P(A_n))$ can be said to describe the probability distribution for the position of the particle after n steps.

Note that in the symmetric case $(p = q = \frac{1}{2})$ when the probabilities of the individual paths are equal to 2^{-n},

$$P(A_k) = C_n^{[n+k]/2} \cdot 2^{-n}.$$

Let us investigate the asymptotic behavior of these probabilities for large n.

If the number of steps is $2n$, it follows from the properties of the binomial coefficients that the largest of the probabilities $P(A_k)$, $|k| \le 2n$, is

$$P(A_0) = C_{2n}^n \cdot 2^{-2n}.$$

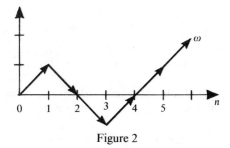

Figure 2

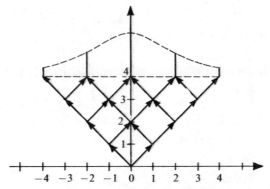

Figure 3. Beginning of the binomial distribution.

From Stirling's formula (see formula (6) in Section 4)

$$n! \sim \sqrt{2\pi n}\; e^{-n} n^n.\dagger$$

Consequently

$$C_{2n}^n = \frac{(2n)!}{(n!)^2} \sim 2^{2n} \cdot \frac{1}{\sqrt{\pi n}}$$

and therefore for large n

$$P(A_0) \sim \frac{1}{\sqrt{\pi n}}.$$

Figure 3 represents the beginning of the binomial distribution for $2n$ steps of a random walk (in contrast to Figure 2, the time axis is now directed upward).

2. Multinomial distribution. Generalizing the preceding model, we now suppose that the sample space is

$$\Omega = \{\omega: \omega = (a_1, \ldots, a_n), a_i = b_1, \ldots, b_r\},$$

where $b_1, \ldots, b_r$ are given numbers. Let $v_i(\omega)$ be the number of elements of $\omega = (a_1, \ldots, a_n)$ that are equal to b_i, $i = 1, \ldots, r$, and define the probability of ω by

$$p(\omega) = p_1^{v_1(\omega)} \cdots p_r^{v_r(\omega)},$$

where $p_i \geq 0$ and $p_1 + \cdots + p_r = 1$. Note that

$$\sum_{\omega \in \Omega} p(\omega) = \sum_{\left\{\substack{n_1 \geq, \ldots, n_r \geq 0, \\ n_1 + \cdots + n_r = n}\right\}} C_n(n_1, \ldots, n_r) p_1^{n_1} \cdots p_r^{n_r},$$

where $C_n(n_1, \ldots, n_r)$ is the number of (ordered) sequences $(a_1, \ldots, a_n)$ in which b_1 occurs n_1 times, $\ldots, b_r$ occurs n_r times. Since n_1 elements b_1 can

† The notation $f(n) \sim g(n)$ means that $f(n)/g(n) \to 1$ as $n \to \infty$.

be distributed into n positions in $C_n^{n_1}$ ways; n_2 elements b_2 into $n - n_1$ positions in $C_{n-n_1}^{n_2}$ ways, etc., we have

$$C_n(n_1, \ldots, n_r) = C_n^{n_1} \cdot C_{n-n_1}^{n_2} \cdots C_{n-(n_1 + \cdots + n_{r-1})}^{n_r}$$

$$= \frac{n!}{n_1! \, (n - n_1)!} \cdot \frac{(n - n_1)!}{n_2! \, (n - n_1 - n_2)!} \cdots 1$$

$$= \frac{n!}{n_1! \cdots n_r!}.$$

Therefore

$$\sum_{\omega \in \Omega} p(\omega) = \sum_{\substack{\{n_1 \geq 0, \ldots, n_r \geq 0, \\ n_1 + \cdots + n_r = n\}}} \frac{n!}{n_1! \cdots n_r!} p_1^{n_1} \cdots p_r^{n_r} = (p_1 + \cdots + p_r)^n = 1,$$

and consequently we have defined an acceptable method of assigning probabilities.

Let

$$A_{n_1, \ldots, n_r} = \{\omega : v_1(\omega) = n_1, \ldots, v_r(\omega) = n_r\}.$$

Then

$$\mathsf{P}(A_{n_1, \ldots, n_r}) = C_n(n_1, \ldots, n_r) p_1^{n_1} \cdots p_r^{n_r}. \qquad (2)$$

The set of probabilities

$$\{\mathsf{P}(A_{n_1, \ldots, n_r})\}$$

is called the *multinomial* (or *polynomial*) distribution.

We emphasize that both this distribution and its special case, the binomial distribution, originate from problems about sampling *with replacement*.

3. The multidimensional hypergeometric distribution occurs in problems that involve sampling *without replacement*.

Consider, for example, an urn containing M balls numbered $1, 2, \ldots, M$, where M_1 balls have the color $b_1, \ldots, M_r$ balls have the color b_r, and $M_1 + \cdots + M_r = M$. Suppose that we draw a sample of size $n < M$ without replacement. The sample space is

$$\Omega = \{\omega : \omega = (a_1, \ldots, a_n), a_k \neq a_l, k \neq l, a_i = 1, \ldots, M\}$$

and $N(\Omega) = (M)_n$. Let us suppose that the sample points are equiprobable, and find the probability of the event $B_{n_1, \ldots, n_r}$ in which n_1 balls have color $b_1, \ldots, n_r$ balls have color b_r, where $n_1 + \cdots + n_r = n$. It is easy to show that

$$N(B_{n_1, \ldots, n_r}) = C_n(n_1, \ldots, n_r)(M_1)_{n_1} \cdots (M_r)_{n_r},$$

and therefore

$$P(B_{n_1, \dots, n_r}) = \frac{N(B_{n_1, \dots, n_r})}{N(\Omega)} = \frac{C_{M_1}^{n_1} \cdots C_{M_r}^{n_r}}{C_M^n}. \tag{3}$$

The set of probabilities $\{P(B_{n_1, \dots, n_r})\}$ is called the *multidimensional hypergeometric distribution*. When $r = 2$ it is simply called the *hypergeometric* distribution because its "generating function" is a hypergeometric function.

The structure of the multidimensional hypergeometric distribution is rather complicated. For example, the probability

$$P(B_{n_1, n_2}) = \frac{C_{M_1}^{n_1} C_{M_2}^{n_2}}{C_M^n}, \qquad n_1 + n_2 = n, \quad M_1 + M_2 = M, \tag{4}$$

contains nine factorials. However, it is easily established that if $M \to \infty$ and $M_1 \to \infty$ in such a way that $M_1/M \to p$ (and therefore $M_2/M \to 1 - p$) then

$$P(B_{n_1, n_2}) \to C_{n_1 + n_2}^{n_1} p^{n_1} (1 - p)^{n_2}. \tag{5}$$

In other words, under the present hypotheses the hypergeometric distribution is approximated by the binomial; this is intuitively clear since when M and M_1 are large (but finite), sampling without replacement ought to give almost the same result as sampling with replacement.

EXAMPLE. Let us use (4) to find the probability of picking six "lucky" numbers in a lottery of the following kind (this is an abstract formulation of the "sportloto," which is well known in Russia):

There are 49 balls numbered from 1 to 49; six of them are lucky (colored red, say, whereas the rest are white). We draw a sample of six balls, without replacement. The question is, What is the probability that all six of these balls are lucky? Taking $M = 49$, $M_1 = 6$, $n_1 = 6$, $n_2 = 0$, we see that the event of interest, namely

$$B_{6,0} = \{6 \text{ balls, all lucky}\}$$

has, by (4), probability

$$P(B_{6,0}) = \frac{1}{C_{49}^6} \approx 7.2 \times 10^{-8}.$$

4. The numbers $n!$ increase extremely rapidly with n. For example,

$$10! = 3,628,800,$$

$$15! = 1,307,674,368,000,$$

and 100! has 158 digits. Hence from either the theoretical or the computational point of view, it is important to know Stirling's formula,

$$n! = \sqrt{2\pi n} \left(\frac{n}{e}\right)^n \exp\left(\frac{\theta_n}{12n}\right), \qquad 0 < \theta_n < 1, \tag{6}$$

whose proof can be found in most textbooks on mathematical analysis (see also [69]).

5. PROBLEMS

1. Prove formula (5).

2. Show that for the multinomial distribution $\{P(A_{n_1}, \ldots, A_{n_r})\}$ the maximum probability is attained at a point $(k_1, \ldots, k_r)$ that satisfies the inequalities $np_i - 1 < k_i \leq (n + r - 1)p_i, i = 1, \ldots, r$.

3. *One-dimensional Ising model.* Consider n particles located at the points $1, 2, \ldots, n$. Suppose that each particle is of one of two types, and that there are n_1 particles of the first type and n_2 of the second ($n_1 + n_2 = n$). We suppose that all $n!$ arrangements of the particles are equally probable.

   Construct a corresponding probabilistic model and find the probability of the event $A_n(m_{11}, m_{12}, m_{21}, m_{22}) = \{v_{11} = m_{11}, \ldots, v_{22} = m_{22}\}$, where v_{ij} is the number of particles of type i following particles of type j ($i, j = 1, 2$).

4. Prove the following inequalities by probabilistic reasoning:

$$\sum_{k=0}^{n} C_n^k = 2^n,$$

$$\sum_{k=0}^{n} (C_n^k)^2 = C_{2n}^n,$$

$$\sum_{k=0}^{n} (-1)^{n-k} C_m^k = C_{m-1}^n, \qquad m \geq n + 1,$$

$$\sum_{k=0}^{n} k(k-1) C_m^k = m(m-1)2^{m-2}, \qquad m \geq 2.$$

§3. Conditional Probability. Independence

1. The concept of probabilities of events lets us answer questions of the following kind: If there are M balls in an urn, M_1 white and M_2 black, what is the probability $P(A)$ of the event A that a selected ball is white? With the classical approach, $P(A) = M_1/M$.

The concept of *conditional probability*, which will be introduced below, lets us answer questions of the following kind: What is the probability that the second ball is white (event B) under the condition that the first ball was also white (event A)? (We are thinking of sampling without replacement.)

It is natural to reason as follows: if the first ball is white, then at the second step we have an urn containing $M - 1$ balls, of which $M_1 - 1$ are white and M_2 black; hence it seems reasonable to suppose that the (conditional) probability in question is $(M_1 - 1)/(M - 1)$.

We now give a definition of conditional probability that is consistent with our intuitive ideas.

Let $(\Omega, \mathscr{A}, \mathsf{P})$ be a (finite) probability space and A an event (i.e. $A \in \mathscr{A}$).

Definition 1. The *conditional probability* of event B assuming event A with $\mathsf{P}(A) > 0$ (denoted by $\mathsf{P}(B|A)$) is

$$\frac{\mathsf{P}(AB)}{\mathsf{P}(A)}. \tag{1}$$

In the classical approach we have $\mathsf{P}(A) = N(A)/N(\Omega)$, $\mathsf{P}(AB) = N(AB)/N(\Omega)$, and therefore

$$\mathsf{P}(B|A) = \frac{N(AB)}{N(A)}. \tag{2}$$

From Definition 1 we immediately get the following properties of conditional probability:

$$\mathsf{P}(A|A) = 1,$$
$$\mathsf{P}(\varnothing|A) = 0,$$
$$\mathsf{P}(B|A) = 1, \quad B \supseteq A,$$
$$\mathsf{P}(B_1 + B_2|A) = \mathsf{P}(B_1|A) + \mathsf{P}(B_2|A).$$

It follows from these properties that for a given set A the conditional probability $\mathsf{P}(\cdot|A)$ has the same properties on the space $(\Omega \cap A, \mathscr{A} \cap A)$, where $\mathscr{A} \cap A = \{B \cap A : B \in \mathscr{A}\}$, that the original probability $\mathsf{P}(\cdot)$ has on $(\Omega, \mathscr{A})$.

Note that

$$\mathsf{P}(B|A) + \mathsf{P}(\bar{B}|A) = 1;$$

however in general

$$\mathsf{P}(B|A) + \mathsf{P}(B|\bar{A}) \neq 1,$$
$$\mathsf{P}(B|A) + \mathsf{P}(\bar{B}|\bar{A}) \neq 1.$$

EXAMPLE 1. Consider a family with two children. We ask for the probability that both children are boys, assuming

(a) that the older child is a boy;
(b) that at least one of the children is a boy.

The sample space is

$$\Omega = \{\text{BB, BG, GB, GG}\},$$

where BG means that the older child is a boy and the younger is a girl, etc.

Let us suppose that all sample points are equally probable:

$$P(\text{BB}) = P(\text{BG}) = P(\text{GB}) = P(\text{GG}) = \tfrac{1}{4}.$$

Let A be the event that the older child is a boy, and B, that the younger child is a boy. Then $A \cup B$ is the event that at least one child is a boy, and AB is the event that both children are boys. In question (a) we want the conditional probability $P(AB|A)$, and in (b), the conditional probability $P(AB|A \cup B)$.

It is easy to see that

$$P(AB|A) = \frac{P(AB)}{P(A)} = \frac{\tfrac{1}{4}}{\tfrac{1}{2}} = \frac{1}{2},$$

$$P(AB|A \cup B) = \frac{P(AB)}{P(A \cup B)} = \frac{\tfrac{1}{2}}{\tfrac{1}{4}} = \frac{1}{3}.$$

2. The simple but important formula (3), below, is called the formula for total probability. It provides the basic means for calculating the probabilities of complicated events by using conditional probabilities.

Consider a decomposition $\mathscr{D} = \{A_1, \ldots, A_n\}$ with $P(A_i) > 0, i = 1, \ldots, n$ (such a decomposition is often called a complete set of disjoint events). It is clear that

$$B = BA_1 + \cdots + BA_n$$

and therefore

$$P(B) = \sum_{i=1}^{n} P(BA_i).$$

But

$$P(BA_i) = P(B|A_i)P(A_i).$$

Hence we have the *formula for total probability*:

$$P(B) = \sum_{i=1}^{n} P(B|A_i)P(A_i). \tag{3}$$

In particular, if $0 < P(A) < 1$, then

$$P(B) = P(B|A)P(A) + P(B|\bar{A})P(\bar{A}). \tag{4}$$

Example 2. An urn contains M balls, m of which are "lucky." We ask for the probability that the second ball drawn is lucky (assuming that the result of the first draw is unknown, that a sample of size 2 is drawn without replacement, and that all outcomes are equally probable). Let A be the event that the first ball is lucky, B the event that the second is lucky. Then

$$P(B|A) = \frac{P(BA)}{P(A)} = \frac{\dfrac{m(m-1)}{M(M-1)}}{\dfrac{m}{M}} = \frac{m-1}{M-1},$$

$$P(B|\bar{A}) = \frac{P(B\bar{A})}{P(\bar{A})} = \frac{\dfrac{m(M-m)}{M(M-1)}}{\dfrac{M-m}{M}} = \frac{m}{M-1}$$

and

$$P(B) = P(B|A)P(A) + P(B|\bar{A})P(\bar{A})$$

$$= \frac{m-1}{M-1} \cdot \frac{m}{M} + \frac{m}{M-1} \cdot \frac{M-m}{M} = \frac{m}{M}.$$

It is interesting to observe that $P(A)$ is precisely m/M. Hence, when the nature of the first ball is unknown, it does not affect the probability that the second ball is lucky.

By the definition of conditional probability (with $P(A) > 0$),

$$P(AB) = P(B|A)P(A). \tag{5}$$

This formula, the *multiplication formula for probabilities*, can be generalized (by induction) as follows: If $A_1, \ldots, A_{n-1}$ are events with $P(A_1 \cdots A_{n-1}) > 0$, then

$$P(A_1 \cdots A_n) = P(A_1)P(A_2|A_1) \cdots P(A_n|A_1 \cdots A_{n-1}) \tag{6}$$

(here $A_1 \cdots A_n = A_1 \cap A_2 \cap \cdots \cap A_n$).

3. Suppose that A and B are events with $P(A) > 0$ and $P(B) > 0$. Then along with (5) we have the parallel formula

$$P(AB) = P(A|B)P(B). \tag{7}$$

From (5) and (7) we obtain *Bayes's formula*

$$P(A|B) = \frac{P(A)P(B|A)}{P(B)}. \tag{8}$$

If the events $A_1, \ldots, A_n$ form a decomposition of Ω, (3) and (8) imply *Bayes's theorem*:

$$P(A_i|B) = \frac{P(A_i)P(B|A_i)}{\sum_{j=1}^{n} P(A_j)P(B|A_j)}. \tag{9}$$

In statistical applications, $A_1, \ldots, A_n$ $(A_1 + \cdots + A_n = \Omega)$ are often called hypotheses, and $P(A_i)$ is called the *a priori*† probability of A_i. The conditional probability $P(A_i|B)$ is considered as the *a posteriori* probability of A_i after the occurrence of event B.

EXAMPLE 3. Let an urn contain two coins: A_1, a fair coin with probability $\frac{1}{2}$ of falling H; and A_2, a biased coin with probability $\frac{1}{3}$ of falling H. A coin is drawn at random and tossed. Suppose that it falls head. We ask for the probability that the fair coin was selected.

Let us construct the corresponding probabilistic model. Here it is natural to take the sample space to be the set $\Omega = \{A_1H, A_1T, A_2H, A_2T\}$, which describes all possible outcomes of a selection and a toss (A_1H means that coin A_1 was selected and fell heads, etc.) The probabilities $p(\omega)$ of the various outcomes have to be assigned so that, according to the statement of the problem,

$$P(A_1) = P(A_2) = \tfrac{1}{2}$$

and

$$P(H|A_1) = \tfrac{1}{2}, \qquad P(H|A_2) = \tfrac{1}{3}.$$

With these assignments, the probabilities of the sample points are uniquely determined:

$$P(A_1H) = \tfrac{1}{4}, \qquad P(A_1T) = \tfrac{1}{4}, \qquad P(A_2H) = \tfrac{1}{6}, \qquad P(A_2T) = \tfrac{1}{3}.$$

Then by Bayes's formula the probability in question is

$$P(A_1|H) = \frac{P(A_1)P(H|A_1)}{P(A_1)P(H|A_1) + P(A_2)P(H|A_2)} = \frac{3}{5},$$

and therefore

$$P(A_2|H) = \tfrac{2}{5}.$$

4. In certain sense, the concept of *independence*, which we are now going to introduce, plays a central role in probability theory: it is precisely this concept that distinguishes probability theory from the general theory of measure spaces.

---

† *A priori*: before the experiment; *a posteriori*: after the experiment.

If A and B are two events, it is natural to say that B is independent of A if knowing that A has occurred has no effect on the probability of B. In other words, "B is independent of A" if

$$P(B|A) = P(B) \qquad (10)$$

(we are supposing that $P(A) > 0$).
    Since

$$P(B|A) = \frac{P(AB)}{P(A)},$$

it follows from (10) that

$$P(AB) = P(A)P(B). \qquad (11)$$

In exactly the same way, if $P(B) > 0$ it is natural to say that "A is independent of B" if

$$P(A|B) = P(A).$$

Hence we again obtain (11), which is symmetric in A and B and still makes sense when the probabilities of these events are zero.
    After these preliminaries, we introduce the following definition.

Definition 2. Events A and B are called *independent* or *statistically independent* (with respect to the probability P) if

$$P(AB) = P(A)P(B).$$

In probability theory it is often convenient to consider not only independence of events (or sets) but also independence of collections of events (or sets).
    Accordingly, we introduce the following definition.

Definition 3. Two algebras $\mathscr{A}_1$ and $\mathscr{A}_2$ of events (or sets) are called *independent* or *statistically independent* (with respect to the probability P) if all pairs of sets A_1 and A_2, belonging respectively to $\mathscr{A}_1$ and $\mathscr{A}_2$, are independent.

    For example, let us consider the two algebras

$$\mathscr{A}_1 = \{A_1, \bar{A}_1, \varnothing, \Omega\} \quad \text{and} \quad \mathscr{A}_2 = \{A_2, \bar{A}_2, \varnothing, \Omega\},$$

where A_1 and A_2 are subsets of Ω. It is easy to verify that $\mathscr{A}_1$ and $\mathscr{A}_2$ are independent if and only if A_1 and A_2 are independent. In fact, the independence of $\mathscr{A}_1$ and $\mathscr{A}_2$ means the independence of the 16 events A_1 and A_2, A_1 and $\bar{A}_2, \ldots, \Omega$ and Ω. Consequently A_1 and A_2 are independent. Conversely, if A_1 and A_2 are independent, we have to show that the other 15 pairs of events are independent. Let us verify, for example, the independence of A_1 and $\bar{A}_2$. We have

$$P(A_1\bar{A}_2) = P(A_1) - P(A_1A_2) = P(A_1) - P(A_1)P(A_2)$$
$$= P(A_1) \cdot (1 - P(A_2)) = P(A_1)P(\bar{A}_2).$$

The independence of the other pairs is verified similarly.

5. The concept of independence of two sets or two algebras of sets can be extended to any finite number of sets or algebras of sets.

Thus we say that the sets $A_1, \ldots, A_n$ are collectively *independent* or *statistically independent* (with respect to the probability P) if for $k = 1, \ldots, n$ and $1 \le i_1 < i_2 < \cdots < i_k \le n$

$$P(A_{i_1} \cdots A_{i_k}) = P(A_{i_1}) \cdots P(A_{i_k}). \tag{12}$$

The algebras $\mathscr{A}_1, \ldots, \mathscr{A}_n$ of sets are called *independent* or *statistically independent* (with respect to the probability P) if all sets $A_1, \ldots, A_n$ belonging respectively to $\mathscr{A}_1, \ldots, \mathscr{A}_n$ are independent.

Note that *pairwise independence* of events *does not imply* their independence. In fact if, for example, $\Omega = \{\omega_1, \omega_2, \omega_3, \omega_4\}$ and all outcomes are equiprobable, it is easily verified that the events

$$A = \{\omega_1, \omega_2\}, \qquad B = \{\omega_1, \omega_3\}, \qquad C = \{\omega_1, \omega_4\}$$

are pairwise independent, whereas

$$P(ABC) = \tfrac{1}{4} \ne (\tfrac{1}{2})^3 = P(A)P(B)P(C).$$

Also note that if

$$P(ABC) = P(A)P(B)P(C)$$

for events A, B and C, it by no means follows that these events are pairwise independent. In fact, let Ω consist of the 36 ordered pairs (i, j), where $i, j = 1, 2, \ldots, 6$ and all the pairs are equiprobable. Then if $A = \{(i,j): j = 1, 2 \text{ or } 5\}$, $B = \{(i,j): j = 4, 5 \text{ or } 6\}$, $C = \{(i, j): i + j = 9\}$ we have

$$P(AB) = \tfrac{1}{6} \ne \tfrac{1}{4} = P(A)P(B),$$
$$P(AC) = \tfrac{1}{36} \ne \tfrac{1}{18} = P(A)P(C),$$
$$P(BC) = \tfrac{1}{12} \ne \tfrac{1}{18} = P(B)P(C),$$

but also

$$P(ABC) = \tfrac{1}{36} = P(A)P(B)P(C).$$

6. Let us consider in more detail, from the point of view of independence, the classical model $(\Omega, \mathscr{A}, P)$ that was introduced in §2 and used as a basis for the binomial distribution.

In this model

$$\Omega = \{\omega: \omega = (a_1, \ldots, a_n), a_i = 0, 1\}, \qquad \mathscr{A} = \{A: A \subseteq \Omega\}$$

and

$$p(\omega) = p^{\sum a_i} q^{n - \sum a_i}. \tag{13}$$

Consider an event $A \subseteq \Omega$. We say that this event depends on a trial at time k if it is determined by the value a_k alone. Examples of such events are

$$A_k = \{\omega: a_k = 1\}, \qquad \bar{A}_k = \{\omega: a_k = 0\}.$$

Let us consider the sequence of algebras $\mathscr{A}_1, \mathscr{A}_2, \ldots, \mathscr{A}_n$, where $\mathscr{A}_k = \{A_k, \bar{A}_k, \varnothing, \Omega\}$ and show that under (13) these algebras are independent.

It is clear that

$$\mathsf{P}(A_k) = \sum_{\{\omega: a_k = 1\}} p(\omega) = \sum_{\{\omega: a_k = 1\}} p^{\sum a_i} q^{n - \sum a_i}$$

$$= p \sum_{(a_1, \ldots, a_{k-1}, a_{k+1}, \ldots, a_n)} p^{a_1 + \cdots + a_{k-1} + a_{k+1} + \cdots + a_n}$$

$$\times q^{(n-1) - (a_1 + \cdots + a_{k-1} + a_{k+1} + \cdots + a_n)} = p \sum_{i=0}^{n-1} C_{n-1}^l p^l q^{(n-1)-l} = p,$$

and a similar calculation shows that $\mathsf{P}(\bar{A}_k) = q$ and that, for $k \neq 1$,

$$\mathsf{P}(A_k A_l) = p^2, \qquad \mathsf{P}(A_k \bar{A}_l) = pq, \qquad \mathsf{P}(\bar{A}_k A_l) = q^2.$$

It is easy to deduce from this that $\mathscr{A}_k$ and $\mathscr{A}_l$ are independent for $k \neq l$.

It can be shown in the same way that $\mathscr{A}_1, \mathscr{A}_2, \ldots, \mathscr{A}_n$ are independent. This is the basis for saying that our model $(\Omega, \mathscr{A}, \mathsf{P})$ corresponds to "n independent trials with two outcomes and probability p of success." James Bernoulli was the first to study this model systematically, and established the law of large numbers (§5) for it. Accordingly, this model is also called the Bernoulli scheme with two outcomes (success and failure) and probability p of success.

A detailed study of the probability space for the Bernoulli scheme shows that it has the structure of a direct product of probability spaces, defined as follows.

Suppose that we are given a collection $(\Omega_1, \mathscr{B}_1, \mathsf{P}_1), \ldots, (\Omega_n, \mathscr{B}_n, \mathsf{P}_n)$ of finite probability spaces. Form the space $\Omega = \Omega_1 \times \Omega_2 \times \cdots \times \Omega_n$ of points $\omega = (a_1, \ldots, a_n)$, where $a_i \in \Omega_i$. Let $\mathscr{A} = \mathscr{B}_1 \otimes \cdots \otimes \mathscr{B}_n$ be the algebra of the subsets of Ω that consists of sums of sets of the form

$$A = B_1 \times B_2 \times \cdots \times B_n$$

with $B_i \in \mathscr{B}_i$. Finally, for $\omega = (a_1, \ldots, a_n)$ take $p(\omega) = p_1(a_1) \cdots p_n(a_n)$ and define $\mathsf{P}(A)$ for the set $A = B_1 \times B_2 \times \cdots \times B_n$ by

$$\mathsf{P}(A) = \sum_{\{a_1 \in B_1, \ldots, a_n \in B_n\}} p_1(a_1) \cdots p_n(a_n).$$

It is easy to verify that $P(\Omega) = 1$ and therefore the triple $(\Omega, \mathscr{A}, P)$ defines a probability space. This space is called the *direct product of the probability spaces* $(\Omega_1, \mathscr{B}_1, P_1), \ldots, (\Omega_n, \mathscr{B}_n, P_n)$.

We note an easily verified property of the direct product of probability spaces: with respect to P, the events

$$A_1 = \{\omega: a_1 \in B_1\}, \ldots, A_n = \{\omega: a_n \in B_n\},$$

where $B_i \in \mathscr{B}_i$, are independent. In the same way, the algebras of subsets of Ω,

$$\mathscr{A}_1 = \{A_1: A_1 = \{\omega: a_1 \in B_1\}, B_1 \in \mathscr{B}_1\},$$
$$\ldots\ldots\ldots\ldots\ldots\ldots\ldots\ldots\ldots\ldots\ldots\ldots$$
$$\mathscr{A}_n = \{A_n: A_n = \{\omega: a_n \in B_n\}, B_n \in \mathscr{B}_n\}$$

are independent.

It is clear from our construction that the Bernoulli scheme

$$(\Omega, \mathscr{A}, P) \quad \text{with} \quad \Omega = \{\omega: \omega = (a_1, \ldots, a_n), a_i = 0 \text{ or } 1\}$$
$$\mathscr{A} = \{A: A \subseteq \Omega\} \quad \text{and} \quad p(\omega) = p^{\Sigma a_i} q^{n - \Sigma a_i}$$

can be thought of as the direct product of the probability spaces $(\Omega_i, \mathscr{B}_i, P_i)$, $i = 1, 2, \ldots, n$, where

$$\Omega_i = \{0, 1\}, \qquad \mathscr{B}_i = \{\{0\}, \{1\}, \varnothing, \Omega_i\},$$
$$P_i(\{1\}) = p, \qquad P_i(\{0\}) = q.$$

7. PROBLEMS

1. Give examples to show that in general the equations

$$P(B|A) + P(B|\bar{A}) = 1,$$
$$P(B|A) + P(\bar{B}|\bar{A}) = 1$$

are false.

2. An urn contains M balls, of which M_1 are white. Consider a sample of size n. Let B_j be the event that the ball selected at the jth step is white, and A_k the event that a sample of size n contains exactly k white balls. Show that

$$P(B_j|A_k) = k/n$$

both for sampling with replacement and for sampling without replacement.

3. Let $A_1, \ldots, A_n$ be independent events. Then

$$P\left(\bigcup_{i=1}^n A_i\right) = 1 - \prod_{i=1}^n P(\bar{A}_i).$$

4. Let $A_1, \ldots, A_n$ be independent events with $P(A_i) = p_i$. Then the probability P_0 that neither event occurs is

$$P_0 = \prod_{i=1}^n (1 - p_i).$$

5. Let A and B be independent events. In terms of $P(A)$ and $P(B)$, find the probabilities of the events that exactly k, at least k, and at most k of A and B occur ($k = 0, 1, 2$).

6. Let event A be independent of itself, i.e. let A and A be independent. Show that $P(A)$ is either 0 or 1.

7. Let event A have $P(A) = 0$ or 1. Show that A and an arbitrary event B are independent.

8. Consider the electric circuit shown in Figure 4:

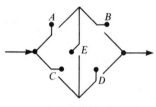

Figure 4

    Each of the switches A, B, C, D, and E is independently open or closed with probabilities p and q, respectively. Find the probability that a signal fed in at "input" will be received at "output". If the signal is received, what is the conditional probability that E is open?

§4. Random Variables and Their Properties

1. Let $(\Omega, \mathscr{A}, P)$ be a probabilistic model of an experiment with a finite number of outcomes, $N(\Omega) < \infty$, where $\mathscr{A}$ is the algebra of all subsets of Ω. We observe that in the examples above, where we calculated the probabilities of various events $A \in \mathscr{A}$, the specific nature of the sample space Ω was of no interest. We were interested only in numerical properties depending on the sample points. For example, we were interested in the probability of some number of successes in a series of n trials, in the probability distribution for the number of objects in cells, etc.

    The concept "random variable," which we now introduce (later it will be given a more general form) serves to define quantities that are subject to "measurement" in random experiments.

Definition 1. Any numerical function $\xi = \xi(\omega)$ defined on a (finite) sample space Ω is called a (simple) *random variable*. (The reason for the term "simple" random variable will become clear after the introduction of the general concept of random variable in §4 of Chapter II.)

EXAMPLE 1. In the model of two tosses of a coin with sample space $\Omega = \{HH, HT, TH, TT\}$, define a random variable $\xi = \xi(\omega)$ by the table

ω	HH	HT	TH	TT
$\xi(\omega)$	2	1	1	0

Here, from its very definition, $\xi(\omega)$ is nothing but the number of heads in the outcome ω.

Another extremely simple example of a random variable is the *indicator* (or *characteristic function*) of a set $A \in \mathscr{A}$:

$$\xi = I_A(\omega),$$

where†

$$I_A(\omega) = \begin{cases} 1, & \omega \in A, \\ 0, & \omega \notin A. \end{cases}$$

When experimenters are concerned with random variables that describe observations, their main interest is in the probabilities with which the random variables take various values. From this point of view they are interested, not in the distribution of the probability P over $(\Omega, \mathscr{A})$, but in its distribution over the range of a random variable. Since we are considering the case when Ω contains only a finite number of points, the range X of the random variable ξ is also finite. Let $X = \{x_1, \ldots, x_m\}$, where the (different) numbers $x_1, \ldots, x_m$ exhaust the values of ξ.

Let $\mathscr{X}$ be the collection of all subsets of X, and let $B \in \mathscr{X}$. We can also interpret B as an event if the sample space is taken to be X, the set of values of ξ.

On $(X, \mathscr{X})$, consider the probability $P_\xi(\cdot)$ induced by ξ according to the formula

$$P_\xi(B) = P\{\omega: \xi(\omega) \in B\}, \qquad B \in \mathscr{X}.$$

It is clear that the values of this probability are completely determined by the probabilities

$$P_\xi(x_i) = P\{\omega: \xi(\omega) = x_i\}, \qquad x_i \in X.$$

The set of numbers $\{P_\xi(x_1), \ldots, P_\xi(x_m)\}$ is called the *probability distribution of the random variable* ξ.

---

† The notation $I(A)$ is also used. For frequently used properties of indicators see Problem 1.

EXAMPLE 2. A random variable ξ that takes the two values 1 and 0 with probabilities p ("success") and q ("failure"), is called a Bernoulli† random variable. Clearly

$$P_\xi(x) = p^x q^{1-x}, \qquad x = 0, 1. \tag{1}$$

A *binomial* (or binomially distributed) *random variable* ξ is a random variable that takes the $n + 1$ values $0, 1, \ldots, n$ with probabilities

$$P_\xi(x) = C_n^x p^x q^{n-x}, \qquad x = 0, 1, \ldots, n. \tag{2}$$

Note that here and in many subsequent examples we do not specify the sample spaces $(\Omega, \mathscr{A}, \mathsf{P})$, but are interested only in the values of the random variables and their probability distributions.

The probabilistic structure of the random variables ξ is completely specified by the probability distributions $\{P_\xi(x_i), i = 1, \ldots, m\}$. The concept of distribution function, which we now introduce, yields an equivalent description of the probabilistic structure of the random variables.

Definition 2. Let $x \in R^1$. The function

$$F_\xi(x) = \mathsf{P}\{\omega: \xi(\omega) \le x\}$$

is called the *distribution function* of the random variable ξ.

Clearly

$$F_\xi(x) = \sum_{\{i:\, x_i \le x\}} P_\xi(x_i)$$

and

$$P_\xi(x_i) = F_\xi(x_i) - F_\xi(x_i -),$$

where $F_\xi(x-) = \lim_{y \uparrow x} F_\xi(y)$.

If we suppose that $x_1 < x_2 < \cdots < x_m$ and put $F_\xi(x_0) = 0$, then

$$P_\xi(x_i) = F_\xi(x_i) - F_\xi(x_{i-1}), \qquad i = 1, \ldots, m.$$

The following diagrams (Figure 5) exhibit $P_\xi(x)$ and $F_\xi(x)$ for a binomial random variable.

It follows immediately from Definition 2 that the distribution $F_\xi = F_\xi(x)$ has the following properties:

(1) $F_\xi(-\infty) = 0,\ F_\xi(+\infty) = 1$;
(2) $F_\xi(x)$ is continuous on the right $(F_\xi(x+) = F_\xi(x))$ and piecewise constant.

---

† We use the terms "Bernoulli, binomial, Poisson, Gaussian, ..., random variables" for what are more usually called random variables with Bernoulli, binomial, Poisson, Gaussian, ..., distributions.

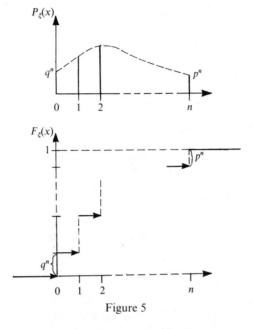

Figure 5

Along with random variables it is often necessary to consider *random vectors* $\xi = (\xi_1, \ldots, \xi_r)$ whose components are random variables. For example, when we considered the multinomial distribution we were dealing with a random vector $v = (v_1, \ldots, v_r)$, where $v_i = v_i(\omega)$ is the number of elements equal to b_i, $i = 1, \ldots, r$, in the sequence $\omega = (a_1, \ldots, a_n)$.

The set of probabilities

$$P_\xi(x_1, \ldots, x_r) = P\{\omega : \xi_1(\omega) = x_1, \ldots, \xi_r(\omega) = x_r\},$$

where $x_i \in X_i$, the range of ξ_i, is called the *probability distribution of the random vector* ξ, and the function

$$F_\xi(x_1, \ldots, x_r) = P\{\omega : \xi_1(\omega) \leq x_1, \ldots, \xi_r(\omega) \leq x_r\},$$

where $x_i \in R^1$, is called the *distribution function of the random vector* $\xi = (\xi_1, \ldots, \xi_r)$.

For example, for the random vector $v = (v_1, \ldots, v_r)$ mentioned above,

$$P_v(n_1, \ldots, n_r) = C_n(n_1, \ldots, n_r)p_1^{n_1} \cdots p_r^{n_r}$$

(see (2.2)).

2. Let $\xi_1, \ldots, \xi_r$ be a set of random variables with values in a (finite) set $X \subseteq R^1$. Let $\mathscr{X}$ be the algebra of subsets of X.

Definition 3. The random variables $\xi_1, \ldots, \xi_r$ are said to be *independent* (*collectively independent*) if

$$P\{\xi_1 = x_1, \ldots, \xi_r = x_r\} = P\{\xi_1 = x_1\} \cdots P\{\xi_r = x_r\}$$

for all $x_1, \ldots, x_r \in X$; or, equivalently, if

$$P\{\xi_1 \in B_1, \ldots, \xi_r \in B_r\} = P\{\xi_1 \in B_1\} \cdots P\{\xi_r \in B_r\}$$

for all $B_1, \ldots, B_r \in \mathscr{X}$.

We can get a very simple example of independent random variables from the Bernoulli scheme. Let

$$\Omega = \{\omega: \omega = (a_1, \ldots, a_n), a_i = 0, 1\}, \quad p(\omega) = p^{\Sigma a_i} q^{n - \Sigma a_i}$$

and $\xi_i(\omega) = a_i$ for $\omega = (a_1, \ldots, a_n), i = 1, \ldots, n$. Then the random variables $\xi_1, \xi_2, \ldots, \xi_n$ are independent, as follows from the independence of the events

$$A_1 = \{\omega: a_1 = 1\}, \ldots, A_n = \{\omega: a_n = 1\},$$

which was established in §3.

3. We shall frequently encounter the problem of finding the probability distributions of random variables that are functions $f(\xi_1, \ldots, \xi_r)$ of random variables $\xi_1, \ldots, \xi_r$. For the present we consider only the determination of the distribution of a sum $\zeta = \xi + \eta$ of random variables.

If ξ and η take values in the respective sets $X = \{x_1, \ldots, x_k\}$ and $Y = \{y_1, \ldots, y_l\}$, the random variable $\zeta = \xi + \eta$ takes values in the set $Z = \{z: z = x_i + y_j, i = 1, \ldots, k; j = 1, \ldots, l\}$. Then it is clear that

$$P_\zeta(z) = P\{\zeta = z\} = P\{\xi + \eta = z\} = \sum_{\{(i, j): x_i + y_j = z\}} P\{\xi = x_i, \eta = y_j\}.$$

The case of independent random variables ξ and η is particularly important. In this case

$$P\{\xi = x_i, \eta = y_j\} = P\{\xi = x_i\}P\{\eta = y_j\},$$

and therefore

$$P_\zeta(z) = \sum_{\{(i, j): x_i + y_j = z\}} P_\xi(x_i)P_\eta(y_j) = \sum_{i=1}^{k} P_\xi(x_i)P_\eta(z - x_i) \tag{3}$$

for all $z \in Z$, where in the last sum $P_\eta(z - x_i)$ is taken to be zero if $z - x_i \notin Y$.

For example, if ξ and η are independent Bernoulli random variables, taking the values 1 and 0 with respective probabilities p and q, then $Z = \{0, 1, 2\}$ and

$$P_\zeta(0) = P_\xi(0)P_\eta(0) = q^2,$$
$$P_\zeta(1) = P_\xi(0)P_\eta(1) + P_\xi(1)P_\eta(0) = 2pq,$$
$$P_\zeta(2) = P_\xi(1)P_\eta(1) = p^2.$$

It is easy to show by induction that if $\xi_1, \xi_2, \ldots, \xi_n$ are independent Bernoulli random variables with $\mathsf{P}\{\xi_i = 1\} = p$, $\mathsf{P}\{\xi_i = 0\} = q$, then the random variable $\zeta = \xi_1 + \cdots + \xi_n$ has the binomial distribution

$$P_\zeta(k) = C_n^k p^k q^{n-k}, \qquad k = 0, 1, \ldots, n. \tag{4}$$

4. We now turn to the important concept of the expectation, or mean value, of a random variable.

Let $(\Omega, \mathscr{A}, \mathsf{P})$ be a (finite) probability space and $\xi = \xi(\omega)$ a random variable with values in the set $X = \{x_1, \ldots, x_k\}$. If we put $A_i = \{\omega: \xi = x_i\}$, $i = 1, \ldots, k$, then ξ can evidently be represented as

$$\xi(\omega) = \sum_{i=1}^{k} x_i I(A_i), \tag{5}$$

where the sets $A_1, \ldots, A_k$ form a decomposition of Ω (i.e., they are pairwise disjoint and their sum is Ω; see Subsection 3 of §1).

Let $p_i = \mathsf{P}\{\xi = x_i\}$. It is intuitively plausible that if we observe the values of the random variable ξ in "n repetitions of identical experiments", the value x_i ought to be encountered about $p_i n$ times, $i = 1, \ldots, k$. Hence the mean value calculated from the results of n experiments is roughly

$$\frac{1}{n} [np_1 x_1 + \cdots + np_k x_k] = \sum_{i=1}^{k} p_i x_i.$$

This discussion provides the motivation for the following definition.

Definition 4. The *expectation*† or *mean value* of the random variable $\xi = \sum_{i=1}^{k} x_i I(A_i)$ is the number

$$\mathsf{E}\xi = \sum_{i=1}^{k} x_i P(A_i). \tag{6}$$

Since $A_i = \{\omega: \xi(\omega) = x_i\}$ and $P_\xi(x_i) = P(A_i)$, we have

$$\mathsf{E}\xi = \sum_{i=1}^{k} x_i P_\xi(x_i). \tag{7}$$

Recalling the definition of $F_\xi = F_\xi(x)$ and writing

$$\Delta F_\xi(x) = F_\xi(x) - F_\xi(x-),$$

we obtain $P_\xi(x_i) = \Delta F_\xi(x_i)$ and consequently

$$\mathsf{E}\xi = \sum_{i=1}^{k} x_i \Delta F_\xi(x_i). \tag{8}$$

---

† Also known as mathematical expectation, or expected value, or (especially in physics) expectation value. (Translator)

Before discussing the properties of the expectation, we remark that it is often convenient to use another representation of the random variable ξ, namely

$$\xi(\omega) = \sum_{j=1}^{l} x_j' I(B_j),$$

where $B_1 + \cdots + B_l = \Omega$, but some of the x_j' may be repeated. In this case $E\xi$ can be calculated from the formula $\sum_{j=1}^{l} x_j' P(B_j)$, which differs formally from (5) because in (5) the x_i are all different. In fact,

$$\sum_{\{j: x_j' = x_i\}} x_j' P(B_j) = x_i \sum_{\{j: x_j' = x_i\}} P(B_j) = x_i P(A_i)$$

and therefore

$$\sum_{i=1}^{l} x_j' P(B_j) = \sum_{i=1}^{k} x_i P(A_i).$$

5. We list the basic properties of the expectation:

(1) *If $\xi \geq 0$ then $E\xi \geq 0$.*
(2) $E(a\xi + b\eta) = aE\xi + bE\eta$, *where a and b are constants.*
(3) *If $\xi \geq \eta$ then $E\xi \geq E\eta$.*
(4) $|E\xi| \leq E|\xi|$.
(5) *If ξ and η are independent, then $E\xi\eta = E\xi \cdot E\eta$.*
(6) $(E|\xi\eta|)^2 \leq E\xi^2 \cdot E\eta^2$ *(Cauchy–Bunyakovskii inequality).*†
(7) *If $\xi = I(A)$ then $E\xi = P(A)$.*

Properties (1) and (7) are evident. To prove (2), let

$$\xi = \sum_i x_i I(A_i), \qquad \eta = \sum_j y_j I(B_j).$$

Then

$$a\xi + b\eta = a\sum_{i,j} x_i I(A_i \cap B_j) + b \sum_{i,j} y_j I(A_i \cap B_j)$$
$$= \sum_{i,j} (ax_i + by_j) I(A_i \cap B_j)$$

and

$$E(a\xi + b\eta) = \sum_{i,j} (ax_i + by_j) P(A_i \cap B_j)$$
$$= \sum_i ax_i P(A_i) + \sum_j by_j P(B_j)$$
$$= a\sum_i x_i P(A_i) + b \sum_j y_j P(B_j) = aE\xi + bE\eta.$$

† Also known as the Cauchy–Schwarz or Schwarz inequality. (Translator)

Property (3) follows from (1) and (2). Property (4) is evident, since

$$|E\xi| = \left| \sum_i x_i P(A_i) \right| \le \sum_i |x_i| P(A_i) = E|\xi|.$$

To prove (5) we note that

$$E\xi\eta = E\left(\sum_i x_i I(A_i) \right) \left(\sum_j y_j I(B_j) \right)$$

$$= E \sum_{i,j} x_i y_j I(A_i \cap B_j) = \sum_{i,j} x_i y_j P(A_i \cap B_j)$$

$$= \sum_{i,j} x_i y_j P(A_i) P(B_j)$$

$$= \left(\sum_i x_i P(A_i) \right) \cdot \left(\sum_j y_j P(B_j) \right) = E\xi \cdot E\eta,$$

where we have used the property that for independent random variables the events

$$A_i = \{\omega : \xi(\omega) = x_i\} \quad \text{and} \quad B_j = \{\omega : \eta(\omega) = y_j\}$$

are independent: $P(A_i \cap B_j) = P(A_i)P(B_j)$.

To prove property (6) we observe that

$$\xi^2 = \sum_i x_i^2 I(A_i), \qquad \eta^2 = \sum_j y_j^2 I(B_j)$$

and

$$E\xi^2 = \sum_i x_i^2 P(A_i), \qquad E\eta^2 = \sum_j y_j^2 P(B_j).$$

Let $E\xi^2 > 0, E\eta^2 > 0$. Put

$$\tilde{\xi} = \frac{\xi}{\sqrt{E\xi^2}}, \qquad \tilde{\eta} = \frac{\eta}{\sqrt{E\eta^2}}.$$

Since $2|\tilde{\xi}\tilde{\eta}| \le \tilde{\xi}^2 + \tilde{\eta}^2$, we have $2E|\tilde{\xi}\tilde{\eta}| \le E\tilde{\xi}^2 + E\tilde{\eta}^2 = 2$. Therefore $E|\tilde{\xi}\tilde{\eta}| \le 1$ and $(E|\xi\eta|)^2 \le E\xi^2 \cdot E\eta^2$.

However, if, say, $E\xi^2 = 0$, this means that $\sum_i x_i^2 P(A_i) = 0$ and consequently the mean value of ξ is 0, and $P\{\omega : \xi(\omega) = 0\} = 1$. Therefore if at least one of $E\xi^2$ or $E\eta^2$ is zero, it is evident that $E|\xi\eta| = 0$ and consequently the Cauchy–Bunyakovskii inequality still holds.

Remark. Property (5) generalizes in an obvious way to any finite number of random variables: if $\xi_1, \ldots, \xi_r$ are independent, then

$$E\xi_1 \cdots \xi_r = E\xi_1 \cdots E\xi_r.$$

The proof can be given in the same way as for the case $r = 2$, or by induction.

EXAMPLE 3. Let ξ be a Bernoulli random variable, taking the values 1 and 0 with probabilities p and q. Then

$$\mathsf{E}\xi = 1 \cdot \mathsf{P}\{\xi = 1\} + 0 \cdot \mathsf{P}\{\xi = 0\} = p.$$

EXAMPLE 4. Let $\xi_1, \ldots, \xi_n$ be n Bernoulli random variables with $\mathsf{P}\{\xi_i = 1\}$ $= p$, $\mathsf{P}\{\xi_i = 0\} = q$, $p + q = 1$. Then if

$$S_n = \xi_1 + \cdots + \xi_n$$

we find that

$$\mathsf{E}S_n = np.$$

This result can be obtained in a different way. It is easy to see that $\mathsf{E}S_n$ is not changed if we assume that the Bernoulli random variables $\xi_1, \ldots, \xi_n$ are independent. With this assumption, we have according to (4)

$$\mathsf{P}(S_n = k) = C_n^k p^k q^{n-k}, \qquad k = 0, 1, \ldots, n.$$

Therefore

$$\mathsf{E}S_n = \sum_{k=0}^{n} k\mathsf{P}(S_n = k) = \sum_{k=0}^{n} k C_n^k p^k q^{n-k}$$

$$= \sum_{k=0}^{n} k \cdot \frac{n!}{k!\,(n-k)!} p^k q^{n-k}$$

$$= np \sum_{k=1}^{n} \frac{(n-1)!}{(k-1)!\,((n-1)-(k-1))!} p^{k-1} q^{(n-1)-(k-1)}$$

$$= np \sum_{l=0}^{n} \frac{(n-1)!}{l!\,((n-1)-l)!} p^l q^{(n-1)-l} = np.$$

However, the first method is more direct.

6. Let $\xi = \sum_i x_i I(A_i)$, where $A_i = \{\omega \colon \xi(\omega) = x_i\}$, and $\varphi = \varphi(\xi(\omega))$ is a function of $\xi(\omega)$. If $B_j = \{\omega \colon \varphi(\xi(\omega)) = y_j\}$, then

$$\varphi(\xi(\omega)) = \sum_j y_j I(B_j),$$

and consequently

$$\mathsf{E}\varphi = \sum_j y_j \mathsf{P}(B_j) = \sum_j y_j \mathsf{P}_\varphi(y_j). \tag{9}$$

But it is also clear that

$$\varphi(\xi(\omega)) = \sum_i \varphi(x_i) I(A_i).$$

Hence, as in (9), the expectation of the random variable $\varphi = \varphi(\xi)$ can be calculated as

$$E\varphi(\xi) = \sum_i \varphi(x_i)P_\xi(x_i).$$

7. The important notion of the variance of a random variable ξ indicates the amount of scatter of the values of ξ around $E\xi$.

Definition 5. The *variance* (also called the *dispersion*) of the random variable ξ (denoted by $V\xi$) is

$$V\xi = E(\xi - E\xi)^2.$$

The number $\sigma = +\sqrt{V\xi}$ is called the standard deviation.
    Since

$$E(\xi - E\xi)^2 = E(\xi^2 - 2\xi \cdot E\xi + (E\xi)^2) = E\xi^2 - (E\xi)^2,$$

we have

$$V\xi = E\xi^2 - (E\xi)^2.$$

Clearly $V\xi \geq 0$. It follows from the definition that

$$V(a + b\xi) = b^2 V\xi, \quad \text{where } a \text{ and } b \text{ are constants.}$$

In particular, $Va = 0$, $V(b\xi) = b^2 V\xi$.
    Let ξ and η be random variables. Then

$$V(\xi + \eta) = E((\xi - E\xi) + (\eta - E\eta))^2$$
$$= V\xi + V\eta + 2E(\xi - E\xi)(\eta - E\eta).$$

Write

$$\text{cov}(\xi, \eta) = E(\xi - E\xi)(\eta - E\eta).$$

This number is called the *covariance* of ξ and η. If $V\xi > 0$ and $V\eta > 0$, then

$$\rho(\xi, \eta) = \frac{\text{cov}(\xi, \eta)}{\sqrt{V\xi \cdot V\eta}}$$

is called the *correlation coefficient* of ξ and η. It is easy to show (see Problem 7 below) that if $\rho(\xi, \eta) = \pm 1$, then ξ and η are linearly dependent:

$$\eta = a\xi + b,$$

with $a > 0$ if $\rho(\xi, \eta) = 1$ and $a < 0$ if $\rho(\xi, \eta) = -1$.
    We observe immediately that if ξ and η are independent, so are $\xi - E\xi$ and $\eta - E\eta$. Consequently by Property (5) of expectations,

$$\text{cov}(\xi, \eta) = E(\xi - E\xi) \cdot E(\eta - E\eta) = 0.$$

Using the notation that we introduced for covariance, we have

$$V(\xi + \eta) = V\xi + V\eta + 2\text{cov}(\xi, \eta); \qquad (10)$$

if ξ and η are independent, the variance of the sum $\xi + \eta$ is equal to the sum of the variances,

$$V(\xi + \eta) = V\xi + V\eta. \qquad (11)$$

It follows from (10) that (11) is still valid under weaker hypotheses than the independence of ξ and η. In fact, it is enough to suppose that ξ and η are uncorrelated, i.e. $\text{cov}(\xi, \eta) = 0$.

Remark. If ξ and η are uncorrelated, it does not follow in general that they are independent. Here is a simple example. Let the random variable α take the values 0, $\pi/2$ and π with probability $\frac{1}{3}$. Then $\xi = \sin \alpha$ and $\eta = \cos \alpha$ are uncorrelated; however, they are not only stochastically dependent (i.e., not independent with respect to the probability P):

$$P\{\xi = 1, \eta = 1\} = 0 \neq \tfrac{1}{9} = P\{\xi = 1\}P\{\eta = 1\},$$

but even functionally dependent: $\xi^2 + \eta^2 = 1$.

Properties (10) and (11) can be extended in the obvious way to any number of random variables:

$$V\left(\sum_{i=1}^{n} \xi_i\right) = \sum_{i=1}^{n} V\xi_i + 2\sum_{i>j} \text{cov}(\xi_i, \xi_j). \qquad (12)$$

In particular, if $\xi_1, \ldots, \xi_n$ are pairwise independent (pairwise uncorrelated is sufficient), then

$$V\left(\sum_{i=1}^{n} \xi_i\right) = \sum_{i=1}^{n} V\xi_i. \qquad (13)$$

EXAMPLE 5. If ξ is a Bernoulli random variable, taking the values 1 and 0 with probabilities p and q, then

$$V\xi = E(\xi - E\xi)^2 = (\xi - p)^2 = (1 - p)^2 p + p^2 q = pq.$$

It follows that if $\xi_1, \ldots, \xi_n$ are independent identically distributed Bernoulli random variables, and $S_n = \xi_1 + \cdots + \xi_n$, then

$$VS_n = npq. \qquad (14)$$

8. Consider two random variables ξ and η. Suppose that only ξ can be observed. If ξ and η are correlated, we may expect that knowing the value of ξ allows us to make some inference about the values of the unobserved variable η.

Any function $f = f(\xi)$ of ξ is called an *estimator* for η. We say that an estimator $f^* = f^*(\xi)$ is *best in the mean-square sense* if

$$E(\eta - f^*(\xi))^2 = \inf_{f} E(\eta - f(\xi))^2.$$

Let us show how to find a best estimator in the class of linear estimators $\lambda(\xi) = a + b\xi$. We consider the function $g(a, b) = E(\eta - (a + b\xi))^2$. Differentiating $g(a, b)$ with respect to a and b, we obtain

$$\frac{\partial g(a, b)}{\partial a} = -2E[\eta - (a + b\xi)],$$

$$\frac{\partial g(a, b)}{\partial b} = -2E[(\eta - (a + b\xi))\xi],$$

whence, setting the derivatives equal to zero, we find that the best mean-square linear estimator is $\lambda^*(\xi) = a^* + b^*\xi$, where

$$a^* = E\eta - b^*E\xi, \qquad b^* = \frac{\text{cov}(\xi, \eta)}{V\xi}. \tag{15}$$

In other words,

$$\lambda^*(\xi) = E\eta + \frac{\text{cov}(\xi, \eta)}{V\xi}(\xi - E\xi). \tag{16}$$

The number $E(\eta - \lambda^*(\xi))^2$ is called the *mean-square error of observation*. An easy calculation shows that it is equal to

$$\Delta^* = E(\eta - \lambda^*(\xi))^2 = V\eta - \frac{\text{cov}^2(\xi, \eta)}{V\xi} = V\eta[1 - \rho^2(\xi, \eta)]. \tag{17}$$

Consequently, the larger (in absolute value) the correlation coefficient $\rho(\xi, \eta)$ between ξ and η, the smaller the mean-square error of observation Δ^*. In particular, if $|\rho(\xi, \eta)| = 1$ then $\Delta^* = 0$ (cf. Problem 7). On the other hand, if ξ and η are uncorrelated ($\rho(\xi, \eta) = 0$), then $\lambda^*(\xi) = E\eta$, i.e. in the absence of correlation between ξ and η the best estimate of η in terms of ξ is simply $E\eta$ (cf. Problem 4).

9. PROBLEMS

1. Verify the following properties of indicators $I_A = I_A(\omega)$:

$$I_\varnothing = 0, \qquad I_\Omega = 1, \qquad I_A + I_{\bar{A}} = 1,$$

$$I_{AB} = I_A \cdot I_B,$$

$$I_{A \cup B} = I_A + I_B - I_{AB}.$$

The indicator of $\bigcup_{i=1}^n A_i$ is $1 - \prod_{i=1}^n (1 - I_{A_i})$, the indicator of $\overline{\bigcup_{i=1}^n A_i}$ is $\prod_{i=1}^n (1 - I_{A_i})$, and the indicator of $\sum_{i=1}^n A_i$ is $\sum_{i=1}^n I_{A_i}$.

$$I_{A \triangle B} = (I_A - I_B)^2,$$

where $A \triangle B$ is the *symmetric difference* of A and B, i.e. the set $(A \backslash B) \cup (B \backslash A)$.

2. Let $\xi_1, \ldots, \xi_n$ be independent random variables and

$$\xi_{\min} = \min(\xi_1, \ldots, \xi_n), \qquad \xi_{\max} = \max(\xi_1, \ldots, \xi_n).$$

Show that

$$P\{\xi_{\min} \geq x\} = \prod_{i=1}^{n} P\{\xi_i \geq x\},$$

$$P\{\xi_{\max} < x\} = \prod_{i=1}^{n} P\{\xi_i < x\}.$$

3. Let $\xi_1, \ldots, \xi_n$ be independent Bernoulli random variables such that

$$P\{\xi_i = 0\} = 1 - \lambda_i \Delta,$$
$$P\{\xi_i = 1\} = \lambda_i \Delta,$$

where Δ is a small number, $\Delta > 0$, $\lambda_i > 0$.
Show that

$$P\{\xi_1 + \cdots + \xi_n = 1\} = \left(\sum_{i=1}^{n} \lambda_i\right)\Delta + O(\Delta^2),$$

$$P\{\xi_1 + \cdots + \xi_n > 1\} = O(\Delta^2).$$

4. Show that $\inf_{-\infty < a < \infty} E(\xi - a)^2$ is attained for $a = E\xi$ and consequently

$$\inf_{-\infty < a < \infty} E(\xi - a)^2 = V\xi.$$

5. Let ξ be a random variable with distribution function $F_\xi(x)$ and let m_e be a median of $F_\xi(x)$, i.e. a point such that

$$F_\xi(m_e-) \leq \tfrac{1}{2} \leq F_\xi(m_e).$$

Show that

$$\inf_{-\infty < a < \infty} E|\xi - a| = E|\xi - m_e|.$$

6. Let $P_\xi(x) = P\{\xi = x\}$ and $F_\xi(x) = P(\xi \leq x)$. Show that

$$P_{a\xi+b}(x) = P_\xi\left(\frac{x-b}{a}\right),$$

$$F_{a\xi+b}(x) = F_\xi\left(\frac{x-b}{a}\right)$$

for $a > 0$ and $-\infty < b < \infty$. If $y \geq 0$, then

$$F_{\xi^2}(y) = F_\xi(+\sqrt{y}) - F_\xi(-\sqrt{y}) + P_\xi(-\sqrt{y}).$$

Let $\xi^+ = \max(\xi, 0)$. Then

$$F_{\xi^+}(x) = \begin{cases} 0, & x < 0, \\ F_\xi(0), & x = 0, \\ F_\xi(x), & x > 0. \end{cases}$$

7. Let ξ and η be random variables with $V\xi > 0$, $V\eta > 0$, and let $\rho = \rho(\xi, \eta)$ be their correlation coefficient. Show that $|\rho| \leq 1$. If $|\rho| = 1$, find constants a and b such that $\eta = a\xi + b$. Moreover, if $\rho = 1$, then

$$\frac{\eta - E\eta}{\sqrt{V\eta}} = \frac{\xi - E\xi}{\sqrt{V\xi}}$$

(and therefore $a > 0$), whereas if $\rho = -1$, then

$$\frac{\eta - E\eta}{\sqrt{V\eta}} = -\frac{\xi - E\xi}{\sqrt{V\xi}}$$

(and therefore $a < 0$).

8. Let ξ and η be random variables with $E\xi = E\eta = 0$, $V\xi = V\eta = 1$ and correlation coefficient $\rho = \rho(\xi, \eta)$. Show that

$$E \max(\xi^2, \eta^2) \leq 1 + \sqrt{1 - \rho^2}.$$

9. Use the equation

$$\left(\text{Indicator of } \overline{\bigcup_{i=1}^{n} A_i}\right) = \prod_{i=1}^{n} (1 - I_{A_i}),$$

to deduce the formula $P(B_0) = 1 - S_1 + S_2 + \cdots \pm S_n$ from Problem 4 of §1.

10. Let $\xi_1, \ldots, \xi_n$ be independent random variables, $\varphi_1 = \varphi_1(\xi_1, \ldots, \xi_k)$ and $\varphi_2 = \varphi_2(\xi_{k+1}, \ldots, \xi_n)$, functions respectively of $\xi_1, \ldots, \xi_k$ and $\xi_{k+1}, \ldots, \xi_n$. Show that the random variables φ_1 and φ_2 are independent.

11. Show that the random variables $\xi_1, \ldots, \xi_n$ are independent if and only if

$$F_{\xi_1, \ldots, \xi_n}(x_1, \ldots, x_n) = F_{\xi_1}(x_1) \cdots F_{\xi_n}(x_n)$$

for all $x_1, \ldots, x_n$, where $F_{\xi_1, \ldots, \xi_n}(x_1, \ldots, x_n) = P\{\xi_1 \leq x_1, \ldots, \xi_n \leq x_n\}$.

12. Show that the random variable ξ is independent of itself (i.e., ξ and ξ are independent) if and only if $\xi = \text{const}$.

13. Under what hypotheses on ξ are the random variables ξ and $\sin \xi$ independent?

14. Let ξ and η be independent random variables and $\eta \neq 0$. Express the probabilities of the events $P\{\xi\eta \leq z\}$ and $P\{\xi/\eta \leq z\}$ in terms of the probabilities $P_\xi(x)$ and $P_\eta(y)$.

§5. The Bernoulli Scheme.   I. The Law of Large Numbers

1. In accordance with the definitions given above, a triple

$$(\Omega, \mathscr{A}, P) \quad \text{with} \quad \Omega = \{\omega : \omega = (a_1, \ldots, a_n), a_i = 0, 1\},$$

$$\mathscr{A} = \{A : A \subseteq \Omega\}, \qquad p(\omega) = p^{\Sigma a_i} q^{n - \Sigma a_i}$$

is called a probabilistic model of n independent experiments with two outcomes, or a Bernoulli scheme.

In this and the next section we study some limiting properties (in a sense described below) for Bernoulli schemes. These are best expressed in terms of random variables and of the probabilities of events connected with them.

We introduce random variables $\xi_1, \ldots, \xi_n$ by taking $\xi_i(\omega) = a_i$, $i = 1, \ldots, n$, where $\omega = (a_1, \ldots, a_n)$. As we saw above, the Bernoulli variables $\xi_i(\omega)$ are independent and identically distributed:

$$\mathsf{P}\{\xi_i = 1\} = p, \qquad \mathsf{P}\{\xi_i = 0\} = q, \qquad i = 1, \ldots, n.$$

It is natural to think of ξ_i as describing the result of an experiment at the ith stage (or at time i).

Let us put $S_0(\omega) \equiv 0$ and

$$S_k = \xi_1 + \cdots + \xi_k, \qquad k = 1, \ldots, n.$$

As we found above, $\mathsf{E}S_n = np$ and consequently

$$\mathsf{E}\frac{S_n}{n} = p. \tag{1}$$

In other words, the mean value of the frequency of "success", i.e. S_n/n, coincides with the probability p of success. Hence we are led to ask how much the frequency S_n/n of success differs from its probability p.

We first note that we cannot expect that, for a sufficiently small $\varepsilon > 0$ and for sufficiently large n, the deviation of S_n/n from p is less than ε for all ω, i.e. that

$$\left| \frac{S_n(\omega)}{n} - p \right| \leq \varepsilon, \qquad \omega \in \Omega. \tag{2}$$

In fact, when $0 < p < 1$,

$$\mathsf{P}\left\{ \frac{S_n}{n} = 1 \right\} = \mathsf{P}\{\xi_1 = 1, \ldots, \xi_n = 1\} = p^n,$$

$$\mathsf{P}\left\{ \frac{S_n}{n} = 0 \right\} = \mathsf{P}\{\xi_1 = 0, \ldots, \xi_n = 0\} = q^n,$$

whence it follows that (2) is not satisfied for sufficiently small $\varepsilon > 0$.

We observe, however, that when n is large the probabilities of the events $\{S_n/n = 1\}$ and $\{S_n/n = 0\}$ are small. It is therefore natural to expect that the total probability of the events for which $|[S_n(\omega)/n] - p| > \varepsilon$ will also be small when n is sufficiently large.

We shall accordingly try to estimate the probability of the event $\{\omega: |[S_n(\omega)/n] - p| > \varepsilon\}$. For this purpose we need the following inequality, which was discovered by Chebyshev.

Chebyshev's inequality. *Let* $(\Omega, \mathscr{A}, \mathsf{P})$ *be a probability space and* $\xi = \xi(\omega)$ *a nonnegative random variable. Then*

$$\mathsf{P}\{\xi \geq \varepsilon\} \leq \mathsf{E}\xi/\varepsilon \tag{3}$$

for all $\varepsilon > 0$.

PROOF. We notice that

$$\xi = \xi I(\xi \geq \varepsilon) + \xi I(\xi < \varepsilon) \geq \xi I(\xi \geq \varepsilon) \geq \varepsilon I(\xi \geq \varepsilon),$$

where $I(A)$ is the indicator of A.

Then, by the properties of the expectation,

$$\mathsf{E}\xi \geq \varepsilon \mathsf{E}I(\xi \geq \varepsilon) = \varepsilon\, \mathsf{P}(\xi \geq \varepsilon),$$

which establishes (3).

Corollary. *If* ξ *is any random variable, we have for* $\varepsilon > 0$,

$$\mathsf{P}\{|\xi| \geq \varepsilon\} \leq \mathsf{E}|\xi|/\varepsilon,$$
$$\mathsf{P}\{|\xi| \geq \varepsilon\} = \mathsf{P}\{\xi^2 \geq \varepsilon^2\} \leq \mathsf{E}\xi^2/\varepsilon^2, \tag{4}$$
$$\mathsf{P}\{|\xi - \mathsf{E}\xi| \geq \varepsilon\} \leq \mathsf{V}\xi/\varepsilon^2.$$

In the last of these inequalities, take $\xi = S_n/n$. Then using (4.14), we obtain

$$\mathsf{P}\left\{\left|\frac{S_n}{n} - p\right| \geq \varepsilon\right\} \leq \frac{\mathsf{V}(S_n/n)}{\varepsilon^2} = \frac{\mathsf{V}S_n}{n^2\varepsilon^2} = \frac{npq}{n^2\varepsilon^2} = \frac{pq}{n\varepsilon^2}.$$

Therefore

$$\mathsf{P}\left\{\left|\frac{S_n}{n} - p\right| \geq \varepsilon\right\} \leq \frac{pq}{n\varepsilon^2} \leq \frac{1}{4n\varepsilon^2}, \tag{5}$$

from which we see that for large n there is rather small probability that the frequency S_n/n of success deviates from the probability p by more than ε.

For $n \geq 1$ and $0 \leq k \leq n$, write

$$P_n(k) = C_n^k p^k q^{n-k}.$$

Then

$$\mathsf{P}\left\{\left|\frac{S_n}{n} - p\right| \geq \varepsilon\right\} = \sum_{\{k:|(k/n)-p|\geq\varepsilon\}} P_n(k),$$

and we have actually shown that

$$\sum_{\{k:|(k/n)-p|\geq\varepsilon\}} P_n(k) \leq \frac{pq}{n\varepsilon^2} \leq \frac{1}{4n\varepsilon^2}, \tag{6}$$

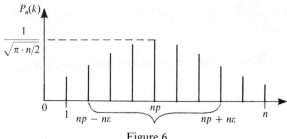

Figure 6

i.e. we have proved an inequality that could also have been obtained analytically, without using the probabilistic interpretation.

It is clear from (6) that

$$\sum_{\{k:|(k/n)-p|\geq\varepsilon\}} P_n(k) \to 0, \qquad n \to \infty. \tag{7}$$

We can clarify this graphically in the following way. Let us represent the binomial distribution $\{P_n(k), 0 \leq k \leq n\}$ as in Figure 6.

Then as n increases the graph spreads out and becomes flatter. At the same time the sum of $P_n(k)$, over k for which $np - n\varepsilon \leq k < np + n\varepsilon$, tends to 1.

Let us think of the sequence of random variables $S_0, S_1, \ldots, S_n$ as the *path* of a wandering particle. Then (7) has the following interpretation.

Let us draw lines from the origin of slopes kp, $k(p + \varepsilon)$, and $k(p - \varepsilon)$. Then on the average the path follows the kp line, and for every $\varepsilon > 0$ we can say that when n is sufficiently large there is a large probability that the point S_n specifying the position of the particle at time n lies in the interval $[n(p - \varepsilon), n(p + \varepsilon)]$; see Figure 7.

We would like to write (7) in the following form:

$$\mathsf{P}\left\{\left|\frac{S_n}{n} - p\right| \geq \varepsilon\right\} \to 0, \qquad n \to \infty, \tag{8}$$

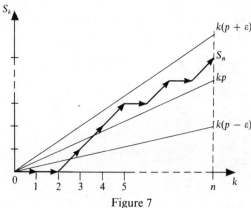

Figure 7

However, we must keep in mind that there is a delicate point involved here. Indeed, the form (8) is really justified only if **P** is a probability on a space $(\Omega, \mathscr{A})$ on which infinitely many sequences of independent Bernoulli random variables $\xi_1, \xi_2, \ldots$, are defined. Such spaces can actually be constructed and (8) can be justified in a completely rigorous probabilistic sense (see Corollary 1 below, the end of §4, Chapter II, and Theorem 1, §9, Chapter II). For the time being, if we want to attach a meaning to the analytic statement (7), using the language of probability theory, we have proved only the following.

Let $(\Omega^{(n)}, \mathscr{A}^{(n)}, \mathsf{P}^{(n)})$, $n \geq 1$, be a sequence of Bernoulli schemes such that

$$\Omega^{(n)} = \{\omega^{(n)}: \omega^{(n)} = (a_1^{(n)}, \ldots, a_n^{(n)}), a_i^{(n)} = 0, 1\},$$

$$\mathscr{A}^{(n)} = \{A: A \subseteq \Omega^{(n)}\},$$

$$p^{(n)}(\omega^{(n)}) = p^{\Sigma a_n^i} \, q^{n - \Sigma a_i^{(n)}}$$

and

$$S_k^{(n)}(\omega^{(n)}) = \xi_1^{(n)}(\omega^{(n)}) + \cdots + \xi_k^{(n)}(\omega^{(n)}),$$

where, for $n \leq 1$, $\xi_1^{(n)}, \ldots, \xi_n^{(n)}$ are sequences of independent identically distributed Bernoulli random variables.

Then

$$\mathsf{P}^{(n)}\left\{\omega^{(n)}: \left|\frac{S_n^{(n)}(\omega^{(n)})}{n} - p\right| \geq \varepsilon\right\} = \sum_{\{k: |(k/n) - p| \geq \varepsilon\}} P_n(k) \to 0, \qquad n \to \infty. \quad (9)$$

Statements like (7)–(9) go by the name of **James Bernoulli's law of large numbers.** We may remark that to be precise, Bernoulli's proof consisted in establishing (7), which he did quite rigorously by using estimates for the "tails" of the binomial probabilities $P_n(k)$ (for the values of k for which $|(k/n) - p| \geq \varepsilon$). A direct calculation of the sum of the tail probabilities of the binomial distribution $\sum_{\{k:|(k/n) - p| \geq \varepsilon\}} P_n(k)$ is rather difficult problem for large n, and the resulting formulas are ill adapted for actual estimates of the probability with which the frequencies S_n/n differ from p by less than ε. Important progress resulted from the discovery by De Moivre (for $p = \frac{1}{2}$) and then by Laplace (for $0 < p < 1$) of simple asymptotic formulas for $P_n(k)$, which led not only to new proofs of the law of large numbers but also to more precise statements of both local and integral limit theorems, the essence of which is that for large n and at least for $k \sim np$,

$$P_n(k) \sim \frac{1}{\sqrt{2\pi npq}} \, e^{-(k - np)^2/(2npq)},$$

and

$$\sum_{\{k: |(k/n) - p| \leq \varepsilon\}} P_n(k) \sim \frac{1}{\sqrt{2\pi}} \int_{-\varepsilon\sqrt{n/pq}}^{\varepsilon\sqrt{n/pq}} e^{-x^2/2} \, dx.$$

2. The next section will be devoted to precise statements and proofs of these results. For the present we consider the question of the real meaning of the law of large numbers, and of its empirical interpretation.

Let us carry out a large number, say N, of series of experiments, each of which consists of "n independent trials with probability p of the event C of interest." Let S_n^i/n be the frequency of event C in the ith series and N_ε the number of series in which the frequency deviates from p by less than ε:
N_ε is the number of i's for which $|(S_n^i/n) - p| \le \varepsilon$. Then

$$N_\varepsilon/N \sim P_\varepsilon \qquad (10)$$

where $P_\varepsilon = \mathsf{P}\{|(S_n^1/n) - p| \le \varepsilon\}$.

It is important to emphasize that an attempt to make (10) precise inevitably involves the introduction of some probability measure, just as an estimate for the deviation of S_n/n from p becomes possible only after the introduction of a probability measure P.

3. Let us consider the estimate obtained above,

$$\mathsf{P}\left\{\left|\frac{S_n}{n} - p\right| \ge \varepsilon\right\} = \sum_{\{k:|(k/n)-p|\ge\varepsilon\}} P_n(k) \le \frac{1}{4n\varepsilon^2}, \qquad (11)$$

as an answer to the following question that is typical of mathematical statistics: what is the least number n of observations that is guaranteed to have (for arbitrary $0 < p < 1$)

$$\mathsf{P}\left\{\left|\frac{S_n}{n} - p\right| \le \varepsilon\right\} \ge 1 - \alpha, \qquad (12)$$

where α is a given number (usually small)?

It follows from (11) that this number is the smallest integer n for which

$$n \ge \frac{1}{4\varepsilon^2\alpha}. \qquad (13)$$

For example, if $\alpha = 0.05$ and $\varepsilon = 0.02$, then 12 500 observations guarantee that (12) will hold independently of the value of the unknown parameter p.

Later (Subsection 5, §6) we shall see that this number is much overstated; this came about because Chebyshev's inequality provides only a very crude upper bound for $\mathsf{P}\{|(S_n/n) - p| \ge \varepsilon\}$.

4. Let us write

$$C(n, \varepsilon) = \left\{\omega: \left|\frac{S_n(\omega)}{n} - p\right| \le \varepsilon\right\}.$$

From the law of large numbers that we proved, it follows that for every $\varepsilon > 0$ and for sufficiently large n, the probability of the set $C(n, \varepsilon)$ is close to 1. In this sense it is natural to call paths (realizations) ω that are in $C(n, \varepsilon)$ *typical* (or (n, ε)-typical).

We ask the following question: How many typical realizations are there, and what is the weight $p(\omega)$ of a typical realization?

For this purpose we first notice that the total number $N(\Omega)$ of points is 2^n, and that if $p = 0$ or 1, the set of typical paths $C(n, \varepsilon)$ contains only the single path $(0, 0, \ldots, 0)$ or $(1, 1, \ldots, 1)$. However, if $p = \frac{1}{2}$, it is intuitively clear that "almost all" paths (all except those of the form $(0, 0, \ldots, 0)$ or $(1, 1, \ldots, 1)$) are typical and that consequently there should be about 2^n of them.

It turns out that we can give a definitive answer to the question whenever $0 < p < 1$; it will then appear that both the number of typical realizations and the weights $p(\omega)$ are determined by a function of p called the entropy.

In order to present the corresponding results in more depth, it will be helpful to consider the somewhat more general scheme of Subsection 2 of §2 instead of the Bernoulli scheme itself.

Let $(p_1, p_2, \ldots, p_r)$ be a finite probability distribution, i.e. a set of nonnegative numbers satisfying $p_1 + \cdots + p_r = 1$. The *entropy* of this distribution is

$$H = - \sum_{i=1}^{r} p_i \ln p_i, \tag{14}$$

with $0 \cdot \ln 0 = 0$. It is clear that $H \geq 0$, and $H = 0$ if and only if every p_i, with one exception, is zero. The function $f(x) = -x \ln x$, $0 \leq x \leq 1$, is convex upward, so that, as know from the theory of convex functions,

$$\frac{f(x_1) + \cdots + f(x_r)}{r} \leq f\left(\frac{x_1 + \cdots + x_r}{r}\right).$$

Consequently

$$H = - \sum_{i=1}^{r} p_i \ln p_i \leq - r \cdot \frac{p_1 + \cdots + p_r}{r} \cdot \ln\left(\frac{p_1 + \cdots + p_r}{r}\right) = \ln r.$$

In other words, the entropy attains its largest value for $p_1 = \cdots = p_r = 1/r$ (see Figure 8 for $H = H(p)$ in the case $r = 2$).

If we consider the probability distribution $(p_1, p_2, \ldots, p_r)$ as giving the probabilities for the occurrence of events $A_1, A_2, \ldots, A_r$, say, then it is quite clear that the "degree of indeterminancy" of an event will be different for

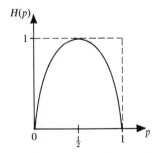

Figure 8. The function $H(p) = -p \ln p - (1 - p)\ln(1 - p)$.

different distributions. If, for example, $p_1 = 1$, $p_2 = \cdots = p_r = 0$, it is clear that this distribution does not admit any indeterminacy: we can say with complete certainty that the result of the experiment will be A_1. On the other hand, if $p_1 = \cdots = p_r = 1/r$, the distribution has maximal indeterminacy, in the sense that it is impossible to discover any preference for the occurrence of one event rather than another.

Consequently it is important to have a quantitative measure of the indeterminacy of different probability distributions, so that we may compare them in this respect. The entropy successfully provides such a measure of indeterminacy; it plays an important role in statistical mechanics and in many significant problems of coding and communication theory.

Suppose now that the sample space is

$$\Omega = \{\omega \colon \omega = (a_1, \ldots, a_n), a_i = 1, \ldots, r\}$$

and that $p(\omega) = p_1^{v_1(\omega)} \cdots p_r^{v_r(\omega)}$, where $v_i(\omega)$ is the number of occurrences of i in the sequence ω, and $(p_1, \ldots, p_r)$ is a probability distribution.

For $\varepsilon > 0$ and $n = 1, 2, \ldots$, let us put

$$C(n, \varepsilon) = \left\{ \omega \colon \left| \frac{v_i(\omega)}{n} - p_i \right| < \varepsilon, i = 1, \ldots, r \right\}.$$

It is clear that

$$\mathsf{P}(C(n, \varepsilon)) \geq 1 - \sum_{i=1}^{r} \mathsf{P}\left\{ \left| \frac{v_i(\omega)}{n} - p_i \right| \geq \varepsilon \right\},$$

and for sufficiently large n the probabilities $\mathsf{P}\{|(v_i(\omega)/n) - p_i| \geq \varepsilon\}$ are arbitrarily small when n is sufficiently large, by the law of large numbers applied to the random variables

$$\xi_k(\omega) = \begin{cases} 1, & a_k = i, \\ 0, & a_k \neq i \end{cases}, \qquad k = 1, \ldots, n.$$

Hence for large n the probability of the event $C(n, \varepsilon)$ is close to 1. Thus, as in the case $n = 2$, a path in $C(n, \varepsilon)$ can be said to be typical.

If all $p_i > 0$, then for every $\omega \in \Omega$

$$p(\omega) = \exp\left\{ -n \sum_{k=1}^{r} \left(-\frac{v_k(\omega)}{n} \ln p_k \right) \right\}.$$

Consequently if ω is a typical path, we have

$$\left| \sum_{k=1}^{r} \left(-\frac{v_k(\omega)}{n} \ln p_k \right) - H \right| \leq -\sum_{k=1}^{r} \left| \frac{v_k(\omega)}{n} - p_k \right| \ln p_k \leq -\varepsilon \sum_{k=1}^{r} \ln p_k.$$

It follows that for typical paths the probability $p(\omega)$ is close to e^{-nH} and — since, by the law of large numbers, the typical paths "almost" exhaust Ω when n is large — the number of such paths must be of order e^{nH}. These considerations lead up to the following proposition.

Theorem (Macmillan). *Let $p_i > 0$, $i = 1, \ldots, r$ and $0 < \varepsilon < 1$. Then there is an $n_0 = n_0(\varepsilon; p_1, \ldots, p_r)$ such that for all $n > n_0$*

(a) $e^{n(H-\varepsilon)} \leq N(C(n, \varepsilon_1)) \leq e^{n(H+\varepsilon)}$;

(b) $e^{-n(H+\varepsilon)} \leq p(\omega) \leq e^{-n(H-\varepsilon)}$, $\omega \in C(n, \varepsilon_1)$;

(c) $\mathsf{P}(C(n, \varepsilon_1)) = \sum\limits_{\omega \in C(n, \varepsilon_n)} p(\omega) \to 1$, $n \to \infty$,

where

$$\varepsilon_1 \text{ is the smaller of } \varepsilon \text{ and } \varepsilon / \left\{ -2 \sum_{k=1}^{r} \ln p_k \right\}.$$

PROOF. Conclusion (c) follows from the law of large numbers. To establish the other conclusions, we notice that if $\omega \in C(n, \varepsilon)$ then

$$np_k - \varepsilon_1 n < v_k(\omega) < np_k + \varepsilon_1 n, \quad k = 1, \ldots, r,$$

and therefore

$$p(\omega) = \exp\{ -\sum v_k \ln p_k \} < \exp\{ -n \sum p_k \ln p_k - \varepsilon_1 n \sum \ln p_k \}$$
$$\leq \exp\{ -n(H - \tfrac{1}{2}\varepsilon) \}.$$

Similarly

$$p(\omega) > \exp\{ -n(H + \tfrac{1}{2}\varepsilon) \}.$$

Consequently (b) is now established.
    Furthermore, since

$$\mathsf{P}(C(n, \varepsilon_1)) \geq N(C(n, \varepsilon_1)) \cdot \min_{\omega \in C(n, \varepsilon_1)} p(\omega),$$

we have

$$N(C(n, \varepsilon_1)) \leq \frac{\mathsf{P}(C(n, \varepsilon_1))}{\min\limits_{\omega \in C(n, \varepsilon_1)} p(\omega)} < \frac{1}{e^{-n(H+(1/2)\varepsilon)}} = e^{n(H+(1/2)\varepsilon)}$$

and similarly

$$N(C(n, \varepsilon_1)) \geq \frac{\mathsf{P}(C(n, \varepsilon_1))}{\max\limits_{\omega \in C(n, \varepsilon_1)} p(\omega)} > \mathsf{P}(C(n, \varepsilon_1)) e^{n(H-(1/2)\varepsilon)}.$$

    Since $\mathsf{P}(C(n, \varepsilon_1)) \to 1$, $n \to \infty$, there is an n_1 such that $\mathsf{P}(C(n, \varepsilon_1)) > 1 - \varepsilon$ for $n > n_1$, and therefore

$$N(C(n, \varepsilon_1)) \geq (1 - \varepsilon) \exp\{ n(H - \tfrac{1}{2}) \}$$
$$= \exp\{ n(H - \varepsilon) + (\tfrac{1}{2}n\varepsilon + \ln(1 - \varepsilon)) \}.$$

Let n_2 be such that

$$\tfrac{1}{2}n\varepsilon + \ln(1 - \varepsilon) > 0.$$

for $n > n_2$. Then when $n \geq n_0 = \max(n_1, n_2)$ we have

$$N(C(n, \varepsilon_1)) \geq e^{n(H - \varepsilon)}.$$

This completes the proof of the theorem.

5. The law of large numbers for Bernoulli schemes lets us give a simple and elegant proof of Weierstrass's theorem on the approximation of continuous functions by polynomials.

Let $f = f(p)$ be a continuous function on the interval $[0, 1]$. We introduce the polynomials

$$B_n(p) = \sum_{k=0}^{n} f\left(\frac{k}{n}\right) C_n^k p^k q^{n-k},$$

which are called Bernstein polynomials after the inventor of this proof of Weierstrass's theorem.

If $\xi_1, \ldots, \xi_n$ is a sequence of independent Bernoulli random variables with $\mathsf{P}\{\xi_i = 1\} = p$, $\mathsf{P}\{\xi_i = 0\} = q$ and $S_n = \xi_1 + \cdots + \xi_n$, then

$$\mathsf{E}f\left(\frac{S_n}{n}\right) = B_n(p).$$

Since the function $f = f(p)$, being continuous on $[0, 1]$, is uniformly continuous, for every $\varepsilon > 0$ we can find $\delta > 0$ such that $|f(x) - f(y)| \leq \varepsilon$ whenever $|x - y| \leq \delta$. It is also clear that the function is bounded: $|f(x)| \leq M < \infty$.

Using this and (5), we obtain

$$|f(p) - B_n(p)| = \left| \sum_{k=0}^{n} \left[f(p) - f\left(\frac{k}{n}\right) \right] C_n^k p^k q^{n-k} \right|$$

$$\leq \sum_{\{k: |(k/n) - p| \leq \delta\}} \left| f(p) - f\left(\frac{k}{n}\right) \right| C_n^k p^k q^{n-k}$$

$$+ \sum_{\{k: |(k/n) - p| > \delta\}} \left| f(p) - f\left(\frac{k}{n}\right) \right| C_n^k p^k q^{n-k}$$

$$\leq \varepsilon + 2M \sum_{\{k: |(k/n) - p| > \delta\}} C_n^k p^k q^{n-k} \leq \varepsilon + \frac{2M}{4n\delta^2} = \varepsilon + \frac{M}{2n\delta^2}.$$

Hence

$$\lim_{n \to \infty} \max_{0 \leq p \leq 1} |f(p) - B_n(p)| = 0,$$

which is the conclusion of Weierstrass's theorem.

6. PROBLEMS

1. Let ξ and η be random variables with correlation coefficient ρ. Establish the following two-dimensional analog of Chebyshev's inequality:

$$P\{|\xi - E\xi| \ge \varepsilon\sqrt{V\xi} \text{ or } |\eta - E\eta| \ge \varepsilon\sqrt{V\eta}\} \le \frac{1}{\varepsilon^2}(1 + \sqrt{1 - \rho^2}).$$

(Hint: Use the result of Problem 8 of §4.)

2. Let $f = f(x)$ be a nonnegative even function that is nondecreasing for positive x. Then for a random variable ξ with $|\xi(\omega)| \le C$,

$$\frac{Ef(\xi) - f(\varepsilon)}{f(C)} \le P\{|\xi - E\xi| \ge \varepsilon\} \le \frac{Ef(\xi - E\xi)}{f(\varepsilon)}.$$

In particular, if $f(x) = x^2$,

$$\frac{E\xi^2 - \varepsilon^2}{C^2} \le P\{|\xi - E\xi| \ge \varepsilon\} \le \frac{V\xi}{\varepsilon^2}.$$

3. Let $\xi_1, \ldots, \xi_n$ be a sequence of independent random variables with $V\xi_i \le C$. Then

$$P\left\{\left|\frac{\xi_1 + \cdots + \xi_n}{n} - \frac{E(\xi_1 + \cdots + \xi_n)}{n}\right| \ge \varepsilon\right\} \le \frac{C}{n\varepsilon^2}. \tag{15}$$

(With the same reservations as in (8), inequality (15) implies the validity of the law of large numbers in more general contexts than Bernoulli schemes.)

4. Let $\xi_1, \ldots, \xi_n$ be independent Bernoulli random variables with $P\{\xi_i = 1\} = p > 0$, $P\{\xi_i = -1\} = 1 - p$. Derive the following *inequality of Bernstein*: there is a number $a > 0$ such that

$$P\left\{\left|\frac{S_n}{n} - (2p - 1)\right| \ge \varepsilon\right\} \le 2e^{-a\varepsilon^2 n},$$

where $S_n = \xi_1 + \cdots + \xi_n$ and $\varepsilon > 0$.

§6. The Bernoulli Scheme. II. Limit Theorems (Local, De Moivre–Laplace, Poisson)

1. As in the preceding section, let

$$S_n = \xi_1 + \cdots + \xi_n.$$

Then

$$E\frac{S_n}{n} = p, \tag{1}$$

and by (4.14)

$$E\left(\frac{S_n}{n} - p\right)^2 = \frac{pq}{n}. \tag{2}$$

It follows from (1) that $S_n/n \sim p$, where the equivalence symbol $\sim$ has been given a precise meaning in the law of large numbers in terms of an inequality for $P\{|(S_n/n) - p| \geq \varepsilon\}$. It is natural to suppose that, in a similar way, the relation

$$\left|\frac{S_n}{n} - p\right| \sim \sqrt{\frac{pq}{n}} \tag{3}$$

which follows from (2), can also be given a precise probabilistic meaning involving, for example, probabilities of the form

$$P\left\{\left|\frac{S_n}{n} - p\right| \leq x\sqrt{\frac{pq}{n}}\right\}, \qquad x \in R^1,$$

or equivalently

$$P\left\{\left|\frac{S_n - ES_n}{\sqrt{VS_n}}\right| \leq x\right\}$$

(since $ES_n = np$ and $VS_n = npq$).

If, as before, we write

$$P_n(k) = C_n^k p^k q^{n-k}, \qquad 0 \leq k \leq n,$$

for $n \geq 1$, then

$$P\left\{\left|\frac{S_n - ES_n}{\sqrt{VS_n}}\right| \leq x\right\} = \sum_{\{k:|(k-np)/\sqrt{npq}|\leq x\}} P_n(k). \tag{4}$$

We set the problem of finding convenient asymptotic formulas, as $n \to \infty$, for $P_n(k)$ and for their sum over the values of k that satisfy the condition on the right-hand side of (4).

The following result provides an answer not only for these values of k (that is, for those satisfying $|k - np| = O(\sqrt{npq})$) but also for those satisfying $|k - np| = o(npq)^{2/3}$.

Local Limit Theorem. *Let* $0 < p < 1$; *then*

$$P_n(k) \sim \frac{1}{\sqrt{2\pi npq}} e^{-(k-np)^2/(2npq)}, \tag{5}$$

uniformly for k such that $|k - np| = o(npq)^{2/3}$, i.e. as $n \to \infty$

$$\sup_{\{k:|k-np|\leq \varphi(n)\}} \left|\frac{P_n(k)}{\dfrac{1}{\sqrt{2\pi npq}} e^{-(k-np)^2/(2npq)}} - 1\right| \to 0,$$

where $\varphi(n) = o(npq)^{2/3}$.

The proof depends on Stirling's formula (2.6)

$$n! = \sqrt{2\pi n}\, e^{-n} n^n (1 + R(n)),$$

where $R(n) \to 0$ as $n \to \infty$.

Then if $n \to \infty$, $k \to \infty$, $n - k \to \infty$, we have

$$C_n^k = \frac{n!}{k!(n-k)!}$$

$$= \frac{\sqrt{2\pi n}\, e^{-n} n^n}{\sqrt{2\pi k \cdot 2\pi(n-k)}\, e^{-k} k^k \cdot e^{-(n-k)}(n-k)^{n-k}} \cdot \frac{1 + R(n)}{(1 + R(k))(1 + R(n-k))}$$

$$= \frac{1}{\sqrt{2\pi n \dfrac{k}{n}\left(1 - \dfrac{k}{n}\right)}} \cdot \frac{1 + \varepsilon(n, k, n-k)}{\left(\dfrac{k}{n}\right)^k \left(1 - \dfrac{k}{n}\right)^{n-k}},$$

where $\varepsilon = \varepsilon(n, k, n-k)$ is defined in an evident way and $\varepsilon \to 0$ as $n \to \infty$, $k \to \infty$, $n - k \to \infty$.

Therefore

$$P_n(k) = C_n^k p^k q^{n-k} = \frac{1}{\sqrt{2\pi n \dfrac{k}{n}\left(1 - \dfrac{k}{n}\right)}} \cdot \frac{p^k (1 - p)^{n-k}}{\left(\dfrac{k}{n}\right)^k \left(1 - \dfrac{k}{n}\right)^{n-k}} (1 + \varepsilon).$$

Write $\hat{p} = k/n$. Then

$$P_n(k) = \frac{1}{\sqrt{2\pi n \hat{p}(1 - \hat{p})}} \left(\frac{p}{\hat{p}}\right)^k \left(\frac{1-p}{1-\hat{p}}\right)^{n-k} (1 + \varepsilon)$$

$$= \frac{1}{\sqrt{2\pi n \hat{p}(1 - \hat{p})}} \exp\left\{k \ln \frac{p}{\hat{p}} + (n-k) \ln \frac{1-p}{1-\hat{p}}\right\} \cdot (1 + \varepsilon)$$

$$= \frac{1}{\sqrt{2\pi n \hat{p}(1 - \hat{p})}} \exp\left\{n\left[\frac{k}{n} \ln \frac{p}{\hat{p}} + \left(1 - \frac{k}{n}\right) \ln \frac{1-p}{1-\hat{p}}\right]\right\} (1 + \varepsilon)$$

$$= \frac{1}{\sqrt{2\pi n \hat{p}(1 - \hat{p})}} \exp\{-n H(\hat{p})\}(1 + \varepsilon),$$

where

$$H(x) = x \ln \frac{x}{p} + (1 - x) \ln \frac{1-x}{1-p}.$$

We are considering values of k such that $|k - np| = o(npq)^{2/3}$, and consequently $p - \hat{p} \to 0$, $n \to \infty$.

Since, for $0 < x < 1$,

$$H'(x) = \ln \frac{x}{p} - \ln \frac{1-x}{1-p},$$

$$H''(x) = \frac{1}{x} + \frac{1}{1-x},$$

$$H'''(x) = -\frac{1}{x^2} + \frac{1}{(1-x)^2},$$

if we write $H(\hat{p})$ in the form $H(p + (\hat{p} - p))$ and use Taylor's formula, we find that for sufficiently large n

$$H(\hat{p}) = H(p) + H'(p)(\hat{p} - p) + \tfrac{1}{2}H''(p)(\hat{p} - p)^2 + O(|\hat{p} - p|^3)$$

$$= \frac{1}{2}\left(\frac{1}{p} + \frac{1}{q}\right)(\hat{p} - p)^2 + O(|\hat{p} - p|^3).$$

Consequently

$$P_n(k) = \frac{1}{\sqrt{2\pi n \hat{p}(1 - \hat{p})}} \exp\left\{ -\frac{n}{2pq}(\hat{p} - p)^2 + nO(|\hat{p} - p|^3) \right\}(1 + \varepsilon).$$

Notice that

$$\frac{n}{2pq}(\hat{p} - p)^2 = \frac{n}{2pq}\left(\frac{k}{n} - p\right)^2 = \frac{(k - np)^2}{2npq}.$$

Therefore

$$P_n(k) = \frac{1}{\sqrt{2\pi npq}} e^{-(k-np)^2/(2npq)}(1 + \varepsilon'(n, k, n - k)),$$

where

$$1 + \varepsilon'(n, k, n - k) = (1 + \varepsilon(n, k, n - k))\exp\{n\, O(|p - \hat{p}|^3)\} \sqrt{\frac{p(1 - p)}{\hat{p}(1 - \hat{p})}}$$

and, as is easily seen,

$$\sup|\varepsilon'(n, k, n - k)| \to 0, \qquad n \to \infty,$$

if the sup is taken over the values of k for which

$$|k - np| \le \varphi(n), \qquad \varphi(n) = o(npq)^{2/3}.$$

This completes the proof.

Corollary. *The conclusion of the local limit theorem can be put in the following equivalent form: For all* $x \in \mathbf{R}^1$ *such that* $x = o(npq)^{1/6}$, *and for* $np + x\sqrt{npq}$ *an integer from the set* $\{0, 1, \ldots, n\}$,

$$P_n(np + x\sqrt{npq}) \sim \frac{1}{\sqrt{2\pi npq}} e^{-x^2/2}, \qquad (7)$$

i.e. as $n \to \infty$,

$$\sup_{\{x:|x| \leq \psi(n)\}} \left| \frac{P_n(np + x\sqrt{npq})}{\frac{1}{\sqrt{2\pi npq}} e^{-x^2/2}} - 1 \right| \to 0, \qquad (8)$$

where $\psi(n) = o(npq)^{1/6}$.

   With the reservations made in connection with formula (5.8), we can reformulate these results in probabilistic language in the following way:

$$P\{S_n = k\} \sim \frac{1}{\sqrt{2\pi npq}} e^{-(k-np)^2/(2npq)}, \qquad |k - np| = o(npq)^{2/3}, \quad (9)$$

$$P\left\{ \frac{S_n - np}{\sqrt{npq}} = x \right\} \sim \frac{1}{\sqrt{2\pi npq}} e^{-x^2/2}, \qquad x = o(npq)^{1/6}. \qquad (10)$$

(In the last formula $np + x\sqrt{npq}$ is assumed to have one of the values $0, 1, \ldots, n$.)

   If we put $t_k = (k - np)/\sqrt{npq}$ and $\Delta t_k = t_{k+1} - t_k = 1/\sqrt{npq}$, the preceding formula assumes the form

$$P\left\{ \frac{S_n - np}{\sqrt{npq}} = t_k \right\} \sim \frac{\Delta t_k}{\sqrt{2\pi}} e^{-t_k^2/2}, \qquad t_k = o(npq)^{1/6}. \qquad (11)$$

   It is clear that $\Delta t_k = 1/\sqrt{npq} \to 0$ and the set of points $\{t_k\}$ as it were "fills" the real line. It is natural to expect that (11) can be used to obtain the integral formula

$$P\left\{ a < \frac{S_n - np}{\sqrt{npq}} \leq b \right\} \sim \frac{1}{\sqrt{2\pi}} \int_a^b e^{-x^2/2} \, dx, \qquad -\infty < a \leq b < \infty.$$

   Let us now give a precise statement.

2. For $-\infty < a \leq b < \infty$ let

$$P_n(a, b] = \sum_{a < x \leq b} P_n(np + x\sqrt{npq}),$$

where the summation is over those x for which $np + x\sqrt{npq}$ is an integer.

It follows from the local theorem (see also (11)) that for all t_k defined by $k = np + t_k\sqrt{npq}$ and satisfying $|t_k| \leq T < \infty$,

$$P_n(np + t_k\sqrt{npq}) = \frac{\Delta t_k}{\sqrt{2\pi}} e^{-t_k^2/2}[1 + \varepsilon(t_k, n)], \qquad (12)$$

where

$$\sup_{|t_k| \leq T} |\varepsilon(t_k, n)| \to 0, \qquad n \to \infty. \qquad (13)$$

Consequently, if a and b are given so that $-T \leq a \leq b \leq T$, then

$$\sum_{a < t_k \leq b} P_n(np + t_k\sqrt{npq}) = \sum_{a < t_k \leq b} \frac{\Delta t_k}{\sqrt{2\pi}} e^{-t_k^2/2} + \sum_{a < t_k \leq b} \varepsilon(t_k, n) \frac{\Delta t_k}{\sqrt{2\pi}} e^{-t_k^2/2}$$

$$= \frac{1}{\sqrt{2\pi}} \int_a^b e^{-x^2/2} \, dx + R_n^{(1)}(a, b) + R_n^{(2)}(a, b), \quad (14)$$

where

$$R_n^{(1)}(a, b) = \sum_{a < t_k \leq b} \frac{\Delta t_k}{\sqrt{2\pi}} e^{-t_k^2/2} - \frac{1}{\sqrt{2\pi}} \int_a^b e^{-x^2/2} \, dx,$$

$$R_n^{(2)}(a, b) = \sum_{a < t_k \leq b} \varepsilon(t_k, n) \frac{\Delta t_k}{\sqrt{2\pi}} e^{-t_k^2/2}.$$

From the standard properties of Riemann sums,

$$\sup_{-T \leq a \leq b \leq T} |R_n^{(1)}(a, b)| \to 0, \qquad n \to \infty. \qquad (15)$$

It also clear that

$$\sup_{-T \leq a \leq b \leq T} |R_n^{(2)}(a, b)|$$

$$\leq \sup_{|t_k| \leq T} |\varepsilon(t_k, n)| \cdot \sum_{|t_k| \leq T} \frac{\Delta t_k}{\sqrt{2\pi}} e^{-t_k^2/2}$$

$$\leq \sup_{|t_k| \leq T} |\varepsilon(t_k, n)|$$

$$\times \left[\frac{1}{\sqrt{2\pi}} \int_{-T}^T e^{-x^2/2} \, dx + \sup_{-T \leq a \leq b \leq T} |R_n^{(1)}(a, b)| \right] \to 0, \quad (16)$$

where the convergence of the right-hand side to zero follows from (15) and from

$$\frac{1}{\sqrt{2\pi}} \int_{-T}^T e^{-x^2/2} \, dx \leq \frac{1}{\sqrt{2\pi}} \int_{-\infty}^\infty e^{-x^2/2} \, dx = 1, \qquad (17)$$

the value of the last integral being well known.

We write

$$\Phi(x) = \frac{1}{\sqrt{2\pi}} \int_{-\infty}^{x} e^{-t^2/2}\, dt.$$

Then it follows from (14)–(16) that

$$\sup_{-T \le a \le b \le T} |P_n(a, b] - (\Phi(b) - \Phi(a))| \to 0, \qquad n \to \infty. \tag{18}$$

We now show that this result holds for $T = \infty$ as well as for finite T. By (17), corresponding to a given $\varepsilon > 0$ we can find a finite $T = T(\varepsilon)$ such that

$$\frac{1}{\sqrt{2\pi}} \int_{-T}^{T} e^{-x^2/2}\, dx > 1 - \tfrac{1}{4}\, \varepsilon. \tag{19}$$

According to (18), we can find an N such that for all $n > N$ and $T = T(\varepsilon)$ we have

$$\sup_{-T \le a \le b \le T} |P_n(a, b] - (\Phi(b) - \Phi(a))| < \tfrac{1}{4}\, \varepsilon. \tag{20}$$

It follows from this and (19) that

$$P_n(-T, T] > 1 - \tfrac{1}{2}\, \varepsilon,$$

and consequently

$$P_n(-\infty, T] + P_n(T, \infty) \le \tfrac{1}{2}\, \varepsilon,$$

where $P_n(-\infty, T] = \lim_{S \downarrow -\infty} P_n(S, T]$ and $P_n(T, \infty) = \lim_{S \uparrow \infty} P_n(T, S]$.
Therefore for $-\infty \le a \le -T < T \le b \le \infty$,

$$\left| P_n(a, b] - \frac{1}{\sqrt{2\pi}} \int_{a}^{b} e^{-x^2/2}\, dx \right|$$

$$\le \left| P_n(-T, T] - \frac{1}{\sqrt{2\pi}} \int_{-T}^{T} e^{-x^2/2}\, dx \right|$$

$$+ \left| P_n(a, -T] - \frac{1}{\sqrt{2\pi}} \int_{a}^{-T} e^{-x^2/2}\, dx \right| + \left| P_n(T, b] - \frac{1}{\sqrt{2\pi}} \int_{T}^{b} e^{-x^2/2}\, dx \right|$$

$$\le \frac{1}{4}\varepsilon + P_n(-\infty, -T] + \frac{1}{\sqrt{2\pi}} \int_{-\infty}^{-T} e^{-x^2/2}\, dx + P_n(T, \infty)$$

$$+ \frac{1}{\sqrt{2\pi}} \int_{T}^{\infty} e^{-x^2/2}\, dx \le \frac{1}{4}\varepsilon + \frac{1}{2}\varepsilon + \frac{1}{8}\varepsilon + \frac{1}{8}\varepsilon = \varepsilon.$$

By using (18) it is now easy to see that $P_n(a, b]$ tends uniformly to $\Phi(b) - \Phi(a)$ for $-\infty \le a < b \le \infty$.

Thus we have proved the following theorem.

De Moivre–Laplace Integral Theorem. *Let* $0 < p < 1$,

$$P_n(k) = C_n^k p^k q^{n-k}, \qquad P_n(a, b] = \sum_{a < x \le b} P_n(np + x\sqrt{npq}),$$

Then

$$\sup_{-\infty \le a < b \le \infty} \left| P_n(a, b] - \frac{1}{\sqrt{2\pi}} \int_a^b e^{-x^2/2}\, dx \right| \to 0, \qquad n \to \infty. \qquad (21)$$

With the same reservations as in (5.8), (21) can be stated in probabilistic language in the following way:

$$\sup_{-\infty \le a < b \le \infty} \left| \mathbf{P}\left\{ a < \frac{S_n - \mathsf{E}S_n}{\sqrt{\mathsf{V}S_n}} \le b \right\} - \frac{1}{\sqrt{2\pi}} \int_a^b e^{-x^2/2}\, dx \right| \to 0, \qquad n \to \infty.$$

It follows at once from this formula that

$$\mathbf{P}\{A < S_n \le B\} - \left[\Phi\left(\frac{B - np}{\sqrt{npq}} \right) - \Phi\left(\frac{A - np}{\sqrt{npq}} \right) \right] \to 0, \qquad (22)$$

as $n \to \infty$, whenever $-\infty \le A < B \le \infty$.

EXAMPLE. A true die is tossed 12 000 times. We ask for the probability P that the number of 6's lies in the interval $(1800, 2100]$.

The required probability is

$$P = \sum_{1800 < k \le 2100} C_{12\,000}^k \left(\frac{1}{6} \right)^k \left(\frac{5}{6} \right)^{12\,000 - k}.$$

An exact calculation of this sum would obviously be rather difficult. However, if we use the integral theorem we find that the probability P in question is ($n = 12\,000$, $p = \frac{1}{6}$, $a = 1800$, $b = 2100$)

$$\Phi\left(\frac{2100 - 2000}{\sqrt{12\,000 \cdot \frac{1}{6} \cdot \frac{5}{6}}} \right) - \Phi\left(\frac{1800 - 2000}{\sqrt{12\,000 \cdot \frac{1}{6} \cdot \frac{5}{6}}} \right) = \Phi(\sqrt{6}) - \Phi(-2\sqrt{6})$$

$$\approx \Phi(2.449) - \Phi(-4.898) \approx 0.992,$$

where the values of $\Phi(2.449)$ and $\Phi(-4.898)$ were taken from tables of $\Phi(x)$ (this is the normal distribution function; see Subsection 6 below).

3. We have plotted a graph of $P_n(np + x\sqrt{npq})$ (with x assumed such that $np + x\sqrt{npq}$ is an integer) in Figure 9.

Then the local theorem says that when $x = o(npq)^{1/6}$, the curve $(1/\sqrt{2\pi npq})e^{-x^2/2}$ provides a close fit to $P_n(np + x\sqrt{npq})$. On the other hand the integral theorem says that $P_n(a, b] = \mathbf{P}\{a\sqrt{npq} < S_n - np \le b\sqrt{npq}\} = \mathbf{P}\{np + a\sqrt{npq} < S_n \le np + b\sqrt{npq}\}$ is closely approximated by the integral $(1/\sqrt{2\pi})\int_a^b e^{-x^2/2}\, dx$.

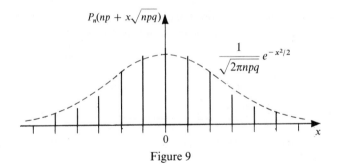

Figure 9

We write

$$F_n(x) = P_n(-\infty, x] \quad \left(= P\left\{\frac{S_n - np}{\sqrt{npq}} \leq x\right\}\right).$$

Then it follows from (21) that

$$\sup_{-\infty \leq x \leq \infty} |F_n(x) - \Phi(x)| \to 0, \qquad n \to \infty. \tag{23}$$

It is natural to ask how rapid the approach to zero is in (21) and (23), as $n \to \infty$. We quote a result in this direction (a special case of the Berry–Esseen theorem: see §6 in Chapter III):

$$\sup_{-\infty \leq x \leq \infty} |F_n(x) - \Phi(x)| \leq \frac{p^2 + q^2}{\sqrt{npq}}. \tag{24}$$

It is important to recognize that the order of the estimate $(1/\sqrt{npq})$ cannot be improved; this means that the approximation of $F_n(x)$ by $\Phi(x)$ can be poor for values of p that are close to 0 or 1, even when n is large. This suggests the question of whether there is a better method of approximation for the probabilities of interest when p or q is small, something better than the normal approximation given by the local and integral theorems. In this connection we note that for $p = \frac{1}{2}$, say, the binomial distribution $\{P_n(k)\}$ is symmetric (Figure 10). However, for small p the binomial distribution is asymmetric (Figure 10), and hence it is not reasonable to expect that the normal approximation will be satisfactory.

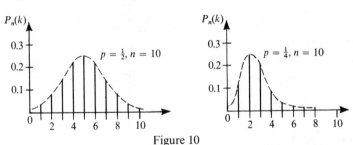

Figure 10

4. It turns out that for small values of p the distribution known as the Poisson distribution provides a good approximation to $\{P_n(k)\}$.

Let

$$P_n(k) = \begin{cases} C_n^k p^k q^{n-k}, & k = 0, 1, \ldots, n, \\ 0, & k = n + 1, n + 2, \ldots, \end{cases}$$

and suppose that p is a function $p(n)$ of n.

Poisson's Theorem. *Let* $p(n) \to 0$, $n \to \infty$, *in such a way that* $np(n) \to \lambda$, *where* $\lambda > 0$. *Then for* $k = 1, 2, \ldots,$

$$P_n(k) \to \pi_k, \qquad n \to \infty, \tag{25}$$

where

$$\pi_k = \frac{\lambda^k e^{-\lambda}}{k!}, \qquad k = 0, 1, \ldots. \tag{26}$$

The proof is extremely simple. Since $p(n) = (\lambda/n) + o(1/n)$ by hypothesis, for a given $k = 0, 1, \ldots$ and sufficiently large n,

$$P_n(k) = C_n^k p^k q^{n-k}$$

$$= \frac{n(n-1)\cdots(n-k+1)}{k!} \left[\frac{\lambda}{n} + o\!\left(\frac{1}{n}\right) \right]^k \cdot \left[1 - \frac{\lambda}{n} + o\!\left(\frac{1}{n}\right) \right]^{n-k}.$$

But

$$n(n-1)\cdots(n-k+1) \left[\frac{\lambda}{n} + o\!\left(\frac{1}{n}\right) \right]^k$$

$$= \frac{n(n-1)\cdots(n-k+1)}{n^k} [\lambda + o(1)]^k \to \lambda^k, \qquad n \to \infty,$$

and

$$\left[1 - \frac{\lambda}{n} + o\!\left(\frac{1}{n}\right) \right]^{n-k} \to e^{-\lambda}, \qquad n \to \infty,$$

which establishes (25).

The set of numbers $\{\pi_k, \; k = 0, 1, \ldots\}$ defines the *Poisson probability distribution* ($\pi_k \geq 0$, $\sum_{k=0}^{\infty} \pi_k = 1$). Notice that all the (discrete) distributions considered previously were concentrated at only a finite number of points. The Poisson distribution is the first example that we have encountered of a (discrete) distribution concentrated at a countable number of points.

The following result of Prohorov exhibits the rapidity with which $P_n(k)$ converges to π_k as $n \to \infty$: if $np(n) = \lambda > 0$, then

$$\sum_{k=0}^{\infty} |P_n(k) - \pi_k| \leq \frac{2\lambda}{n} \cdot \min(2, \lambda). \tag{27}$$

(For the proof of (27), see §7 of Chapter III.)

5. Let us return to the De Moivre–Laplace limit theorem, and show how it implies the law of large numbers (with the same reservation that was made in connection with (5.8)). Since

$$P\left\{\left|\frac{S_n}{n} - p\right| \le \varepsilon\right\} = P\left\{\left|\frac{S_n - np}{\sqrt{npq}}\right| \le \varepsilon\sqrt{\frac{n}{pq}}\right\},$$

it is clear from (21) that when $\varepsilon > 0$

$$P\left\{\left|\frac{S_n}{n} - p\right| \le \varepsilon\right\} - \frac{1}{\sqrt{2\pi}}\int_{-\varepsilon\sqrt{n/pq}}^{\varepsilon\sqrt{n/pq}} e^{-x^2/2}\,dx \to 0, \qquad n \to \infty, \qquad (28)$$

whence

$$P\left\{\left|\frac{S_n}{n} - p\right| \le \varepsilon\right\} \to 1, \qquad n \to \infty,$$

which is the conclusion of the law of large numbers.

From (28)

$$P\left\{\left|\frac{S_n}{n} - p\right| \le \varepsilon\right\} \sim \frac{1}{\sqrt{2\pi}}\int_{-\varepsilon\sqrt{n/pq}}^{\varepsilon\sqrt{n/pq}} e^{-x^2/2}\,dx, \qquad n \to \infty, \qquad (29)$$

whereas Chebyshev's inequality yielded only

$$P\left\{\left|\frac{S_n}{n} - p\right| \le \varepsilon\right\} \ge 1 - \frac{pq}{n\varepsilon^2}.$$

It was shown at the end of §5 that Chebyshev's inequality yielded the estimate

$$n \ge \frac{1}{4\varepsilon^2\alpha}$$

for the number of observations needed for the validity of the inequality

$$P\left\{\left|\frac{S_n}{n} - p\right| \le \varepsilon\right\} \ge 1 - \alpha.$$

Thus with $\varepsilon = 0.02$ and $\alpha = 0.05$, 12 500 observations were needed. We can now solve the same problem by using the approximation (29).

We define the number $k(\alpha)$ by

$$\frac{1}{\sqrt{2\pi}}\int_{-k(\alpha)}^{k(\alpha)} e^{-x^2/2}\,dx = 1 - \alpha.$$

Since $\varepsilon\sqrt{(n/pq)} \ge 2\varepsilon\sqrt{n}$, if we define n as the smallest integer satisfying

$$2\varepsilon\sqrt{n} \ge k(\alpha) \qquad (30)$$

we find that

$$P\left\{\left|\frac{S_n}{n} - p\right| \le \varepsilon\right\} \gtrsim 1 - \alpha. \qquad (31)$$

We find from (30) that the smallest integer n satisfying

$$n \geq \frac{k^2(\alpha)}{4\varepsilon^2}$$

guarantees that (31) is satisfied, and the accuracy of the approximation can easily be established by using (24).

Taking $\varepsilon = 0.02$, $\alpha = 0.05$, we find that in fact 2500 observations suffice, rather than the 12 500 found by using Chebyshev's inequality. The values of $k(\alpha)$ have been tabulated. We quote a number of values of $k(\alpha)$ for various values of α:

α	$k(a)$
0.50	0.675
0.3173	1.000
0.10	1.645
0.05	1.960
0.0454	2.000
0.01	2.576
0.0027	3.000

6. The function

$$\Phi(x) = \frac{1}{\sqrt{2\pi}} \int_{-\infty}^{x} e^{-t^2/2} \, dt, \tag{32}$$

which was introduced above and occurs in the De Moivre–Laplace integral theorem, plays an exceptionally important role in probability theory. It is known as the *normal* or *Gaussian distribution* on the real line, with the (normal or Gaussian) density

$$\varphi(x) = \frac{1}{\sqrt{2\pi}} e^{-x^2/2}, \qquad x \in \mathbf{R}^1.$$

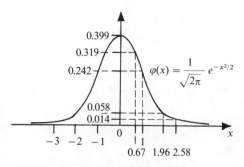

Figure 11. Graph of the normal probability density $\varphi(x)$.

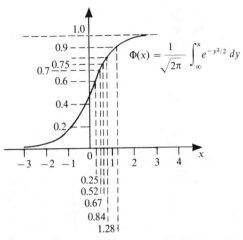

Figure 12. Graph of the normal distribution $\Phi(x)$.

We have already encountered (discrete) distributions concentrated on a finite or countable set of points. The normal distribution belongs to another important class of distributions that arise in probability theory. We have mentioned its exceptional role; this comes about, first of all, because under rather general hypotheses, sums of a large number of independent random variables (not necessarily Bernoulli variables) are closely approximated by the normal distribution (§4 of Chapter III). For the present we mention only some of the simplest properties of $\varphi(x)$ and $\Phi(x)$, whose graphs are shown in Figures 11 and 12.

The function $\varphi(x)$ is a symmetric bell-shaped curve, decreasing very rapidly with increasing $|x|$: thus $\varphi(1) = 0.24197$, $\varphi(2) = 0.053991$, $\varphi(3) = 0.004432$, $\varphi(4) = 0.000134$, $\varphi(5) = 0.000016$. Its maximum is attained at $x = 0$ and is equal to $(2\pi)^{-1/2} \approx 0.399$.

The curve $\Phi(x) = (1/\sqrt{2\pi}) \int_{-\infty}^{x} e^{-t^2/2} \, dt$ approximates 1 very rapidly as x increases: $\Phi(1) = 0.841345$, $\Phi(2) = 0.977250$, $\Phi(3) = 0.998650$, $\Phi(4) = 0.999968$, $\Phi(4, 5) = 0.999997$.

For tables of $\varphi(x)$ and $\Phi(x)$, as well as of other important functions that are used in probability theory and mathematical statistics, see [A1].

7. PROBLEMS

1. Let $n = 100$, $p = \frac{1}{10}, \frac{2}{10}, \frac{3}{10}, \frac{4}{10}, \frac{5}{10}$. Using tables (for example, those in [A1]) of the binomial and Poisson distributions, compare the values of the probabilities

$$P\{10 < S_{100} \leq 12\}, \qquad P\{20 < S_{100} \leq 22\},$$

$$P\{33 < S_{100} \leq 35\}, \qquad P\{40 < S_{100} \leq 42\},$$

$$P\{50 < S_{100} \leq 52\}$$

with the corresponding values given by the normal and Poisson approximations.

2. Let $p = \frac{1}{2}$ and $Z_n = 2S_n - n$ (the excess of 1's over 0's in n trials). Show that

$$\sup_j |\sqrt{\pi n}\, P\{Z_{2n} = j\} - e^{-j^2/4n}| \to 0, \qquad n \to \infty.$$

3. Show that the rate of convergence in Poisson's theorem is given by

$$\sup_k \left| P_n(k) - \frac{\lambda^k e^{-\lambda}}{k!} \right| \le \frac{2\lambda^2}{n}.$$

§7. Estimating the Probability of Success in the Bernoulli Scheme

1. In the Bernoulli scheme $(\Omega, \mathscr{A}, \mathsf{P})$ with $\Omega = \{\omega : \omega = (x_1, \ldots, x_n), x_i = 0, 1)\}$, $\mathscr{A} = A : A \subseteq \Omega\}$,

$$p(\omega) = p^{\Sigma x_i} q^{n - \Sigma x_i},$$

we supposed that p (the probability of success) was known.

Let us now suppose that p is not known in advance and that we want to determine it by observing the outcomes of experiments; or, what amounts to the same thing, by observations of the random variables $\xi_1, \ldots, \xi_n$, where $\xi_i(\omega) = x_i$. This is a typical problem of mathematical statistics, and can be formulated in various ways. We shall consider two of the possible formulations: the problem of *estimation* and the problem of *constructing confidence intervals*.

In the notation used in mathematical statistics, the unknown parameter is denoted by θ, assuming *a priori* that θ belongs to the set $\Theta = [0, 1]$. We say that the set $(\Omega, \mathscr{A}, \mathsf{P}_\theta; \theta \in \Theta)$ with $p_\theta(\omega) = \theta^{\Sigma x_i}(1 - \theta)^{n - \Sigma x_i}$ is a probabilistic-statistical model (corresponding to "n independent trials" with probability of "success" $\theta \in \Theta$), and any function $T_n = T_n(\omega)$ with values in Θ is called an *estimator*.

If $S_n = \xi_1 + \cdots + \xi_n$ and $T_n^* = S_n/n$, it follows from the law of large numbers that T_n^* is *consistent*, in the sense that $(\varepsilon > 0)$

$$\mathsf{P}_\theta\{|T_n^* - \theta| \ge \varepsilon\} \to 0, \qquad n \to \infty. \tag{1}$$

Moreover, this estimator is *unbiased*: for every θ

$$\mathsf{E}_\theta T_n^* = \theta, \tag{2}$$

where E_θ is the expectation corresponding to the probability P_θ.

The property of being unbiased is quite natural: it expresses the fact that any reasonable estimate ought, at least "on the average," to lead to the desired result. However, it is easy to see that T_n^* is not the only unbiased estimator. For example, the same property is possessed by every estimator

$$T_n = \frac{b_1 x_1 + \cdots + b_n x_n}{n},$$

where $b_1 + \cdots + b_n = n$. Moreover, the law of large numbers (1) is also satisfied by such estimators (at least if $|b_i| \le K < \infty$; see Problem 2(b), §3, Chapter III) and so these estimators T_n are just as "good" as T_n^*.

In this connection there arises the question of how to compare different unbiased estimators, and which of them to describe as best, or optimal.

With the same meaning of "estimator," it is natural to suppose that an estimator is better, the smaller its deviation from the parameter that is being estimated. On this basis, we call an estimator $\tilde{T}_n$ *efficient* (in the class of unbiased estimators T_n) if,

$$\mathsf{V}_\theta \tilde{T}_n = \inf_{T_n} \mathsf{V}_\theta T_n, \qquad \theta \in \Theta, \tag{3}$$

where $\mathsf{V}_\theta T_n$ is the dispersion of T_n, i.e. $\mathsf{E}_\theta (T_n - \theta)^2$.

Let us show that the estimator T_n^*, considered above, is efficient. We have

$$\mathsf{V}_\theta T_n^* = \mathsf{V}_\theta \left(\frac{S_n}{n} \right) = \frac{\mathsf{V}_\theta S_n}{n^2} = \frac{n\theta(1 - \theta)}{n^2} = \frac{\theta(1 - \theta)}{n}. \tag{4}$$

Hence to establish that T_n^* is efficient, we have only to show that

$$\inf_{T_n} \mathsf{V}_\theta T_n \ge \frac{\theta(1 - \theta)}{n}. \tag{5}$$

This is obvious for $\theta = 0$ or 1. Let $\theta \in (0, 1)$ and

$$p_\theta(x_i) = \theta^{x_i}(1 - \theta)^{1 - x_i}.$$

It is clear that

$$p_\theta(\omega) = \prod_{i=1}^n p_\theta(x_i).$$

Let us write

$$L_\theta(\omega) = \ln p_\theta(\omega).$$

Then

$$L_\theta(\omega) = \ln \theta \cdot \sum x_i + \ln(1 - \theta) \sum (1 - x_i)$$

and

$$\frac{\partial L_\theta(\omega)}{\partial \theta} = \frac{\sum (x_i - \theta)}{\theta(1 - \theta)}.$$

Since

$$1 = \mathsf{E}_\theta 1 = \sum_\omega p_\theta(\omega),$$

and since T_n is unbiased,

$$\theta \equiv \mathsf{E}_\theta T_n = \sum_\omega T_n(\omega) p_\theta(\omega).$$

After differentiating with respect to θ, we find that

$$0 = \sum_\omega \frac{\partial p_\theta(\omega)}{\partial \theta} = \sum_\omega \frac{\left(\dfrac{\partial p_\theta(\omega)}{\partial \theta}\right)}{p_\theta(\omega)} p_\theta(\omega) = \mathsf{E}_\theta\left[\frac{\partial L_\theta(\omega)}{\partial \theta}\right],$$

$$1 = \sum_\omega T_n \frac{\left(\dfrac{\partial p_\theta(\omega)}{\partial \theta}\right)}{p_\theta(\omega)} p_\theta(\omega) = \mathsf{E}_\theta\left[T_n \frac{\partial L_\theta(\omega)}{\partial \theta}\right].$$

Therefore

$$1 = \mathsf{E}_\theta\left[(T_n - \theta)\frac{\partial L_\theta(\omega)}{\partial \theta}\right]$$

and by the Cauchy–Bunyakovskii inequality,

$$1 \leq \mathsf{E}_\theta[T_n - \theta]^2 \cdot \mathsf{E}_\theta\left[\frac{\partial L_\theta(\omega)}{\partial \theta}\right]^2,$$

whence

$$\mathsf{E}_\theta[T_n - \theta]^2 \geq \frac{1}{I_n(\theta)}, \tag{6}$$

where

$$I_n(\theta) = \left[\frac{\partial L_\theta(\omega)}{\partial \theta}\right]^2$$

is known as *Fisher's information*.

From (6) we can obtain a special case of the Rao–Cramér inequality for unbiased estimators T_n:

$$\inf_{T_n} \mathsf{V}_\theta T_n \geq \frac{1}{I_n(\theta)}. \tag{7}$$

In the present case

$$I_n(\theta) = \mathsf{E}_\theta\left[\frac{\partial L_\theta(\omega)}{\partial \theta}\right]^2 = \mathsf{E}_\theta\left[\frac{\sum(\xi_i - 0)}{\theta(1 - \theta)}\right]^2 = \frac{n\theta(1 - \theta)}{[\theta(1 - \theta)]^2} = \frac{n}{\theta(1 - \theta)},$$

which also establishes (5), from which, as we already noticed, there follows the efficiency of the unbiased estimator $T_n^* = S_n/n$ for the unknown parameter θ.

2. It is evident that, in considering T_n^* as a pointwise estimator for θ, we have introduced a certain amount of inaccuracy. It can even happen that the numerical value of T_n^* calculated from observations of $x_1, \ldots, x_n$ differs rather severely from the true value θ. Hence it would be advisable to determine the size of the error.

It would be too much to hope that $T_n^*(\omega)$ differs little from the true value θ for all sample points ω. However, we know from the law of large numbers that for every $\delta > 0$ and for sufficiently large n, the probability of the event $\{|\theta - T_n^*(\omega)| > \delta\}$ will be arbitrarily small.

By Chebyshev's inequality

$$P_\theta\{|\theta - T_n^*| > \delta\} \leq \frac{V_\theta T_n^*}{\delta^2} = \frac{\theta(1-\theta)}{n\delta^2}$$

and therefore, for every $\lambda > 0$,

$$P_\theta\left\{|\theta - T_n^*| \leq \lambda \sqrt{\frac{\theta(1-\theta)}{n}}\right\} \geq 1 - \frac{1}{\lambda^2}.$$

If we take, for example, $\lambda = 3$, then with P_θ-probability greater than 0.888 $(1 - (1/3^2) = \frac{8}{9} \approx 0.8889)$ the event

$$|\theta - T_n^*| \leq 3\sqrt{\frac{\theta(1-\theta)}{n}}$$

will be realized, and a fortiori the event

$$|\theta - T_n^*| \leq \frac{3}{2\sqrt{n}},$$

since $\theta(1 - \theta) \leq \frac{1}{4}$.

Therefore

$$P_\theta\left\{|\theta - T_n^*| \leq \frac{3}{2\sqrt{n}}\right\} = P_\theta\left\{T_n^* - \frac{3}{2\sqrt{n}} \leq \theta \leq T_n^* + \frac{3}{2\sqrt{n}}\right\} \geq 0.8888.$$

In other words, we can say with probability greater than 0.8888 that the exact value of θ is in the interval $[T_n^* - (3/2\sqrt{n}), T_n^* + (3/2\sqrt{n})]$. This statement is sometimes written in the symbolic form

$$\theta \simeq T_n^* \pm \frac{3}{2\sqrt{n}} \quad (\geq 88\%),$$

where "$\geq 88\%$" means "in more than 88% of all cases."

The interval $[T_n^* - (3/2\sqrt{n}), T_n^* + (3/2\sqrt{n})]$ is an example of what are called confidence intervals for the unknown parameter.

Definition. An interval of the form

$$[\psi_1(\omega), \psi_2(\omega)]$$

where $\psi_1(\omega)$ and $\psi_2(\omega)$ are functions of sample points, is called a *confidence interval of reliability* $1 - \delta$ (or of *significance level* δ) if

$$P_\theta\{\psi_1(\omega) \leq \theta \leq \psi_2(\omega)\} \geq 1 - \delta.$$

for all $\theta \in \Theta$.

The preceding discussion shows that the interval

$$\left[T_n^* - \frac{\lambda}{2\sqrt{n}}, T_n^* + \frac{\lambda}{2\sqrt{n}} \right]$$

has reliability $1 - (1/\lambda^2)$. In point of fact, the reliability of this confidence interval is considerably higher, since Chebyshev's inequality gives only crude estimates of the probabilities of events.

To obtain more precise results we notice that

$$\left\{ \omega : |\theta - T_n^*| \le \lambda \sqrt{\frac{\theta(1 - \theta)}{n}} \right\} = \{ \omega : \psi_1(T_n^*, n) \le \theta \le \psi_2(T_n^*, n) \},$$

where $\psi_1 = \psi_1(T_n^*, n)$ and $\psi_2 = \psi_2(T_n^*, n)$ are the roots of the quadratic equation

$$(\theta - T_n^*)^2 = \frac{\lambda^2}{n} \theta(1 - \theta),$$

which describes an ellipse situated as shown in Figure 13.

Now let

$$F_\theta^n(x) = \mathsf{P}_\theta \left\{ \frac{S_n - n\theta}{\sqrt{n\theta(1 - \theta)}} \le x \right\}.$$

Then by (6.24)

$$\sup_x |F_\theta^n(x) - \Phi(x)| \le \frac{1}{\sqrt{n\theta(1 - \theta)}}.$$

Therefore if we know *a priori* that

$$0 < \Delta \le \theta \le 1 - \Delta < 1,$$

where Δ is a constant, then

$$\sup_x |F_\theta^n(x) - \Phi(x)| \le \frac{1}{\Delta\sqrt{n}}$$

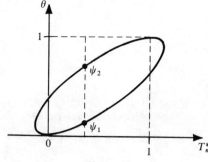

Figure 13

and consequently

$$P_\theta\{\psi_1(T_n^*, n) \le \theta \le \psi_2(T_n^*, n)\} = P_\theta\left\{|\theta - T_n^*| \le \lambda\sqrt{\frac{\theta(1 - \theta)}{n}}\right\}$$

$$= P_\theta\left\{\frac{|S_n - n\theta|}{\sqrt{n\theta(1 - \theta)}} \le \lambda\right\}$$

$$\ge (2\Phi(\lambda) - 1) - \frac{2}{\Delta\sqrt{n}}.$$

Let λ^* be the smallest λ for which

$$(2\Phi(\lambda) - 1) - \frac{2}{\Delta\sqrt{n}} \ge 1 - \delta^*,$$

where δ^* is a given significance level. Putting $\delta = \delta^* - (2/\Delta\sqrt{n})$, we find that λ^* satisfies the equation

$$\Phi(\lambda) = 1 - \frac{1}{2}\delta.$$

For large n we may neglect the term $2/\Delta\sqrt{n}$ and assume that λ^* satisfies

$$\Phi(\lambda^*) = 1 - \frac{1}{2}\delta^*.$$

In particular, if $\lambda^* = 3$ then $\delta^* = 0.9973\ldots$. Then with probability approximately 0.9973

$$T_n^* - 3\sqrt{\frac{\theta(1 - \theta)}{n}} \le \theta \le T_n^* + 3\sqrt{\frac{\theta(1 - \theta)}{n}} \qquad (8)$$

or, after iterating and then suppressing terms of order $O(n^{-3/4})$, we obtain

$$T_n^* - 3\sqrt{\frac{T_n^*(1 - T_n^*)}{n}} \le \theta \le T_n^* + 3\sqrt{\frac{T_n^*(1 - T_n^*)}{n}}. \qquad (9)$$

Hence it follows that the confidence interval

$$\left[T_n^* - \frac{3}{2\sqrt{n}}, T_n^* + \frac{3}{2\sqrt{n}}\right] \qquad (10)$$

has (for large n) reliability 0.9973 (whereas Chebyshev's inequality only provided reliability approximately 0.8889).

Thus we can make the following practical application. Let us carry out a large number N of series of experiments, in each of which we estimate the parameter θ after n observations. Then in about 99.73% of the N cases, in each series the estimate will differ from the true value of the parameter by at most $3/2\sqrt{n}$. (On this topic see also the end of §5.)

3. PROBLEMS

1. Let it be known *a priori* that θ has a value in the set $\Theta_0 \subseteq [0, 1]$. Construct an unbiased estimator for θ, taking values only in Θ_0.

2. Under the hypotheses of the preceding problem, find an analog of the Rao–Cramér inequality and discuss the problem of efficient estimators.

3. Under the hypotheses of the first problem, discuss the construction of confidence intervals for θ.

§8. Conditional Probabilities and Mathematical Expectations with Respect to Decompositions

1. Let $(\Omega, \mathscr{A}, \mathsf{P})$ be a finite probability space and

$$\mathscr{D} = \{D_1, \ldots, D_k\}$$

a decomposition of Ω ($D_i \in \mathscr{A}, \mathsf{P}(D_i) > 0, i = 1, \ldots, k$, and $D_1 + \cdots + D_k = \Omega$). Also let A be an event from $\mathscr{A}$ and $\mathsf{P}(A|D_i)$ the conditional probability of A with respect to D_i.

With a set of conditional probabilities $\{\mathsf{P}(A|D_i), i = 1, \ldots, k\}$ we may associate the random variable

$$\pi(\omega) = \sum_{i=1}^{k} \mathsf{P}(A|D_i) I_{D_i}(\omega) \tag{1}$$

(cf. (4.5)), that takes the values $\mathsf{P}(A|D_i)$ on the atoms of D_i. To emphasize that this *random variable* is associated specifically with the decomposition $\mathscr{D}$, we denote it by

$$\mathsf{P}(A|\mathscr{D}) \quad \text{or} \quad \mathsf{P}(A|\mathscr{D})(\omega)$$

and call it the *conditional probability of the event A with respect to the decomposition $\mathscr{D}$.*

This concept, as well as the more general concept of conditional probabilities with respect to a σ-algebra, which will be introduced later, plays an important role in probability theory, a role that will be developed progressively as we proceed.

We mention some of the simplest properties of conditional probabilities:

$$\mathsf{P}(A + B|\mathscr{D}) = \mathsf{P}(A|\mathscr{D}) + \mathsf{P}(B|\mathscr{D}); \tag{2}$$

if $\mathscr{D}$ is the trivial decomposition consisting of the single set Ω then

$$\mathsf{P}(A|\Omega) = \mathsf{P}(A). \tag{3}$$

The definition of $P(A|\mathscr{D})$ as a random variable lets us speak of its expectation; by using this, we can write the *formula* (3.3) *for total probability* in the following compact form:

$$EP(A|\mathscr{D}) = P(A). \tag{4}$$

In fact, since

$$P(A|\mathscr{D}) = \sum_{i=1}^{k} P(A|D_i)I_{D_i}(\omega),$$

then by the definition of expectation (see (4.5) and (4.6))

$$EP(A|\mathscr{D}) = \sum_{i=1}^{k} P(A|D_i)P(D_i) = \sum_{i=1}^{k} P(AD_i) = P(A).$$

Now let $\eta = \eta(\omega)$ be a random variable that takes the values $y_1, \ldots, y_k$ with positive probabilities:

$$\eta(\omega) = \sum_{j=1}^{k} y_j I_{D_j}(\omega),$$

where $D_j = \{\omega\colon \eta(\omega) = y_j\}$. The decomposition $\mathscr{D}_\eta = \{D_1, \ldots, D_k\}$ is called the decomposition induced by η. The conditional probability $P(A|\mathscr{D}_\eta)$ will be denoted by $P(A|\eta)$ or $P(A|\eta)(\omega)$, and called the *conditional probability of A with respect to the random variable* η. We also denote by $P(A|\eta = y_j)$ the conditional probability $P(A|D_j)$, where $D_j = \{\omega\colon \eta(\omega) = y_j\}$.

Similarly, if $\eta_1, \eta_2, \ldots, \eta_m$ are random variables and $\mathscr{D}_{\eta_1, \eta_2, \ldots, \eta_m}$ is the decomposition induced by $\eta_1, \eta_2, \ldots, \eta_m$ with atoms

$$D_{y_1, y_2, \ldots, y_m} = \{\omega\colon \eta_1(\omega) = y_1, \ldots, \eta_m(\omega) = y_m\},$$

then $P(A|D_{\eta_1, \eta_2, \ldots, \eta_m})$ will be denoted by $P(A|\eta_1, \eta_2, \ldots, \eta_m)$ and called the conditional probability of A with respect to $\eta_1, \eta_2, \ldots, \eta_m$.

EXAMPLE 1. Let ξ and η be independent identically distributed random variables, each taking the values 1 and 0 with probabilities p and q. For $k = 0, 1, 2$, let us find the conditional probability $P(\xi + \eta = k|\eta)$ of the event $A = \{\omega\colon \xi + \eta = k\}$ with respect to η.

To do this, we first notice the following useful general fact: if ξ and η are independent random variables with respective values x and y, then

$$P(\xi + \eta = z|\eta = y) = P(\xi + y = z). \tag{5}$$

In fact,

$$P(\xi + \eta = f|\eta = y) = \frac{P(\xi + \eta = z, \eta = y)}{P(\eta = y)}$$

$$= \frac{P(\xi + y = z, \eta = y)}{P(\eta = y)} = \frac{P(\xi + y = z)P(y = \eta)}{P(\eta = y)}$$

$$= P(\xi + y = z).$$

Using this formula for the case at hand, we find that

$$P(\xi + \eta = k | \eta) = P(\xi + \eta = k | \eta = 0)I_{\{\eta = 0\}}(\omega)$$
$$+ P(\xi + \eta = k | \eta = 1)I_{\{\eta = 1\}}(\omega)$$
$$= P(\xi = k)I_{\{\eta = 0\}}(\omega) + P\{\xi = k - 1\}I_{\{\eta = 1\}}(\omega).$$

Thus

$$P(\xi + \eta = k | \eta) = \begin{cases} qI_{\{\eta = 0\}}(\omega), & k = 0, \\ pI_{\{\eta = 0\}}(\omega) + qI_{\{\eta = 1\}}(\omega), & k = 1, \\ pI_{\{\eta = 1\}}(\omega), & k = 2, \end{cases} \tag{6}$$

or equivalently

$$P(\xi + \eta = k | \eta) = \begin{cases} q(1 - \eta), & k = 0, \\ p(1 - \eta) + q\eta, & k = 1, \\ p\eta, & k = 2, \end{cases} \tag{7}$$

2. Let $\xi = \xi(\omega)$ be a random variable with values in the set $X = \{x_1, \ldots, x_n\}$:

$$\xi = \sum_{j=1}^{l} x_j I_{A_j}(\omega), \qquad A_j = \{\omega : \xi = x_j\}$$

and let $\mathscr{D} = \{D_1, \ldots, D_k\}$ be a decomposition. Just as we defined the expectation of ξ with respect to the probabilities $P(A_j), j = 1, \ldots, l$.

$$E\xi = \sum_{j=1}^{l} x_j P(A_j), \tag{8}$$

it is now natural to define the *conditional expectation of ξ with respect to $\mathscr{D}$* by using the conditional probabilities $P(A_j | \mathscr{D})$, $j = 1, \ldots, l$. We denote this expectation by $E(\xi | \mathscr{D})$ or $E(\xi | \mathscr{D})(\omega)$, and define it by the formula

$$E(\xi | \mathscr{D}) = \sum_{j=1}^{l} x_j P(A_j | \mathscr{D}). \tag{9}$$

According to this definition the conditional expectation $E(\xi | \mathscr{D})(\omega)$ is a random variable which, at all sample points ω belonging to the same atom D_i, takes the same value $\sum_{j=1}^{l} x_j P(A_j | D_i)$. This observation shows that the definition of $E(\xi | D_i)$ could have been expressed differently. In fact, we could first define $E(\xi | D_i)$, the conditional expectation of ξ with respect to D_i, by

$$E(\xi | D_i) = \sum_{j=1}^{l} x_j P(A_j | D_i) \left(= \frac{E[\xi I_{D_i}]}{P(D_i)} \right), \tag{10}$$

and then define

$$E(\xi | \mathscr{D})(\omega) = \sum_{i=1}^{k} E(\xi | D_i) I_{D_i}(\omega) \tag{11}$$

(see the diagram in Figure 14).

$$P(\cdot) \xrightarrow{\quad (8) \quad} E\xi$$

$$\Big\downarrow (3.1)$$

$$P(\cdot|D) \xrightarrow{\quad (10) \quad} E(\xi|D)$$

$$\Big\downarrow (1) \qquad\qquad \Big\downarrow (11)$$

$$P(\cdot|\mathscr{D}) \xrightarrow{\quad (9) \quad} E(\xi|\mathscr{D})$$

Figure 14

It is also useful to notice that $E(\xi|D)$ and $E(\xi|\mathscr{D})$ are independent of the representation of ξ.

The following properties of conditional expectations follow immediately from the definitions:

$$E(a\xi + b\eta|\mathscr{D}) = aE(\xi|\mathscr{D}) + bE(\eta|\mathscr{D}), \qquad a \text{ and } b \text{ constants}; \quad (12)$$

$$E(\xi|\Omega) = E\xi; \tag{13}$$

$$E(C|\mathscr{D}) = C, \qquad C \text{ constant}; \tag{14}$$

if $\xi = I_A(\omega)$ then

$$E(\xi|\mathscr{D}) = P(A|\mathscr{D}). \tag{15}$$

The last equation shows, in particular, that properties of conditional probabilities can be deduced directly from properties of conditional expectations.

The following important property generalizes the *formula for total probability* (5):

$$EE(\xi|\mathscr{D}) = E\xi. \tag{16}$$

For the proof, it is enough to notice that by (5)

$$EE(\xi|\mathscr{D}) = E \sum_{j=1}^{l} x_j P(A_j|\mathscr{D}) = \sum_{j=1}^{l} x_j EP(A_j|\mathscr{D}) = \sum_{j=1}^{l} x_j P(A_j) = E\xi.$$

Let $\mathscr{D} = \{D_1, \ldots, D_k\}$ be a decomposition and $\eta = \eta(\omega)$ a random variable. We say that η is measurable with respect to this decomposition, or $\mathscr{D}$-measurable, if $\mathscr{D}_\eta \preccurlyeq \mathscr{D}$, i.e. $\eta = \eta(\omega)$ can be represented in the form

$$\eta(\omega) = \sum_{i=1}^{k} y_i I_{D_i}(\omega),$$

where some y_i might be equal. In other words, a random variable is $\mathscr{D}$-measurable if and only if it takes constant values on the atoms of $\mathscr{D}$.

EXAMPLE 2. If $\mathscr{D}$ is the trivial decomposition, $\mathscr{D} = \{\Omega\}$, then η is $\mathscr{D}$-measurable if and only if $\eta \equiv C$, where C is a constant. Every random variable η is measurable with respect to $\mathscr{D}_\eta$.

Suppose that the random variable η is $\mathscr{D}$-measurable. Then

$$\mathsf{E}(\xi\eta \mid \mathscr{D}) = \eta \mathsf{E}(\xi \mid \mathscr{D}) \tag{17}$$

and in particular

$$\mathsf{E}(\eta \mid \mathscr{D}) = \eta \qquad (\mathsf{E}(\eta \mid \mathscr{D}_n) = \eta). \tag{18}$$

To establish (17) we observe that if $\xi = \sum_{j=1}^{l} x_j I_{A_j}$, then

$$\xi\eta = \sum_{j=1}^{l} \sum_{i=1}^{k} x_j y_i I_{A_j D_i}$$

and therefore

$$\begin{aligned}
\mathsf{E}(\xi\eta \mid \mathscr{D}) &= \sum_{j=1}^{l} \sum_{i=1}^{k} x_j y_i \mathsf{P}(A_j D_i \mid \mathscr{D}) \\
&= \sum_{j=1}^{l} \sum_{i=1}^{k} x_j y_i \sum_{m=1}^{k} \mathsf{P}(A_j D_i \mid D_m) I_{D_m}(\omega) \\
&= \sum_{j=1}^{l} \sum_{i=1}^{k} x_j y_i \mathsf{P}(A_j D_i \mid D_i) I_{D_i}(\omega) \\
&= \sum_{j=1}^{l} \sum_{i=1}^{k} x_j y_i \mathsf{P}(A_j \mid D_i) I_{D_i}(\omega).
\end{aligned} \tag{19}$$

On the other hand, since $I_{D_i}^2 = I_{D_i}$ and $I_{D_i} \cdot I_{D_m} = 0$, $i \neq m$, we obtain

$$\begin{aligned}
\eta \mathsf{E}(\xi \mid \mathscr{D}) &= \left[\sum_{i=1}^{k} y_i I_{D_i}(\omega) \right] \cdot \left[\sum_{j=1}^{l} x_j \mathsf{P}(A_j \mid \mathscr{D}) \right] \\
&= \left[\sum_{i=1}^{k} y_i I_{D_i}(\omega) \right] \cdot \sum_{m=1}^{k} \left[\sum_{j=1}^{l} x_j \mathsf{P}(A_j \mid D_m) \right] \cdot I_{D_m}(\omega) \\
&= \sum_{i=1}^{k} \sum_{j=1}^{l} y_i x_j \mathsf{P}(A_j \mid D_i) \cdot I_{D_i}(\omega),
\end{aligned}$$

which, with (19), establishes (17).

We shall establish another important property of conditional expectations. Let $\mathscr{D}_1$ and $\mathscr{D}_2$ be two decompositions, with $\mathscr{D}_1 \preccurlyeq \mathscr{D}_2$ ($\mathscr{D}_2$ is "finer" than $\mathscr{D}_1$). Then

$$\mathsf{E}[\mathsf{E}(\xi \mid \mathscr{D}_2) \mid \mathscr{D}_1] = \mathsf{E}(\xi \mid \mathscr{D}_1). \tag{20}$$

For the proof, suppose that

$$\mathscr{D}_1 = \{D_{11}, \ldots, D_{1m}\}, \qquad \mathscr{D}_2 = \{D_{21}, \ldots, D_{2n}\}.$$

Then if $\xi = \sum_{j=1}^{l} x_j I_{A_j}$, we have

$$\mathsf{E}(\xi \mid \mathscr{D}_2) = \sum_{j=1}^{l} x_j \mathsf{P}(A_j \mid \mathscr{D}_2),$$

and it is sufficient to establish that

$$E[P(A_j|\mathscr{D}_2)|\mathscr{D}_1] = P(A_j|\mathscr{D}_1). \tag{21}$$

Since

$$P(A_j|\mathscr{D}_2) = \sum_{q=1}^{n} P(A_j|D_{2q})I_{D_{2q}},$$

we have

$$E[P(A_j|\mathscr{D}_2)|\mathscr{D}_1] = \sum_{q=1}^{n} P(A_j|D_{2q})P(D_{2q}|\mathscr{D}_1)$$

$$= \sum_{q=1}^{n} P(A_j|D_{2q})\left[\sum_{p=1}^{m} P(D_{2q}|D_{1p})I_{D_{1p}}\right]$$

$$= \sum_{p=1}^{m} I_{D_{1p}} \cdot \sum_{q=1}^{n} P(A_j|D_{2q})P(D_{2q}|D_{1p})$$

$$= \sum_{p=1}^{m} I_{D_{1p}} \cdot \sum_{\{q:\, D_{2q}\subseteq D_{1p}\}} P(A_j|D_{2q})P(D_{2q}|D_{1p})$$

$$= \sum_{p=1}^{m} I_{D_{1p}} \cdot \sum_{\{q:\, D_{2q}\subseteq D_{1p}\}} \frac{P(A_jD_{2q})}{P(D_{2q})} \cdot \frac{P(D_{2q})}{P(D_{1p})}$$

$$= \sum_{p=1}^{m} I_{D_{1p}} \cdot P(A_j|D_{1p}) = P(A_j|\mathscr{D}_1),$$

which establishes (21).

When $\mathscr{D}$ is induced by the random variables $\eta_1, \ldots, \eta_k$ ($\mathscr{D} = \mathscr{D}_{\eta_1,\ldots,\eta_k}$), the conditional expectation $E(\xi|\mathscr{D}_{\eta_1,\ldots,\eta_k})$ is denoted by $E(\xi|\eta_1,\ldots,\eta_k)$, or $E(\xi|\eta_1,\ldots,\eta_k)(\omega)$, and is called the *conditional expectation of* ξ *with respect to* $\eta_1,\ldots,\eta_k$.

It follows immediately from the definition of $E(\xi|\eta)$ that if ξ and η are *independent*, then

$$E(\xi|\eta) = E\xi. \tag{22}$$

From (18) it also follows that

$$E(\eta|\eta) = \eta. \tag{23}$$

Property (22) admits the following generalization. Let ξ be independent of $\mathscr{D}$ (i.e. for each $D_i \in \mathscr{D}$ the random variables ξ and I_{D_i} are independent). Then

$$E(\xi|\mathscr{D}) = E\xi. \tag{24}$$

As a special case of (20) we obtain the following useful formula:

$$E[E(\xi|\eta_1,\eta_2)|\eta_1] = E(\xi|\eta_1). \tag{25}$$

EXAMPLE 3. Let us find $E(\xi + \eta | \eta)$ for the random variables ξ and η considered in Example 1. By (22) and (23),

$$E(\xi + \eta | \eta) = E\xi + \eta = p + \eta.$$

This result can also be obtained by starting from (8):

$$E(\xi + \eta | \eta) = \sum_{k=0}^{2} kP(\xi + \eta = k | \eta) = p(1 - \eta) + q\eta + 2p\eta = p + \eta.$$

EXAMPLE 4. Let ξ and η be independent and identically distributed random variables. Then

$$E(\xi | \xi + \eta) = E(\eta | \xi + \eta) = \frac{\xi + \eta}{2}. \tag{26}$$

In fact, if we assume for simplicity that ξ and η take the values $1, 2, \ldots, m$, we find ($1 \le k \le m, 2 \le l \le 2m$)

$$\begin{aligned}
P(\xi = k | \xi + \eta = l) &= \frac{P(\xi = k, \xi + \eta = l)}{P(\xi + \eta = l)} = \frac{P(\xi = k, \eta = l - k)}{P(\xi + \eta = l)} \\
&= \frac{P(\xi = k)P(\eta = l - k)}{P(\xi + \eta = l)} = \frac{P(\eta = k)P(\xi = l - k)}{P(\xi + \eta = l)} \\
&= P(\eta = k | \xi + \eta = l).
\end{aligned}$$

This establishes the first equation in (26). To prove the second, it is enough to notice that

$$2E(\xi | \xi + \eta) = E(\xi | \xi + \eta) + E(\eta | \xi + \eta) = E(\xi + \eta | \xi + \eta) = \xi + \eta.$$

3. We have already noticed in §1 that to each decomposition $\mathscr{D} = \{D_1, \ldots, D_k\}$ of the finite set Ω there corresponds an algebra $\alpha(\mathscr{D})$ of subsets of Ω. The converse is also true: every algebra $\mathscr{B}$ of subsets of the finite space Ω generates a decomposition $\mathscr{D}$ ($\mathscr{B} = \alpha(\mathscr{D})$). Consequently there is a one-to-one correspondence between algebras and decompositions of a finite space Ω. This should be kept in mind in connection with the concept, which will be introduced later, of conditional expectation with respect to the special systems of sets called σ-algebras.

For finite spaces, the concepts of algebra and σ-algebra coincide. It will turn out that if $\mathscr{B}$ is an algebra, the conditional expectation $E(\xi | \mathscr{B})$ of a random variable ξ with respect to $\mathscr{B}$ (to be introduced in §7 of Chapter II) simply coincides with $E(\xi | \mathscr{D})$, the expectation of ξ with respect to the decomposition $\mathscr{D}$ such that $\mathscr{B} = \alpha(\mathscr{D})$. In this sense we can, in dealing with finite spaces in the future, not distinguish between $E(\xi | \mathscr{B})$ and $E(\xi | \mathscr{D})$, understanding in each case that $E(\xi | \mathscr{B})$ is simply defined to be $E(\xi | \mathscr{D})$.

4. PROBLEMS

1. Give an example of random variables ξ and η which are not independent but for which

$$E(\xi|\eta) = E\xi.$$

(Cf. (22).)

2. The conditional variance of ξ with respect to $\mathscr{D}$ is the random variable

$$V(\xi|\mathscr{D}) = E[(\xi - E(\xi|\mathscr{D}))^2|\mathscr{D}].$$

Show that

$$V\xi = EV(\xi|\mathscr{D}) + VE(\xi|\mathscr{D}).$$

3. Starting from (17), show that for every function $f = f(\eta)$ the conditional expectation $E(\xi|\eta)$ has the property

$$E[f(\eta)E(\xi|\eta)] = E[\xi f(\eta)].$$

4. Let ξ and η be random variables. Show that $\inf_f E(\eta - f(\xi))^2$ is attained for $f^*(\xi) = E(\eta|\xi)$. (Consequently, the best estimator for η in terms of ξ, in the mean-square sense, is the conditional expectation $E(\eta|\xi)$).

5. Let $\xi_1, \ldots, \xi_n, \tau$ be independent random variables, where $\xi_1, \ldots, \xi_n$ are identically distributed and τ takes the values $1, 2, \ldots, n$. Show that if $S_\tau = \xi_1 + \cdots + \xi_\tau$ is the sum of a random number of the random variables,

$$E(S_\tau|\tau) = \tau E\xi_1, \qquad V(S_\tau|\tau) = \tau V\xi_1$$

and

$$ES_\tau = E\tau \cdot E\xi_1, \qquad VS_\tau = E\tau \cdot V\xi_1 + V\tau \cdot (E\xi_1)^2.$$

6. Establish equation (24).

§9. Random Walk. I. Probabilities of Ruin and Mean Duration in Coin Tossing

1. The value of the limit theorems of §6 for Bernoulli schemes is not just that they provide convenient formulas for calculating probabilities $P(S_n = k)$ and $P(A < S_n \leq B)$. They have the additional significance of being of a universal nature, i.e. they remain useful not only for independent Bernoulli random variables that have only two values, but also for variables of much more general character. In this sense the Bernoulli scheme appears as the simplest model, on the basis of which we can recognize many probabilistic regularities which are inherent also in much more general models.

In this and the next section we shall discuss a number of new probabilistic regularities, some of which are quite surprising. The ones that we discuss are again based on the Bernoulli scheme, although many results on the nature of random oscillations remain valid for random walks of a more general kind.

2. Consider the Bernoulli scheme $(\Omega, \mathscr{A}, \mathsf{P})$, where $\Omega = \{\omega \colon \omega = (x_1, \ldots, x_n),$ $x_i = \pm 1\}$, $\mathscr{A}$ consists of all subsets of Ω, and $p(\omega) = p^{\nu(\omega)} q^{n - \nu(\omega)}$, $\nu(\omega) = (\sum x_i + n)/2$. Let $\xi_i(\omega) = x_i$, $i = 1, \ldots, n$. Then, as we know, the sequence $\xi_1, \ldots, \xi_n$ is a sequence of independent Bernoulli random variables,

$$\mathsf{P}(\xi_i = 1) = p, \qquad \mathsf{P}(\xi_i = -1) = q, \qquad p + q = 1.$$

Let us put $S_0 = 0$, $S_k = \xi_1 + \cdots + \xi_k$, $1 \leq k \leq n$. The sequence S_0, $S_1, \ldots, S_n$ can be considered as the path of the random motion of a particle starting at zero. Here $S_{k+1} = S_k + \xi_k$, i.e. if the particle has reached the point S_k at time k, then at time $k + 1$ it is displaced either one unit up (with probability p) or one unit down (with probability q).

Let A and B be integers, $A \leq 0 \leq B$. An interesting problem about this random walk is to find the probability that after n steps the moving particle has left the interval (A, B). It is also of interest to ask with what probability the particle leaves (A, B) at A or at B.

That these are natural questions to ask becomes particularly clear if we interpret them in terms of a gambling game. Consider two players (first and second) who start with respective bankrolls $(-A)$ and B. If $\xi_i = +1$, we suppose that the second player pays one unit to the first; if $\xi_i = -1$, the first pays the second. Then $S_k = \xi_1 + \cdots + \xi_k$ can be interpreted as the amount won by the first player from the second (if $S_k < 0$, this is actually the amount lost by the first player to the second) after k turns.

At the instant $k \leq n$ at which for the first time $S_k = B$ ($S_k = A$) the bankroll of the second (first) player is reduced to zero; in other words, that player is ruined. (If $k < n$, we suppose that the game ends at time k, although the random walk itself is well defined up to time n, inclusive.)

Before we turn to a precise formulation, let us introduce some notation. Let x be an integer in the interval $[A, B]$ and for $0 \leq k \leq n$ let $S_k^x = x + S_k$,

$$\tau_k^x = \min\{0 \leq l \leq k \colon S_l^x = A \text{ or } B\}, \tag{1}$$

where we agree to take $\tau_k^x = k$ if $A < S_l^x < B$ for all $0 \leq l \leq k$.

For each k in $0 \leq k \leq n$ and $x \in [A, B]$, the instant τ_k^x, called a *stopping time* (see §11), is an integer-valued random variable defined on the sample space Ω (the dependence of τ_k^x on Ω is not explicitly indicated).

It is clear that for all $l < k$ the set $\{\omega \colon \tau_k^x = l\}$ is the event that the random walk $\{S_i^x, 0 \leq i \leq k\}$, starting at time zero at the point x, leaves the interval (A, B) at time l. It is also clear that when $l \leq k$ the sets $\{\omega \colon \tau_k^x = l, S_l^x = A\}$ and $\{\omega \colon \tau_k^x = l, S_l^x = B\}$ represent the events that the wandering particle leaves the interval (A, B) at time l through A or B respectively.

For $0 \leq k \leq n$, we write

$$\mathscr{A}_k^x = \sum_{0 \leq l \leq k} \{\omega : \tau_k^x = l, S_l^x = A\},$$

$$\mathscr{B}_k^x = \sum_{0 \leq l \leq k} \{\omega : \tau_k^x = l, S_l^x = B\},$$

(2)

and let

$$\alpha_k(x) = \mathsf{P}(\mathscr{A}_k^x), \qquad \beta_k(x) = \mathsf{P}(\mathscr{B}_k^x)$$

be the probabilities that the particle leaves (A, B), through A or B respectively, during the time interval $[0, k]$. For these probabilities we can find recurrent relations from which we can successively determine $\alpha_1(x), \ldots, \alpha_n(x)$ and $\beta_1(x), \ldots, \beta_n(x)$.

Let, then, $A < x < B$. It is clear that $\alpha_0(x) = \beta_0(x) = 0$. Now suppose $1 \leq k \leq n$. Then by (8.5),

$$\begin{aligned}
\beta_k(x) = \mathsf{P}(\mathscr{B}_k^x) &= \mathsf{P}(\mathscr{B}_k^x | S_1^x = x + 1)\mathsf{P}(\xi_1 = 1) \\
&\quad + \mathsf{P}(\mathscr{B}_k^x | S_1^x = x - 1)\mathsf{P}(\xi_1 = -1) \\
&= p\mathsf{P}(\mathscr{B}_k^x = x + 1) + q\mathsf{P}(\mathscr{B}_k^x | S_1^x = x - 1).
\end{aligned}$$

(3)

We now show that

$$\mathsf{P}(\mathscr{B}_k^x | S_1^x = x + 1) = \mathsf{P}(\mathscr{B}_{k-1}^{x+1}), \qquad \mathsf{P}(\mathscr{B}_k^x | S_1^x = x - 1) = \mathsf{P}(\mathscr{B}_{k-1}^{x-1}).$$

To do this, we notice that $\mathscr{B}_k^x$ can be represented in the form

$$\mathscr{B}_k^x = \{\omega : (x, x + \xi_1, \ldots, x + \xi_1 + \cdots + \xi_k) \in B_k^x\},$$

where B_k^x is the set of paths of the form

$$(x, x + x_1, \ldots, x + x_1 + \cdots x_k)$$

with $x_1 = \pm 1$, which during the time $[0, k]$ first leave (A, B) at B (Figure 15).

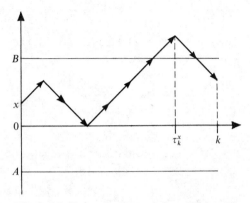

Figure 15. Example of a path from the set B_k^x.

We represent B_k^x in the form $B_k^{x,x+1} + B_k^{x,x-1}$, where $B_k^{x,x+1}$ and $B_k^{x,x-1}$ are the paths in B_k^x for which $x_1 = +1$ or $x_1 = -1$, respectively.

Notice that the paths $(x, x + 1, x + 1 + x_2, \ldots, x + 1 + x_2 + \cdots + x_k)$ in $B_k^{x,x+1}$ are in one-to-one correspondence with the paths

$$(x + 1, x + 1 + x_2, \ldots, x + 1 + x_2, \ldots, x + 1 + x_2 + \cdots + x_k)$$

in B_{k-1}^{x+1}. The same is true for the paths in $B_k^{x,x-1}$. Using these facts, together with independence, the identical distribution of $\xi_1, \ldots, \xi_k$, and (8.6), we obtain

$$\mathsf{P}(\mathcal{B}_k^x | S_1^x = x + 1)$$
$$= \mathsf{P}(\mathcal{B}_k^x | \xi_1 = 1)$$
$$= \mathsf{P}\{(x, x + \xi_1, \ldots, x + \xi_1 + \cdots + \xi_k) \in B_k^x | \xi_1 = 1\}$$
$$= \mathsf{P}\{(x + 1, x + 1 + \xi_2, \ldots, x + 1 + \xi_2 + \cdots + \xi_k) \in B_{k-1}^{x+1}\}$$
$$= \mathsf{P}\{(x + 1, x + 1 + \xi_1, \ldots, x + 1 + \xi_1 + \cdots + \xi_{k-1}) \in B_{k-1}^{x+1}\}$$
$$= \mathsf{P}(\mathcal{B}_{k-1}^{x+1}).$$

In the same way,

$$\mathsf{P}(\mathcal{B}_k^x | S_1^x = x - 1) = \mathsf{P}(\mathcal{B}_{k-1}^{x-1}).$$

Consequently, by (3) with $x \in (A, B)$ and $k \leq n$,

$$\beta_k(x) = p\beta_{k-1}(x + 1) + q\beta_{k-1}(x - 1), \tag{4}$$

where

$$\beta_l(B) = 1, \qquad \beta_l(A) = 0, \qquad 0 \leq l \leq n. \tag{5}$$

Similarly

$$\alpha_k(x) = p\alpha_{k-1}(x + 1) + q\alpha_{k-1}(x - 1) \tag{6}$$

with

$$\alpha_1(A) = 1, \qquad \alpha_l(B) = 0, \qquad 0 \leq l \leq n.$$

Since $\alpha_0(x) = \beta_0(x) = 0$, $x \in (A, B)$, these recurrent relations can (at least in principle) be solved for the probabilities

$$\alpha_1(x), \ldots, \alpha_n(x) \quad \text{and} \quad \beta_1(x), \ldots, \beta_n(x).$$

Putting aside any explicit calculation of the probabilities, we ask for their values for large n.

For this purpose we notice that since $\mathcal{B}_{k-1}^x \subset \mathcal{B}_k^x$, $k \leq n$, we have $\beta_{k-1}(x) \leq \beta_k(x) \leq 1$. It is therefore natural to expect (and this is actually the case; see Subsection 3) that for sufficiently large n the probability $\beta_n(x)$ will be close to the solution $\beta(x)$ of the equation

$$\beta(x) = p\beta(x + 1) + q\beta(x - 1) \tag{7}$$

with the boundary conditions

$$\beta(B) = 1, \qquad \beta(A) = 0, \tag{8}$$

that result from a formal approach to the limit in (4) and (5).

To solve the problem in (7) and (8), we first suppose that $p \neq q$. We see easily that the equation has the two particular solutions a and $b(q/p)^x$, where a and b are constants. Hence we look for a solution of the form

$$\beta(x) = a + b(q/p)^x. \tag{9}$$

Taking account of (8), we find that for $A \leq x \leq B$

$$\beta(x) = \frac{(q/p)^x - (q/p)^A}{(q/p)^B - (q/p)^A}. \tag{10}$$

Let us show that this is the *only* solution of our problem. It is enough to show that all solutions of the problem in (7) and (8) admit the representation (9).

Let $\tilde{\beta}(x)$ be a solution with $\tilde{\beta}(A) = 0$, $\tilde{\beta}(B) = 1$. We can always find constants $\tilde{a}$ and $\tilde{b}$ such that

$$\tilde{a} + \tilde{b}(q/p)^A = \tilde{b}(A), \qquad \tilde{a} + \tilde{b}(q/p)^{A+1} = \tilde{\beta}(A + 1).$$

Then it follows from (7) that

$$\tilde{\beta}(A + 2) = \tilde{a} + \tilde{b}(q/p)^{A+2}$$

and generally

$$\tilde{\beta}(x) = \tilde{a} + \tilde{b}(q/p)^x.$$

Consequently the solution (10) is the only solution of our problem.

A similar discussion shows that the only solution of

$$\alpha(x) = p\alpha(x + 1) + q\alpha(x - 1), \qquad x \in (A, B) \tag{11}$$

with the boundary conditions

$$\alpha(A) = 1, \qquad \alpha(B) = 0 \tag{12}$$

is given by the formula

$$\alpha(x) = \frac{(p/q)^B - (q/p)^x}{(p/q)^B - (p/p)^A}, \qquad A \leq x \leq B. \tag{13}$$

If $p = q = \frac{1}{2}$, the only solutions $\beta(x)$ and $\alpha(x)$ of (7), (8) and (11), (12) are respectively

$$\beta(x) = \frac{x - A}{B - A} \tag{14}$$

and

$$\alpha(x) = \frac{B - x}{B - A}. \tag{15}$$

We note that

$$\alpha(x) + \beta(x) = 1 \tag{16}$$

for $0 \le p \le 1$.

We call $\alpha(x)$ and $\beta(x)$ the *probabilities of ruin for the first and second players*, respectively (when the first player's bankroll is $x - A$, and the second player's is $B - x$) under the assumption of infinitely many turns, which of course presupposes an infinite sequence of independent Bernoulli random variables $\xi_1, \xi_2, \dots$, where $\xi_i = +1$ is treated as a gain for the first player, and $\xi_i = -1$ as a loss. The probability space $(\Omega, \mathscr{A}, \mathsf{P})$ considered at the beginning of this section turns out to be too small to allow such an infinite sequence of independent variables. We shall see later that such a sequence can actually be constructed and that $\beta(x)$ and $\alpha(x)$ are in fact the probabilities of ruin in an unbounded number of steps.

We now take up some corollaries of the preceding formulas.

If we take $A = 0$, $0 \le x \le B$, then the definition of $\beta(x)$ implies that this is the probability that a particle starting at x arrives at B before it reaches 0. It follows from (10) and (14) (Figure 16) that

$$\beta(x) = \begin{cases} x/B, & p = q = \tfrac{1}{2}, \\ \dfrac{(q/p)^x - 1}{(q/p)^B - 1}, & p \ne q. \end{cases} \tag{17}$$

Now let $q > p$, which means that the game is unfavorable for the first player, whose limiting probability of being ruined, namely $\alpha = \alpha(0)$, is given by

$$\alpha = \frac{(q/p)^B - 1}{(q/p)^B - (q/p)^A}.$$

Next suppose that the rules of the game are changed: the original bankrolls of the players are still $(-A)$ and B, but the payoff for each player is now $\tfrac{1}{2}$,

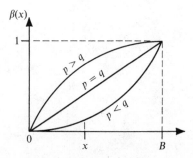

Figure 16. Graph of $\beta(x)$, the probability that a particle starting from x reaches B before reaching 0.

rather than 1 as before. In other words, now let $P(\xi_i = \frac{1}{2}) = p$, $P(\xi_i = -\frac{1}{2}) = q$. In this case let us denote the limiting probability of ruin for the first player by $\alpha_{1/2}$. Then

$$\alpha_{1/2} = \frac{(q/p)^{2B} - 1}{(q/p)^{2B} - (q/p)^{2A}},$$

and therefore

$$\alpha_{1/2} = \alpha \cdot \frac{(q/p)^B + 1}{(q/p)^B + (q/p)^A} > \alpha,$$

if $q > p$.

Hence we can draw the following conclusion: *if the game is unfavorable to the first player (i.e., $q > p$) then doubling the stake decreases the probability of ruin.*

3. We now turn to the question of how fast $\alpha_n(x)$ and $\beta_n(x)$ approach their limiting values $\alpha(x)$ and $\beta(x)$.

Let us suppose for simplicity that $x = 0$ and put

$$\alpha_n = \alpha_n(0), \qquad \beta_n = \beta_n(0), \qquad \gamma_n = 1 - (\alpha_n + \beta_n).$$

It is clear that

$$\gamma_n = P\{A < S_k < B, 0 \le k \le n\},$$

where $\{A < S_k < B, 0 \le k \le n\}$ denotes the event

$$\bigcap_{0 \le k \le n} \{A < S_k < B\}.$$

Let $n = rm$, where r and m are integers and

$$\zeta_1 = \xi_1 + \cdots + \xi_m,$$
$$\zeta_2 = \xi_{m+1} + \cdots + \xi_{2m},$$
$$\dots\dots\dots\dots\dots\dots\dots\dots$$
$$\zeta_r = \xi_{m(r-1)+1} + \cdots + \xi_{rm}.$$

Then if $C = |A| + B$, it is easy to see that

$$\{A < S_k < B, 1 \le k \le rm\} \subseteq \{|\zeta_1| < C, \dots, |\zeta_r| < C\},$$

and therefore, since $\zeta_1, \dots, \zeta_r$ are independent and identically distributed,

$$\gamma_n \le P\{|\zeta_1| < C, \dots, |\zeta_r| < C\} = \prod_{i=1}^{r} P\{|\zeta_i| < C\} = (P\{|\zeta_1| < C\})^r. \quad (18)$$

We notice that $V\zeta_1 = m[1 - (p - q)^2]$. Hence, for $0 < p < 1$ and sufficiently large m,

$$P\{|\zeta_1| < c\} \le \varepsilon_1, \quad (19)$$

where $\varepsilon_1 < 1$, since $V\zeta_1 \le C^2$ if $P\{|\zeta_1| \le C\} = 1$.

If $p = 0$ or $p = 1$, then $\mathbf{P}\{|\zeta_1| < C\} = 0$ for sufficiently large m, and consequently (19) is satisfied for $0 \leq p \leq 1$.

It follows from (18) and (19) that for sufficiently large n

$$\gamma_n \leq \varepsilon^n, \tag{20}$$

where $\varepsilon = \varepsilon_1^{1/m} < 1$.

According to (16), $\alpha + \beta = 1$. Therefore

$$(\alpha - \alpha_n) + (\beta - \beta_n) = \gamma_n,$$

and since $\alpha \geq \alpha_n$, $\beta \geq \beta_n$, we have

$$0 \leq \alpha - \alpha_n \leq \gamma_n \leq \varepsilon^n,$$

$$0 \leq \beta - \beta_n \leq \gamma_n \leq \varepsilon^n, \qquad \varepsilon < 1.$$

There are similar inequalities for the differences $\alpha(x) - \alpha_n(x)$ and $\beta(x) - \beta_n(x)$.

4. We now consider the question of the *mean duration* of the random walk.

Let $m_k(x) = \mathbf{E}\tau_k^x$ be the expectation of the stopping time $\tau_k^x, k \leq n$. Proceeding as in the derivation of the recurrent relations for $\beta_x(x)$, we find that, for $x \in (A, B)$,

$$m_k(x) = \mathbf{E}\tau_k^x = \sum_{1 \leq l \leq k} l\mathbf{P}(\tau_k^x = l)$$

$$= \sum_{1 \leq l \leq k} l \cdot [p\mathbf{P}(\tau_k^x = l | \xi_1 = 1) + q\mathbf{P}(\tau_k^x = l | \xi_1 = -1)]$$

$$= \sum_{1 \leq l \leq k} l \cdot [p\mathbf{P}(\tau_{k-1}^{x+1} = l - 1) + q\mathbf{P}(\tau_{k-1}^{x-1} = l - 1)]$$

$$= \sum_{0 \leq l \leq k-1} (l + 1)[p\mathbf{P}(\tau_{k-1}^{x+1} = l) + q\mathbf{P}(\tau_{k-1}^{x-1} = l)]$$

$$= pm_{k-1}(x + 1) + qm_{k-1}(x - 1)$$

$$\quad + \sum_{0 \leq l \leq k-1} [p\mathbf{P}(\tau_{k-1}^{x+1} = l) + q\mathbf{P}(\tau_{k-1}^{x-1} = l)]$$

$$= pm_{k-1}(x + 1) + qm_{k-1}(x - 1) + 1.$$

Thus, for $x \in (A, B)$ and $0 \leq k \leq n$, the functions $m_k(x)$ satisfy the recurrent relations

$$m_k(x) = 1 + pm_{k-1}(x + 1) + qm_{k-1}(x - 1), \tag{21}$$

with $m_0(x) = 0$. From these equations together with the boundary conditions

$$m_k(A) = m_k(B) = 0, \tag{22}$$

we can successively find $m_1(x), \ldots, m_n(x)$.

Since $m_k(x) \leq m_{k+1}(x)$, the limit

$$m(x) = \lim_{n \to \infty} m_n(x)$$

exists, and by (21) it satisfies the equation

$$m(x) + 1 + pm(x + 1) + qm(x - 1) \qquad (23)$$

with the boundary conditions

$$m(A) = m(B) = 0. \qquad (24)$$

To solve this equation, we first suppose that

$$m(x) < \infty, \qquad x \in (A, B). \qquad (25)$$

Then if $p \neq q$ there is a particular solution of the form $\alpha/(q - p)$ and the general solution (see (9)) can be written in the form

$$m(x) = \frac{x}{q - p} + a + b\left(\frac{q}{p}\right)^x.$$

Then by using the boundary conditions $m(A) = m(B) = 0$ we find that

$$m(x) = \frac{1}{p - q}(B\beta(x) + A\alpha(x) - x], \qquad (26)$$

where $\beta(x)$ and $\alpha(x)$ are defined by (10) and (13). If $p = q = \frac{1}{2}$, the general solution of (23) has the form

$$m(x) = a + bx - x^2,$$

and since $m(A) = m(B) = 0$ we have

$$m(x) = (B - x)(x - A). \qquad (27)$$

It follows, in particular, that if the players start with equal bankrolls $(B = -A)$, then

$$m(0) = B^2.$$

If we take $B = 10$, and suppose that each turn takes a second, then the (limiting) time to the ruin of one player is rather long: 100 seconds.

We obtained (26) and (27) under the assumption that $m(x) < \infty, x \in (A, B)$. Let us now show that in fact $m(x)$ is finite for all $x \in (A, B)$. We consider only the case $x = 0$; the general case can be analyzed similarly.

Let $p = q = \frac{1}{2}$. We introduce the random variable S_{τ_n} defined in terms of the sequence $S_0, S_1, \ldots, S_n$ and the stopping time $\tau_n = \tau_n^0$ by the equation

$$S_{\tau_n} = \sum_{k=0}^{n} S_k I_{\{\tau_n = k\}}(\omega). \qquad (28)$$

The descriptive meaning of S_{τ_n} is clear: it is the position reached by the random walk at the stopping time τ_n. Thus, if $\tau_n < n$, then $S_{\tau_n} = A$ or B; if $\tau_n = n$, then $A \leq S_{\tau_n} \leq B$.

Let us show that when $p = q = \frac{1}{2}$,

$$\mathsf{E}S_{\tau_n} = 0, \tag{29}$$

$$\mathsf{E}S_{\tau_n}^2 = \mathsf{E}\tau_n. \tag{30}$$

To establish the first equation we notice that

$$\mathsf{E}S_{\tau_n} = \sum_{k=0}^{n} \mathsf{E}[S_k I_{\{\tau_n = k\}}(\omega)]$$

$$= \sum_{k=0}^{n} \mathsf{E}[S_n I_{\{\tau_n = k\}}(\omega)] + \sum_{k=0}^{n} \mathsf{E}[(S_k - S_n)I_{\{\tau_n = k\}}(\omega)]$$

$$= \mathsf{E}S_n + \sum_{k=0}^{n} \mathsf{E}[(S_k - S_n)I_{\{\tau_n = k\}}(\omega)], \tag{31}$$

where we evidently have $\mathsf{E}S_n = 0$. Let us show that

$$\sum_{k=0}^{n} \mathsf{E}[(S_k - S_n)I_{\{\tau_n = k\}}(\omega)] = 0.$$

To do this, we notice that $\{\tau_n > k\} = \{A < S_1 < B, \ldots, A < S_k < B\}$ when $0 \le k < n$. The event $\{A < S_1 < B, \ldots, A < S_k < B\}$ can evidently be written in the form

$$\{\omega : (\xi_1, \ldots, \xi_k) \in A_k\}, \tag{32}$$

where A_k is a subset of $\{-1, +1\}^k$. In other words, this set is determined by just the values of $\xi_1, \ldots, \xi_k$ and does not depend on $\xi_{k+1}, \ldots, \xi_n$. Since

$$\{\tau_n = k\} = \{\tau_n > k - 1\} \backslash \{\tau_n > k\},$$

this is also a set of the form (32). It then follows from the independence of $\xi_1, \ldots, \xi_n$ and from Problem 9 of §4 that the random variables $S_n - S_k$ and $I_{\{\tau_n = k\}}$ are independent, and therefore

$$\mathsf{E}[(S_n - S_k)I_{\{\tau_n = k\}}] = \mathsf{E}[S_n - S_k] \cdot \mathsf{E}I_{\{\tau_n = k\}} = 0.$$

Hence we have established (29).

We can prove (30) by the same method:

$$\mathsf{E}S_{\tau_n}^2 = \sum_{k=0}^{n} \mathsf{E}S_k^2 I_{\{\tau_n = k\}} = \sum_{k=0}^{n} \mathsf{E}([S_n + (S_k - S_n)]^2 I_{\{\tau_n = k\}})$$

$$= \sum_{k=0}^{n} [\mathsf{E}S_n^2 I_{\{\tau_n = k\}} + 2\mathsf{E}S_n(S_k - S_n)I_{\{\tau_n = k\}}$$

$$+ \mathsf{E}(S_n - S_k)^2 I_{\{\tau_n = k\}}] = \mathsf{E}S_n^2 - \sum_{k=0}^{n} \mathsf{E}(S_n - S_k)^2 I_{\{\tau_n = k\}}$$

$$= n - \sum_{k=0}^{n} (n - k)\mathsf{P}(\tau_n = k) = \sum_{k=0}^{n} k\mathsf{P}(\tau_n = k) = \mathsf{E}\tau_n.$$

Thus we have (29) and (30) when $p = q = \frac{1}{2}$. For general p and q $(p + q = 1)$ it can be shown similarly that

$$\mathsf{E}S_{\tau_n} = (p - q) \cdot \mathsf{E}\tau_n, \tag{33}$$

$$\mathsf{E}[S_{\tau_n} - \tau_n \cdot \mathsf{E}\xi_1]^2 = \mathsf{V}\xi_1 \cdot \mathsf{E}\tau_n, \tag{34}$$

where $\mathsf{E}\xi_1 = p - q$, $\mathsf{V}\xi_1 = 1 - (p - q)^2$.

With the aid of the results obtained so far we can now show that $\lim_{n \to \infty} m_n(0) = m(0) < \infty$.

If $p = q = \frac{1}{2}$, then by (30)

$$\mathsf{E}\tau_n \le \max(A^2, B^2). \tag{35}$$

If $p \ne q$, then by (33),

$$\mathsf{E}\tau_n \le \frac{\max(|A|, B)}{|p - q|}, \tag{36}$$

from which it is clear that $m(0) < \infty$.

We also notice that when $p = q = \frac{1}{2}$

$$\mathsf{E}\tau_n = \mathsf{E}S_{\tau_n}^2 = A^2 \cdot \alpha_n + B^2 \cdot \beta_n + \mathsf{E}[S_n^2 I_{\{A < S_n < B\}}]$$

and therefore

$$A^2 \cdot \alpha_n + B^2 \cdot \beta_n \le \mathsf{E}\tau_n \le A^2 \cdot \alpha_n + B^2 \cdot \beta_n + \max(A^2, B^2) \cdot \gamma_n.$$

It follows from this and (20) that as $n \to \infty$, $\mathsf{E}\tau_n$ converges with exponential rapidity to

$$m(0) = A^2\alpha + B^2\beta = A^2 \cdot \frac{B}{B - A} - B^2 \cdot \frac{A}{B - A} = |AB|.$$

There is a similar result when $p \ne q$:

$$\mathsf{E}\tau_n \to m(0) = \frac{\alpha A + \beta B}{p - q}, \quad \text{exponentially fast.}$$

5. PROBLEMS

1. Establish the following generalizations of (33) and (34):

$$\mathsf{E}S_{\tau_n}^x = x + (p - q)\mathsf{E}\tau_n^x,$$

$$\mathsf{E}[S_{\tau_n^x} - \tau_n^x \cdot \mathsf{E}\xi_1]^2 = \mathsf{V}\xi_1 \cdot \mathsf{E}\tau_n^x.$$

2. Investigate the limits of $\alpha(x)$, $\beta(x)$, and $m(x)$ when the level $A \downarrow -\infty$.

3. Let $p = q = \frac{1}{2}$ in the Bernoulli scheme. What is the order of $\mathsf{E}|S_n|$ for large n?

4. Two players each toss their own symmetric coins, independently. Show that the probability that each has the same number of heads after n tosses is $2^{-2n}\sum_{k=0}^{n}(C_n^k)^2$. Hence deduce the equation $\sum_{k=0}^{n}(C_n^k)^2 = C_{2n}^n$.

Let σ_n be the first time when the number of heads for the first player coincides with the number of heads for the second player (if this happens within n tosses; $\sigma_n = n+1$ if there is no such time). Find $E\min(\sigma_n, n)$.

§10. Random Walk. II. Reflection Principle. Arcsine Law

1. As in the preceding section, we suppose that $\xi_1, \xi_2, \ldots, \xi_{2n}$ is a sequence of independent identically distributed Bernoulli random variables with

$$P(\xi_i = 1) = p, \qquad P(\xi_i = -1) = q,$$

$$S_k = \xi_1 + \cdots + \xi_k, \qquad 1 \le k \le 2n; \qquad S_0 = 0.$$

We define

$$\sigma_{2n} = \min\{1 \le k \le 2n : S_k = 0\},$$

putting $\sigma_{2n} = \infty$ if $S_k \ne 0$ for $1 \le k \le 2n$.

The descriptive meaning of σ_{2n} is clear: it is the time of first return to zero. Properties of this time are studied in the present section, where we assume that the random walk is symmetric, i.e. $p = q = \frac{1}{2}$.

For $0 \le k \le n$ we write

$$u_{2k} = P(S_{2k} = 0), \qquad f_{2k} = P(\sigma_{2n} = 2k). \tag{1}$$

It is clear that $u_0 = 1$ and

$$u_{2k} = C_{2k}^k \cdot 2^{-2k}.$$

Our immediate aim is to show that for $1 \le k \le n$ the probability f_{2k} is given by

$$f_{2k} = \frac{1}{2k} u_{2(k-1)}. \tag{2}$$

It is clear that

$$\{\sigma_{2n} = 2k\} = \{S_1 \ne 0, S_2 \ne 0, \ldots, S_{2k-1} \ne 0, S_{2k} = 0\}$$

for $1 \le k \le n$, and by symmetry

$$f_{2k} = P\{S_1 \ne 0, \ldots, S_{2k-1} \ne 0, S_{2k} = 0\}$$

$$= 2P\{S_1 > 0, \ldots, S_{2k-1} > 0, S_{2k} = 0\}. \tag{3}$$

A sequence $(S_0, \ldots, S_k)$ is called a *path* of length k; we denote by $L_k(A)$ the number of paths of length k having some specified property A. Then

$$f_{2k} = 2 \sum_{(a_{2k+1}, \ldots, a_n)} L_{2n}(S_1 > 0, \ldots, S_{2k-1} > 0, S_{2k} = 0,$$

$$\text{and } S_{2k+1} = a_{2k+1}, \ldots, S_{2n} = a_{2k+1} + \cdots + a_{2n}) \cdot 2^{-2n}$$

$$= 2L_{2k}(S_1 > 0, \ldots, S_{2k-1} > 0, S_{2k} = 0) \cdot 2^{-2k}, \tag{4}$$

where the summation is over all sets $(a_{2k+1}, \ldots, a_{2n})$ with $a_i = \pm 1$.

Consequently the determination of the probability f_{2k} reduces to calculating the number of paths $L_{2k}(S_1 > 0, \ldots, S_{2k-1} > 0, S_{2k} = 0)$.

Lemma 1. *Let a and b be nonnegative integers, $a - b > 0$ and $k = a + b$. Then*

$$L_k(S_1 > 0, \ldots, S_{k-1} > 0, S_k = a - b) = \frac{a - b}{k} C_k^a. \tag{5}$$

PROOF. In fact,

$$L_k(S_1 > 0, \ldots, S_{k-1} > 0, S_k = a - b)$$
$$= L_k(S_1 = 1, S_2 > 0, \ldots, S_{k-1} > 0, S_k = a - b)$$
$$= L_k(S_1 = 1, S_k = a - b) - L_k(S_1 = 1, S_k = a - b;$$
$$\text{and } \exists\, i, 2 \le i \le k - 1, \text{ such that } S_i \le 0). \tag{6}$$

In other words, the number of positive paths $(S_1, S_2, \ldots, S_k)$ that originate at $(1, 1)$ and terminate at $(k, a - b)$ is the same as the total number of paths from $(1, 1)$ to $(k, a - b)$ after excluding the paths that touch or intersect the time axis.*

We now notice that

$$L_k(S_1 = 1, S_k = a - b; \exists\, i, 2 \le i \le k - 1, \text{ such that } S_i \le 0)$$
$$= L_k(S_1 = -1, S_k = a - b), \tag{7}$$

i.e. the number of paths from $\alpha = (1, 1)$ to $\beta = (k, a - b)$, neither touching nor intersecting the time axis, is equal to the total number of paths that connect $\alpha^* = (1, -1)$ with β. The proof of this statement, known as the *reflection principle*, follows from the easily established one-to-one correspondence between the paths $A = (S_1, \ldots, S_a, S_{a+1}, \ldots, S_k)$ joining α and β, and paths $B = (-S_1, \ldots, -S_a, S_{a+1}, \ldots, S_k)$ joining α^* and β (Figure 17); a is the first point where A and B reach zero.

---

* A path $(S_1, \ldots, S_k)$ is called *positive* (or nonnegative) if all $S_i > 0$ ($S_i \ge 0$); a path is said to *touch* the time axis if $S_j \ge 0$ or else $S_j \le 0$, for $1 \le j \le k$, and there is an i, $1 \le i \le k$, such that $S_i = 0$; and a path is said to *intersect* the time axis if there are two times i and j such that $S_i > 0$ and $S_j < 0$.

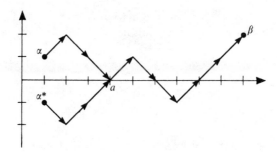

Figure 17. The reflection principle.

From (6) and (7) we find

$$L_k(S_1 > 0, \ldots, S_{k-1} > 0, S_k = a - b)$$
$$= L_k(S_1 = 1, S_k = a - b) - L_k(S_1 = -1, S_k = a - b)$$
$$= C_{k-1}^{a-1} - C_{k-1}^{a} = \frac{a - b}{k} C_k^a,$$

which establishes (5).

Turning to the calculation of f_{2k}, we find that by (4) and (5) (with $a = k$, $b = k - 1$),

$$f_{2k} = 2L_{2k}(S_1 > 0, \ldots, S_{2k-1} > 0, S_{2k} = 0) \cdot 2^{-2k}$$
$$= 2L_{2k-1}(S_1 > 0, \ldots, S_{2k-1} = 1) \cdot 2^{-2k}$$
$$= 2 \cdot 2^{-2k} \cdot \frac{1}{2k - 1} C_{2k-1}^k = \frac{1}{2k} u_{2(k-1)}.$$

Hence (2) is established.

We present an alternative proof of this formula, based on the following observation. A straightforward verification shows that

$$\frac{1}{2k} u_{2(k-1)} = u_{2(k-1)} - u_{2k}, \tag{8}$$

At the same time, it is clear that

$$\{\sigma_{2n} = 2k\} = \{\sigma_{2n} > 2(k - 1)\} \backslash \{\sigma_{2n} > 2k\},$$
$$\{\sigma_{2n} > 2l\} = \{S_1 \neq 0, \ldots, S_{2l} \neq 0\}$$

and therefore

$$\{\sigma_{2n} = 2k\} = \{S_1 \neq 0, \ldots, S_{2(k-1)} \neq 0\} \backslash \{S_1 \neq 0, \ldots, S_{2k} \neq 0\}.$$

Hence

$$f_{2k} = \mathsf{P}\{S_1 \neq 0, \ldots, S_{2(k-1)} \neq 0\} - \mathsf{P}\{S_1 \neq 0, \ldots, S_{2k} \neq 0\},$$

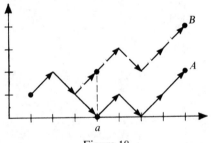

Figure 18

and consequently, because of (8), in order to show that $f_{2k} = (1/2k)u_{2(k-1)}$ it is enough to show only that

$$L_{2k}(S_1 \neq 0, \ldots, S_{2k} \neq 0) = L_{2k}(S_{2k} = 0). \qquad (9)$$

For this purpose we notice that evidently

$$L_{2k}(S_1 \neq 0, \ldots, S_{2k} \neq 0) = 2L_{2k}(S_1 > 0, \ldots, S_{2k} > 0).$$

Hence to verify (9) we need only establish that

$$2L_{2k}(S_1 > 0, \ldots, S_{2k} > 0) = L_{2k}(S_1 \geq 0, \ldots, S_{2k} \geq 0) \qquad (10)$$

and

$$L_{2k}(S_1 \geq 0, \ldots, S_{2k} \geq 0) = L_{2k}(S_{2k} = 0). \qquad (11)$$

Now (10) will be established if we show that we can establish a one-to-one correspondence between the paths $A = (S_1, \ldots, S_{2k})$ for which at least one $S_i = 0$, and the positive paths $B = (S_1, \ldots, S_{2k})$.

Let $A = (S_1, \ldots, S_{2k})$ be a nonnegative path for which the first zero occurs at the point a (i.e., $S_a = 0$). Let us construct the path, starting at $(a, 2)$, $(S_a + 2, S_{a+1} + 2, \ldots, S_{2k} + 2)$ (indicated by the broken lines in Figure 18). Then the path $B = (S_1, \ldots, S_{a-1}, S_a + 2, \ldots, S_{2k} + 2)$ is positive.

Conversely, let $B = (S_1, \ldots, S_{2k})$ be a positive path and b the last instant at which $S_b = 1$ (Figure 19). Then the path

$$A = (S_1, \ldots, S_b, S_{b+1} - 2, \ldots, S_k - 2)$$

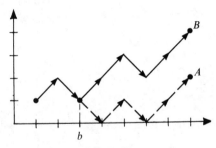

Figure 19

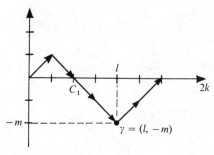

Figure 20

is nonnegative. It follows from these constructions that there is a one-to-one correspondence between the positive paths and the nonnegative paths with at least one $S_i = 0$. Therefore formula (10) is established.

We now establish (11). From symmetry and (10) it is enough to show that

$$L_{2k}(S_1 > 0, \ldots, S_{2k} > 0) + L_{2k}(S_1 \geq 0, \ldots, S_{2k} \geq 0 \text{ and } \exists\, i,$$
$$1 \leq i \leq 2k, \text{ such that } S_i = 0) = L_{2k}(S_{2k} = 0).$$

The set of paths $(S_{2k} = 0)$ can be represented as the sum of the two sets $\mathscr{C}_1$ and $\mathscr{C}_2$, where $\mathscr{C}_1$ contains the paths $(S_0, \ldots, S_{2k})$ that have just one minimum, and $\mathscr{C}_2$ contains those for which the minimum is attained at at least two points.

Let $C_1 \in \mathscr{C}_1$ (Figure 20) and let γ be the minimum point. We put the path $C_1 = (S_0, S_1, \ldots, S_{2k})$ in correspondence with the path C_1^* obtained in the following way (Figure 21). We reflect $(S_0, S_1, \ldots, S_l)$ around the vertical line through the point l, and displace the resulting path to the right and upward, thus releasing it from the point $(2k, 0)$. Then we move the origin to the point $(l, -m)$. The resulting path C_1^* will be positive.

In the same way, if $C_2 \in \mathscr{C}_2$ we can use the same device to put it into correspondence with a nonnegative path C_2^*.

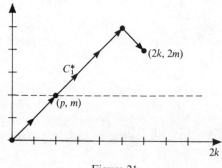

Figure 21

Conversely, let $C_1^* = (S_1 > 0, \ldots, S_{2k} > 0)$ be a positive path with $S_{2k} = 2m$ (see Figure 21). We make it correspond to the path C_1 that is obtained in the following way. Let p be the last point at which $S_p = m$. Reflect $(S_p, \ldots, S_{2m})$ with respect to the vertical line $x = p$ and displace the resulting path downward and to the left until its right-hand end coincides with the point $(0, 0)$. Then we move the origin to the left-hand end of the resulting path (this is just the path drawn in Figure 20). The resulting path $C_1 = (S_0, \ldots, S_{2k})$ has a minimum at $S_{2k} = 0$. A similar construction applied to paths $(S_1 \geq 0, \ldots, S_{2k} \geq 0$ and $\exists \, i, 1 \leq i \leq 2k$, with $S_i = 0)$ leads to paths for which there are at least two minima and $S_{2k} = 0$. Hence we have established a one-to-one correspondence, which establishes (11).

Therefore we have established (9) and consequently also the formula
$$f_{2k} = u_{2(k-1)} - u_{2k} = (1/2k)u_{2(k-1)}.$$
By Stirling's formula

$$u_{2k} = C_{2k}^k \cdot 2^{-2k} \sim \frac{1}{\sqrt{\pi k}}, \qquad k \to \infty.$$

Therefore

$$f_{2k} \sim \frac{1}{2\sqrt{\pi} k^{3/2}}, \qquad k \to \infty.$$

Hence it follows that the expectation of the first time when zero is reached, namely

$$E\min(\sigma_{2n}, 2n) = \sum_{k=1}^{n} 2kP(\sigma_{2n} = 2k) + 2nu_{2n}$$

$$= \sum_{k=1}^{n} u_{2(k-1)} + 2nu_{2n},$$

can be arbitrarily large.

In addition, $\sum_{k=1}^{\infty} u_{2(k-1)} = \infty$, and consequently the limiting value of the mean time for the walk to reach zero (in an unbounded number of steps) is ∞.

This property accounts for many of the unexpected properties of the symmetric random walk that we have been discussing. For example, it would be natural to suppose that after time $2n$ the number of zero net scores in a game between two equally matched players ($p = q = \frac{1}{2}$), i.e. the number of instants i at which $S_i = 0$, would be proportional to $2n$. However, in fact the number of zeros has order $\sqrt{2n}$ (see [F1]). Hence it follows, in particular, that, contrary to intuition, the "typical" walk $(S_0, S_1, \ldots, S_n)$ does not have a sinusoidal character (so that roughly half the time the particle would be on the positive side and half the time on the negative side), but instead must resemble a stretched-out wave. The precise formulation of this statement is given by the arcsine law, which we proceed to investigate.

2. Let $P_{2k, 2n}$ be the probability that during the interval $[0, 2n]$ the particle spends $2k$ units of time on the positive side.*

Lemma 2. *Let* $u_0 = 1$ *and* $0 \leq k \leq n$. *Then*

$$P_{2k, 2n} = u_{2k} \cdot u_{2n-2k} \tag{12}$$

PROOF. It was shown above that $f_{2k} = u_{2(k-1)} - u_{2k}$. Let us show that

$$u_{2k} = \sum_{r=1}^{k} f_{2r} \cdot u_{2(k-r)}. \tag{13}$$

Since $\{S_{2k} = 0\} \subseteq \{\sigma_{2n} \leq 2k\}$, we have

$$\{S_{2k} = 0\} = \{S_{2k} = 0\} \cap \{\sigma_{2n} \leq 2k\} = \sum_{1 \leq l \leq k} \{S_{2k} = 0\} \cap \{\sigma_{2n} = 2l\}.$$

Consequently

$$u_{2k} = \mathsf{P}(S_{2k} = 0) = \sum_{1 \leq l \leq k} \mathsf{P}(S_{2k} = 0, \sigma_{2n} = 2l)$$

$$= \sum_{1 \leq l \leq k} \mathsf{P}(S_{2k} = 0 | \sigma_{2k} = 2l)\mathsf{P}(\sigma_{2n} = 2l).$$

But

$$\mathsf{P}(S_{2k} = 0 | \sigma_{2n} = 2l) = \mathsf{P}(S_{2k} = 0 | S_1 \neq 0, \ldots, S_{2l-1} \neq 0, S_{2l} = 0)$$
$$= \mathsf{P}(S_{2l} + (\xi_{2l+1} + \cdots + \xi_{2k}) = 0 | S_1 \neq 0, \ldots, S_{2l-1} \neq 0, S_{2l} = 0)$$
$$= \mathsf{P}(S_{2l} + (\xi_{2l+1} + \cdots + \xi_{2k}) = 0 | S_{2l} = 0)$$
$$= \mathsf{P}(\xi_{2l+1} + \cdots + \xi_{2k} = 0) = \mathsf{P}(S_{2(k-1)} = 0).$$

Therefore

$$u_{2k} = \sum_{1 \leq l \leq k} \mathsf{P}(S_{2(k-1)} = 0)\mathsf{P}(\sigma_{2n} = 2l),$$

which establishes (13).

We turn now to the proof of (12). It is obviously true for $k = 0$ and $k = n$. Now let $1 \leq k \leq n - 1$. If the particle is on the positive side for exactly $2k$ instants, it must pass through zero. Let $2r$ be the time of first passage through zero. There are two possibilities: either $S_k \geq 0$, $k \leq 2r$, or $S_k \leq 0$, $k \leq 2r$.

The number of paths of the first kind is easily seen to be

$$(\tfrac{1}{2} 2^{2r} f_{2r}) \cdot 2^{2(n-r)} P_{2(k-r), 2(n-r)} = \tfrac{1}{2} \cdot 2^{2n} \cdot f_{2r} \cdot P_{2(k-r), 2(n-r)}.$$

---

* We say that the particle is on the positive side in the interval $[m - 1, m]$ if one, at least, of the values S_{m-1} and S_m is positive.

The corresponding number of paths of the second kind is

$$\tfrac{1}{2} \cdot 2^{2n} \cdot f_{2r} \cdot P_{2k,\,2(n-r)}.$$

Consequently, for $1 \le k \le n - 1$,

$$P_{2k,\,2n} = \frac{1}{2} \sum_{r=1}^{k} f_{2r} \cdot P_{2(k-r),\,2(n-r)} + \frac{1}{2} \sum_{r=1}^{k} f_{2r} \cdot P_{2k,\,2(n-r)}. \qquad (14)$$

Let us suppose that $P_{2k,\,2m} = u_{2k} \cdot u_{2m-2k}$ holds for $m = 1, \ldots, n - 1$. Then we find from (13) and (14) that

$$P_{2k,\,2n} = \tfrac{1}{2} u_{2n-2k} \cdot \sum_{r=1}^{k} f_{2r} \cdot u_{2k-2r} + \tfrac{1}{2} u_{2k} \cdot \sum_{r=1}^{k} f_{2r} \cdot u_{2n-2r-2k}$$

$$= \tfrac{1}{2} u_{2n-2k} \cdot u_{2k} + \tfrac{1}{2} u_{2k} \cdot u_{2n-2k} = u_{2k} \cdot u_{2n-2k}.$$

This completes the proof of the lemma.

Now let $\gamma(2n)$ be the number of time units that the particle spends on the positive axis in the interval $[0, 2n]$. Then, when $x < 1$,

$$\mathsf{P}\left\{ \frac{1}{2} < \frac{\gamma(2n)}{2n} \le x \right\} = \sum_{\{k,\, 1/2 < (2k/2n) \le x\}} P_{2k,\,2n}.$$

Since

$$u_{2k} \sim \frac{1}{\sqrt{\pi k}}$$

as $k \to \infty$, we have

$$P_{2k,\,2n} = u_{2k} \cdot u_{2(n-k)} \sim \frac{1}{\pi \sqrt{k(n-k)}},$$

as $k \to \infty$ and $n - k \to \infty$.

Therefore

$$\sum_{\{k:\, 1/2 < (2k/2n) \le x\}} P_{2k,\,2n} - \sum_{\{k:\, 1/2 < (2k/2n) \ge x\}} \frac{1}{\pi n} \cdot \left[\frac{k}{n}\left(1 - \frac{k}{n}\right) \right]^{-1/2} \to 0, \qquad n \to \infty,$$

whence

$$\sum_{\{k:\, 1/2 < (2k/2n) \le n\}} P_{2k,\,2n} - \frac{1}{\pi} \int_{1/2}^{x} \frac{dt}{\sqrt{t(1-t)}} \to 0, \qquad n \to \infty.$$

But, by symmetry,

$$\sum_{\{k:\, k/n \le 1/2\}} P_{2k,\,2n} \to \tfrac{1}{2}.$$

and

$$\frac{1}{\pi} \int_{1/2}^{x} \frac{dt}{\sqrt{t(1-t)}} = \frac{2}{\pi} \arcsin \sqrt{x} - \tfrac{1}{2}.$$

Consequently we have proved the following theorem.

Theorem (Arcsine Law). *The probability that the fraction of the time spent by the particle on the positive side is at most x tends to $2\pi^{-1} \arcsin \sqrt{x}$:*

$$\sum_{\{k:k/n\le x\}} P_{2k,\,2n} \to 2\pi^{-1} \arcsin \sqrt{x}. \tag{15}$$

We remark that the integrand $p(t)$ in the integral

$$\frac{1}{\pi} \int_{0}^{x} \frac{dt}{\sqrt{t(1-t)}}$$

represents a U-shaped curve that tends to infinity as $t \to 0$ or 1.
  Hence it follows that, for large n,

$$P\left\{0 < \frac{\gamma(2n)}{2n} \le \Delta\right\} > P\left\{\frac{1}{2} < \frac{\gamma(2n)}{2n} \le \tfrac{1}{2} + \Delta\right\},$$

i.e., it is more likely that the fraction of the time spent by the particle on the positive side is close to zero or one, than to the intuitive value $\tfrac{1}{2}$.
  Using a table of arcsines and noting that the convergence in (15) is indeed quite rapid, we find that

$$P\left\{\frac{\gamma(2n)}{2n} \le 0.024\right\} \approx 0.1,$$

$$P\left\{\frac{\gamma(2n)}{2n} \le 0.1\right\} \approx 0.2,$$

$$P\left\{\frac{\gamma(2n)}{2n} \le 0.2\right\} \approx 0.3,$$

$$P\left\{\frac{\gamma(2n)}{2n} \le 0.65\right\} \approx 0.6.$$

  Hence if, say, $n = 1000$, then in about one case in ten, the particle spends only 24 units of time on the positive axis and therefore spends the greatest amount of time, 976 units, on the negative axis.

3. Problems

1. How fast does $E\min(\sigma_{2n}, 2n) \to \infty$ as $n \to \infty$?

2. Let $\tau_n = \min\{1 \le k \le n: S_k = 1\}$, where we take $\tau_n = \infty$ if $S_k < 1$ for $1 \le k \le n$. What is the limit of $E\min(\tau_n, n)$ as $n \to \infty$ for symmetric $(p = q = \tfrac{1}{2})$ and for unsymmetric $(p \ne q)$ walks?

§11. Martingales. Some Applications to the Random Walk

1. The Bernoulli random walk discussed above was generated by a sequence $\xi_1, \ldots, \xi_n$ of *independent* random variables. In this and the next section we introduce two important classes of *dependent* random variables, those that constitute martingales and Markov chains.

The theory of martingales will be developed in detail in Chapter VII. Here we shall present only the essential definitions, prove a theorem on the preservation of the martingale property for stopping times, and apply this to deduce the "ballot theorem." In turn, the latter theorem will be used for another proof of proposition (10.5), which was obtained above by applying the reflection principle.

2. Let $(\Omega, \mathscr{A}, \mathsf{P})$ be a finite probability space and $\mathscr{D}_1 \preccurlyeq \mathscr{D}_2 \preccurlyeq \cdots \preccurlyeq \mathscr{D}_n$ a sequence of decompositions.

Definition 1. A sequence of random variables $\xi_1, \ldots, \xi_n$ is called a *martingale* (with respect to the decomposition $\mathscr{D}_1 \preccurlyeq \mathscr{D}_2 \preccurlyeq \cdots \preccurlyeq \mathscr{D}_n$) if

(1) ξ_k is $\mathscr{D}_k$-measurable,
(2) $\mathsf{E}(\xi_{k+1}|\mathscr{D}_k) = \xi_k$, $1 \le k \le n - 1$.

In order to emphasize the system of decompositions with respect to which the random variables form a martingale, we shall use the notation

$$\xi = (\xi_k, \mathscr{D}_k)_{1 \le k \le n}, \tag{1}$$

where for the sake of simplicity we often do not mention explicitly that $1 \le k \le n$.

When $\mathscr{D}_k$ is induced by $\xi_1, \ldots, \xi_n$, i.e.

$$\mathscr{D}_k = \mathscr{D}_{\xi_1, \ldots, \xi_k},$$

instead of saying that $\xi = (\xi_k, \mathscr{D}_k)$ is a martingale, we simply say that the sequence $\xi = (\xi_k)$ is a martingale.

Here are some examples of martingales.

EXAMPLE 1. Let $\eta_1, \ldots, \eta_n$ be independent Bernoulli random variables with

$$\mathsf{P}(\eta_k = 1) = \mathsf{P}(\eta_k = -1) = \tfrac{1}{2},$$

$$S_k = \eta_1 + \cdots + \eta_k \quad \text{and} \quad \mathscr{D}_k = \mathscr{D}_{\eta_1, \ldots, \eta_k}.$$

We observe that the decompositions $\mathscr{D}_k$ have a simple structure:

$$\mathscr{D}_1 = \{D^+, D^-\},$$

where

$$D^+ = \{\omega: \eta_1 = +1\}, \qquad D^- = \{\omega: \eta_1 = -1\},$$
$$\mathscr{D}_2 = \{D^{++}, D^{+-}, D^{-+}, D^{--}\},$$

where

$$D^{++} = \{\omega: \eta_1 = +1, \eta_2 = +1\}, \ldots, D^{--} = \{\omega: \eta_1 = -1, \eta_2 = -1\},$$

etc.

It is also easy to see that $\mathscr{D}_{\eta_1,\ldots,\eta_k} = \mathscr{D}_{S_1,\ldots,S_k}$.

Let us show that $(S_k, \mathscr{D}_k)$ forms a martingale. In fact, S_k is $\mathscr{D}_k$-measurable, and by (8.12), (8.18) and (8.24),

$$E(S_{k+1}|\mathscr{D}_k) = E(S_k + \eta_{k+1}|\mathscr{D}_k)$$
$$= E(S_k|\mathscr{D}_k) + E(\eta_{k+1}|\mathscr{D}_k) = S_k + E\eta_{k+1} = S_k.$$

If we put $S_0 = 0$ and take $D_0 = \{\Omega\}$, the trivial decomposition, then the sequence $(S_k, \mathscr{D}_k)_{0 \le k \le n}$ also forms a martingale.

EXAMPLE 2. Let $\eta_1, \ldots, \eta_n$ be independent Bernoulli random variables with $P(\eta_i = 1) = p$, $P(\eta_i = -1) = q$. If $p \ne q$, each of the sequences $\xi = (\xi_k)$ with

$$\xi_k = \left(\frac{q}{p}\right)^{S_k}, \qquad \xi_k = S_k - k(p - q), \qquad \text{where} \quad S_k = \eta_1 + \cdots + \eta_n,$$

is a martingale.

EXAMPLE 3. Let η be a random variable, $\mathscr{D}_1 \preccurlyeq \cdots \preccurlyeq \mathscr{D}_n$, and

$$\xi_k = E(\eta|\mathscr{D}_k). \tag{2}$$

Then the sequence $\xi = (\xi_k, \mathscr{D}_k)$ is a martingale. In fact, it is evident that $E(\eta|\mathscr{D}_k)$ is $\mathscr{D}_k$-measurable, and by (8.20)

$$E(\xi_{k+1}|\mathscr{D}_k) = E[E(\eta|\mathscr{D}_{k+1})|\mathscr{D}_k] = E(\eta|\mathscr{D}_k) = \xi_k.$$

In this connection we notice that if $\xi = (\xi_k, \mathscr{D}_k)$ is any martingale, then by (8.20)

$$\xi_k = E(\xi_{k+1}|\mathscr{D}_k) = E[E(\xi_{k+2}|\mathscr{D}_{k+1})|\mathscr{D}_k]$$
$$= E(\xi_{k+2}|\mathscr{D}_k) = \cdots = E(\xi_n|\mathscr{D}_k). \tag{3}$$

Consequently the set of martingales $\xi = (\xi_k, \mathscr{D}_k)$ is exhausted by the martingales of the form (2). (We note that for infinite sequences $\xi = (\xi_k, \mathscr{D}_k)_{k \ge 1}$ this is, in general, no longer the case; see Problem 7 in §1 of Chapter VII.)

EXAMPLE 4. Let $\eta_1, \ldots, \eta_n$ be a sequence of independent identically distributed random variables, $S_k = \eta_1 + \cdots + \eta_k$, and $\mathscr{D}_1 = \mathscr{D}_{S_n}$, $\mathscr{D}_2 = \mathscr{D}_{S_n, S_{n-1}}, \ldots,$ $\mathscr{D}_n = \mathscr{D}_{S_n, S_{n-1}, \ldots, S_1}$. Let us show that the sequence $\xi = (\xi_k, \mathscr{D}_k)$ with

$$\xi_1 = \frac{S_n}{n}, \xi_2 = \frac{S_{n-1}}{n-1}, \ldots, \xi_k = \frac{S_{n+1-k}}{n+1-k}, \ldots, \xi_n = S_1$$

is a martingale. In the first place, it is clear that $\mathscr{D}_k \preccurlyeq \mathscr{D}_{k+1}$ and ξ_k is $\mathscr{D}_k$-measurable. Moreover, we have by symmetry, for $j \leq n - k + 1$,

$$\mathsf{E}(\eta_j | \mathscr{D}_k) = \mathsf{E}(\eta_1 | \mathscr{D}_k) \tag{4}$$

(compare (8.26)). Therefore

$$(n - k + 1)\mathsf{E}(\eta_1 | \mathscr{D}_k) = \sum_{j=1}^{n-k+1} \mathsf{E}(\eta_j | \mathscr{D}_k) = \mathsf{E}(S_{n-k+1} | \mathscr{D}_k) = S_{n-k+1},$$

and consequently

$$\xi_k = \frac{S_{n-k+1}}{n-k+1} = \mathsf{E}(\eta_1 | \mathscr{D}_k),$$

and it follows from Example 3 that $\xi = (\xi_k, \mathscr{D}_k)$ is a martingale.

EXAMPLE 5. Let $\eta_1, \ldots, \eta_n$ be independent Bernoulli random variables with

$$\mathsf{P}(\eta_i = +1) = \mathsf{P}(\eta_i = -1) = \tfrac{1}{2},$$

$S_k = \eta_1 + \cdots + \eta_k$. Let A and B be integers, $A < 0 < B$. Then with $0 < \lambda < \pi/2$, the sequence $\xi = (\xi_k, \mathscr{D}_k)$ with $\mathscr{D}_k = \mathscr{D}_{S_1, \ldots, S_k}$ and

$$\xi_k = (\cos \lambda)^{-k} \exp\left\{i\lambda\left(S_k - \frac{B+A}{2}\right)\right\} \tag{5}$$

is a complex martingale (i.e., the real and imaginary parts of ξ_k form martingales).

3. It follows from the definition of a martingale that the expectation $\mathsf{E}\xi_k$ is the same for every k:

$$\mathsf{E}\xi_k = \mathsf{E}\xi_1.$$

It turns out that this property persists if time k is replaced by a random time.

In order to formulate this property we introduce the following definition.

Definition 2. A random variable $\tau = \tau(\omega)$ that takes the values $1, 2, \ldots, n$ is called a *stopping time* (with respect to a decomposition $(\mathscr{D}_k)_{1 \leq k \leq n}$, $\mathscr{D}_1 \preccurlyeq \mathscr{D}_2 \preccurlyeq \cdots \preccurlyeq \mathscr{D}_n$) if, for $k = 1, \ldots, n$, the random variable $I_{\{\tau = k\}}(\omega)$ is $\mathscr{D}_k$-measurable.

If we consider $\mathscr{D}_k$ as the decomposition induced by observations for k steps (for example, $\mathscr{D}_k = \mathscr{D}_{\eta_1, \ldots, \eta_k}$, the decomposition induced by the variables $\eta_1, \ldots, \eta_k$), then the $\mathcal{D}_k$-measurability of $I_{\{\tau=k\}}(\omega)$ means that the realization or nonrealization of the event $\{\tau = k\}$ is determined only by observations for k steps (and is independent of the "future").

If $\mathcal{B}_k = \alpha(\mathcal{D}_k)$, then the $\mathcal{D}_k$-measurability of $I_{\{\tau=k\}}(\omega)$ is equivalent to the assumption that

$$\{\tau = k\} \in \mathcal{B}_k. \tag{6}$$

We have already introduced specific examples of stopping times: the times τ_k^x, σ_{2n} introduced in §§9 and 10. Those times are special cases of stopping times of the form

$$\tau^A = \min\{0 < k \le n : \xi_k \in A\},$$
$$\sigma^A = \min\{0 \le k \le n : \xi_k \in A\}, \tag{7}$$

which are the times (respectively the first time after zero and the first time) for a sequence $\xi_0, \xi_1, \ldots, \xi_n$ to attain a point of the set A.

4. Theorem 1. *Let* $\xi = (\xi_k, \mathcal{D}_k)_{1 \le k \le n}$ *be a martingale and* τ *a stopping time with respect to the decomposition* $(\mathcal{D}_k)_{1 \le k \le n}$. *Then*

$$\mathsf{E}(\xi_\tau | \mathcal{D}_1) = \xi_1, \tag{8}$$

where

$$\xi_\tau = \sum_{k=1}^{n} \xi_k I_{\{\tau=k\}}(\omega) \tag{9}$$

and

$$\mathsf{E}\xi_\tau = \mathsf{E}\xi_1. \tag{10}$$

PROOF (compare the proof of (9.29)). Let $D \in \mathcal{D}_1$. Using (3) and the properties of conditional expectations, we find that

$$\mathsf{E}(\xi_\tau | D) = \frac{\mathsf{E}(\xi_\tau I_D)}{P(D)}$$

$$= \frac{1}{P(D)} \cdot \sum_{l=1}^{n} \mathsf{E}(\xi_l \cdot I_{\{\tau=l\}} \cdot I_D)$$

$$= \frac{1}{P(D)} \sum_{l=1}^{n} \mathsf{E}[\mathsf{E}(\xi_n | \mathcal{D}_l) \cdot I_{\{\tau=l\}} \cdot I_D]$$

$$= \frac{1}{P(D)} \sum_{l=1}^{n} \mathsf{E}[\mathsf{E}(\xi_n I_{\{\tau=l\}} \cdot I_D | \mathcal{D}_l)]$$

$$= \frac{1}{P(D)} \sum_{l=1}^{n} \mathsf{E}[\xi_n I_{\{\tau=l\}} \cdot I_D]$$

$$= \frac{1}{P(D)} \mathsf{E}(\xi_n I_D) = \mathsf{E}(\xi_n | D),$$

and consequently

$$E(\xi_\tau|\mathscr{D}_1) = E(\xi_n|\mathscr{D}_1) = \xi_1.$$

The equation $E\xi_\tau = E\xi_1$ then follows in an obvious way.

This completes the proof of the theorem.

Corollary. *For the martingale* $(S_k, \mathscr{D}_k)_{1 \leq k \leq n}$ *of Example 1, and any stopping time* τ *(with respect to* $(\mathscr{D}_k)$*) we have the formulas*

$$ES_\tau = 0, \qquad ES_\tau^2 = E\tau, \tag{11}$$

known as Wald's identities (cf. (9.29) and (9.30); see also Problem 1 and Theorem 3 in §2 of Chapter VII).

5. Let us use Theorem 1 to establish the following proposition.

Theorem 2 (Ballot Theorem). *Let* $\eta_1, \ldots, \eta_n$ *be a sequence of independent identically distributed random variables whose values are nonnegative integers,* $S_k = \eta_1 + \cdots + \eta_k, 1 \leq k \leq n$. *Then*

$$P\{S_k < k \text{ for all } k, 1 \leq k \leq n | S_n\} = \left(1 - \frac{S_n}{n}\right)^+, \tag{12}$$

where $a^+ = \max(a, 0)$.

PROOF. On the set $\{\omega: S_n \geq n\}$ the formula is evident. We therefore prove (12) for the sample points at which $S_n < n$.

Let us consider the martingale $\xi = (\xi_k, \mathscr{D}_k)_{1 \leq k \leq n}$ introduced in Example 4, with $\xi_k = S_{n+1-k}/(n + 1 - k)$ and $\mathscr{D}_k = \mathscr{D}_{S_{n+1-k}, \ldots, S_n}$.

We define

$$\tau = \min\{1 \leq k \leq n: \xi_k \geq 1\},$$

taking $\tau = n$ on the set $\{\xi_k < 1$ for all k such that $1 \leq k \leq n\} = \{\max_{1 \leq l \leq n}(S_l/l) < 1\}$. It is clear that $\xi_\tau = \xi_n = S_1 = 0$ on this set, and therefore

$$\left\{\max_{1 \leq l \leq n} \frac{S_l}{l} < 1\right\} = \left\{\max_{1 \leq l \leq n} \frac{S_l}{l} < 1, S_n < n\right\} \subseteq \{\xi_\tau = 0\}. \tag{13}$$

Now let us consider those outcomes for which simultaneously $\max_{1 \leq l \leq n}(S_l/l) \geq 1$ and $S_n < n$. Write $\sigma = n + 1 - \tau$. It is easy to see that

$$\sigma = \max\{1 \leq k \leq n: S_k \geq k\}$$

and therefore (since $S_n < n$) we have $\sigma < n$, $S_\sigma \geq \sigma$, and $S_{\sigma+1} < \sigma + 1$. Consequently $\eta_{\sigma+1} = S_{\sigma+1} - S_\sigma < (\sigma + 1) - \sigma = 1$, i.e. $\eta_{\sigma+1} = 0$. Therefore $\sigma \leq S_\sigma = S_{\sigma+1} < \sigma + 1$, and consequently $S_\sigma = \sigma$ and

$$\xi_\tau = \frac{S_{n+1-\tau}}{n + 1 - \tau} = \frac{S_\sigma}{\sigma} = 1.$$

Therefore

$$\left\{ \max_{1 \leq l \leq n} \frac{S_l}{l} \geq 1, S_n < n \right\} \subseteq \{\xi_\tau = 1\}. \tag{14}$$

From (13) and (14) we find that

$$\left\{ \max_{1 \leq l \leq n} \frac{S_l}{l} \geq 1, S_n < n \right\} = \{\xi_\tau = 1\} \cap \{S_n < n\}.$$

Therefore, on the set $\{S_n < n\}$, we have

$$\mathsf{P}\left\{ \max_{1 \leq l \leq n} \frac{S_l}{l} \geq 1 | S_n \right\} = \mathsf{P}\{\xi_\tau = 1 | S_n\} = \mathsf{E}(\xi_\tau | S_n),$$

where the last equation follows because ξ_τ takes only the two values 0 and 1.

Let us notice now that $\mathsf{E}(\xi_\tau | S_n) = \mathsf{E}(\xi_\tau | \mathscr{D}_1)$, and (by Theorem 1) $\mathsf{E}(\xi_\tau | \mathscr{D}_1) = \xi_1 = S_n/n$. Consequently, on the set $\{S_n < n\}$ we have $\mathsf{P}\{S_k < k$ *for all k such that $1 \leq k \leq n | S_n\} = 1 - (S_n/n)$.*

This completes the proof of the theorem.

We now apply this theorem to obtain a different proof of Lemma 1 of §10, and explain why it is called the ballot theorem.

Let $\xi_1, \ldots, \xi_n$ be independent Bernoulli random variables with

$$\mathsf{P}(\xi_1 = 1) = \mathsf{P}(\xi_i = -1) = \tfrac{1}{2},$$

$S_k = \xi_1 + \cdots + \xi_k$ and a, b nonnegative integers such that $a - b > 0$, $a + b = n$. We are going to show that

$$\mathsf{P}\{S_1 > 0, \ldots, S_n > 0 | S_n = a - b\} = \frac{a - b}{a + b}. \tag{15}$$

In fact, by symmetry,

$$\mathsf{P}\{S_1 > 0, \ldots, S_n > 0 | S_n = a - b\}$$

$$= \mathsf{P}\{S_1 < 0, \ldots, S_n < 0 | S_n = -(a - b)\}$$

$$= \mathsf{P}\{S_1 + 1 < 1, \ldots, S_n + n < n | S_n + n = n - (a - b)\}$$

$$= \mathsf{P}\{\eta_1 < 1, \ldots, \eta_1 + \cdots + \eta_n < n | \eta_1 + \cdots + \eta_n = n - (a - b)\}$$

$$= \left[1 - \frac{n - (a - b)}{n} \right]^+ = \frac{a - b}{n} = \frac{a - b}{a + b},$$

where we have put $\eta_k = \xi_k + 1$ and applied (12).

Now formula (10.5) follows from (15) in an evident way; the formula was also established in Lemma 1 of §10 by using the reflection principle.

Let us interpret $\xi_i = +1$ as a vote for candidate A and $\xi_i = -1$ as a vote for B. Then S_k is the difference between the numbers of votes cast for A and B at the time when k votes have been recorded, and

$$P\{S_1 > 0, \ldots, S_n > 0 | S_n = a - b\}$$

is the probability that A was always ahead of B, with the understanding that A received a votes in all, B received b votes, and $a - b > 0$, $a + b = n$. According to (15) this probability is $(a - b)/n$.

6. PROBLEMS

1. Let $\mathscr{D}_0 \preccurlyeq \mathscr{D}_1 \preccurlyeq \cdots \preccurlyeq \mathscr{D}_n$ be a sequence of decompositions with $\mathscr{D}_0 = \{\Omega\}$, and let η_k be $\mathscr{D}_k$-measurable variables, $1 \le k \le n$. Show that the sequence $\xi = (\xi_k, \mathscr{D}_k)$ with

$$\xi_k = \sum_{l=1}^{k} [\eta_l - E(\eta_l | \mathscr{D}_{l-1})]$$

is a martingale.

2. Let the random variables $\eta_1, \ldots, \eta_k$ satisfy $E(\eta_k | \eta_1, \ldots, \eta_{k-1}) = 0$. Show that the sequence $\xi = (\xi_k)_{1 \le k \le n}$ with $\xi_1 = \eta_1$ and

$$\xi_{k+1} = \sum_{i=1}^{k} \eta_{i+1} f_i(\eta_1, \ldots, \eta_i),$$

where f_i are given functions, is a martingale.

3. Show that every martingale $\xi = (\xi_i, \mathscr{D}_k)$ has uncorrelated increments: if $a < b < c < d$ then

$$\mathrm{cov}(\xi_d - \xi_c, \xi_b - \xi_a) = 0.$$

4. Let $\xi = (\xi_1, \ldots, \xi_n)$ be a random sequence such that ξ_k is $\mathscr{D}_k$-measurable $(\mathscr{D} \preccurlyeq \mathscr{D}_2 \preccurlyeq \cdots \preccurlyeq \mathscr{D}_n)$. Show that a necessary and sufficient condition for this sequence to be a martingale (with respect to the system $(\mathscr{D}_k)$) is that $E\xi_\tau = E\xi_1$ for every stopping time τ (with respect to $(\mathscr{D}_k)$). (The phrase "for every stopping time" can be replaced by "for every stopping time that assumes two values.")

5. Show that if $\xi = (\xi_k, \mathscr{D}_k)_{1 \le k \le n}$ is a martingale and τ is a stopping time, then

$$E[\xi_n I_{\{\tau = k\}}] = E[\xi_k I_{\{\tau = k\}}]$$

for every k.

6. Let $\xi = (\xi_k, \mathscr{D}_k)$ and $\eta = (\eta_k, \mathscr{D}_k)$ be two martingales, $\xi_1 = \eta_1 = 0$. Show that

$$E\xi_n \eta_n = \sum_{k=2}^{n} E(\xi_k - \xi_{k-1})(\eta_k - \eta_{k-1})$$

and in particular that

$$E\xi_n^2 = \sum_{k=2}^{n} E(\xi_k - \xi_{k-1})^2.$$

7. Let $\eta_1, \ldots, \eta_n$ be a sequence of independent identically distributed random variables with $E\eta_i = 0$. Show that the sequence $\xi = (\xi_k)$ with

$$\xi_k = \left(\sum_{i=1}^{k} \eta_i \right)^2 - kE\eta_i^2,$$

$$\xi_k = \frac{\exp \lambda(\eta_1 + \cdots + \eta_k)}{(E \exp \lambda\eta_1)^k}$$

is a martingale.

8. Let $\eta_1, \ldots, \eta_n$ be a sequence of independent identically distributed random variables taking values in a finite set Y. Let $f_0(y) = P(\eta_1 = y)$, $y \in Y$, and let $f_1(y)$ be a nonnegative function with $\sum_{y \in Y} f_1(y) = 1$. Show that the sequence $\xi = (\xi_k, \mathscr{D}_k^\eta)$ with $\mathscr{D}_k^\eta = D_{\eta_1, \ldots, \eta_k}$,

$$\xi_k = \frac{f_1(\eta_1) \cdots f_1(\eta_k)}{f_0(\eta_1) \cdots f_0(\eta_k)},$$

is a martingale. (The variables ξ_k, known as *likelihood ratios*, are extremely important in mathematical statistics.)

§12. Markov Chains. Ergodic Theorem. Strong Markov Property

1. We have discussed the Bernoulli scheme with

$$\Omega = \{\omega : \omega = (x_1, \ldots, x_n), x_i = 0, 1\},$$

where the probability $p(\omega)$ of each outcome is given by

$$p(\omega) = p(x_1) \cdots p(x_n), \tag{1}$$

with $p(x) = p^x q^{1-x}$. With these hypotheses, the variables $\xi_1, \ldots, \xi_n$ with $\xi_i(\omega) = x_i$ are *independent* and *identically distributed* with

$$P(\xi_1 = x) = \cdots = P(\xi_n = x) = p(x), \qquad x = 0, 1.$$

If we replace (1) by

$$p(\omega) = p_1(x_1) \cdots p_n(x_n),$$

where $p_i(x) = p_i^x(1 - p_i)$, $0 \le p_i \le 1$, the random variables $\xi_1, \ldots, \xi_n$ are still *independent*, but in general are *differently distributed*:

$$P(\xi_1 = x) = p_1(x), \ldots, P(\xi_n = x) = p_n(x).$$

We now consider a generalization that leads to *dependent* random variables that form what is known as a Markov chain.

Let us suppose that

$$\Omega = \{\omega : \omega = (x_0, x_1, \ldots, x_n), x_i \in X\},$$

where X is a finite set. Let there be given nonnegative functions $p_0(x)$, $p_1(x, y), \ldots, p_n(x, y)$ such that

$$\sum_{x \in X} p_0(x) = 1,$$

$$\sum_{y \in X} p_k(x, y) = 1, \qquad k = 1, \ldots, n; \quad y \in X. \tag{2}$$

For each $\omega = (x_0, x_1, \ldots, x_n)$, put

$$p(\omega) = p_0(x_0)p_1(x_0, x_1) \cdots p_n(x_{n-1}, x_n). \tag{3}$$

It is easily verified that $\sum_{\omega \in \Omega} p(\omega) = 1$, and consequently the set of numbers $p(\omega)$ together with the space Ω and the collection of its subsets defines a probabilistic model, which it is usual to call a *model of experiments that form a Markov chain.*

Let us introduce the random variables $\xi_0, \xi_1, \ldots, \xi_n$ with $\xi_i(\omega) = x_i$. A simple calculation shows that

$$\mathsf{P}(\xi_0 = a) = p_0(a),$$

$$\mathsf{P}(\xi_0 = a_0, \ldots, \xi_k = a_k) = p_0(a_0)p_1(a_0, a_1) \cdots p_k(a_{k-1}, a_k). \tag{4}$$

We now establish the validity of the following fundamental property of conditional probabilities:

$$\mathsf{P}\{\xi_{k+1} = a_{k+1} | \xi_k = a_k, \ldots, \xi_0 = a_0\} = \mathsf{P}\{\xi_{k+1} = a_{k+1} | \xi_k = a_k\} \tag{5}$$

(under the assumption that $\mathsf{P}(\xi_k = a_k, \ldots, \xi_0 = a_0) > 0$).

By (4),

$$\mathsf{P}\{\xi_{k+1} = a_{k+1} | \xi_k = a_k, \ldots, \xi_0 = a_0\}$$

$$= \frac{\mathsf{P}\{\xi_{k+1} = a_{k+1}, \ldots, \xi_0 = a_0\}}{\mathsf{P}\{\xi_k = a_k, \ldots, \xi_0 = a_0\}}$$

$$= \frac{p_0(a_0)p_1(a_0, a_1) \cdots p_{k+1}(a_k, a_{k+1})}{p_0(a_0) \cdots p_k(a_{k-1}, a_k)} = p_{k+1}(a_k, a_{k+1}).$$

In a similar way we verify

$$\mathsf{P}\{\xi_{k+1} = a_{k+1} | \xi_k = a_k\} = p_{k+1}(a_k, a_{k+1}), \tag{6}$$

which establishes (5).

Let $\mathscr{D}_k^\xi = \mathscr{D}_{\xi_0, \ldots, \xi_k}$ be the decomposition induced by $\xi_0, \ldots, \xi_k$, and $\mathscr{B}_k^\xi = \alpha(\mathscr{D}_k^\xi)$.

Then, in the notation introduced in §8, it follows from (5) that

$$\mathsf{P}\{\xi_{k+1} = a_{k+1} | \mathscr{B}_k^\xi\} = \mathsf{P}\{\xi_{k+1} = a_{k+1} | \xi_k\} \tag{7}$$

or

$$\mathsf{P}\{\xi_{k+1} = a_{k+1} | \xi_0, \ldots, \xi_k\} = \mathsf{P}\{\xi_{k+1} = a_{k+1} | \xi_k\}.$$

If we use the evident equation

$$P(AB|C) = P(A|BC)P(B|C),$$

we find from (7) that

$$P\{\xi_n = a_n, \ldots, \xi_{k+1} = a_{k+1}|\mathscr{B}_k^\xi\} = P\{\xi_n = a_n, \ldots, \xi_{k+1} = a_{k+1}|\xi_k\} \quad (8)$$

or

$$P\{\xi_n = a_n, \ldots, \xi_{k+1} = a_{k+1}|\xi_0, \ldots, \xi_k\} = P\{\xi_n = a_n, \ldots, \xi_{k+1} = a_{k+1}|\xi_k\}.$$
$$(9)$$

This equation admits the following intuitive interpretation. Let us think of ξ_k as the position of a particle "at present," $(\xi_0, \ldots, \xi_{k-1})$ as the "past," and $(\xi_{k+1}, \ldots, \xi_n)$ as the "future." Then (9) says that if the past and the present are given, the future depends only on the present and is independent of how the particle arrived at ξ_k, i.e. is independent of the past $(\xi_0, \ldots, \xi_{k-1})$.

Let $F = (\xi_n = a_n, \ldots, \xi_{k+1} = a_{k+1})$, $N = \{\xi_k = a_k\}$,

$$B = \{\xi_{k-1} = a_{k-1}, \ldots, \xi_0 = a_0\}.$$

Then it follows from (9) that

$$P(F|NB) = P(F|N),$$

from which we easily find that

$$P(FB|N) = P(F|N)P(B|N). \quad (10)$$

In other words, it follows from (7) that for a given present N, the future F and the past B are independent. It is easily shown that the converse also holds: if (10) holds for all $k = 0, 1, \ldots, n - 1$, then (7) holds for every $k = 0, 1, \ldots, n - 1$.

The property of the independence of future and past, or, what is the same thing, the lack of dependence of the future on the past when the present is given, is called the *Markov property*, and the corresponding sequence of random variables $\xi_0, \ldots, \xi_n$ is a *Markov chain*.

Consequently if the probabilities $p(\omega)$ of the sample points are given by (3), the sequence $(\xi_0, \ldots, \xi_n)$ with $\xi_i(\omega) = x_i$ forms a Markov chain.

We give the following formal definition.

Definition. Let $(\Omega, \mathscr{A}, P)$ be a (finite) probability space and let $\xi = (\xi_0, \ldots, \xi_n)$ be a sequence of random variables with values in a (finite) set X. If (7) is satisfied, the sequence $\xi = (\xi_0, \ldots, \xi_n)$ is called a (finite) *Markov chain*.

The set X is called the *phase space* or *state space* of the chain. The set of probabilities $(p_n(x))$, $x \in X$, with $p_0(x) = P(\xi_0 = x)$ is the *initial distribution*, and the matrix $\|p_k(x, y)\|$, $x, y \in X$, with $p(x, y) = P\{\xi_k = y|\xi_{k-1} = x\}$ is the *matrix of transition probabilities* (from state x to state y) at time $k = 1, \ldots, n$.

When the transition probabilities $p_k(x, y)$ are independent of k, that is, $p_k(x, y) = p(x, y)$, the sequence $\xi = (\xi_0, \ldots, \xi_n)$ is called a *homogeneous* Markov chain with transition matrix $\|p(x, y)\|$.

Notice that the matrix $\|(x, y)\|$ is *stochastic*: its elements are nonnegative and the sum of the elements in each row is 1: $\sum_y p(x, y) = 1, x \in X$.

We shall suppose that the phase space X is a finite set of integers $(X = \{0, 1, \ldots, N\}, X = \{0, \pm 1, \ldots, \pm N\}$, etc.), and use the traditional notation $p_i = p_0(i)$ and $p_{ij} = p(i, j)$.

It is clear that the properties of homogeneous Markov chains completely determine the initial distributions p_i and the transition probabilities p_{ij}. In specific cases we describe the evolution of the chain, not by writing out the matrix $\|p_{ij}\|$ explicitly, but by a (directed) graph whose vertices are the states in X, and an arrow from state i to state j with the number p_{ij} over it indicates that it is possible to pass from point i to point j with probability p_{ij}. When $p_{ij} = 0$, the corresponding arrow is omitted.

EXAMPLE 1. Let $X = \{0, 1, 2\}$ and

$$\|p_{ij}\| = \begin{pmatrix} 1 & 0 & 0 \\ \frac{1}{2} & 0 & \frac{1}{2} \\ \frac{2}{3} & 0 & \frac{1}{3} \end{pmatrix}.$$

The following graph corresponds to this matrix:

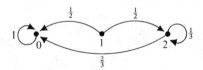

Here state 0 is said to be absorbing: if the particle gets into this state it remains there, since $p_{00} = 1$. From state 1 the particle goes to the adjacent states 0 or 2 with equal probabilities; state 2 has the property that the particle remains there with probability $\frac{1}{3}$ and goes to state 0 with probability $\frac{2}{3}$.

EXAMPLE 2. Let $X = \{0, \pm 1, \ldots, \pm N\}$, $p_0 = 1$, $p_{NN} = p_{(-N)(-N)} = 1$, and, for $|i| < N$,

$$p_{ij} = \begin{cases} p, & j = i + 1, \\ q, & j = i - 1, \\ 0 & \text{otherwise.} \end{cases} \tag{11}$$

The transitions corresponding to this chain can be presented graphically in the following way ($N = 3$):

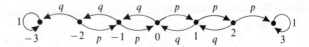

This chain corresponds to the two-player game discussed earlier, when each player has a bankroll N and at each turn the first player wins $+1$ from the second with probability p, and loses (wins -1) with probability q. If we think of state i as the amount won by the first player from the second, then reaching state N or $-N$ means the ruin of the second or first player, respectively.

In fact, if $\eta_1, \eta_2, \ldots, \eta_n$ are independent Bernoulli random variables with $\mathsf{P}(\eta_i = +1) = p$, $\mathsf{P}(\eta_i = -1) = q$, $S_0 = 0$ and $S_k = \eta_1 + \cdots + \eta_k$ the amounts won by the first player from the second, then the sequence S_0, $S_1, \ldots, S_n$ is a Markov chain with $p_0 = 1$ and transition matrix (11), since

$$\mathsf{P}\{S_{k+1} = j \mid S_k = i_k, S_{k-1} = i_{k-1}, \ldots\}$$
$$= \mathsf{P}\{S_k + \eta_{k+1} = j \mid S_k = i_k, S_{k-1} = i_{k-1}, \ldots\}$$
$$= \mathsf{P}\{S_k + \eta_{k+1} = j \mid S_k = i_k\} = \mathsf{P}\{\eta_{k+1} = j - i_k\}.$$

This Markov chain has a very simple structure:

$$S_{k+1} = S_k + \eta_{k+1}, \qquad 0 \le k \le n - 1,$$

where $\eta_1, \eta_2, \ldots, \eta_n$ is a sequence of independent random variables.

The same considerations show that if $\xi_0, \eta_1, \ldots, \eta_n$ are independent random variables then the sequence $\xi_0, \xi_1, \ldots, \xi_n$ with

$$\xi_{k+1} = f_k(\xi_k, \eta_{k+1}), \qquad 0 \le k \le n - 1, \tag{12}$$

is also a Markov chain.

It is worth noting in this connection that a Markov chain constructed in this way can be considered as a natural probabilistic analog of a (deterministic) sequence $x = (x_0, \ldots, x_n)$ generated by the recurrent equations

$$x_{k+1} = f_k(x_k).$$

We now give another example of a Markov chain of the form (12); this example arises in queueing theory.

EXAMPLE 3. At a taxi stand let taxis arrive at unit intervals of time (one at a time). If no one is waiting at the stand, the taxi leaves immediately. Let η_k be the number of passengers who arrive at the stand at time k, and suppose that $\eta_1, \ldots, \eta_n$ are independent random variables. Let ξ_k be the length of the waiting line at time k, $\xi_0 = 0$. Then if $\xi_k = i$, at the next time $k + 1$ the length ξ_{k+1} of the waiting line is equal to

$$j = \begin{cases} \eta_{k+1} & \text{if } i = 0, \\ i - 1 + \eta_{k+1} & \text{if } i \geq 1. \end{cases}$$

In other words,

$$\xi_{k+1} = (\xi_k - 1)^+ + \eta_{k+1}, \qquad 0 \leq k \leq n - 1,$$

where $a^+ = \max(a, 0)$, and therefore the sequence $\xi = (\xi_0, \ldots, \xi_n)$ is a Markov chain.

EXAMPLE 4. This example comes from the theory of *branching processes*. A branching process with discrete times is a sequence of random variables $\xi_0, \xi_1, \ldots, \xi_n$, where ξ_k is interpreted as the number of particles in existence at time k, and the process of creation and annihilation of particles is as follows: each particle, independently of the other particles and of the "prehistory" of the process, is transformed into j particles with probability p_j, $j = 0, 1, \ldots, M$.

We suppose that at the initial time there is just one particle, $\xi_0 = 1$. If at time k there are ξ_k particles (numbered $1, 2, \ldots, \xi_k$), then by assumption ξ_{k+1} is given as a random sum of random variables,

$$\xi_{k+1} = \eta_1^{(k)} + \cdots + \eta_{\xi_k}^{(k)},$$

where $\eta_i^{(k)}$ is the number of particles produced by particle number i. It is clear that if $\xi_k = 0$ then $\xi_{k+1} = 0$. If we suppose that all the random variables $\eta_j^{(k)}$, $k \geq 0$, are independent of each other, we obtain

$$\mathsf{P}\{\xi_{k+1} = i_{k+1} | \xi_k = i_k, \xi_{k-1} = i_{k-1}, \ldots\} = \mathsf{P}\{\xi_{k+1} = i_{k+1} | \xi_k = i_k\}$$
$$= \mathsf{P}\{\eta_1^{(k)} + \cdots + \eta_{i_k}^{(k)} = i_{k+1}\}.$$

It is evident from this that the sequence $\xi_0, \xi_1, \ldots, \xi_n$ is a Markov chain.

A particularly interesting case is that in which each particle either vanishes with probability q or divides in two with probability p, $p + q = 1$. In this case it is easy to calculate that

$$p_{ij} = \mathsf{P}\{\xi_{k+1} = j | \xi_k = i\}$$

is given by the formula

$$p_{ij} = \begin{cases} C_i^{j/2} p^{j/2} q^{i-j/2}, & j = 0, \ldots, 2i, \\ 0 & \text{in all other cases.} \end{cases}$$

2. Let $\xi = (\xi_k, \Pi, \mathsf{P})$ be a homogeneous Markov chain with starting vectors (rows) $\Pi = (p_i)$ and transition matrix $\Pi = \|p_{ij}\|$. It is clear that

$$p_{ij} = \mathsf{P}\{\xi_1 = j | \xi_0 = i\} = \cdots = \mathsf{P}\{\xi_n = j | \xi_{n-1} = i\}.$$

We shall use the notation

$$p_{ij}^{(k)} = \mathsf{P}\{\xi_k = j | \xi_0 = i\} \quad (= \mathsf{P}\{\xi_{k+l} = j | \xi_l = i\})$$

for the probability of a transition from state i to state j in k steps, and

$$p_j^{(k)} = \mathsf{P}\{\xi_k = j\}$$

for the probability of finding the particle at point j at time k. Also let

$$\Pi^{(k)} = \|p_i^{(k)}\|, \qquad \mathbb{P}^{(k)} = \|p_{ij}^{(k)}\|.$$

Let us show that the transition probabilities $p_{ij}^{(k)}$ satisfy the *Kolmogorov–Chapman equation*

$$p_{ij}^{(k+l)} = \sum_\alpha p_{i\alpha}^{(k)} p_{\alpha j}^{(l)}, \tag{13}$$

or, in matrix form,

$$\mathbb{P}^{(k+l)} = \mathbb{P}^{(k)} \cdot \mathbb{P}^{(l)} \tag{14}$$

The proof is extremely simple: using the formula for total probability and the Markov property, we obtain

$$p_{ij}^{(k+l)} = \mathsf{P}(\xi_{k+l} = j | \xi_0 = i) = \sum_\alpha \mathsf{P}(\xi_{k+l} = j, \xi_k = \alpha | \xi_0 = i)$$

$$= \sum_\alpha \mathsf{P}(\xi_{k+l} = j | \xi_k = \alpha) \mathsf{P}(\xi_k = \alpha | \xi_0 = i) = \sum_\alpha p_{\alpha j}^{(l)} p_{i\alpha}^{(k)}.$$

The following two cases of (13) are particularly important:

the *backward equation*

$$p_{ij}^{(l+1)} = \sum_v p_{i\alpha} p_{\alpha j}^{(l)} \tag{15}$$

and the *forward equation*

$$p_{ij}^{(k+1)} = \sum_\alpha p_{i\alpha}^{(k)} p_{\alpha j} \tag{16}$$

(see Figures 22 and 23). The forward and backward equations can be written in the following matrix forms

$$\mathbb{P}^{(k+1)} = \mathbb{P}^{(k)} \cdot \mathbb{P}, \tag{17}$$

$$\mathbb{P}^{(k+1)} = \mathbb{P} \cdot \mathbb{P}^{(k)}. \tag{18}$$

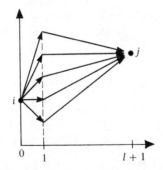

Figure 22. For the backward equation.

Similarly, we find for the (unconditional) probabilities $p_j^{(k)}$ that

$$p_j^{(k+l)} = \sum_\alpha p_\alpha^{(k)} p_{\alpha j}^{(l)}, \tag{19}$$

or in matrix form

$$\Pi^{(k+l)} = \Pi^{(k)} \cdot \mathbb{P}^{(l)}.$$

In particular,

$$\Pi^{(k+1)} = \Pi^{(k)} \cdot \mathbb{P}$$

(*forward equation*) and

$$\Pi^{(k+1)} = \Pi^{(1)} \cdot \mathbb{P}^{(k)}$$

(*backward equation*). Since $\mathbb{P}^{(1)} = \mathbb{P}, \Pi^{(1)} = \Pi$, it follows from these equations that

$$\mathbb{P}^{(k)} = \mathbb{P}^k, \qquad \Pi^{(k)} = \Pi^k.$$

Consequently for homogeneous Markov chains the k-step transition probabilities $p_{ij}^{(k)}$ are the elements of the kth powers of the matrix $\mathbb{P}$, so that many properties of such chains can be investigated by the methods of matrix analysis.

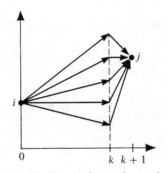

Figure 23. For the forward equation.

EXAMPLE 5. Consider a homogeneous Markov chain with the two states 0 and 1 and the matrix

$$\mathbb{P} = \begin{pmatrix} p_{00} & p_{01} \\ p_{10} & p_{11} \end{pmatrix}.$$

It is easy to calculate that

$$\mathbb{P}^2 = \begin{pmatrix} p_{00}^2 + p_{01}p_{10} & p_{01}(p_{00} + p_{11}) \\ p_{10}(p_{00} + p_{11}) & p_{11}^2 + p_{01}p_{10} \end{pmatrix}$$

and (by induction)

$$\mathbb{P}^n = \frac{1}{2 - p_{00} - p_{11}} \begin{pmatrix} 1 - p_{11} & 1 - p_{00} \\ 1 - p_{11} & 1 - p_{00} \end{pmatrix}$$
$$+ \frac{(p_{00} + p_{11} - 1)^n}{2 - p_{00} - p_{11}} \begin{pmatrix} 1 - p_{00} & -(1 - p_{00}) \\ -(1 - p_{11}) & 1 - p_{11} \end{pmatrix}$$

(under the hypothesis that $|p_{00} + p_{11} - 1| < 1$).

Hence it is clear that if the elements of $\mathbb{P}$ satisfy $|p_{00} + p_{11} - 1| < 1$ (in particular, if all the transition probabilities p_{ij} are positive), then as $n \to \infty$

$$\mathbb{P}^n \to \frac{1}{2 - p_{00} - p_{11}} \begin{pmatrix} 1 - p_{11} & 1 - p_{00} \\ 1 - p_{11} & 1 - p_{00} \end{pmatrix}, \tag{20}$$

and therefore

$$\lim_n p_{i0}^{(n)} = \frac{1 - p_{11}}{2 - p_{00} - p_{11}}, \qquad \lim_n p_{i1}^{(n)} = \frac{1 - p_{00}}{2 - p_{00} - p_{11}}.$$

Consequently if $|p_{00} + p_{11} - 1| < 1$, such a Markov chain exhibits regular behavior of the following kind: the influence of the initial state on the probability of finding the particle in one state or another eventually becomes negligible ($p_{ij}^{(n)}$ approach limits π_j, *independent of i* and forming a probability distribution: $\pi_0 \geq 0$, $\pi_1 \geq 0$, $\pi_0 + \pi_1 = 1$); if also all $p_{ij} > 0$ then $\pi_0 > 0$ and $\pi_1 > 0$.

3. The following theorem describes a wide class of Markov chains that have the property called *ergodicity*: the limits $\pi_j = \lim_n p_{ij}$ not only exist, are independent of i, and form a probability distribution ($\pi_j \geq 0$, $\sum_j \pi_j = 1$), but also $\pi_j > 0$ for all j (such a distribution π_j is said to be *ergodic*).

Theorem 1 (Ergodic Theorem). *Let* $\mathbb{P} = \|p_{ij}\|$ *be the transition matrix of a chain with a finite state space* $X = \{1, 2, \ldots, N\}$.

(a) *If there is an* n_0 *such that*

$$\min_{i,j} p_{ij}^{(n_0)} > 0, \tag{21}$$

then there are numbers $\pi_1, \ldots, \pi_N$ such that

$$\pi_j > 0, \qquad \sum_j \pi_j = 1 \tag{22}$$

and

$$p_{ij}^{(n)} \to \pi_j, \qquad n \to \infty \tag{23}$$

for every $i \in X$.

(b) *Conversely, if there are numbers $\pi_1, \ldots, \pi_N$ satisfying (22) and (23), there is an n_0 such that (21) holds.*

(c) *The numbers $(\pi_1, \ldots, \pi_N)$ satisfy the equations*

$$\pi_j = \sum_\alpha \pi_\alpha p_{\alpha j}, \qquad j = 1, \ldots, N. \tag{24}$$

PROOF. (a) Let

$$m_j^{(n)} = \min_i p_{ij}^{(n)}, \qquad M_j^{(n)} = \max_i p_{ij}^{(n)}.$$

Since

$$p_{ij}^{(n+1)} = \sum_\alpha p_{i\alpha} p_{\alpha j}^{(n)}, \tag{25}$$

we have

$$m_j^{(n+1)} = \min_i p_{ij}^{(n+1)} = \min_i \sum_\alpha p_{i\alpha} p_{\alpha j}^{(n)} \geq \min_i \sum_\alpha p_{i\alpha} \min_\alpha p_{\alpha j}^{(n)} = m_j^{(n)},$$

whence $m_j^{(n)} \leq m_j^{(n+1)}$ and similarly $M_j^{(n)} \geq M_j^{(n+1)}$. Consequently, to establish (23) it will be enough to prove that

$$M_j^{(n)} - m_j^{(n)} \to 0, \qquad n \to \infty, \quad j = 1, \ldots, N.$$

Let $\varepsilon = \min_{i,j} p_{ij}^{(n_0)} > 0$. Then

$$p_{ij}^{(n_0+n)} = \sum_\alpha p_{i\alpha}^{(n_0)} p_{\alpha j}^{(n)} = \sum_\alpha [p_{i\alpha}^{(n_0)} - \varepsilon p_{j\alpha}^{(n)}] p_{\alpha j}^{(n)} + \varepsilon \sum_\alpha p_{j\alpha}^{(n)} p_{\alpha j}^{(n)}$$

$$= \sum_\alpha [p_{i\alpha}^{(n_0)} - \varepsilon p_{j\alpha}^{(n)}] p_{\alpha j}^{(n)} + \varepsilon p_{jj}^{(2n)}.$$

But $p_{i\alpha}^{(n_0)} - \varepsilon p_{j\alpha}^{(n)} \geq 0$; therefore

$$p_{ij}^{(n_0+n)} \geq m_j^{(n)} \cdot \sum_\alpha [p_{i\alpha}^{(n_0)} - \varepsilon p_{j\alpha}^{(n)}] + \varepsilon p_{jj}^{(2n)} = m_j^{(n)}(1 - \varepsilon) + \varepsilon p_{jj}^{(2n)},$$

and consequently

$$m_j^{(n_0+n)} \geq m_j^{(n)}(1 - \varepsilon) + \varepsilon p_{jj}^{(2n)}.$$

In a similar way

$$M_j^{(n_0+n)} \leq M_j^{(n)}(1 - \varepsilon) + \varepsilon p_{jj}^{(2n)}.$$

Combining these inequalities, we obtain

$$M_j^{(n_0+n)} - m_j^{(n_0+n)} \leq (M_j^{(n)} - m_j^{(n)}) \cdot (1 - \varepsilon)$$

and consequently

$$M_j^{(kn_0+n)} - m_j^{(kn_0+n)} \le (M_j^{(n)} - m_j^{(n)})(1 - \varepsilon)^k \downarrow 0, \qquad k \to \infty.$$

Thus $M_j^{(n_\beta)} - m_j^{(n_\beta)} \to 0$ for some subsequence n_β, $n_\beta \to \infty$. But the difference $M_j^{(n)} - m_j^{(n)}$ is monotonic in n, and therefore $M_j^{(n)} - m_j^{(n)} \to 0$, $n \to \infty$.

If we put $\pi_j = \lim_n m_j^{(n)}$, it follows from the preceding inequalities that

$$|p_{ij}^{(n)} - \pi_j| \le M_j^{(n)} - m_j^{(n)} \le (1 - \varepsilon)^{[n/n_0]-1}$$

for $n \ge n_0$, that is, $p_{ij}^{(n)}$ converges to its limit π_j geometrically (i.e., as fast as a geometric progression).

It is also clear that $m_j^{(n)} \ge m_j^{(n_0)} \ge \varepsilon > 0$ for $n \ge n_0$, and therefore $\pi_j > 0$.

(b) Inequality (21) follows from (23) and (25).

(c) Equation (24) follows from (23) and (25).

This completes the proof of the theorem.

4. Equations (24) play a major role in the theory of Markov chains. A nonnegative solution $(\pi_1, \ldots, \pi_N)$ satisfying $\sum_\alpha \pi_\alpha = 1$ is said to be a *stationary* or *invariant* probability distribution for the Markov chain with transition matrix $\|p_{ij}\|$. The reason for this terminology is as follows.

Let us select an initial distribution $(\pi_1, \ldots, \pi_N)$ and take $p_j = \pi_j$. Then

$$p_j^{(1)} = \sum_\alpha \pi_\alpha p_{\alpha j} = \pi_j$$

and in general $p_j^{(n)} = \pi_j$. In other words, if we take $(\pi_1, \ldots, \pi_N)$ as the initial distribution, this distribution is unchanged as time goes on, i.e. for any k

$$\mathsf{P}(\xi_k = j) = \mathsf{P}(\xi_0 = j), \qquad j = 1, \ldots, N.$$

Moreover, with this initial distribution the Markov chain $\xi = (\xi, \sqcap, \mathbb{P})$ is really *stationary*: the joint distribution of the vector $(\xi_k, \xi_{k+1}, \ldots, \xi_{k+l})$ is independent of k for all l (assuming that $k + l \le n$).

Property (21) guarantees both the existence of limits $\pi_j = \lim p_{ij}^{(n)}$, which are independent of i, and the existence of an ergodic distribution, i.e. one with $\pi_j > 0$. The distribution $(\pi_1, \ldots, \pi_N)$ is also a *stationary* distribution. Let us now show that the set $(\pi_1, \ldots, \pi_N)$ is the *only* stationary distribution.

In fact, let $(\tilde\pi_1, \ldots, \tilde\pi_N)$ be another stationary distribution. Then

$$\tilde\pi_j = \sum_\alpha \tilde\pi_\alpha p_{\alpha j} = \cdots = \sum_\alpha \tilde\pi_\alpha p_{\alpha j}^{(n)},$$

and since $p_{\alpha j}^{(n)} \to \pi_j$ we have

$$\tilde\pi_j = \sum_\alpha (\tilde\pi_\alpha \cdot \pi_j) = \pi_j.$$

These problems will be investigated in detail in Chapter VIII for Markov chains with countably many states as well as with finitely many states.

We note that a stationary probability distribution (even unique) may exist for a nonergodic chain. In fact, if

$$\mathbb{P} = \begin{pmatrix} 0 & 1 \\ 1 & 0 \end{pmatrix},$$

then

$$\mathbb{P}^{2n} = \begin{pmatrix} 0 & 1 \\ 1 & 0 \end{pmatrix}, \qquad \mathbb{P}^{2n+1} = \begin{pmatrix} 1 & 0 \\ 0 & 1 \end{pmatrix},$$

and consequently the limits $\lim p_{ij}^{(n)}$ do not exist. At the same time, the system

$$\pi_j = \sum_{\alpha} \pi_{\alpha} p_{\alpha j}, \qquad j = 1, 2,$$

reduces to

$$\pi_1 = \pi_2,$$
$$\pi_2 = \pi_1,$$

of which the unique solution satisfying $\pi_1 + \pi_2 = 1$ is $(\tfrac{1}{2}, \tfrac{1}{2})$.

We also notice that for this example the system (24) has the form

$$\pi_0 = \pi_0 p_{00} + \pi_1 p_{10}.$$
$$\pi_1 = \pi_0 p_{01} + \pi_1 p_{11},$$

from which, by the condition $\pi_0 = \pi_1 = 1$, we find that the unique stationary distribution (π_0, π_1) coincides with the one obtained above:

$$\pi_0 = \frac{1 - p_{11}}{2 - p_{00} - p_{11}}, \qquad \pi_1 = \frac{1 - p_{00}}{2 - p_{00} - p_{11}}.$$

We now consider some corollaries of the ergodic theorem.

Let A be a set of states, $A \subseteq X$ and

$$I_A(x) = \begin{cases} 1, & x \in A, \\ 0, & x \notin A. \end{cases}$$

Consider

$$v_A(n) = \frac{I_A(\xi_0) + \cdots + I_A(\xi_n)}{n + 1}$$

which is the fraction of the time spent by the particle in the set A. Since

$$\mathsf{E}[I_A(\xi_k) | \xi_0 = i] = \mathsf{P}(\xi_k \in A | \xi_0 = i) = \sum_{j \in A} p_{ij}^{(k)} (= p_i^{(k)}(A)),$$

we have

$$E[v_A(n)|\xi_0 = i] = \frac{1}{n+1} \sum_{k=0}^{n} p_i^{(k)}(A)$$

and in particular

$$E[v_{\{j\}}(n)|\xi_0 = i] = \frac{1}{n+1} \sum_{k=0}^{n} p_{ij}^{(n)}.$$

It is known from analysis (see also Lemma 1 in §3 of Chapter IV) that if $a_n \to a$ then $(a_0 + \cdots + a_n)/(n+1) \to a$, $n \to \infty$. Hence if $p_{ij}^{(k)} \to \pi_j$, $k \to \infty$, then

$$E v_{\{j\}}(n) \to \pi_j, \qquad E v_A(n) \to \pi_A, \qquad \text{where} \quad \pi_A = \sum_{j \in A} \pi_j.$$

For ergodic chains one can in fact prove more, namely that the following result holds for $I_A(\xi_0), \ldots, I_A(\xi_n), \ldots$.

Law of Large Numbers. *If $\xi_0, \xi_1, \ldots$ form a finite ergodic Markov chain, then*

$$P\{|v_A(n) - \pi_A| > \varepsilon\} \to 0, \qquad n \to \infty, \qquad (26)$$

for every $\varepsilon > 0$ and every initial distribution.

Before we undertake the proof, let us notice that we cannot apply the results of §5 directly to $I_A(\xi_0), \ldots, I_A(\xi_n), \ldots$, since these variables are, in general, dependent. However, the proof can be carried through along the same lines as for independent variables if we again use Chebyshev's inequality, and apply the fact that for an ergodic chain with finitely many states there is a number ρ, $0 < \rho < 1$, such that

$$|p_{ij}^{(n)} - \pi_j| \le C \cdot \rho^n. \qquad (27)$$

Let us consider states i and j (which might be the same) and show that, for $\varepsilon > 0$,

$$P\{|v_{\{j\}}(n) - \pi_j| > \varepsilon|\xi_0 = i\} \to 0, \qquad n \to \infty. \qquad (28)$$

By Chebyshev's inequality,

$$P\{|v_{\{j\}}(n) - \pi_j| > \varepsilon|\xi_0 = i\} < \frac{E\{|v_{\{j\}}(n) - \pi_j|^2|\xi_0 = i\}}{\varepsilon^2}.$$

Hence we have only to show that

$$E\{|v_{\{j\}}(n) - \pi_j|^2|\xi_0 = i\} \to 0, \qquad n \to \infty.$$

A simple calculation shows that

$$\mathsf{E}\{|v_{(j)}(n) - \pi_j|^2|\xi_0 = i\} = \frac{1}{(n+1)^2} \cdot \mathsf{E}\left\{\left[\sum_{k=0}^{n}(I_{(j)}(\xi_k) - \pi_j)\right]^2 \Big| \xi_0 = i\right\}$$

$$= \frac{1}{(n+1)^2}\sum_{k=0}^{n}\sum_{l=0}^{n} m_{ij}^{(k,l)},$$

where

$$m_{ij}^{(k,l)} = \mathsf{E}\{[I_{(j)}(\xi_k)I_{(j)}(\xi_l)]|\xi_0 = i\}$$
$$- \pi_j \cdot \mathsf{E}[I_{(j)}(\xi_k)|\xi_0 = i] - \pi_j \cdot \mathsf{E}[I_{(j)}(\xi_l)|\xi_0 = l] + \pi_j^2$$
$$= p_{ij}^{(s)} \cdot p_{jj}^{(t)} - \pi_j \cdot p_{ij}^{(k)} - \pi_j \cdot p_{ij}^{(l)} + \pi_j^2,$$

$$s = \min(k,l) \quad \text{and} \quad t = |k - l|.$$

By (27),

$$p_{ij}^{(n)} = \pi_j + \varepsilon_{ij}^{(n)}, \qquad |\varepsilon_{ij}^{(n)}| \le C\rho^n.$$

Therefore

$$|m_{ij}^{(k,l)}| \le C_1[\rho^s + \rho^t + \rho^k + \rho^l],$$

where C_1 is a constant. Consequently

$$\frac{1}{(n+1)^2}\sum_{k=0}^{n}\sum_{l=0}^{n} m_{ij}^{(k,l)} \le \frac{C_1}{(n+1)^2}\sum_{k=0}^{n}\sum_{l=0}^{n}[\rho^s + \rho^t + \rho^k + \rho^l]$$

$$\le \frac{4C_1}{(n+1)^2}\cdot\frac{2(n+1)}{1-\rho} = \frac{8C_1}{(n+1)(1-\rho)} \to 0, \quad n \to \infty.$$

Then (28) follows from this, and we obtain (26) in an obvious way.

5. In §9 we gave, for a random walk $S_0, S_1, \ldots$ generated by a Bernoulli scheme, recurrent equations for the probability and the expectation of the exit time at either boundary. We now derive similar equations for Markov chains.

Let $\xi = (\xi_0, \ldots, \xi_n)$ be a Markov chain with transition matrix $\|p_{ij}\|$ and phase space $X = \{0, \pm 1, \ldots, \pm N\}$. Let A and B be two integers, $-N \le A \le 0 \le B \le N$, and $x \in X$. Let $\mathscr{B}_{k+1}$ be the set of paths $(x_0, x_1, \ldots, x_k)$, $x_i \in X$, that leave the interval (A, B) for the first time at the upper end, i.e. leave (A, B) by going into the set $(B, B+1, \ldots, N)$.

For $A \le x \le B$, put

$$\beta_k(x) = \mathsf{P}\{(\xi_0, \ldots, \xi_k) \in \mathscr{B}_{k+1}|\xi_0 = x\}.$$

In order to find these probabilities (for the first exit of the Markov chain from (A, B) through the upper boundary) we use the method that was applied in the deduction of the backward equations.

We have

$$\beta_k(x) = \mathsf{P}\{(\xi_0, \ldots, \xi_k) \in \mathscr{B}_{k+1} | \xi_0 = x\}$$
$$= \sum_y p_{xy} \cdot \mathsf{P}\{(\xi_0, \ldots, \xi_k) \in \mathscr{B}_{k+1} | \xi_0 = x, \xi_1 = y\},$$

where, as is easily seen by using the Markov property and the homogeneity of the chain,

$$\mathsf{P}\{(\xi_0, \ldots, \xi_k) \in \mathscr{B}_{k+1} | \xi_0 = x, \xi_1 = y\}$$
$$= \mathsf{P}\{(x, y, \xi_2, \ldots, \xi_k) \in \mathscr{B}_{k+1} | \xi_0 = x, \xi_1 = y\}$$
$$= \mathsf{P}\{(y, \xi_2, \ldots, \xi_k) \in \mathscr{B}_k | \xi_1 = y\}$$
$$= \mathsf{P}\{(y, \xi_1, \ldots, \xi_{k-1}) \in \mathscr{B}_k | \xi_0 = y\} = \beta_{k-1}(y).$$

Therefore

$$\beta_k(x) = \sum_y p_{xy} \beta_{k-1}(y)$$

for $A < x < B$ and $1 \le k \le n$. Moreover, it is clear that

$$\beta_k(x) = 1, \qquad x = B, B + 1, \ldots, N,$$

and

$$\beta_k(x) = 0, \qquad x = -N, \ldots, A.$$

In a similar way we can find equations for $\alpha_k(x)$, the probabilities for first exit from (A, B) through the lower boundary.

Let $\tau_k = \min\{0 \le l \le k : \xi_l \notin (A, B)\}$, where $\tau_k = k$ if the set $\{\cdot\} = \varnothing$. Then the same method, applied to $m_k(x) = \mathsf{E}(\tau_k | \xi_0 = x)$, leads to the following recurrent equations:

$$m_k(x) = 1 + \sum_y m_{k-1}(y) p_{xy}$$

(here $1 \le k \le n$, $A < x < B$). We define

$$m_k(x) = 0, \qquad x \notin (A, B).$$

It is clear that if the transition matrix is given by (11) the equations for $\alpha_k(x)$, $\beta_k(x)$ and $m_k(x)$ become the corresponding equations from §9, where they were obtained by essentially the same method that was used here.

These equations have the most interesting applications in the limiting case when the walk continues for an unbounded length of time. Just as in §9, the corresponding equations can be obtained by a formal limiting process $(k \to \infty)$.

By way of example, we consider the Markov chain with states $\{0, 1, \ldots, B\}$ and transition probabilities

$$p_{00} = 1, \qquad p_{BB} = 1,$$

and

$$p_{ij} = \begin{cases} p_i > 0, & j = i + 1, \\ r_i, & j = i, \\ q_i > 0, & j = i - 1, \end{cases}$$

for $1 \le i \le B - 1$, where $p_i + q_i + r_i = 1$.

For this chain, the corresponding graph is

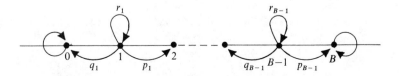

It is clear that states 0 and B are absorbing, whereas for every other state i the particle stays there with probability r_i, moves one step to the right with probability p_i, and to the left with probability q_i.

Let us find $\alpha(x) = \lim_{k \to \infty} \alpha_k(x)$, the limit of the probability that a particle starting at the point x arrives at state zero before reaching state B. Taking limits as $k \to \infty$ in the equations for $\alpha_k(x)$, we find that

$$\alpha(j) = q_j \alpha(j - 1) + r_j \alpha(j) + p_j \alpha(j + 1)$$

when $0 < j < B$, with the boundary conditions

$$\alpha(0) = 1, \qquad \alpha(B) = 0.$$

Since $r_j - 1 - q_j - p_j$, we have

$$p_j(\alpha(j + 1) - \alpha(j)) = q_j(\alpha(j) - \alpha(j - 1))$$

and consequently

$$\alpha(j + 1) - \alpha(j) = \rho_j(\alpha(1) - 1),$$

where

$$\rho_j = \frac{q_1 \cdots q_j}{p_1 \cdots p_j}, \qquad \rho_0 = 1.$$

But

$$\alpha(j + 1) - 1 = \sum_{i = 0}^{j} (\alpha(i + 1) - \alpha(i)).$$

Therefore

$$\alpha(j + 1) - 1 = (\alpha(1) - 1) \cdot \sum_{i = 1}^{j} \rho_i.$$

If $j = B - 1$, we have $\alpha(j + 1) = \alpha(B) = 0$, and therefore

$$\alpha(1) = 1 = -\frac{1}{\sum_{i=1}^{B-1} \rho_i},$$

whence

$$\alpha(1) = \frac{\sum_{i=1}^{B-1} \rho_i}{\sum_{i=0}^{B-1} \rho_i} \quad \text{and} \quad \alpha(j) = \frac{\sum_{i=j}^{B-1} \rho_i}{\sum_{i=1}^{B-1} \rho_i}, \qquad j = 1, \ldots, B.$$

(This should be compared with the results of §9.)

Now let $m(x) = \lim_k m_k(x)$, the limiting value of the average time taken to arrive at one of the states 0 or B. Then $m(0) = m(B) = 0$,

$$m(x) = 1 + \sum_y m(y) p_{xy}$$

and consequently for the example that we are considering,

$$m(j) = 1 + q_j m(j - 1) + r_j m(j) + p_j m(j + 1)$$

for $j = 1, 2, \ldots, B - 1$. To find $m(j)$ we put

$$M(j) = m(j) - m(j - 1), \qquad j = 0, 1, \ldots, B.$$

Then

$$p_j M(j + 1) = q_j M(j) - 1, \qquad j = 1, \ldots, B - 1,$$

and consequently we find that

$$M(j + 1) = \rho_j M(1) - R_j,$$

where

$$\rho_j = \frac{q_1 \cdots q_j}{p_1 \cdots p_j}, \qquad R_j = \frac{1}{p_j}\left[1 + \frac{q_j}{p_{j-1}} + \cdots + \frac{q_j \cdots q_2}{p_j \cdots p_1} \right].$$

Therefore

$$m(i) = m(j) - m(0) = \sum_{i=0}^{j-1} M(i + 1)$$

$$= \sum_{i=0}^{j-1} (\rho_i m(1) - R_i) = m(1) \sum_{i=0}^{j-1} \rho_i - \sum_{i=0}^{j-1} R_i.$$

It remains only to determine $m(1)$. But $m(B) = 0$, and therefore

$$m(1) = \frac{\sum_{i=0}^{B-1} R_i}{\sum_{i=0}^{B-1} \rho_i},$$

and for $1 < j \leq B$,

$$m(j) = \sum_{i=0}^{j-1} \rho_i \cdot \frac{\sum_{i=0}^{B-1} R_i}{\sum_{i=0}^{B-1} \rho_i} - \sum_{i=0}^{j-1} R_i.$$

(This should be compared with the results in §9 for the case $r_i = 0$, $p_i = p$, $q_i = q$.)

6. In this subsection we consider a stronger version of the Markov property (8), namely that it remains valid if time k is replaced by a random time (see also Theorem 2). The significance of this, the *strong Markov property*, can be illustrated in particular by the example of the derivation of the recurrent relations (38), which play an important role in the classification of the states of Markov chains (Chapter VIII).

Let $\xi = (\xi_1, \ldots, \xi_n)$ be a homogeneous Markov chain with transition matrix $\|p_{ij}\|$; let $\mathscr{D}^\xi = (\mathscr{D}_k^\xi)_{0 \le k \le n}$ be a system of decompositions, $\mathscr{D}_k^\xi = \mathscr{D}_{\xi_0, \ldots, \xi_k}$. Let $\mathscr{B}_k^\xi$ denote the algebra $\alpha(\mathscr{D}_k^\xi)$ generated by the decomposition $\mathscr{D}_k^\xi$.

We first put the Markov property (8) into a somewhat different form. Let $B \in \mathscr{B}_k^\xi$. Let us show that then

$$P\{\xi_n = a_n, \ldots, \xi_{k+1} = a_{k+1} | B \cap (\xi_k = a_k)\}$$
$$= P\{\xi_n = a_n, \ldots, \xi_{k+1} = a_{k+1} | \xi_k = a_k\} \qquad (29)$$

(assuming that $P\{B \cap (\xi_k = a_k)\} > 0$). In fact, B can be represented in the form

$$B = \sum{}^* \{\xi_0^* = a_0^*, \ldots, \xi_k = a_k^*\},$$

where $\sum^*$ extends over some set $(a_0^*, \ldots, a_k^*)$. Consequently

$$P\{\xi_n = a_n, \ldots, \xi_{k+1} = a_{k+1} | B \cap (\xi_k = a_k)\}$$
$$= \frac{P\{(\xi_n = a_n, \ldots, \xi_k = a_k) \cap B\}}{P\{(\xi_k = a_k) \cap B\}}$$
$$= \frac{\sum^* P\{(\xi_n = a_n, \ldots, \xi_k = a_k) \cap (\xi_0 = a_0^*, \ldots, \xi_k = a_k^*)\}}{P\{(\xi_k = a_k) \cap B\}}. \qquad (30)$$

But, by the Markov property,

$$P\{(\xi_n = a_n, \ldots, \xi_k = a_k) \cap (\xi_0 = a_0^*, \ldots, \xi_k = a_k^*)\}$$

$$= \begin{cases} P\{\xi_n = a_n, \ldots, \xi_{k+1} = a_{k+1} | \xi_0 = a_0^*, \ldots, \xi_k = a_k^*\} \\ \quad \times P\{\xi_0 = a_0^*, \ldots, \xi_k = a_k^*\} & \text{if } a_k = a_k^*, \\ 0 & \text{if } a_k \ne a_k^*, \end{cases}$$

$$= \begin{cases} P\{\xi_n = a_n, \ldots, \xi_{k+1} = a_{k+1} | \xi_k = a_k\} P\{\xi_0 = a_0^*, \ldots, \xi_k = a_k^*\} \\ \quad \text{if } a_k = a_k^*, \\ 0 & \text{if } a_k \ne a_k^*, \end{cases}$$

$$= \begin{cases} P\{\xi_n = a_n, \ldots, \xi_{k+1} = a_{k+1} | \xi_k = a_k\} P\{(\xi_k = a_k) \cap B\} \\ \quad \text{if } a_k = a_k^*, \\ 0 & \text{if } a_k \ne a_k^*. \end{cases}$$

Therefore the sum $\sum^*$ in (30) is equal to

$$P\{\xi_n = a_n, \dots, \xi_{k+1} = a_{k+1} | \xi_k = a_k\} P\{(\xi_k = a_k) \cap B\},$$

This establishes (29).

Let τ be a stopping time (with respect to the system $D^\xi = (D^\xi_k)_{0 \le k \le n}$; see Definition 2 in §11).

Definition. We say that a set B in the algebra $\mathscr{B}^\xi_n$ belongs to the system of sets $\mathscr{B}^\xi_\tau$ if, for each k, $0 \le k \le n$,

$$B \cap \{\tau = k\} \in \mathscr{B}^\xi_k. \tag{31}$$

It is easily verified that the collection of such sets B forms an algebra (called the algebra of events observed at time τ).

Theorem 2. *Let $\xi = (\xi_0, \dots, \xi_n)$ be a homogeneous Markov chain with transition matrix $\|p_{ij}\|$, τ a stopping time (with respect to $\mathscr{D}^\xi$), $B \in \mathscr{B}^\xi_\tau$ and $A = \{\omega: \tau + l \le n\}$. Then if $P\{A \cap B \cap (\xi_\tau = a_0)\} > 0$, we have*

$$P\{\xi_{\tau+l} = a_l, \dots, \xi_{\tau+1} = a_1 | A \cap B \cap (\xi_\tau = a_0)\}$$
$$= P\{\xi_{\tau+l} = a_l, \dots, \xi_{\tau+1} = a_1 | A \cap (\xi_\tau = a_0)\}, \tag{32}$$

and if $P\{A \cap (\xi_\tau = a_0)\} > 0$ then

$$P\{\xi_{\tau+l} = a_l, \dots, \xi_{\tau+1} = a_1 | A \cap (\xi_\tau = a_0)\} = p_{a_0 a_1} \cdots p_{a_{l-1} a_l}. \tag{33}$$

For the sake of simplicity, we give the proof only for the case $l = 1$. Since $B \cap (\tau = k) \in \mathscr{B}^\xi_k$, we have, according to (29),

$$P\{\xi_{\tau+1} = a_1, A \cap B \cap (\xi_\tau = a_0)\}$$
$$= \sum_{k \le n-1} P\{\xi_{k+1} = a_1, \xi_k = a_0, \tau = k, B\}$$
$$= \sum_{k \le n-1} P\{\xi_{k+1} = a_1 | \xi_k = a_0, \tau = k, B\} P\{\xi_k = a_0, \tau = k, B\}$$
$$= \sum_{k \le n-1} P\{\xi_{k+1} = a_1 | \xi_k = a_0\} P\{\xi_k = a_0, \tau = k, B\}$$
$$= p_{a_0 a_1} \cdot \sum_{k \le n-1} P\{\xi_k = a_0, \tau = k, B\} = p_{a_0 a_1} \cdot P\{A \cap B \cap (\xi_\tau = a_0)\},$$

which simultaneously establishes (32) and (33) (for (33) we have to take $B = \Omega$).

Remark. When $l = 1$, the strong Markov property (32), (33) is evidently equivalent to the property that

$$P\{\xi_{\tau+1} \in C | A \cap B \cap (\xi_\tau = a_0)\} = P_{a_0}(C), \tag{34}$$

for every $C \subseteq X$, where

$$P_{a_0}(C) = \sum_{a_1 \in C} p_{a_0 a_1}.$$

In turn, (34) can be restated as follows: on the set $A = \{\tau \leq n - 1\}$,

$$P\{\xi_{\tau+1} \in C | \mathscr{B}_\tau^\xi\} = P_{\xi_\tau}(C), \tag{35}$$

which is a form of the strong Markov property that is commonly used in the general theory of homogeneous Markov processes.

7. Let $\xi = (\xi_0, \ldots, \xi_n)$ be a homogeneous Markov chain with transition matrix $\|p_{ij}\|$, and let

$$f_{ii}^{(k)} = P\{\xi_k = i, \xi_l \neq i, 1 \leq l \leq k - 1 | \xi_0 = i\} \tag{36}$$

and

$$f_{ij}^{(k)} = P\{\xi_k = j, \xi_l \neq j, 1 \leq l \leq k - 1 | \xi_0 = i\} \tag{37}$$

for $i \neq j$ be respectively the probability of first return to state i at time k and the probability of first arrival at state j at time k.
   Let us show that

$$p_{ij}^{(n)} = \sum_{k=1}^{n} f_{ij}^{(k)} p_{jj}^{(n-k)}, \qquad \text{where} \quad p_{jj}^{(0)} = 1. \tag{38}$$

The intuitive meaning of the formula is clear: to go from state i to state j in n steps, it is necessary to reach state j for the first time in k steps ($1 \leq k \leq n$) and then to go from state j to state j in $n - k$ steps. We now give a rigorous derivation.
   Let j be given and

$$\tau = \min\{1 \leq k \leq n: \xi_k = j\},$$

assuming that $\tau = n + 1$ if $\{\cdot\} = \varnothing$. Then $f_{ij}^{(k)} = P\{\tau = k | \xi_0 = i\}$ and

$$\begin{aligned} p_{ij}^{(n)} &= P\{\xi_n = j | \xi_0 = i\} \\ &= \sum_{1 \leq k \leq n} P\{\xi_n = j, \tau = k | \xi_0 = i\} \\ &= \sum_{1 \leq k \leq n} P\{\xi_{\tau+n-k} = j, \tau = k | \xi_0 = i\}, \end{aligned} \tag{39}$$

where the last equation follows because $\xi_{\tau+n-k} = \xi_n$ on the set $\{\tau = k\}$. Moreover, the set $\{\tau = k\} = \{\tau = k, \xi_\tau = j\}$ for every $k, 1 \leq k \leq n$. Therefore if $P\{\xi_0 = i, \tau = k\} > 0$, it follows from Theorem 2 that

$$\begin{aligned} P\{\xi_{\tau+n-k} = j | \xi_0 = i, \tau = k\} &= P\{\xi_{\tau+n-k} = j | \xi_0 = i, \tau = k, \xi_\tau = j\} \\ &= P\{\xi_{\tau+n-k} = j | \xi_\tau = j\} = p_{jj}^{(n-k)} \end{aligned}$$

128   I. Elementary Probability Theory

and by (37)

$$p_{ij}^{(n)} = \sum_{k=1}^{n} \mathsf{P}\{\xi_{\tau+n-k} = j \,|\, \xi_0 = i, \tau = k\}\mathsf{P}\{\tau = k \,|\, \xi_0 = i\}$$

$$= \sum_{k=1}^{n} p_{jj}^{(n-k)} f_{ij}^{(k)},$$

which establishes (38).

8. Problems

1. Let $\xi = (\xi_0, \ldots, \xi_n)$ be a Markov chain with values in X and $f = f(x)$ $(x \in X)$ a function. Will the sequence $(f(\xi_0), \ldots, f(\xi_n))$ form a Markov chain? Will the "reversed" sequence

$$(\xi_n, \xi_{n-1}, \ldots, \xi_0)$$

form a Markov chain?

2. Let $\mathbb{P} = \|p_{ij}\|$, $1 \leq i, j \leq r$, be a stochastic matrix and λ an eigenvalue of the matrix, i.e. a root of the characteristic equation $\det\|\mathbb{P} - \lambda E\| = 0$. Show that $\lambda_0 = 1$ is an eigenvalue and that all the other eigenvalues have moduli not exceeding 1. If all the eigenvalues $\lambda_1, \ldots, \lambda_r$ are distinct, then $p_{ij}^{(k)}$ admits the representation

$$p_{ij}^{(k)} = \pi_j + a_{ij}(1)\lambda_1^k + \cdots + a_{ij}(r)\lambda_r^k,$$

where $\pi_j, a_{ij}(1), \ldots, a_{ij}(r)$ can be expressed in terms of the elements of $\mathbb{P}$. (It follows from this algebraic approach to the study of Markov chains that, in particular, when $|\lambda_1| < 1, \ldots, |\lambda_r| < 1$, the limit $\lim p_{ij}^{(k)}$ exists for every j and is independent of i.)

3. Let $\xi = (\xi_0, \ldots, \xi_n)$ be a homogeneous Markov chain with state space X and transition matrix $\mathbb{P} = \|p_{xy}\|$. Let

$$T\varphi(x) = \mathsf{E}[\varphi(\xi_1) \,|\, \xi_0 = x] \quad \left(= \sum_y \varphi(y)p_{xy}\right).$$

Let the nonnegative function φ satisfy
$$T\varphi(x) = \varphi(x), \qquad x \in X.$$

Show that the sequence of random variables

$$\zeta = (\zeta_k, \mathscr{D}_k^\xi) \qquad \text{with} \quad \zeta_k = \varphi(\xi_k)$$

is a martingale.

4. Let $\xi = (\xi_n, \sqcap, \mathbb{P})$ and $\tilde{\xi} = (\xi_n, \sqcap, \mathbb{P})$ be two Markov chains with different initial distributions $\sqcap = (p_1, \ldots, p_r)$ and $\tilde{\sqcap} = (\tilde{p}_1, \ldots, \tilde{p}_r)$. Show that if $\min_{i,j} p_{ij} \geq \varepsilon > 0$ then

$$\sum_{i=1}^{r} |\tilde{p}_i^{(n)} - p_i^{(n)}| \leq 2(1 - \varepsilon)^n.$$

CHAPTER II

Mathematical Foundations of Probability Theory

§1. Probabilistic Model for an Experiment with Infinitely Many Outcomes. Kolmogorov's Axioms

1. The models introduced in the preceding chapter enabled us to give a probabilistic–statistical description of experiments with a finite number of outcomes. For example, the triple $(\Omega, \mathscr{A}, \mathbf{P})$ with

$$\Omega = \{\omega : \omega = (a_1, \ldots, a_n), a_i = 0, 1\}, \quad \mathscr{A} = \{A : A \subseteq \Omega\}$$

and $p(\omega) = p^{\Sigma a_i} q^{n - \Sigma a_i}$ is a model for the experiment in which a coin is tossed n times "independently" with probability p of falling head. In this model the number $N(\Omega)$ of outcomes, i.e. the number of points in Ω, is the finite number 2^n.

We now consider the problem of constructing a probabilistic model for the experiment consisting of an infinite number of independent tosses of a coin when at each step the probability of falling head is p.

It is natural to take the set of outcomes to be the set

$$\Omega = \{\omega : \omega = (a_1, a_2, \ldots), a_i = 0, 1\},$$

i.e. the space of sequences $\omega = (a_1, a_2, \ldots)$ whose elements are 0 or 1.

What is the cardinality $N(\Omega)$ of Ω? It is well known that every number $a \in [0, 1)$ has a unique binary expansion (containing an infinite number of zeros)

$$a = \frac{a_1}{2} + \frac{a_2}{2^2} + \cdots \qquad (a_i = 0, 1).$$

Hence it is clear that there is a one-to-one correspondence between the points ω of Ω and the points a of the set $[0, 1)$, and therefore Ω has the cardinality of the continuum.

Consequently if we wish to construct a probabilistic model to describe experiments like tossing a coin infinitely often, we must consider spaces Ω of a rather complicated nature.

We shall now try to see what probabilities ought reasonably to be assigned (or assumed) in a model of infinitely many independent tosses of a fair coin $(p + q = \frac{1}{2})$.

Since we may take Ω to be the set $[0, 1)$, our problem can be considered as the problem of choosing points at random from this set. For reasons of symmetry, it is clear that all outcomes ought to be equiprobable. But the set $[0, 1)$ is uncountable, and if we suppose that its probability is 1, then it follows that the probability $p(\omega)$ of each outcome certainly must equal zero. However, this assignment of probabilities $(p(\omega) = 0, \ \omega \in [0, 1))$ does not lead very far. The fact is that we are ordinarily not interested in the probability of one outcome or another, but in the probability that the result of the experiment is in one or another specified set A of outcomes (an event). In elementary probability theory we use the probabilities $p(\omega)$ to find the probability $\mathsf{P}(A)$ of the event A: $\mathsf{P}(A) = \sum_{\omega \in A} p(\omega)$. In the present case, with $p(\omega) = 0, \ \omega \in [0, 1)$, we cannot define, for example, the probability that a point chosen at random from $[0, 1)$ belongs to the set $[0, \frac{1}{2})$. At the same time, it is intuitively clear that this probability should be $\frac{1}{2}$.

These remarks should suggest that in constructing probabilistic models for uncountable spaces Ω we must assign probabilities, not to individual outcomes but to subsets of Ω. The same reasoning as in the first chapter shows that the collection of sets to which probabilities are assigned must be closed with respect to unions, intersections and complements. Here the following definition is useful.

Definition 1. Let Ω be a set of points ω. A system $\mathscr{A}$ of subsets of Ω is called an *algebra* if

(a) $\Omega \in \mathscr{A}$,
(b) $A, B \in \mathscr{A} \Rightarrow A \cup B \in \mathscr{A}, \qquad A \cap B \in \mathscr{A}$,
(c) $A \in \mathscr{A} \Rightarrow \bar{A} \in \mathscr{A}$

(Notice that in condition (b) it is sufficient to require only that either $A \cup B \in \mathscr{A}$ or that $A \cap B \in \mathscr{A}$, since $A \cup B = \overline{\bar{A} \cap \bar{B}}$ and $A \cap B = \overline{\bar{A} \cup \bar{B}}$.)

The next definition is needed in formulating the concept of a probabilistic model.

Definition 2. Let $\mathscr{A}$ be an algebra of subsets of Ω. A set function $\mu = \mu(A)$, $A \in \mathscr{A}$, taking values in $[0, \infty]$, is called a *finitely additive measure* defined on $\mathscr{A}$ if

$$\mu(A + B) = \mu(A) + \mu(B). \qquad (1)$$

for every pair of disjoint sets A and B in $\mathscr{A}$.

A finitely additive measure μ with $\mu(\Omega) < \infty$ is called finite, and when $\mu(\Omega) = 1$ it is called a finitely additive probability measure, or a finitely additive probability.

2. We now define a probabilistic model (in the extended sense).

Definition 3. An ordered triple $(\Omega, \mathscr{A}, P)$, where

(a) Ω is a set of points ω;
(b) $\mathscr{A}$ is an algebra of subsets of Ω;
(c) P is a finitely additive probability on A,

is a *probabilistic model in the extended sense.*

It turns out, however, that this model is too broad to lead to a fruitful mathematical theory. Consequently we must restrict both the class of subsets of Ω that we consider, and the class of admissible probability measures.

Definition 4. A system $\mathscr{F}$ of subsets of Ω is a *σ-algebra* if it is an algebra and satisfies the following additional condition (stronger than (b) of Definition 1):

(b*) if $A_n \in \mathscr{F}, n = 1, 2, \ldots$, then

$$\bigcup A_n \in \mathscr{F}, \qquad \bigcap A_n \in \mathscr{F}$$

(it is sufficient to require either that $\bigcup A_n \in \mathscr{F}$ or that $\bigcap A_n \in \mathscr{F}$).

Definition 5. The space Ω together with a σ-algebra $\mathscr{F}$ of its subsets is a *measurable space*, and is denoted by $(\Omega, \mathscr{F})$.

Definition 6. A finitely additive measure μ defined on an algebra $\mathscr{A}$ of subsets of Ω is *countably additive* (or *σ-additive*), or simply a measure, if, for all pairwise disjoint subsets $A_1, A_2, \ldots$ of A,

$$\mu\left(\sum_{n=1}^{\infty} A_n \right) = \sum_{n=1}^{\infty} \mu(A_n).$$

A finitely additive measure μ is said to be *σ-finite* if Ω can be represented in the form

$$\Omega = \sum_{n=1}^{\infty} \Omega_n, \qquad \Omega_n \in \mathscr{A},$$

with $\mu(\Omega_n) < \infty, n = 1, 2, \ldots$.

If a countably additive measure P on the algebra A satisfies $P(\Omega) = 1$, it is called a *probability measure* or a *probability* (defined on the sets that belong to the algebra $\mathscr{A}$).

Probability measures have the following properties.

If $\varnothing$ is the empty set then

$$P(\varnothing) = 0.$$

If $A, B \in \mathscr{A}$ then

$$P(A \cup B) = P(A) + P(B) - P(A \cap B).$$

If $A, B \in \mathscr{A}$ and $B \subseteq A$ then

$$P(B) \le P(A).$$

If $A_n \in \mathscr{A}, n = 1, 2, \ldots,$ and $\bigcup A_n \in \mathscr{A}$, then

$$P(A_1 \cup A_2 \cup \cdots) \le P(A_1) + P(A_2) + \cdots.$$

The first three properties are evident. To establish the last one it is enough to observe that $\sum_{n=1}^{\infty} A_n = \sum_{n=1}^{\infty} B_n$, where $B_1 = A_1$, $B_n = \bar{A}_1 \cap \cdots \cap \bar{A}_{n-1} \cap A_n, n \ge 2, B_i \cap B_j = \varnothing, i \ne j$, and therefore

$$P\left(\bigcap_{n=1}^{\infty} A_n\right) = P\left(\sum_{n=1}^{\infty} B_n\right) = \sum_{n=1}^{\infty} P(B_n) \le \sum_{n=1}^{\infty} P(A_n).$$

The next theorem, which has many applications, provides conditions under which a finitely additive set function is actually countably additive.

Theorem. *Let P be a finitely additive set function defined over the algebra $\mathscr{A}$, with $P(\Omega) = 1$. The following four conditions are equivalent:*

(1) P *is σ-additive (P is a probability);*

(2) P *is continuous from below, i.e. for any sets $A_1, A_2, \ldots \in \mathscr{A}$ such that $A_n \subseteq A_{n+1}$ and $\bigcup_{n=1}^{\infty} A_n \in \mathscr{A}$,*

$$\lim_n P(A_n) = P\left(\bigcup_{n=1}^{\infty} A_n\right);$$

(3) P *is continuous from above, i.e. for any sets $A_1, A_2, \ldots$ such that $A_n \supseteq A_{n+1}$ and $\bigcap_{n=1}^{\infty} A_n \in \mathscr{A}$,*

$$\lim_n P(A_n) = P\left(\bigcap_{n=1}^{\infty} A_n\right);$$

(4) P *is continuous at* $\varnothing$, *i.e. for any sets* $A_1, A_2, \ldots \in \mathscr{A}$ *such that* $A_{n+1} \subseteq A_n$ *and* $\bigcap_{n=1}^{\infty} A_n = \varnothing$,

$$\lim_n P(A_n) = 0.$$

PROOF. (1) $\Rightarrow$ (2). Since

$$\bigcup_{n=1}^{\infty} A_n = A_1 + (A_2 \backslash A_1) + (A_3 \backslash A_2) + \cdots,$$

we have

$$P\left(\bigcup_{n=1}^{\infty} A_n\right) = P(A_1) + P(A_2 \backslash A_1) + P(A_3 \backslash A_2) + \cdots$$

$$= P(A_1) + P(A_2) - P(A_1) + P(A_3) - P(A_2) + \cdots$$

$$= \lim_n P(A_n).$$

(2) $\Rightarrow$ (3). Let $n \geq 1$; then

$$P(A_n) = P(A_1 \backslash (A_1 \backslash A_n)) = P(A_1) - P(A_1 \backslash A_n).$$

The sequence $\{A_1 \backslash A_n\}_{n \geq 1}$ of sets is nondecreasing (see the table in Subsection 3 below) and

$$\bigcup_{n=1}^{\infty} (A_1 \backslash A_n) = A_1 \backslash \bigcap_{n=1}^{\infty} A_n.$$

Then, by (2)

$$\lim_n P(A_1 \backslash A_n) = P\left(\bigcup_{n=1}^{\infty} (A_l \backslash A_n)\right)$$

and therefore

$$\lim_n P(A_n) = P(A_1) - \lim_n P(A_1 \backslash A_n)$$

$$= P(A_1) - P\left(\bigcup_{n=1}^{\infty} (A_1 \backslash A_n)\right) = P(A_1) - P\left(A_1 \backslash \bigcap_{n=1}^{\infty} A_n\right)$$

$$= P(A_1) - P(A_1) + P\left(\bigcap_{n=1}^{\infty} A_n\right) = P\left(\bigcap_{n=1}^{\infty} A_n\right).$$

(3) $\Rightarrow$ (4). Obvious.

(4) $\Rightarrow$ (1). Let $A_1, A_2, \ldots \in \mathscr{A}$ be pairwise disjoint and let $\sum_{n=1}^{\infty} A_n \in \mathscr{A}$. Then

$$P\left(\sum_{i=1}^{\infty} A_i\right) = P\left(\sum_{i=1}^{n} A_i\right) + P\left(\sum_{i=n+1}^{\infty} A_i\right),$$

Table

Notation	Set-theoretic interpretation	Interpretation in probability theory
ω	element or point	outcome, sample point, elementary event
Ω	set of points	sample space; certain event
$\mathscr{F}$	σ-algebra of subsets	σ-algebra of events
$A \in \mathscr{F}$	set of points	event (if $\omega \in A$, we say that event A occurs)
$\bar{A} = \Omega \setminus A$	complement of A, i.e. the set of points ω that are not in A	event that A does not occur
$A \cup B$	union of A and B, i.e. the set of points ω belonging either to A or to B	event that either A or B occurs
$A \cap B$ (or AB)	intersection of A and B, i.e. the set of points ω belonging to both A and B	event that both A and B occur
$\varnothing$	empty set	impossible event
$A \cap B \equiv \varnothing$	A and B are disjoint	events A and B are mutually exclusive, i.e. cannot occur simultaneously
$A + B$	sum of sets, i.e. union of disjoint sets	event that one of two mutually exclusive events occurs
$A \setminus B$	difference of A and B, i.e. the set of points that belong to A but not to B	event that A occurs and B does not
$A \triangle B$	symmetric difference of sets, i.e. $(A \setminus B) \cup (B \setminus A)$	event that A or B occurs, but not both
$\bigcup_{n=1}^{\infty} A_n$	union of the sets $A_1, A_2, \dots$	event that at least one of $A_1, A_2, \dots$ occurs

$\sum\limits_{n=1}^{\infty} A_n$ — sum, i.e. union of pairwise disjoint sets $A_1, A_2, \ldots$ — event that one of the mutually exclusive events $A_1, A_2, \ldots$ occurs

$\bigcap\limits_{n=1}^{\infty} A_n$ — intersection of $A_1, A_2, \ldots$ — event that all the events $A_1, A_2, \ldots$ occur

$A_n \uparrow A$ $\left(\text{or } A = \lim\limits_{n} \uparrow A_n\right)$ — the increasing sequence of sets A_n converges to A, i.e. $A_1 \subseteq A_2 \subseteq \cdots$ and $A = \bigcup\limits_{n=1}^{\infty} A_n$ — the increasing sequence of events converges to event A

$A_n \downarrow A$ $\left(\text{or } A = \lim\limits_{n} \downarrow A_n\right)$ — the decreasing sequence of sets A_n converges to A, i.e. $A_1 \supseteq A_2 \supseteq \cdots$ and $A = \bigcap\limits_{n=1}^{\infty} A_n$ — the decreasing sequence of events converges to event A

$\overline{\lim} \, A_n$ (or $\limsup A_n$ or* $\{A_n \text{ i.o.}\}$) — the set $\bigcap\limits_{n=1}^{\infty} \bigcup\limits_{k=n}^{\infty} A_k$ — event that infinitely many of events $A_1, A_2, \ldots$ occur

$\underline{\lim}\limits_{n} A_n$ (or $\liminf A_n$) — the set $\bigcup\limits_{n=1}^{\infty} \bigcap\limits_{k=n}^{\infty} A_k$ — event that all the events $A_1, A_2, \ldots$ occur with the possible exception of a finite number of them

* i.o. = infinitely often.

and since $\sum_{i=n+1}^{\infty} A_i \downarrow \varnothing$, $n \to \infty$, we have

$$\sum_{i=1}^{\infty} P(A_i) = \lim_n \sum_{i=1}^{n} P(A_i) = \lim_n P\left(\sum_{i=1}^{n} A_i\right)$$

$$= \lim_n \left[P\left(\sum_{i=1}^{\infty} A_i\right) - P\left(\sum_{i=n+1}^{\infty} A_i\right) \right]$$

$$= P\left(\sum_{i=1}^{\infty} A_i\right) - \lim_n P\left(\sum_{i=n+1}^{\infty} A_i\right) = P\left(\sum_{i=1}^{\infty} A_i\right).$$

3. We can now formulate Kolmogorov's generally accepted axiom system, which forms the basis for the concept of a probability space.

Fundamental Definition. *An ordered triple* $(\Omega, \mathscr{F}, P)$ *where*

(a) Ω *is a set of points* ω,
(b) $\mathscr{F}$ *is a σ-algebra of subsets of* Ω,
(c) P *is a probability on* $\mathscr{F}$,

is called a probabilistic model or a probability space. Here Ω is the sample space or space of elementary events, the sets A in $\mathscr{F}$ are events, and $P(A)$ is the probability of the event A.

It is clear from the definition that the axiomatic formulation of probability theory is based on set theory and measure theory. Accordingly, it is useful to have a table (pp. 134–135) displaying the ways in which various concepts are interpreted in the two theories. In the next two sections we shall give examples of the measurable spaces that are most important for probability theory and of how probabilities are assigned on them.

4. PROBLEMS

1. Let $\Omega = \{r : r \in [0, 1]\}$ be the set of rational points of $[0, 1]$, $\mathscr{A}$ the algebra of sets each of which is a finite sum of disjoint sets A of one of the forms $\{r : a < r < b\}$, $\{r : a \le r < b\}$, $\{r : a < r \le b\}$, $\{r : a \le r \le b\}$, and $P(A) = b - a$. Show that $P(A)$, $A \in \mathscr{A}$, is finitely additive set function but not countably additive.

2. Let Ω be a countable set and $\mathscr{F}$ the collection of all its subsets. Put $\mu(A) = 0$ if A is finite and $\mu(A) = \infty$ if A is infinite. Show that the set function μ is finitely additive but not countably additive.

3. Let μ be a finite measure on a σ-algebra $\mathscr{F}$, $A_n \in \mathscr{F}$, $n = 1, 2, \ldots$, and $A = \lim_n A_n$ (i.e., $A = \underline{\lim}_n A_n = \overline{\lim}_n A_n$). Show that $\mu(A) = \lim_n \mu(A_n)$.

4. Prove that $P(A \triangle B) = P(A) + P(B) - 2P(A \cap B)$.

5. Show that the "distances" $\rho_1(A, B)$ and $\rho_2(A, B)$ defined by

$$\rho_1(A, B) = \mathsf{P}(A \triangle B),$$

$$\rho_2(A, B) = \begin{cases} \dfrac{\mathsf{P}(A \triangle B)}{\mathsf{P}(A \cup B)} & \text{if } \mathsf{P}(A \cup B) \neq 0, \\ 0 & \text{if } \mathsf{P}(A \cup B) = 0 \end{cases}$$

satisfy the triangle inequality.

6. Let μ be a finitely additive measure on an algebra $\mathscr{A}$, and let the sets $A_1, A_2, \ldots \in \mathscr{A}$ be pairwise disjoint and satisfy $A = \sum_{i=1}^{\infty} A_i \in \mathscr{A}$. Then $\mu(A) \geq \sum_{i=1}^{\infty} \mu(A_i)$.

7. Prove that

$$\overline{\lim \sup A_n} = \lim \inf \overline{A}_n, \qquad \overline{\lim \inf A_n} = \lim \sup \overline{A}_n,$$

$$\lim \inf A_n \subseteq \lim \sup A_n, \qquad \lim \sup(A_n \cup B_n) = \lim \sup A_n \cup \lim \sup B_n,$$

$$\lim \sup A_n \cap \lim \inf B_n \subseteq \lim \sup(A_n \cap B_n) \subseteq \lim \sup A_n \cap \lim \sup B_n.$$

If $A_n \uparrow A$ or $A_n \downarrow A$, then

$$\lim \inf A_n = \lim \sup A_n.$$

8. Let $\{x_n\}$ be a sequence of numbers and $A_n = (-\infty, x_n)$. Show that $x = \lim \sup x_n$ and $A = \lim \sup A_n$ are related in the following way: $(-\infty, x) \subseteq A \subseteq (-\infty, x]$. In other words, A is equal to either $(-\infty, x)$ or to $(-\infty, x]$.

9. Give an example to show that if a measure takes the value $+\infty$, it does not follow in general that countable additivity implies continuity at $\varnothing$.

§2. Algebras and σ-Algebras. Measurable Spaces

1. Algebras and σ-algebras are the components out of which probabilistic models are constructed. We shall present some examples and a number of results for these systems.

Let Ω be a sample space. Evidently each of the collections of sets

$$\mathscr{F}_* = \{\varnothing, \Omega\}, \qquad \mathscr{F}^* = \{A : A \subseteq \Omega\}$$

is both an algebra and a σ-algebra. In fact, $\mathscr{F}_*$ is trivial, the "poorest" σ-algebra, whereas $\mathscr{F}^*$ is the "richest" σ-algebra, consisting of all subsets of Ω.

When Ω is a finite space, the σ-algebra $\mathscr{F}^*$ is fully surveyable, and commonly serves as the system of events in the elementary theory. However, when the space is uncountable the class $\mathscr{F}^*$ is much too large, since it is impossible to define "probability" on such a system of sets in any consistent way.

If $A \subseteq \Omega$, the system

$$\mathscr{F}_A = \{A, \overline{A}, \varnothing, \Omega\}$$

is another example of an algebra (and a σ-algebra), the algebra (or σ-algebra) generated by A.

This system of sets is a special case of the systems generated by decompositions. In fact, let

$$\mathcal{D} = \{D_1, D_2, \ldots\}$$

be a *countable* decomposition of Ω into nonempty sets:

$$\Omega = D_1 + D_2 + \cdots ; \qquad D_i \cap D_j = \varnothing, \qquad i \neq j.$$

Then the system $\mathcal{A} = \alpha(\mathcal{D})$, formed by the sets that are unions of finite numbers of elements of the decomposition, is an algebra.

The following lemma is particularly useful since it establishes the important principle that there is a smallest algebra, or σ-algebra, containing a given collection of sets.

Lemma 1. *Let $\mathcal{E}$ be a collection of subsets of Ω. Then there are a smallest algebra $\alpha(\mathcal{E})$ and a smallest σ-algebra $\sigma(\mathcal{E})$ containing all the sets that are in $\mathcal{E}$.*

PROOF. The class $\mathcal{F}^*$ of all subsets of Ω is a σ-algebra. Therefore there are at least one algebra and one σ-algebra containing $\mathcal{E}$. We now define $\alpha(\mathcal{E})$ (or $\sigma(\mathcal{E})$) to consist of all sets that belong to every algebra (or σ-algebra) containing $\mathcal{E}$. It is easy to verify that this system is an algebra (or σ-algebra) and indeed the smallest.

Remark. The algebra $\alpha(E)$ (or $\sigma(E)$, respectively) is often referred to as the smallest algebra (or σ-algebra) generated by $\mathcal{E}$.

We often need to know what additional conditions will make an algebra, or some other system of sets, into a σ-algebra. We shall present several results of this kind.

Definition 1. A collection $\mathcal{M}$ of subsets of Ω is a *monotonic class* if $A_n \in \mathcal{M}$, $n = 1, 2, \ldots$, together with $A_n \uparrow A$ or $A_n \downarrow A$, implies that $A \in \mathcal{M}$.

Let $\mathcal{E}$ be a system of sets. Let $\mu(\mathcal{E})$ be the smallest monotonic class containing $\mathcal{E}$. (The proof of the existence of this class is like the proof of Lemma 1.)

Lemma 2. *A necessary and sufficient condition for an algebra $\mathcal{A}$ to be a σ-algebra is that it is a monotonic class.*

PROOF. A σ-algebra is evidently a monotonic class. Now let $\mathcal{A}$ be a monotonic class and $A_n \in \mathcal{A}$, $n = 1, 2, \ldots$. It is clear that $B_n = \bigcup_{i=1}^{n} A_i \in \mathcal{A}$ and $B_n \subseteq B_{n+1}$. Consequently, by the definition of a monotonic class, $B_n \uparrow \bigcup_{i=1}^{\infty} A_i \in \mathcal{A}$. Similarly we could show that $\bigcap_{i=1}^{\infty} A_i \in \mathcal{A}$.

By using this lemma, we can prove that, starting with an algebra $\mathcal{A}$, we can construct the σ-algebra $\sigma(\mathcal{A})$ by means of monotonic limiting processes.

Theorem 1. *Let $\mathscr{A}$ be an algebra. Then*

$$\mu(\mathscr{A}) = \sigma(\mathscr{A}). \tag{1}$$

PROOF. By Lemma 2, $\mu(\mathscr{A}) \subseteq \sigma(\mathscr{A})$. Hence it is enough to show that $\mu(\mathscr{A})$ is a σ-algebra. But $\mathscr{M} = \mu(\mathscr{A})$ is a monotonic class, and therefore, by Lemma 2 again, it is enough to show that $\mu(\mathscr{A})$ is an algebra.

Let $A \in \mathscr{M}$; we show that $\bar{A} \in \mathscr{M}$. For this purpose, we shall apply a principle that will often be used in the future, the *principle of appropriate sets*, which we now illustrate.

Let

$$\tilde{\mathscr{M}} = \{B : B \in \mathscr{M}, \bar{B} \in \mathscr{M}\}$$

be the sets that have the property that concerns us. It is evident that $\mathscr{A} \subseteq \tilde{\mathscr{M}} \subseteq \mathscr{M}$. Let us show that $\tilde{\mathscr{M}}$ is a monotonic class.

Let $B_n \in \tilde{\mathscr{M}}$; then $B_n \in \mathscr{M}$, $\bar{B}_n \in \mathscr{M}$, and therefore

$$\lim \uparrow B_n \in \mathscr{M}, \quad \lim \uparrow \bar{B}_n \in \mathscr{M}, \quad \lim \downarrow B_n \in \mathscr{M}, \quad \lim \downarrow \bar{B}_n \in \mathscr{M}.$$

Consequently

$$\overline{\lim \uparrow B_n} = \lim \downarrow \bar{B}_n \in \mathscr{M}, \quad \overline{\lim \downarrow B_n} = \lim \uparrow \bar{B}_n \in \mathscr{M},$$

$$\overline{\lim \uparrow \bar{B}_n} = \lim \downarrow B_n \in \mathscr{M}, \quad \overline{\lim \downarrow \bar{B}_n} = \lim \uparrow B_n \in \mathscr{M},$$

and therefore $\tilde{\mathscr{M}}$ is a monotonic class. But $\tilde{\mathscr{M}} \subseteq \mathscr{M}$ and $\mathscr{M}$ is the smallest monotonic class. Therefore $\tilde{\mathscr{M}} = \mathscr{M}$, and if $A \in \mathscr{M} = \mu(\mathscr{A})$, then we also have $\bar{A} \in \mathscr{M}$, i.e. $\mathscr{M}$ is closed under the operation of taking complements.

Let us now show that $\mathscr{M}$ is closed under intersections.

Let $A \in \mathscr{M}$ and

$$\mathscr{M}_A = \{B : B \in \mathscr{M}, A \cap B \in \mathscr{M}\}.$$

From the equations

$$\lim \downarrow (A \cap B_n) = A \cap \lim \downarrow B_n,$$

$$\lim \uparrow (A \cap B_n) = A \cap \lim \uparrow B_n$$

it follows that $\mathscr{M}_A$ is a monotonic class.

Moreover, it is easily verified that

$$(A \in \mathscr{M}_B) \Leftrightarrow (B \in \mathscr{M}_A). \tag{2}$$

Now let $A \in \mathscr{A}$; then since $\mathscr{A}$ is an algebra, for every $B \in \mathscr{A}$ the set $A \cap B \in \mathscr{A}$ and therefore

$$\mathscr{A} \subseteq \mathscr{M}_A \subseteq \mathscr{M}.$$

But $\mathscr{M}_A$ is a monotonic class (since $\lim \uparrow AB_n = A \lim \uparrow B_n$ and $\lim \downarrow AB_n = A \lim \downarrow B_n$), and $\mathscr{M}$ is the smallest monotonic class. Therefore $\mathscr{M}_A = \mathscr{M}$ for all $A \in \mathscr{A}$. But then it follows from (2) that

$$(A \in \mathscr{M}_B) \Leftrightarrow (B \in \mathscr{M}_A = \mathscr{M}).$$

whenever $A \in \mathcal{A}$ and $B \in \mathcal{M}$. Consequently if $A \in \mathcal{A}$ then

$$A \in \mathcal{M}_B$$

for every $B \in \mathcal{M}$. Since A is any set in $\mathcal{A}$, it follows that

$$A \subseteq \mathcal{M}_B \subseteq \mathcal{M}.$$

Therefore for every $B \in \mathcal{M}$

$$\mathcal{M}_B = \mathcal{M},$$

i.e. if $B \in \mathcal{M}$ and $C \in \mathcal{M}$ then $C \cap B \in \mathcal{M}$.

Thus $\mathcal{M}$ is closed under complementation and intersection (and therefore under unions). Consequently $\mathcal{M}$ is an algebra, and the theorem is established.

Definition 2. Let Ω be a space. A class $\mathcal{D}$ of subsets of Ω is a *d-system* if

(a) $\Omega \in \mathcal{D}$;
(b) $A, B, \in \mathcal{D}, A \subseteq B \Rightarrow B \backslash A \in \mathcal{D}$;
(c) $A_n \in \mathcal{D}, A_n \subseteq A_{n+1} \Rightarrow \bigcup A_n \in \mathcal{D}$.

If $\mathcal{E}$ is a collection of sets then $d(\mathcal{E})$ denotes the smallest *d*-system containing $\mathcal{E}$.

Theorem 2. *If the collection $\mathcal{E}$ of sets is closed under intersections, then*

$$d(\mathcal{E}) = \sigma(\mathcal{E}) \tag{3}$$

PROOF. Every σ-algebra is a *d*-system, and consequently $d(\mathcal{E}) \subseteq \sigma(\mathcal{E})$. Hence if we prove that $d(\mathcal{E})$ is closed under intersections, $d(\mathcal{E})$ must be a σ-algebra and then, of course, the opposite inclusion $\sigma(\mathcal{E}) \subseteq d(\mathcal{E})$ is valid.

The proof once again uses the principle of appropriate sets.

Let

$$\mathcal{E}_1 = \{B \in d(\mathcal{E}): B \cap A \in d(\mathcal{E}) \text{ for all } A \in \mathcal{E}\}.$$

If $B \in \mathcal{E}$ then $B \cap A \in \mathcal{E}$ for all $A \in \mathcal{E}$ and therefore $\mathcal{E} \subseteq \mathcal{E}_1$. But $\mathcal{E}_1$ is a *d*-system. Hence $d(\mathcal{E}) \subseteq \mathcal{E}_1$. On the other hand, $\mathcal{E}_1 \subseteq d(\mathcal{E})$ by definition. Consequently

$$\mathcal{E}_1 = d(\mathcal{E}).$$

Now let

$$\mathcal{E}_2 = \{B \in d(\mathcal{E}): B \cap A \in d(\mathcal{E}) \text{ for all } A \in d(\mathcal{E})\}.$$

Again it is easily verified that $\mathcal{E}_2$ is a *d*-system. If $B \in \mathcal{E}$, then by the definition of $\mathcal{E}_1$ we obtain that $B \cap A \in d(\mathcal{E})$ for all $A \in \mathcal{E}_1 = d(\mathcal{E})$. Consequently $\mathcal{E} \subseteq \mathcal{E}_2$ and $d(\mathcal{E}) \subseteq \mathcal{E}_2$. But $d(\mathcal{E}) \supseteq \mathcal{E}_2$; hence $d(\mathcal{E}) = \mathcal{E}_2$, and therefore whenever A and B are in $d(\mathscr{E})$, the set $A \cap B$ also belongs to $d(\mathscr{E})$, i.e. $d(\mathscr{E})$ is closed under intersections.

This completes the proof of the theorem.

We next consider some measurable spaces $(\Omega, \mathscr{F})$ which are extremely important for probability theory.

2. The measurable space $(R, \mathscr{B}(R))$. Let $R = (-\infty, \infty)$ be the real line and

$$(a, b] = \{x \in R : a < x \le b\}$$

for all a and b, $-\infty \le a < b < \infty$. The interval $(a, \infty]$ is taken to be (a, ∞). (This convention is required if the complement of an interval $(-\infty, b]$ is to be an interval of the same form, i.e. open on the left and closed on the right.)

Let $\mathscr{A}$ be the system of subsets of R which are finite sums of disjoint intervals of the form $(a, b]$:

$$A \in \mathscr{A} \text{ if } A = \sum_{i=1}^{n} (a_i, b_i], \qquad n < \infty.$$

It is easily verified that this system of sets, in which we also include the empty set $\varnothing$, is an algebra. However, it is not a σ-algebra, since if $A_n = (0, 1 - 1/n] \in \mathscr{A}$, we have $\bigcup_n A_n = (0, 1) \notin \mathscr{A}$.

Let $\mathscr{B}(R)$ be the smallest σ-algebra $\sigma(\mathscr{A})$ containing $\mathscr{A}$. This σ-algebra, which plays an important role in analysis, is called the *Borel* algebra of subsets of the real line, and its sets are called *Borel sets*.

If $\mathscr{I}$ is the system of intervals $\mathscr{I}$ of the form $(a, b]$, and $\sigma(\mathscr{I})$ is the smallest σ-algebra containing $\mathscr{I}$, it is easily verified that $\sigma(\mathscr{I})$ is the Borel algebra. In other words, we can obtain the Borel algebra from $\mathscr{I}$ without going through the algebra $\mathscr{A}$, since $\sigma(\mathscr{I}) = \sigma(\alpha(\mathscr{I}))$.

We observe that

$$(a, b) = \bigcup_{n=1}^{\infty} \left(a, b - \frac{1}{n} \right], \qquad a < b,$$

$$[a, b] = \bigcap_{n=1}^{\infty} \left(a - \frac{1}{n}, b \right], \qquad a < b,$$

$$\{a\} = \bigcap_{n=1}^{\infty} \left(a - \frac{1}{n}, a \right].$$

Thus the Borel algebra contains not only intervals $(a, b]$ but also the singletons $\{a\}$ and all sets of the six forms

$$(a, b), \quad [a, b], \quad [a, b), \quad (-\infty, b), \quad (-\infty, b], \quad (a, \infty). \tag{4}$$

Let us also notice that the construction of $\mathscr{B}(R)$ could have been based on any of the six kinds of intervals instead of on $(a, b]$, since all the minimal σ-algebras generated by systems of intervals of any of the forms (4) are the same as $\mathscr{B}(R)$.

Sometimes it is useful to deal with the σ-algebra $\mathscr{B}(\bar{R})$ of subsets of the extended real line $\bar{R} = [-\infty, \infty]$. This is the smallest σ-algebra generated by intervals of the form

$$(a, b] = \{x \in \bar{R} : a < x \leq b\}, \qquad -\infty \leq a < b \leq \infty,$$

where $(-\infty, b]$ is to stand for the set $\{x \in \bar{R} : -\infty \leq x \leq b\}$.

Remark 1. The measurable space $(R, \mathscr{B}(R))$ is often denoted by $(R, \mathscr{B})$ or $(R^1, \mathscr{B}_1)$.

Remark 2. Let us introduce the metric

$$\rho_1(x, y) = \frac{|x - y|}{1 + |x - y|}$$

on the real line R (this is equivalent to the usual metric $|x - y|$) and let $\mathscr{B}_0(R)$ be the smallest σ-algebra generated by the open sets $S_\rho(x^0) = \{x \in R : \rho_1(x, x^0) < \rho\}, \rho > 0, x^0 \in R$. Then $\mathscr{B}_0(R) = \mathscr{B}(R)$ (see Problem 7).

3. The measurable space $(R^n, \mathscr{B}(R^n))$. Let $R^n = R \times \cdots \times R$ be the direct, or Cartesian, product of n copies of the real line, i.e. the set of ordered n-tuples $x = (x_1, \ldots, x_n)$, where $-\infty < x_k < \infty, k = 1, \ldots, n$. The set

$$I = I_1 \times \cdots \times I_n,$$

where $I_k = (a_k, b_k]$, i.e. the set $\{x \in R^n : x_k \in I_k, k = 1, \ldots, n\}$, is called a rectangle, and I_k is a side of the rectangle. Let $\mathscr{I}$ be the set of all rectangles I. The smallest σ-algebra $\sigma(\mathscr{I})$ generated by the system $\mathscr{I}$ is the *Borel algebra* of subsets of R^n and is denoted by $\mathscr{B}(R^n)$. Let us show that we can arrive at this Borel algebra by starting in a different way.

Instead of the rectangles $I = I_1 \times \cdots \times I_n$ let us consider the rectangles $B = B_1 \times \cdots \times B_n$ with Borel sides (B_k is the Borel subset of the real line that appears in the kth place in the direct product $R \times \cdots \times R$). The smallest σ-algebra containing all rectangles with Borel sides is denoted by

$$\mathscr{B}(R) \otimes \cdots \otimes \mathscr{B}(R)$$

and called the *direct product* of the σ-algebras $\mathscr{B}(R)$. Let us show that in fact

$$\mathscr{B}(R^n) = \mathscr{B}(R) \otimes \cdots \otimes \mathscr{B}(R).$$

In other words, the smallest σ-algebra generated by the rectangles $I = I_1 \times \cdots \times I_n$ and the (broader) class of rectangles $B = B_1 \times \cdots \times B_n$ with Borel sides are actually the same.

The proof depends on the following proposition.

Lemma 3. *Let $\mathscr{E}$ be a class of subsets of Ω, let $B \subseteq \Omega$, and define*

$$\mathscr{E} \cap B = \{A \cap B \colon A \in \mathscr{E}\}. \tag{5}$$

Then

$$\sigma(\mathscr{E} \cap B) = \sigma(\mathscr{E}) \cap B. \tag{6}$$

PROOF. Since $\mathscr{E} \subseteq \sigma(\mathscr{E})$, we have

$$\mathscr{E} \cap B \subseteq \sigma(\mathscr{E}) \cap B. \tag{7}$$

But $\sigma(\mathscr{E}) \cap B$ is a σ-algebra; hence it follows from (7) that

$$\sigma(\mathscr{E} \cap B) \subseteq \sigma(\mathscr{E}) \cap B.$$

To prove the conclusion in the opposite direction, we again use the principle of appropriate sets.

Define

$$\mathscr{C}_B = \{A \in \sigma(\mathscr{E}) \colon A \cap B \in \sigma(\mathscr{E} \cap B)\}.$$

Since $\sigma(\mathscr{E})$ and $\sigma(\mathscr{E} \cap B)$ are σ-algebras, $\mathscr{C}_B$ is also a σ-algebra, and evidently

$$\mathscr{E} \subseteq \mathscr{C}_B \subseteq \sigma(\mathscr{E}),$$

whence $\sigma(\mathscr{E}) \subseteq \sigma(\mathscr{C}_B) = \mathscr{C}_B \subseteq \sigma(\mathscr{E})$ and therefore $\sigma(\mathscr{E}) = \mathscr{C}_B$. Therefore

$$A \cap B \in \sigma(\mathscr{E} \cap B)$$

for every $A \subseteq \sigma(\mathscr{E})$, and consequently $\sigma(\mathscr{E}) \cap B \subseteq \sigma(\mathscr{E} \cap B)$.

This completes the proof of the lemma.

Proof that $\mathscr{B}(R^n)$ and $\mathscr{B} \otimes \cdots \otimes \mathscr{B}$ are the same. This is obvious for $n = 1$. We now show that it is true for $n = 2$.

Since $\mathscr{B}(R^2) \subseteq \mathscr{B} \otimes \mathscr{B}$, it is enough to show that the Borel rectangle $B_1 \times B_2$ belongs to $\mathscr{B}(R^2)$.

Let $R^2 = R_1 \times R_2$, where R_1 and R_2 are the "first" and "second" real lines, $\tilde{\mathscr{B}}_1 = \mathscr{B}_1 \times R_2$, $\tilde{\mathscr{B}}_2 = R_1 \times \mathscr{B}_2$, where $\mathscr{B}_1 \times R_2$ (or $R_1 \times \mathscr{B}_2$) is the collection of sets of the form $B_1 \times R_2$ (or $R_1 \times B_2$), with $B_1 \in \mathscr{B}_1$ (or $B_2 \in \mathscr{B}_2$). Also let $\mathscr{I}_1$ and $\mathscr{I}_2$ be the sets of intervals in R_1 and R_2, and $\tilde{\mathscr{I}}_1 = \mathscr{I}_1 \times R_2$, $\tilde{\mathscr{I}}_2 = R_1 \times \mathscr{I}_2$. Then, by (6),

$$\begin{aligned} B_1 \times B_2 = \tilde{B}_1 \cap \tilde{B}_2 \in \tilde{\mathscr{B}}_1 \cap \tilde{\mathscr{B}}_2 &= \sigma(\tilde{\mathscr{I}}_1) \cap \tilde{B}_2 \\ &= \sigma(\tilde{\mathscr{I}}_1 \cap \tilde{B}_2) \subseteq \sigma(\tilde{\mathscr{I}}_1 \cap \tilde{\mathscr{I}}_2) \\ &= \sigma(\mathscr{I}_1 \times \mathscr{I}_2), \end{aligned}$$

as was to be proved.

The case of any n, $n > 2$, can be discussed in the same way.

Remark. Let $\mathscr{B}_0(R^n)$ be the smallest σ-algebra generated by the open sets

$$S_\rho(x^0) = \{x \in R^n : \rho_n(x, x^0) < \rho\}, \qquad x^0 \in R^n, \quad \rho > 0,$$

in the metric

$$\rho_n(x, x^0) = \sum_{k=1}^{n} 2^{-k} \rho_1(x_k, x_k^0),$$

where $x = (x_1, \ldots, x_n)$, $x^0 = (x_1^0, \ldots, x_n^0)$.
Then $\mathscr{B}_0(R_n) = \mathscr{B}(R^n)$ (Problem 7).

4. The measurable space $(R^\infty, \mathscr{B}(R^\infty))$ plays a significant role in probability theory, since it is used as the basis for constructing probabilistic models of experiments with infinitely many steps.

The space R^∞ is the space of *ordered* sequences of numbers,

$$x = (x_1, x_2, \ldots), \qquad -\infty < x_k < \infty, \quad k = 1, 2, \ldots$$

Let I_k and B_k denote, respectively, the intervals $(a_k, b_k]$ and the Borel subsets of the kth line (with coordinate x_k). We consider the *cylinder sets*

$$\mathscr{I}(I_1 \times \cdots \times I_n) = \{x : x = (x_1, x_2, \ldots), x_1 \in I_1, \ldots, x_n \in I_n\}, \quad (8)$$

$$\mathscr{I}(B_1 \times \cdots \times B_n) = \{x : x = (x_1, x_2 \cdots), x_1 \in B_1, \ldots, x_n \in B_n\}, \quad (9)$$

$$\mathscr{I}(B^n) = \{x : (x_1, \ldots, x_n) \in B^n\}, \quad (10)$$

where B^n is a Borel set in $\mathscr{B}(R^n)$. Each cylinder $\mathscr{I}(B_1 \times \cdots \times B_n)$, or $\mathscr{I}(B^n)$, can also be thought of as a cylinder with base in $R^{n+1}, R^{n+2}, \ldots$, since

$$\mathscr{I}(B_1 \times \cdots \times B_n) = \mathscr{I}(B_1 \times \cdots \times B_n \times R),$$

$$\mathscr{I}(B^n) = \mathscr{I}(B^{n+1}),$$

where $B^{n+1} = B^n \times R$.

It follows that both systems of cylinders $\mathscr{I}(B_1 \times \cdots \times B_n)$ and $\mathscr{I}(B^n)$ are algebras. It is easy to verify that the unions of disjoint cylinders

$$\mathscr{I}(I_1 \times \cdots \times I_n)$$

also form an algebra. Let $\mathscr{B}(R^\infty)$, $\mathscr{B}_1(R^\infty)$ and $\mathscr{B}_2(R^\infty)$ be the smallest σ-algebras containing all the sets (8), (9) or (10), respectively. (The σ-algebra $\mathscr{B}_1(R^\infty)$ is often denoted by $\mathscr{B}(R) \otimes \mathscr{B}(R) \times \cdots$.) It is clear that $\mathscr{B}(R^\infty) \subseteq \mathscr{B}_1(R^\infty) \subseteq \mathscr{B}_2(R^\infty)$. As a matter of fact, all three σ-algebras are the same.

To prove this, we put

$$\mathscr{C}_n = \{A \in R^n : \{x : (x_1, \ldots, x_n) \in A\} \in \mathscr{B}(R^\infty)\}$$

for $n = 1, 2, \ldots$. Let $B^n \in \mathscr{B}(R^n)$. Then

$$B^n \in \mathscr{C}_n \subseteq \mathscr{B}(R^\infty).$$

But $\mathscr{C}_n$ is a σ-algebra, and therefore

$$\mathscr{B}(R^n) \subseteq \sigma(\mathscr{C}_n) = \mathscr{C}_n \subseteq \mathscr{B}(R^\infty);$$

consequently

$$\mathscr{B}_2(R^\infty) \subseteq \mathscr{B}(R^\infty).$$

Thus $\mathscr{B}(R^\infty) = \mathscr{B}_1(R^\infty) = \mathscr{B}_2(R^\infty)$.
From now on we shall describe sets in $\mathscr{B}(R^\infty)$ as Borel sets (in R^∞).

Remark. Let $\mathscr{B}_0(R^\infty)$ be the smallest σ-algebra generated by the *open* sets

$$S_\rho(x^0) = \{x \in R^\infty : \rho_\infty(x, x^0) < \rho\}, \qquad x^0 \in R^\infty, \quad \rho > 0,$$

in the metric

$$\rho_\infty(x, x^0) = \sum_{k=1}^\infty 2^{-k}\rho_1(x_k, x_k^0),$$

where $x = (x_1, x_2, \ldots)$, $x^0 = (x_1^0, x_2^0, \ldots)$. Then $\mathscr{B}(R^\infty) = \mathscr{B}_0(R^\infty)$ (Problem 7).

Here are some examples of Borel sets in R^∞:

(a) $\{x \in R^\infty : \sup x_n > a\}$,
$\quad \{x \in R^\infty : \inf x_n < a\}$;

(b) $\{x \in R^\infty : \overline{\lim} x_n \le a\}$,
$\quad \{x \in R^\infty : \underline{\lim} x_n > a\}$,

where, as usual,

$$\overline{\lim} \, x_n = \inf_n \sup_{m \ge n} x_m, \qquad \underline{\lim} \, x_n = \sup_n \inf_{m \ge n} x_m;$$

(c) $\{x \in R^\infty : x_n \to\}$, the set of $x \in R^\infty$ for which $\lim x_n$ exists and is finite;
(d) $\{x \in R^\infty : \lim x_n > a\}$;
(e) $\{x \in R^\infty : \sum_{n=1}^\infty |x_n| > a\}$;
(f) $\{x \in R^\infty : \sum_{k=1}^n x_k = 0 \text{ for at least one } n \ge 1\}$.

To be convinced, for example, that sets in (a) belong to the system $\mathscr{B}(R^\infty)$, it is enough to observe that

$$\{x : \sup x_n > a\} = \bigcup_n \{x : x_n > a\} \in \mathscr{B}(R^\infty),$$

$$\{x : \inf x_n < a\} = \bigcup_n \{x : x_n < a\} \in \mathscr{B}(R^\infty).$$

5. The measurable space $(R^T, \mathscr{B}(R^T))$, where T is an arbitrary set. The space R^T is the collection of real functions $x = (x_t)$ defined for $t \in T$†. In general we shall be interested in the case when T is an uncountable subset of the real

---

† We shall also use the notations $x = (x_t)_{t \in R^T}$ and $x = (x_t)$, $t \in R^T$, for elements of R^T.

line. For simplicity and definiteness we shall suppose for the present that $T = [0, \infty)$.

We shall consider three types of cylinder sets

$$\mathscr{I}_{t_1,\ldots,t_n}(I_1 \times \cdots \times I_n) = \{x: x_{t_1} \in I_1, \ldots, x_{t_n} \in I_1\}, \qquad (11)$$

$$\mathscr{I}_{t_1,\ldots,t_n}(B_1 \times \cdots \times B_n) = \{x: x_{t_1} \in B_1, \ldots, x_{t_n} \in B_n\}, \qquad (12)$$

$$\mathscr{I}_{t_1,\ldots,t_n}(B^n) = \{x: (x_{t_1}, \ldots, x_{t_n}) \in B^n\}, \qquad (13)$$

where I_k is a set of the form $(a_k, b_k]$, B_k is a Borel set on the line, and B^n is a Borel set in R^n.

The set $\mathscr{I}_{t_1,\ldots,t_n}(I_1 \times \cdots \times I_n)$ is just the set of functions that, at times $t_1, \ldots, t_n$, "get through the windows" $I_1, \ldots, I_n$ and at other times have arbitrary values (Figure 24).

Let $\mathscr{B}(R^T)$, $\mathscr{B}_1(R^T)$ and $\mathscr{B}_2(R^T)$ be the smallest σ-algebras corresponding respectively to the cylinder sets (11), (12) and (13). It is clear that

$$\mathscr{B}(R^T) \subseteq \mathscr{B}_1(R^T) \subseteq \mathscr{B}_2(R^T). \qquad (14)$$

As a matter of fact, all three of these σ-algebras are the same. Moreover, we can give a complete description of the structure of their sets.

Theorem 3. *Let T be any uncountable set. Then $\mathscr{B}(R^T) = \mathscr{B}_1(R^T) = \mathscr{B}_2(R^T)$, and every set $A \in \mathscr{B}(R^T)$ has the following structure: there are a countable set of points $t_1, t_2, \ldots$ of T and a Borel set B in $\mathscr{B}(R^\infty)$ such that*

$$A = \{x: (x_{t_1}, x_{t_2}, \ldots) \in B\}. \qquad (15)$$

PROOF. Let $\mathscr{E}$ denote the collection of sets of the form (15) (for various aggregates $(t_1, t_2, \ldots)$ and Borel sets B in $\mathscr{B}(R^\infty)$). If $A_1, A_2, \ldots \in \mathscr{E}$ and the corresponding aggregates are $T^{(1)} = (t_1^{(1)}, t_2^{(1)}, \ldots)$, $T^{(2)} = (t_1^{(2)}, t_2^{(2)}, \ldots), \ldots,$

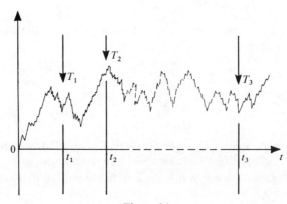

Figure 24

then the set $T^{(\infty)} = \bigcup_k T^{(k)}$ can be taken as a basis, so that every $A^{(i)}$ has a representation

$$A_i = \{x \colon (x_{\tau_1}, x_{\tau_2}, \ldots) \in B_i\},$$

where B_i is a set in one and the same σ-algebra $\mathscr{B}(R^\infty)$, and $\tau_i \in T^{(\infty)}$.

Hence it follows that the system $\mathscr{E}$ is a σ-algebra. Clearly this σ-algebra contains all cylinder sets of the form (1) and, since $\mathscr{B}_2(R^T)$ is the smallest σ-algebra containing these sets, and since we have (14), we obtain

$$\mathscr{B}(R^T) \subseteq \mathscr{B}_1(R^T) \subseteq \mathscr{B}_2(R^T) \subseteq \mathscr{E}. \tag{16}$$

Let us consider a set A from $\mathscr{E}$, represented in the form (15). For a given aggregate $(t_1, t_2, \ldots)$, the same reasoning as for the space $(R^\infty, \mathscr{B}(R^\infty))$ shows that A is an element of the σ-algebra generated by the cylinder sets (11). But this σ-algebra evidently belongs to the σ-algebra $\mathscr{B}(R^T)$; together with (16), this established both conclusions of the theorem.

Thus every Borel set A in the σ-algebra $\mathscr{B}(R^T)$ is determined by restrictions imposed on the functions $x = (x_t), t \in T$, on an at most countable set of points $t_1, t_2, \ldots$. Hence it follows, in particular, that the sets

$$A_1 = \{x \colon \sup x_t < C \text{ for all } t \in [0, 1]\},$$

$$A_2 = \{x \colon x_t = 0 \text{ for at least one } t \in [0, 1]\},$$

$$A_3 = \{x \colon x_t \text{ is continuous at a given point } t_0 \in [0, 1]\},$$

which depend on the behavior of the function on an uncountable set of points, cannot be Borel sets. And indeed *none of these three sets belongs to* $\mathscr{B}(R^{[0, 1]})$.

Let us establish this for A_1. If $A_1 \in \mathscr{B}(R^{[0, 1]})$, then by our theorem there are a point $(t_1^0, t_2^0, \ldots)$ and a set $B^0 \in \mathscr{B}(R^\infty)$ such that

$$\left\{ x \colon \sup_t x_t < C, t \in [0, 1] \right\} = \{x \colon (x_{t_1^0}, x_{t_2^0}, \ldots) \in B^0\}.$$

It is clear that the function $y_t \equiv C - 1$ belongs to A_1, and consequently $(y_{t_1^0}, \ldots) \in B^0$. Now form the function

$$z_t = \begin{cases} C - 1, & t \in (t_1^0, t_2^0, \ldots), \\ C + 1, & t \notin (t_1^0, t_2^0, \ldots). \end{cases}$$

It is clear that

$$(y_{t_1^0}, y_{t_2^0}, \ldots) = (z_{t_1^0}, z_{t_2^0}, \ldots),$$

and consequently the function $z = (z_t)$ belongs to the set $\{x \colon (x_{t_1^0}, \ldots) \in B^0\}$. But at the same time it is clear that it does not belong to the set $\{x \colon \sup x_t < C\}$. This contradiction shows that $A_1 \notin \mathscr{B}(R^{[0, 1]})$.

Since the sets A_1, A_2 and A_3 are nonmeasurable with respect to the σ-algebra $\mathcal{B}[R^{[0, 1]})$ in the space of all functions $x = (x_t)$, $t \in [0, 1]$, it is natural to consider a smaller class of functions for which these sets are measurable. It is intuitively clear that this will be the case if we take the intial space to be, for example, the space of continuous functions.

6. The measurable space $(C, \mathcal{B}(C))$. Let $T = [0, 1]$ and let C be the space of continuous functions $x = (x_t)$, $0 \le t \le 1$. This is a metric space with the metric $\rho(x, y) = \sup_{t \in T} |x_t - y_t|$. We introduce two σ-algebras in C: $\mathcal{B}(C)$ is the σ-algebra generated by the cylinder sets, and $\mathcal{B}_0(C)$ is generated by the open sets (open with respect to the metric $\rho(x, y)$). Let us show that in fact these σ-algebras are the same: $\mathcal{B}(C) = \mathcal{B}_0(C)$.

Let $B = \{x: x_{t_0} < b\}$ be a cylinder set. It is easy to see that this set is open. Hence it follows that $\{x: x_{t_1} < b_1, \ldots, x_{t_n} < b_n\} \in \mathcal{B}_0(C)$, and therefore $\mathcal{B}(C) \subseteq \mathcal{B}_0(C)$.

Conversely, consider a set $B_\rho = \{y: y \in S_\rho(x^0)\}$ where x^0 is an element of C and $S_\rho(x^0) = \{x \in C: \sup_{t \in T} |x_t - x_t^0| < \rho\}$ is an open ball with center at x^0. Since the functions in C are continuous,

$$B_\rho = \{y \in C: y \in S_\rho(x^0)\} = \left\{y \in C: \max_t |y_t - x_t^0| < \rho\right\}$$
$$= \bigcap_{t_k} \{y \in C: |y_{t_k} - x_{t_k}^0| < \rho\} \in \mathcal{B}(C), \quad (17)$$

where t_k are the rational points of $[0, 1]$. Therefore $\mathcal{B}_0(C) \subseteq \mathcal{B}(C)$.

The following example is fundamental.

7. The measurable space $(D, \mathcal{B}(D))$, where D is the space of functions $x = (x_t)$, $t \in [0, 1]$, that are continuous on the right ($x_t = x_{t_+}$ for all $t < 1$) and have limits from the left (at every $t > 0$).

Just as for C, we can introduce a metric $d(x, y)$ on D such that the σ-algebra $\mathcal{B}_0(D)$ generated by the open sets will coincide with the σ-algebra $\mathcal{B}(D)$ generated by the cylinder sets. This metric $d(x, y)$, which was introduced by Skorohod, is defined as follows:

$$d(x, y) = \inf\{\varepsilon > 0: \exists \lambda \in \Lambda: \sup_t |x_t - y_{\lambda(t)}| + \sup_t |t - \lambda(t)| \le \varepsilon\}, \quad (18)$$

where Λ is the set of strictly increasing functions $\lambda = \lambda(t)$ that are continuous on $[0, 1]$ and have $\lambda(0) = 0$, $\lambda(1) = 1$.

8. The measurable space $(\prod_{t \in T} \Omega_t, \bigotimes_{t \in T} \mathcal{F}_t)$. Along with the space $(R^T, \mathcal{B}(R^T))$, which is the direct product of T copies of the real line together with the system of Borel sets, probability theory also uses the measurable space $(\prod_{t \in T} \Omega_t, \bigotimes_{t \in T} \mathcal{F}_t)$, which is defined in the following way.

Let T be any set of indices and $(\Omega_t, \mathscr{F}_t)$ a measurable space, $t \in T$. Let $\Omega = \prod_{t \in T} \Omega_t$, the set of functions $\omega = (\omega_t)$, $t \in T$, such that $\omega_t \in \Omega_t$ for each $t \in T$.

The collection of cylinder sets

$$\mathscr{I}_{t_1, \ldots, t_n}(B_1 \times \cdots \times B_n) = \{\omega : \omega_{t_1} \in B_1, \ldots, \omega_{t_n} \in B_n\},$$

where $B_{t_i} \in \mathscr{F}_{t_i}$, is easily shown to be an algebra. The smallest σ-algebra containing all these cylinder sets is denoted by $\bigotimes_{t \in T} \mathscr{F}_t$, and the measurable space $(\prod \Omega_i, \bigotimes \mathscr{F}_t)$ is called the *direct product* of the measurable spaces $(\Omega_t, \mathscr{F}_t)$, $t \in T$.

9. PROBLEMS

1. Let $\mathscr{B}_1$ and $\mathscr{B}_2$ be σ-algebras of subsets of Ω. Are the following systems of sets σ-algebras?

$$\mathscr{B}_1 \cap \mathscr{B}_2 \equiv \{A : A \in \mathscr{B}_1 \text{ and } A \in \mathscr{B}_2\},$$

$$\mathscr{B}_1 \cup \mathscr{B}_2 \equiv \{A : A \in \mathscr{B}_1 \text{ or } A \in \mathscr{B}_2\}.$$

2. Let $\mathscr{D} = \{D_1, D_2, \ldots\}$ be a countable decomposition of Ω and $\mathscr{B} = \sigma(\mathscr{D})$. Are there also only countably many sets in $\mathscr{B}$?

3. Show that

$$\mathscr{B}(R^n) \otimes \mathscr{B}(R) = \mathscr{B}(R^{n+1}).$$

4. Prove that the sets (b)–(f) (see Subsection 4) belong to $\mathscr{B}(R^\infty)$.

5. Prove that the sets A_2 and A_3 (see Subsection 5) do not belong to $\mathscr{B}(R^{[0, 1]})$.

6. Prove that the function (15) actually defines a metric.

7. Prove that $\mathscr{B}_0(R^n) = \mathscr{B}(R^n)$, $n \geq 1$, and $\mathscr{B}_0(R^\infty) = \mathscr{B}(R^\infty)$.

8. Let $C = C[0, \infty)$ be the space of continuous functions $x = (x_t)$ defined for $t \geq 0$. Show that with the metric

$$\rho(x, y) = \sum_{n=1}^{\infty} 2^{-n} \min\left[\sup_{0 \leq t \leq n} |x_t - y_t|, 1\right], \qquad x, y \in C,$$

this is a complete separable metric space and that the σ-algebra $\mathscr{B}_0(C)$ generated by the open sets coincides with the σ-algebra $\mathscr{B}(C)$ generated by the cylinder sets.

§3. Methods of Introducing Probability Measures on Measurable Spaces

1. The measurable space $(R, \mathscr{B}(R))$. Let $\mathsf{P} = \mathsf{P}(A)$ be a probability measure defined on the Borel subsets A of the real line. Take $A = (-\infty, x]$ and put

$$F(x) = \mathsf{P}(-\infty, x], \qquad x \in R. \tag{1}$$

This function has the following properties:

(1) $F(x)$ is *nondecreasing*;
(2) $F(-\infty) = 0$, $F(+\infty) = 1$, *where*

$$F(-\infty) = \lim_{x \downarrow -\infty} F(x), \qquad F(+\infty) = \lim_{x \uparrow \infty} F(x);$$

(3) $F(x)$ *is continuous on the right and has a limit on the left at each* $x \in R$.

The first property is evident, and the other two follow from the continuity properties of probability measures.

Definition 1. Every function $F = F(x)$ satisfying conditions (1)–(3) is called a *distribution function* (on the real line R).

Thus to every probability measure P on $(R, \mathscr{B}(R))$ there corresponds (by (1)) a distribution function. It turns out that the converse is also true.

Theorem 1. *Let* $F = F(x)$ *be a distribution function on the real line R. There exists a unique probability measure P on $(R, \mathscr{B}(R))$ such that*

$$P(a, b] = F(b) - F(a) \tag{2}$$

for all a, b, $-\infty \le a < b < \infty$.

PROOF. Let $\mathscr{A}$ be the algebra of the subsets A of R that are finite sums of disjoint intervals of the form $(a, b]$:

$$A = \sum_{k=1}^{n} (a_k, b_k].$$

On these sets we define a set function P_0 by putting

$$P_0(A) = \sum_{k=1}^{n} [F(b_k) - F(a_k)], \qquad A \in \mathscr{A}. \tag{3}$$

This formula defines, evidently uniquely, a finitely additive set function on $\mathscr{A}$. Therefore if we show that this function is also countably additive on this algebra, the existence and uniqueness of the required measure P on $\mathscr{B}(R)$ will follow immediately from a general result of measure theory (which we quote without proof).

Carathéodory's Theorem. *Let Ω be a space, $\mathscr{A}$ an algebra of its subsets, and $\mathscr{B} = \sigma(\mathscr{A})$ the smallest σ-algebra containing $\mathscr{A}$. Let μ_0 be a σ-finite measure on $(\Omega, \mathscr{A})$. Then there is a unique measure μ on $(\Omega, \sigma(\mathscr{A}))$ which is an extension of μ_0, i.e. satisfies*

$$\mu(A) = \mu_0(A), \qquad A \in \mathscr{A}.$$

We are now to show that P_0 is countably additive on $\mathscr{A}$. By a theorem from §1 it is enough to show that P_0 is continuous at $\varnothing$, i.e. to verify that

$$P_0(A_n) \downarrow 0, \qquad A_n \downarrow \varnothing, \qquad A_n \in \mathscr{A}.$$

Let $A_1, A_2, \ldots$ be a sequence of sets from $\mathscr{A}$ with the property $A_n \downarrow \varnothing$. Let us suppose first that the sets A_n belong to a closed interval $[-N, N], N < \infty$. Since A is the sum of finitely many intervals of the form $(a, b]$ and since

$$P_0(a', b] = F(b) - F(a') \to F(b) - F(a) = P_0(a, b]$$

as $a' \downarrow a$, because $F(x)$ is continuous on the right, we can find, for every A_n, a set $B_n \in \mathscr{A}$ such that its closure $[B_n] \subseteq A_n$ and

$$P_0(A_n) - P_0(B_n) \le \varepsilon \cdot 2^{-n},$$

where ε is a preassigned positive number.

By hypothesis, $\bigcap A_n = \varnothing$ and therefore $\bigcap [B_n] = \varnothing$. But the sets $[B_n]$ are closed, and therefore there is a finite $n_0 = n_0(\varepsilon)$ such that

$$\bigcap_{n=1}^{n_0} [B_n] = \varnothing. \tag{4}$$

(In fact, $[-N, N]$ is compact, and the collection of sets $\{[-N, N]\backslash[B_n]\}_{n \ge 1}$ is an open covering of this compact set. By the Heine–Borel theorem there is a finite subcovering:

$$\bigcup_{n=1}^{n_0} ([-N, N]\backslash[B_n]) = [-N, N]$$

and therefore $\bigcap_{n=1}^{n_0} [B_n] = \varnothing$).

Using (4) and the inclusions $A_{n_0} \subseteq A_{n_0 - 1} \subseteq \cdots \subseteq A_1$, we obtain

$$P_0(A_{n_0}) = P_0\left(A_{n_0}\backslash \bigcap_{k=1}^{n_0} B_k\right) + P_0\left(\bigcap_{k=1}^{n_0} B_k\right)$$

$$= P_0\left(A_{n_0}\backslash \bigcap_{k=1}^{n_0} B_k\right) \le P_0\left(\bigcup_{k=1}^{n_0} (A_k\backslash B_k)\right)$$

$$\le \sum_{k=1}^{n_0} P_0(A_k\backslash B_k) \le \sum_{k=1}^{n_0} \varepsilon \cdot 2^{-k} \le \varepsilon.$$

Therefore $P_0(A_n) \downarrow 0, n \to \infty$.

We now abandon the assumption that $A_n \subseteq [-N, N]$ for some N. Take an $\varepsilon > 0$ and choose N so that $P_0[-N, N] > 1 - \varepsilon/2$. Then, since

$$A_n = A_n \cap [-N, N] + A_n \cap \overline{[-N, N]},$$

we have

$$P_0(A_n) = P_0(A_n[-N, N]) + P_0(A_n \cap \overline{[-N, N]})$$
$$\le P_0(A_n \cap [-N, N]) + \varepsilon/2$$

and, applying the preceding reasoning (replacing A_n by $A_n \cap [-N, N]$), we find that $P_0(A_n \cap [-N, N]) \leq \varepsilon/2$ for sufficiently large n. Hence once again $P_0(A_n) \downarrow 0, n \to \infty$. This completes the proof of the theorem.

Thus there is a one-to-one correspondence between probability measures P on $(R, \mathscr{B}(R))$ and distribution functions F on the real line R. The measure P constructed from the function F is usually called the Lebesgue–Stieltjes probability measure corresponding to the distribution function F.

The case when

$$F(x) = \begin{cases} 0, & x < 0, \\ x, & 0 \leq x \leq 1, \\ 1, & x > 1. \end{cases}$$

is particularly important. In this case the corresponding probability measure (denoted by λ) is *Lebesgue measure* on $[0, 1]$. Clearly $\lambda(a, b] = b - a$. In other words, the Lebesgue measure of $(a, b]$ (as well as of any of the intervals $(a, b), [a, b]$ or $[a, b)$) is simply its length $b - a$.

Let

$$\mathscr{B}([0, 1]) = \{A \cap [0, 1] : A \in \mathscr{B}(R)\}$$

be the collection of Borel subsets of $[0, 1]$. It is often necessary to consider, besides these sets, the Lebesgue measurable subsets of $[0, 1]$. We say that a set $\Lambda \subseteq [0, 1]$ belongs to $\bar{\mathscr{B}}([0, 1)]$ if there are Borel sets A and B such that $A \subseteq \Lambda \subseteq B$ and $\lambda(B \backslash A) = 0$. It is easily verified that $\bar{\mathscr{B}}([0, 1])$ is a σ-algebra. It is known as the system of *Lebesgue measurable subsets of* $[0, 1]$. Clearly $\mathscr{B}([0, 1]) \subseteq \bar{\mathscr{B}}([0, 1])$.

The measure λ, defined so far only for sets in $\mathscr{B}([0, 1])$, extends in a natural way to the system $\bar{\mathscr{B}}([0, 1])$ of Lebesgue measurable sets. Specifically, if $\Lambda \in \bar{\mathscr{B}}([0, 1])$ and $A \subseteq \Lambda \subseteq B$, where A and $B \in \bar{\mathscr{B}}([0, 1])$ and $\lambda(B \backslash A) = 0$, we define $\bar{\lambda}(\Lambda) = \lambda(A)$. The set function $\bar{\lambda} = \bar{\lambda}(\Lambda), \Lambda \in \bar{\mathscr{B}}([0, 1])$, is easily seen to be a probability measure on $([0, 1], \bar{\mathscr{B}}([0, 1]))$. It is usually called *Lebesgue measure* (on the system of Lebesgue-measurable sets).

Remark. This process of completing (or extending) a measure can be applied, and is useful, in other situations. For example, let $(\Omega, \mathscr{F}, P)$ be a probability space. Let $\bar{\mathscr{F}}^P$ be the collection of all the subsets A of Ω for which there are sets B_1 and B_2 of $\mathscr{F}$ such that $B_1 \subseteq A \subseteq B_2$ and $P(B_2 \backslash B_1) = 0$. The probability measure can be defined for sets $A \in \bar{\mathscr{F}}^P$ in a natural way (by $P(A) = P(B_1)$). The resulting probability space is the completion of $(\Omega, \mathscr{F}, P)$ with respect to P.

A probability measure such that $\bar{\mathscr{F}}^P = \mathscr{F}$ is called *complete*, and the corresponding space $(\Omega, \mathscr{F}, P)$ is a *complete probability space*.

The correspondence between probability measures P and distribution functions F established by the equation $P(a, b] = F(b) - F(a)$ makes it

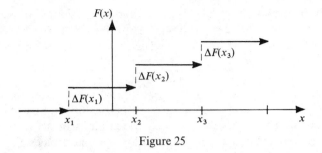

Figure 25

possible to construct various probability measures by obtaining the corresponding distribution functions.

Discrete measures are measures P for which the corresponding distributions $F = F(x)$ are piecewise constant (Figure 25), changing their values at the points $x_1, x_2, \ldots$ $(\Delta F(x_i) > 0$, where $\Delta F(x) = F(x) - F(x-)$. In this case the measure is concentrated at the points $x_1, x_2, \ldots$:

$$P(\{x_k\}) = \Delta F(x_k) > 0, \qquad \sum_k P(\{x_k\}) = 1.$$

The set of numbers $(p_1, p_2, \ldots)$, where $p_k = P(\{x_k\})$, is called a *discrete probability distribution* and the corresponding distribution function $F = F(x)$ is called *discrete*.

We present a table of the commonest types of discrete probability distribution, with their names.

Table 1

Distribution	Probabilities p_k	Parameters
Discrete uniform	$1/N, \quad k = 1, 2, \ldots, N$	$N = 1, 2, \ldots$
Bernoulli	$p_1 = p, \quad p_0 = q$	$0 \le p \le 1, q = 1 - p$
Binomial	$C_n^k p^k q^{n-k}, \quad k = 0, 1, \ldots, n$	$0 \le p \le 1, \quad q = 1 - p,$ $n = 1, 2, \ldots$
Poisson	$e^{-k}/k!, \quad k = 0, 1, \ldots$	$\lambda > 0$
Geometric	$q^{k-1} p, \quad k = 0, 1, \ldots$	$0 \le p \le 1, \quad q = 1 - p$
Negative binomial	$C_{k-1}^{r-1} p^r q^{k-r}, \quad k = r, r + 1, \ldots$	$0 \le p \le 1, \quad q = 1 - p,$ $r = 1, 2, \ldots$

Absolutely continuous measures. These are measures for which the corresponding distribution functions are such that

$$F(x) = \int_{-\infty}^x f(t)\, dt, \tag{5}$$

where $f = f(t)$ are nonnegative functions and the integral is at first taken in the Riemann sense, but later (see §6) in that of Lebesgue.

The function $f = f(x)$, $x \in R$, is the *density* of the distribution function $F = F(x)$ (or the density of the probability distribution, or simply the density) and $F = F(x)$ is called absolutely continuous.

It is clear that every nonnegative $f = f(x)$ that is Riemann integrable and such that $\int_{-\infty}^{\infty} f(x)\, dx = 1$ defines a distribution function by (5). Table 2 presents some important examples of various kinds of densities $f = f(x)$ with their names and parameters (a density $f(x)$ is taken to be zero for values of x not listed in the table).

Table 2

Distribution	Density	Parameters
Uniform on $[a, b]$	$1/(b - a), \quad a \le x \le b$	$a, b \in R; \quad a < b$
Normal or Gaussian	$(2\pi\sigma)^{-1/2} e^{-(x-m)^2/(2\sigma^2)}, \quad x \in R$	$m \in R, \sigma > 0$
Gamma	$\dfrac{x^{\alpha-1} e^{-x/\beta}}{\Gamma(\alpha)\beta^\alpha}, \quad x \ge 0$	$\alpha > 0, \beta > 0$
Beta	$\dfrac{x^{r-1}(1 - x)^{s-1}}{B(r, s)}, \quad 0 \le x \le 1$	$r > 0, s > 0$
Exponential (gamma with $\alpha = 1, \beta = 1/\lambda$)	$\lambda e^{-\lambda x}, \quad x \ge 0$	$\lambda > 0$
Bilateral exponential	$\frac{1}{2}\lambda e^{-\lambda |x|}, \quad x \in R$	$\lambda > 0$
Chi-squared, χ^2 (gamma with a $\alpha = n/2, \beta = 2$)	$2^{-n/2} x^{n/2-1} e^{-x/2}/\Gamma(n/2), \quad x \ge 0$	$n = 1, 2, \ldots$
Student, t	$\dfrac{\Gamma(\frac{1}{2}(n + 1))}{(n\pi)^{1/2}\Gamma(n/2)} \left(1 + \dfrac{x^2}{n}\right)^{-(n+1)/2}, \quad x \in R$	$n = 1, 2, \ldots$
F	$\dfrac{(m/n)^{m/2}}{B(m/2, n/2)} \dfrac{x^{m/2-1}}{(1 + mx/n)^{(m+n)/2}}$	$m, n = 1, 2, \ldots$
Cauchy	$\dfrac{\theta}{\pi(x^2 + \theta^2)}, \quad x \in R$	$\theta > 0$

Singular measures. These are measures whose distribution functions are continuous but have all their points of increases on sets of *zero Lebesgue measure*. We do not discuss this case in detail; we merely give an example of such a function.

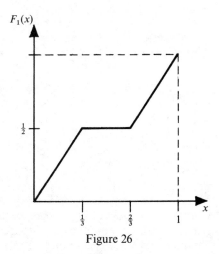

Figure 26

We consider the interval $[0, 1]$ and construct $F(x)$ by the following procedure originated by Cantor.

We divide $[0, 1]$ into thirds and put (Figure 26)

$$F_2(x) = \begin{cases} \frac{1}{2}, & x \in (\frac{1}{3}, \frac{2}{3}), \\ \frac{1}{4}, & x \in (\frac{1}{9}, \frac{2}{9}), \\ \frac{3}{4}, & x \in (\frac{7}{9}, \frac{8}{9}), \\ 0, & x = 0, \\ 1, & x = 1 \end{cases}$$

defining it in the intermediate intervals by linear interpolation.

Then we divide each of the intervals $[0, \frac{1}{3}]$ and $[\frac{2}{3}, 1]$ into three parts and define the function (Figure 27) with its values at other points determined by linear interpolation.

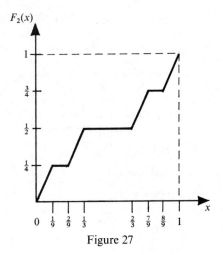

Figure 27

Continuing this process, we construct a sequence of functions $F_n(x)$, $n = 1, 2, \ldots$, which converges to a nondecreasing continuous function $F(x)$ (the Cantor function), whose points of increase (x is a point of increase of $F(x)$ if $F(x + \varepsilon) - F(x - \varepsilon) > 0$ for every $\varepsilon > 0$) form a set of Lebesgue measure zero. In fact, it is clear from the construction of $F(x)$ that the total length of the intervals $(\frac{1}{3}, \frac{2}{3}), (\frac{1}{9}, \frac{2}{9}), (\frac{7}{9}, \frac{8}{9}), \ldots$ on which the function is constant is

$$\frac{1}{3} + \frac{2}{9} + \frac{4}{27} + \cdots = \frac{1}{3}\sum_{n=0}^{\infty}\left(\frac{2}{3}\right)^n = 1. \tag{6}$$

Let $\mathcal{N}$ be the set of points of increase of the Cantor function $F(x)$. It follows from (6) that $\lambda(\mathcal{N}) = 0$. At the same time, if μ is the measure corresponding to the Cantor function $F(x)$, we have $\mu(\mathcal{N}) = 1$. (We then say that the measure is *singular* with respect to Lebesgue measure λ.)

Without any further discussion of possible types of distribution functions, we merely observe that in fact the *three types* that have been mentioned cover all possibilities. More precisely, every distribution function can be represented in the form $p_1 F_1 + p_2 F_2 + p_3 F_3$, where F_1 is discrete, F_2 is absolutely continuous, and F_3 is singular, and p_i are nonnegative numbers, $p_1 + p_2 + p_3 = 1$.

2. Theorem 1 establishes a one-to-one correspondence between probability measures on $(R, \mathcal{B}(R))$ and distribution functions on R. An analysis of the proof of the theorem shows that in fact a stronger theorem is true, one that in particular lets us introduce Lebesgue measure on the real line.

Let μ be a σ-finite measure on $(\Omega, \mathcal{A})$, where $\mathcal{A}$ is an algebra of subsets of Ω. It turns out that the conclusion of Carathéodory's theorem on the extension of a measure and an algebra $\mathcal{A}$ to a minimal σ-algebra $\sigma(\mathcal{A})$ remains valid with a σ-finite measure; this makes it possible to generalize Theorem 1.

A *Lebesgue–Stieltjes measure* on $(R, \mathcal{B}(R))$ is a (countably additive) measure μ such that the measure $\mu(I)$ of every bounded interval I is finite. A *generalized distribution function* on the real line R is a nondecreasing function $G = G(x)$, with values on $(-\infty, \infty)$, that is continuous on the right.

Theorem 1 can be generalized to the statement that the formula

$$\mu(a, b] = G(b) - G(a), \qquad a < b,$$

again establishes a one-to-one correspondence between Lebesgue–Stieltjes measures μ and generalized distribution functions G.

In fact, if $G(+\infty) - G(-\infty) < \infty$, the proof of Theorem 1 can be taken over without any change, since this case reduces to the case when $G(+\infty) - G(-\infty) = 1$ and $G(-\infty) = 0$.

Now let $G(+\infty) - G(-\infty) = \infty$. Put

$$G_n(x) = \begin{cases} G(x), & |x| \leq n, \\ G(n) & x = n, \\ G(-n), & x = -n. \end{cases}$$

On the algebra $\mathscr{A}$ let us define a finitely additive measure μ_0 such that $\mu_0(a, b] = G(b) - G(a)$, and let μ_n be the finitely additive measure previously constructed (by Theorem 1) from $G_n(x)$.

Evidently $\mu_n \uparrow \mu_0$ on $\mathscr{A}$. Now let $A_1, A_2, \ldots$ be disjoint sets in $\mathscr{A}$ and $A \equiv \sum A_n \in \mathscr{A}$. Then (Problem 6 of §1)

$$\mu_0(A) \geq \sum_{n=1}^{\infty} \mu_0(A_n).$$

If $\sum_{n=1}^{\infty} \mu_0(A_n) = \infty$ then $\mu_0(A) = \sum_{n=1}^{\infty} \mu_0(A_n)$. Let us suppose that $\sum \mu_0(A_n) < \infty$. Then

$$\mu_0(A) = \lim_n \mu_n(A) = \lim_n \sum_{k=1}^{\infty} \mu_n(A_k).$$

By hypothesis, $\sum \mu_0(A_n) < \infty$. Therefore

$$0 \leq \mu_0(A) - \sum_{k=1}^{\infty} \mu_0(A_k) = \lim_n \left[\sum_{k=1}^{\infty} (\mu_n(A_k) - \mu_0(A_k)) \right] \leq 0,$$

since $\mu_n \leq \mu_0$.

Thus a σ-finite finitely additive measure μ_0 is countably additive on $\mathscr{A}$, and therefore (by Carathéodory's theorem) it can be extended to a countably additive measure μ on $\sigma(\mathscr{A})$.

The case $G(x) = x$ is particularly important. The measure λ corresponding to this generalized distribution function is Lebesgue measure on $(R, \mathscr{B}(R))$. As for the interval $[0, 1]$ of the real line, we can define the system $\bar{\mathscr{B}}(R)$ by writing $A \in \bar{\mathscr{B}}(R)$ if there are Borel sets A and B such that $A \subseteq \Lambda \subseteq B$, $\lambda(B \backslash A) = 0$. Then Lebesgue measure $\bar{\lambda}$ on $\mathscr{B}(R)$ is defined by $\bar{\lambda}(\Lambda) = \lambda(A)$ if $A \subseteq \Lambda \subseteq B$, $\lambda \in \bar{\mathscr{B}}(R)$ and $\Lambda(B \backslash A) = 0$.

3. The measurable space $(R^n, \mathscr{B}(R^n))$. Let us suppose, as for the real line, that P is a probability measure on $(R^n, \mathscr{B}(R^n))$.

Let us write

$$F_n(x_1, \ldots, x_n) = P((-\infty, x_1] \times \cdots \times (-\infty, x_n]),$$

or, in a more compact form,

$$F_n(x) = P(-\infty, x],$$

where $x = (x_1, \ldots, x_n)$, $(-\infty, x] = (-\infty, x_1] \times \cdots \times (-\infty, x_n]$.

Let us introduce the difference operator $\Delta_{a_i, b_i} \colon R^n \to R$, defined by the formula

$$\Delta_{a_i, b_i} F_n(x_1, \ldots, x_n) = F_n(x_1, \ldots, x_{i-1}, b_i, x_{i+1} \ldots) \\ - F_n(x_1, \ldots, x_{i-1}, a_i, x_{i+1} \ldots)$$

where $a_i \leq b_i$. A simple calculation shows that

$$\Delta_{a_1 b_1} \cdots \Delta_{a_n b_n} F_n(x_1 \cdots x_n) = \mathsf{P}(a, b], \tag{7}$$

where $(a, b] = (a_1, b_1] \times \cdots \times (a_n, b_n]$. Hence it is clear, in particular, that (in contrast to the one-dimensional case) $\mathsf{P}(a, b]$ is in general not equal to $F_n(b) - F_n(a)$.

Since $\mathsf{P}(a, b] \geq 0$, it follows from (7) that

$$\Delta_{a_1 b_1} \cdots \Delta_{a_n b_n} F_n(x_1, \ldots, x_n) \geq 0 \tag{8}$$

for arbitrary $a = (a_1, \ldots, a_n), b = (b_1, \ldots, b_n)$.

It also follows from the continuity of P that $F_n(x_1, \ldots, x_n)$ is continuous on the right with respect to the variables collectively, i.e. if $x^{(k)} \downarrow x$, $x^{(k)} = (x_1^{(k)}, \ldots, x_n^{(k)})$, then

$$F_n(x^{(k)}) \downarrow F_n(x), \qquad k \to \infty. \tag{9}$$

It is also clear that

$$F_n(+\infty, \ldots, +\infty) = 1 \tag{10}$$

and

$$\lim_{x \downarrow y} F_n(x_1, \ldots, x_n) = 0, \tag{11}$$

if at least one coordinate of y is $-\infty$.

Definition 2. An n-dimensional distribution function (on R^n) is a function $F = F(x_1, \ldots, x_n)$ with properties (8)–(11).

The following result can be established by the same reasoning as in Theorem 1.

Theorem 2. Let $F = F_n(x_1, \ldots, x_n)$ be a distribution function on R^n. Then there is a unique probability measure P on $(R^n, \mathscr{B}(R^n))$ such that

$$\mathsf{P}(a, b] = \Delta_{a_1 b_1} \cdots \Delta_{a_n b_n} F_n(x_1, \ldots, x_n). \tag{12}$$

Here are some examples of n-dimensional distribution functions.
Let $F^1, \ldots, F^n$ be one-dimensional distribution functions (on R) and

$$F_n(x_1, \ldots, x_n) = F^1(x_1) \cdots F^n(x_n).$$

It is clear that this function is continuous on the right and satisfies (10) and (11). It is also easy to verify that

$$\Delta_{a_1 b_1} \cdots \Delta_{a_n b_n} F_n(x_1, \ldots, x_n) = \prod [F^k(b_k) - F^k(a_k)] \geq 0.$$

Consequently $F_n(x_1, \ldots, x_n)$ is a distribution function.

The case when

$$F^k(x_k) = \begin{cases} 0 & x_k < 0, \\ x_k, & 0 \le x_k \le 1, \\ 1, & x_k > 1 \end{cases}$$

is particularly important. In this case

$$F_n(x_1, \ldots, x_n) = x_1 \cdots x_n.$$

The probability measure corresponding to this n-dimensional distribution function is n-dimensional Lebesgue measure on $[0, 1]^n$.

Many n-dimensional distribution functions appear in the form

$$F_n(x_1, \ldots, x_n) = \int_{-\infty}^{x_1} \cdots \int_{-\infty}^{x_n} f_n(t_1, \ldots, t_n) \, dt_1 \cdots dt_n,$$

where $f_n(t_1, \ldots, t_n)$ is a nonnegative function such that

$$\int_{-\infty}^{\infty} \cdots \int_{-\infty}^{\infty} f_n(t_1, \ldots, t_n) \, dt_1 \cdots dt_n = 1,$$

and the integrals are Riemann (more generally, Lebesgue) integrals. The function $f = f_n(t_1, \ldots, t_n)$ is called the *density* of the n-dimensional distribution function, the density of the n-dimensional probability distribution, or simply an n-dimensional density.

When $n = 1$, the function

$$f(x) = \frac{1}{\sigma\sqrt{2\pi}} e^{-(x-m)^2/(2\sigma^2)}, \qquad x \in R,$$

with $\sigma > 0$ is the density of the (nondegenerate) *Gaussian* or *normal distribution*. There are natural analogs of this density when $n > 1$.

Let $\mathbb{R} = \|r_{ij}\|$ be a nonnegative definite symmetric $n \times n$ matrix:

$$\sum_{i,j=1}^{n} r_{ij}\lambda_i\lambda_j \ge 0, \qquad \lambda_i \in R, \quad i = 1, \ldots, n, \qquad r_{ij} = r_{ji}.$$

When $\mathbb{R}$ is a positive definite matrix, $|\mathbb{R}| = \det \mathbb{R} > 0$ and consequently there is an inverse matrix $A = \|a_{ij}\|$.

$$f_n(x_1, \ldots, x_n) = \frac{|A|^{1/2}}{(2\pi)^{n/2}} \exp\{-\tfrac{1}{2} \sum a_{ij}(x_i - m_i)(x_j - m_j)\}, \qquad (13)$$

where $m_i \in R$, $i = 1, \ldots, n$, has the property that its (Riemann) integral over the whole space equals 1 (this will be proved in §13) and therefore, since it is also positive, it is a density.

This function is the *density of the n-dimensional* (nondegenerate) *Gaussian* or *normal distribution* (with vector mean $m = (m_1, \ldots, m_n)$ and covariance matrix $\mathbb{R} = A^{-1}$).

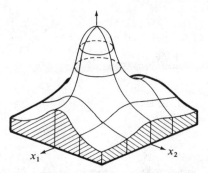

Figure 28. Density of the two-dimensional Gaussian distribution.

When $n = 2$ the density $f_2(x_1, x_2)$ can be put in the form

$$f_2(x_1, x_2) = \frac{1}{2\pi\sigma_1\sigma_2\sqrt{1 - \rho^2}}$$

$$\times \exp\left\{-\frac{1}{2(1 - \rho^2)}\left[\frac{(x_1 - m_1)^2}{\sigma_1^2} - \right.\right.$$

$$\left.\left. - 2\rho\frac{(x_1 - m_1)(x_2 - m_2)}{\sigma_1\sigma_2} + \frac{(x_2 - m_2)^2}{\sigma_2^2}\right]\right\}, \qquad (14)$$

where $\sigma_i > 0$, $|\rho| < 1$. (The meanings of the parameters m_i, σ_i and ρ will be explained in §8.)

Figure 28 indicates the form of the two-dimensional Gaussian density.

Remark. As in the case $n = 1$, Theorem 2 can be generalized to (similarly defined) Lebesgue–Stieltjes measures on $(R^n, \mathscr{B}(R^n))$ and generalized distribution functions on R^n. When the generalized distribution function $G_n(x_1, \ldots, x_n)$ is $x_1 \cdots x_n$, the corresponding measure is Lebesgue measure on the Borel sets of R^n. It clearly satisfies

$$\lambda(a, b) = \prod_{i=1}^{n} (b_i - a_i),$$

i.e. the Lebesgue measure of the "rectangle"

$$(a, b] = (a_1, b_1] \times \cdots \times (a_n, b_n]$$

is its "content."

4. The measurable space $(R^\infty, \mathscr{B}(R^\infty))$. For the spaces R^n, $n \geq 1$, the probability measures were constructed in the following way: first for elementary sets (rectangles $(a, b]$), then, in a natural way, for sets $A = \sum (a_i, b_i]$, and finally, by using Carathéodory's theorem, for sets in $\mathscr{B}(R^n)$.

A similar construction for probability measures also works for the space $(R^\infty, \mathscr{B}(R^\infty))$.

Let

$$\mathscr{I}_n(B) = \{x \in R^\infty : (x_1, \ldots, x_n) \in B\}, \qquad B \in \mathscr{B}(R^n),$$

denote a cylinder set in R^∞ with base $B \in \mathscr{B}(R^n)$. We see at once that it is natural to take the cylinder sets as *elementary sets* in R^∞, with their probabilities defined by the probability measure on the sets of $\mathscr{B}(R^\infty)$.

Let P be a probability measure on $(R^\infty, \mathscr{B}(R^\infty))$. For $n = 1, 2, \ldots$, we take

$$P_n(B) = \mathsf{P}(\mathscr{I}_n(B)), \qquad B \in \mathscr{B}(R^n). \tag{15}$$

The sequence of probability measures $P_1, P_2, \ldots$ defined respectively on $(R, \mathscr{B}(R)), (R^2, \mathscr{B}(R^2)), \ldots$, has the following evident consistency property: for $n = 1, 2, \ldots$ and $B \in \mathscr{B}(R^n)$,

$$P_{n+1}(B \times R) = P_n(B). \tag{16}$$

It is noteworthy that the converse also holds.

Theorem 3 (Kolmogorov's Theorem on the Extension of Measures in $(R^\infty, \mathscr{B}(R^\infty))$). *Let $P_1, P_2, \ldots$ be a sequence of probability measures on $(R, \mathscr{B}(R)), (R^2, \mathscr{B}(R^2)), \ldots$, possessing the consistency property* (16). *Then there is a unique probability measure P on $(R^\infty, \mathscr{B}(R^\infty))$ such that*

$$\mathsf{P}(\mathscr{I}_n(B)) = P_n(B), \qquad B \in \mathscr{B}(R^n). \tag{17}$$

for $n = 1, 2, \ldots$.

PROOF. Let $B^n \in \mathscr{B}(R^n)$ and let $\mathscr{I}_n(B^n)$ be the cylinder with base B^n. We assign the measure $\mathsf{P}(\mathscr{I}_n(B^n))$ to this cylinder by taking $\mathsf{P}(\mathscr{I}_n(B^n)) = P_n(B^n)$.

Let us show that, in virtue of the consistency condition, this definition is consistent, i.e. the value of $\mathsf{P}(\mathscr{I}_n(B^n))$ is independent of the representation of the set $\mathscr{I}_n(B^n)$. In fact, let the same cylinder be represented in two way:

$$\mathscr{I}_n(B^n) = \mathscr{I}_{n+k}(B^{n+k}).$$

It follows that, if $(x_1, \ldots, x_{n+k}) \in R^{n+k}$, we have

$$(x_1, \ldots, x_n) \in B^n \Leftrightarrow (x_1, \ldots, x_{n+k}) \in B^{n+k}, \tag{18}$$

and therefore, by (16) and (18),

$$\begin{aligned}
P_n(B^n) &= P_{n+1}((x_1, \ldots, x_{n+1}) : (x_1, \ldots, x_n) \in B^n) \\
&= \cdots = P_{n+k}((x_1, \ldots, x_{n+k}) : (x_1, \ldots, x_n) \in B^n) \\
&= P_{n+k}(B^{n+k}).
\end{aligned}$$

Let $\mathscr{A}(R^\infty)$ denote the collection of all cylinder sets $\hat{B}^n = \mathscr{I}_n(B^n), B^n \in \mathscr{B}(R^n)$, $n = 1, 2, \ldots$.

Now let $\hat{B}_1, \ldots, \hat{B}_k$ be disjoint sets in $\mathscr{A}(R^\infty)$. We may suppose without loss of generality that $\hat{B}_i = \mathscr{I}_n(B_i^n)$, $i = 1, \ldots, k$, for some n, where $B_1^n, \ldots, B_k^n$ are disjoint sets in $\mathscr{B}(R^n)$. Then

$$\mathsf{P}\left(\sum_{i=1}^{k} \hat{B}_i\right) = \mathsf{P}\left(\sum_{i=1}^{k} \mathscr{I}_n(B_i^n)\right) = P_n\left(\sum_{i=1}^{k} B_i^n\right) = \sum_{i=1}^{n} P_n(B_i^n) = \sum_{i=1}^{n} \mathsf{P}(\hat{B}_i),$$

i.e. the set function P is finitely additive on the algebra $\mathscr{A}(R^\infty)$.

Let us show that P is "continuous at zero," i.e. if the sequence of sets $\hat{B}_n \downarrow \varnothing$, $n \to \infty$, then $\mathsf{P}(\hat{B}_n) \to 0$, $n \to \infty$. Suppose the contrary, i.e. let $\lim \mathsf{P}(\hat{B}_n) = \delta > 0$. We may suppose without loss of generality that $\{\hat{B}_n\}$ has the form

$$\hat{B}_n = \{x \colon (x_1, \ldots, x_n) \in B_n\}, \qquad B_n \in \mathscr{B}(R^n).$$

We use the following property of probability measures P_n on $(R^n, \mathscr{B}(R^n))$ (see Problem 9): if $B_n \in \mathscr{B}(R^n)$, for a given $\delta > 0$ we can find a compact set $A_n \in \mathscr{B}(R^n)$ such that $A_n \subseteq B_n$ and

$$P_n(B_n \backslash A_n) \le \delta/2^{n+1}.$$

Therefore if

$$\hat{A}_n = \{x \colon (x_1, \ldots, x_n) \in A_n\},$$

we have

$$\mathsf{P}(\hat{B}_n \backslash \hat{A}_n) = P_n(B_n \backslash A_n) \le \delta/2^{n+1}.$$

Form the set $\hat{C}_n = \bigcap_{k=1}^{n} \hat{A}_k$ and let C_n be such that

$$\hat{C}_n = \{x \colon (x_1, \ldots, x_n) \in C_n\}.$$

Then, since the sets $\hat{B}_n$ decrease, we obtain

$$\mathsf{P}(\hat{B}_n \backslash \hat{C}_n) \le \sum_{k=1}^{n} \mathsf{P}(\hat{B}_n \backslash \hat{A}_k) \le \sum_{k=1}^{n} \mathsf{P}(\hat{B}_k \backslash \hat{A}_k) \le \delta/2.$$

But by assumption $\lim_n \mathsf{P}(\hat{B}_n) = \delta > 0$, and therefore $\lim_n \mathsf{P}(\hat{C}_n) \ge \delta/2 > 0$. Let us show that this contradicts the condition $\hat{C}_n \downarrow \varnothing$.

Let us choose a point $\hat{x}^{(n)} = (x_1^{(n)}, x_2^{(n)}, \ldots)$ in $\hat{C}_n$. Then $(x_1^{(n)}, \ldots, x_n^{(n)}) \in C_n$ for $n \ge 1$.

Let (n_1) be a subsequence of (n) such that $x_1^{(n_1)} \to x_1^0$, where x_1^0 is a point in C_1. (Such a sequence exists since $x_1^{(n)} \in C_1$ and C_1 is compact.) Then select a subsequence (n_2) of (n_1) such that $(x_1^{(n_2)}, x_2^{(n_2)}) \to (x_1^0, x_2^0) \in C_2$. Similarly let $(x_1^{(n_k)}, \ldots, x_k^{(n_k)}) \to (x_1^0, \ldots, x_k^0) \in C_k$. Finally form the diagonal sequence (m_k), where m_k is the kth term of (n_k). Then $x_i^{(m_k)} \to x_i^0$ as $m_k \to \infty$ for $i = 1, 2, \ldots$; and $(x_1^0, x_2^0, \ldots) \in \hat{C}_n$ for $n = 1, 2, \ldots$, which evidently contradicts the assumption that $\hat{C}_n \downarrow \varnothing$, $n \to \infty$. This completes the proof of the theorem.

Remark. In the present case, the space R^∞ is a countable product of lines, $R^\infty = R \times R \times \cdots$. It is natural to ask whether Theorem 3 remains true if $(R^\infty, \mathscr{B}(R^\infty))$ is replaced by a direct product of measurable spaces $(\Omega_i, \mathscr{F}_i)$, $i = 1, 2, \ldots$.

We may notice that in the preceding proof the only topological property of the real line that was used was that every set in $\mathscr{B}(R^n)$ contains a compact subset whose probability measure is arbitrarily close to the probability measure of the whole set. It is known, however, that this is a property not only of spaces $(R^n, \mathscr{B}(R^n))$, but also of arbitrary complete separable metric spaces with σ-algebras generated by the open sets.

Consequently Theorem 3 remains valid if we suppose that $P_1, P_2, \ldots$ is a sequence of consistent probability measures on $(\Omega_1, \mathscr{F}_1)$,

$$(\Omega_1 \times \Omega_2, \mathscr{F}_1 \otimes \mathscr{F}_2), \ldots,$$

where $(\Omega_i, \mathscr{F}_i)$ are complete separable metric spaces with σ-algebras $\mathscr{F}_i$ generated by open sets, and $(R^\infty, \mathscr{B}(R^\infty))$ is replaced by

$$(\Omega_1 \times \Omega_2 \times \cdots, \mathscr{F}_1 \otimes \mathscr{F}_2 \otimes \cdots).$$

In §9 (Theorem 2) it will be shown that the result of Theorem 3 remains valid for arbitrary measurable spaces $(\Omega_i, \mathscr{F}_i)$ if the measures P_n are concentrated in a particular way. However, Theorem 3 may fail in the general case (without any hypotheses on the topological nature of the measurable spaces or on the structure of the family of measures $\{P_n\}$). This is shown by the following example.

Let us consider the space $\Omega = (0, 1]$, which is evidently not complete, and construct a sequence $\mathscr{F}_1 \subseteq \mathscr{F}_2 \subseteq \cdots$ of σ-algebras in the following way. For $n = 1, 2, \ldots$, let

$$\varphi_n(\omega) = \begin{cases} 1, & 0 < \omega < 1/n, \\ 0, & 1/n \leq \omega \leq 1, \end{cases}$$

$$\mathscr{C}_n = \{A \in \Omega: A = \{\omega: \varphi_n(\omega) \in B\}, B \in \mathscr{B}(R)\}$$

and let $\mathscr{F}_n = \sigma\{\mathscr{C}_1, \ldots, \mathscr{C}_n\}$ be the smallest σ-algebra containing the sets $\mathscr{C}_1, \ldots, \mathscr{C}_n$. Clearly $\mathscr{F}_1 \subseteq \mathscr{F}_2 \subseteq \cdots$. Let $\mathscr{F} = \sigma(\bigcup \mathscr{F}_n)$ be the smallest σ-algebra containing all the $\mathscr{F}_n$. Consider the measurable space $(\Omega, \mathscr{F}_n)$ and define a probability measure P_n on it as follows:

$$P_n\{\omega: (\varphi_1(\omega), \ldots, \varphi_n(\omega)) \in B^n\} = \begin{cases} 1 & \text{if } (1, \ldots, 1) \in B^n, \\ 0 & \text{otherwise,} \end{cases}$$

where $B^n = \mathscr{B}(R^n)$. It is easy to see that the family $\{P_n\}$ is consistent: if $A \in \mathscr{F}_n$ then $P_{n+1}(A) = P_n(A)$. However, we claim that there is no probability measure P on $(\Omega, \mathscr{F})$ such that its *restriction* $P|\mathscr{F}_n$ (i.e., the measure P

considered only on sets in $\mathscr{F}_n$) coincides with P_n for $n = 1, 2, \ldots$. In fact, let us suppose that such a probability measure P exists. Then

$$P\{\omega: \varphi_1(\omega) = \cdots = \varphi_n(\omega) = 1\} = P_n\{\omega: \varphi_1(\omega) = \cdots = \varphi_n(\omega) = 1\} = 1$$

(19)

for $n = 1, 2, \ldots$. But

$$\{\omega: \varphi_1(\omega) = \cdots = \varphi_n(\omega) = 1\} = (0, 1/n) \downarrow \varnothing,$$

which contradicts (19) and the hypothesis of countable additivity (and therefore continuity at the "zero" $\varnothing$) of the set function P.

We now give an example of a probability measure on $(R^\infty, \mathscr{B}(R^\infty))$. Let $F_1(x), F_2(x), \ldots$ be a sequence of one-dimensional distribution functions. Define the functions $G(x) = F_1(x), G_2(x_1, x_2) = F_1(x_1)F_2(x_2), \ldots$, and denote the corresponding probability measures on $(R, \mathscr{B}(R)), (R^2, \mathscr{B}(R^2)), \ldots$ by $P_1, P_2, \ldots$. Then it follows from Theorem 3 that there is a measure P on $(R^\infty, \mathscr{B}(R^\infty))$ such that

$$P\{x \in R^\infty: (x_1, \ldots, x_n) \in B\} = P_n(B), \qquad B \in \mathscr{B}(R^n)$$

and, in particular,

$$P\{x \in R^\infty: x_1 \leq a_1, \ldots, x_n \leq a_n\} = F_1(a_1) \cdots F_n(a_n).$$

Let us take $F_i(x)$ to be a Bernoulli distribution,

$$F_i(x) = \begin{cases} 0, & x < 0, \\ q, & 0 \leq x < 1, \\ 1, & x \geq 1. \end{cases}$$

Then we can say that there is a probability measure P on the space Ω of sequences of numbers $x = (x_1, x_2, \ldots), x_i = 0$ or 1, together with the σ-algebra of its Borel subsets, such that

$$P\{x: x_1 = a_1, \ldots, x_n = a_n\} = p^{\Sigma a_i} q^{n - \Sigma a_i}.$$

This is precisely the result that was not available in the first chapter for stating the law of large numbers in the form (I.5.8).

5. The measurable space $(R^T, \mathscr{B}(R^T))$. Let T be a set of indices $t \in T$ and R_t a real line corresponding to the index t. We consider a finite unordered set $\tau = [t_1, \ldots, t_n]$ of distinct indices $t_i, t_i \in T, n \geq 1$, and let P_τ be a probability measure on $(R^\tau, \mathscr{B}(R^\tau))$, where $R^\tau = R_{t_1} \times \cdots \times R_{t_n}$.

We say that the family $\{P_\tau\}$ of probability measures, where τ runs through all finite unordered sets, is *consistent* if, for all sets $\tau = [t_1, \ldots, t_n]$ and $\sigma = [s_1, \ldots, s_k]$ such that $\sigma \subseteq \tau$ we have

$$P_\sigma\{(x_{s_1}, \ldots, x_{s_k}): (x_{s_1}, \ldots, x_{s_k}) \in B\} = P_\tau\{(x_{t_1}, \ldots, x_{t_n}): (x_{s_1}, \ldots, x_{s_k}) \in B\}$$

(20)

for every $B \in \mathscr{B}(R^\sigma)$.

Theorem 4 (Kolmogorov's Theorem on the Extension of Measures in $(R^T, \mathcal{B}(R^T))$). *Let* $\{P_\tau\}$ *be a consistent family of probability measures on* $(R^\tau, \mathcal{B}(R^\tau))$. *Then there is a unique probability measure* P *on* $(R^T, \mathcal{B}(R^T))$ *such that*

$$\mathsf{P}(\mathscr{I}_\tau(B)) = P_\tau(B) \qquad (21)$$

for all unordered sets $\tau = [t_1, \dots, t_n]$ *of different indices* $t_i \in T$, $B \in \mathcal{B}(R^\tau)$ *and* $\mathscr{I}_\tau(B) = \{x \in R^T : (x_{t_1}, \dots, x_{t_n}) \in B\}$.

PROOF. Let the set $\hat{B} \in \mathcal{B}(R^T)$. By the theorem of §2 there is an at most countable set $S = \{s_1, s_2, \dots\} \subseteq T$ such that $\hat{B} = \{x : (x_{s_1}, x_{s_2}, \dots) \in B\}$, where $B \in \mathcal{B}(R^S)$, $R^S = R_{s_1} \times R_{s_2} \times \cdots$. In other words, $\hat{B} = \mathscr{I}_S(B)$ is a cylinder set with base $B \in \mathcal{B}(R^S)$.

We can define a set function P on such cylinder sets by putting

$$\mathsf{P}(\mathscr{I}_S(B)) = P_S(B), \qquad (22)$$

where P_S is the probability measure whose existence is guaranteed by Theorem 3. We claim that P is in fact the measure whose existence is asserted in the theorem. To establish this we first verify that the definition (22) is consistent, i.e. that it leads to a unique value of $\mathsf{P}(\hat{B})$ for all possible representations of $\hat{B}$; and second, that this set function is countably additive.

Let $\hat{B} = \mathscr{I}_{S_1}(B_1)$ and $\hat{B} = \mathscr{I}_{S_2}(B_2)$. It is clear that then $\hat{B} = \mathscr{I}_{S_1 \cup S_2}(B_3)$ with some $B_3 \in \mathcal{B}(R^{S_1 \cup S_2})$; therefore it is enough to show that if $S \subseteq S'$ and $B \in \mathcal{B}(R^S)$, then $P_{S'}(B') = P_S(B)$, where

$$B' = \{(x_{s'_1}, x_{s'_2}, \dots) : (x_{s_1}, x_{s_2}, \dots) \in B\}$$

with $S' = \{s'_1, s'_2, \dots\}$, $S = \{s_1, s_2, \dots\}$. But by the assumed consistency of (20) this equation follows immediately from Theorem 3. This establishes that the value of $\mathsf{P}(\hat{B})$ is independent of the representation of $\hat{B}$.

To verify the countable additivity of P, let us suppose that $\{\hat{B}_n\}$ is a sequence of pairwise disjoint sets in $\mathcal{B}(R^T)$. Then there is an at most countable set $S \subseteq T$ such that $\hat{B}_n = \mathscr{I}_S(B_n)$ for all $n \geq 1$, where $B_n \in \mathcal{B}(R^S)$. Since P_S is a probability measure, we have

$$\mathsf{P}(\sum \hat{B}_n) = \mathsf{P}(\sum \mathscr{I}_S(B_n)) = P_S(\sum B_n) = \sum P_S(B_n)$$
$$= \sum \mathsf{P}(I_S(B_n)) = \sum \mathsf{P}(\hat{B}_n).$$

Finally, property (21) follows immediately from the way in which P was constructed.

This completes the proof.

Remark 1. We emphasize that T is *any* set of indices. Hence, by the remark after Theorem 3, the present theorem remains valid if we replace the real lines R_t by arbitrary complete separable metric spaces Ω_t (with σ-algebras generated by open sets).

Remark 2. The original probability measures $\{P_\tau\}$ were assumed defined on *unordered* sets $\tau = [t_1, \ldots, t_n]$ of different indices. It is also possible to start from a family of probability measures $\{P_\tau\}$ where τ runs through all *ordered* sets $\tau = (t_1, \ldots, t_n)$ of different indices. In this case, in order to have Theorem 4 hold we have to adjoin to (20) a further *consistency condition*:

$$P_{(t_1, \ldots, t_n)}(A_{t_1} \times \cdots \times A_{t_n}) = P_{(t_{i_1}, \ldots, t_{i_n})}(A_{t_{i_1}} \times \cdots \times A_{t_{i_n}}), \qquad (23)$$

where $(i, \ldots, i_n)$ is an arbitrary permutation of $(1, \ldots, n)$ and $A_{t_i} \in \mathcal{B}(R_{t_i})$. As a necessary condition for the existence of P this follows from (21) (with $P_{[t_1, \ldots, t_n]}(B)$ replaced by $P_{(t_1, \ldots, t_n)}(B)$).

     From now on we shall assume that the sets τ under consideration are *unordered*. If T is a subset of the real line (or some completely ordered set), we may assume without loss of generality that the set $\tau = [t_1, \ldots, t_n]$ satisfies $t_1 < t_2 < \cdots < t_n$. Consequently it is enough to define "finite-dimensional" probabilities only for sets $\tau = [t_1, \ldots, t_n]$ for which $t_1 < t_2 < \cdots < t_n$.

     Now consider the case $T = [0, \infty)$. Then R^T is the space of all real functions $x = (x_t)_{t \geq 0}$. A fundamental example of a probability measure on $(R^{[0, \infty)}, \mathcal{B}(R^{[0, \infty)}))$ is Wiener measure, constructed as follows.

     Consider the family $\{\varphi_t(y|x)\}_{t \geq 0}$ of Gaussian densities (as functions of y for fixed x):

$$\varphi_t(y|x) = \frac{1}{\sqrt{2\pi t}} e^{-(y-x)^2/2t}, \qquad y \in R,$$

and for each $\tau = [t_1, \ldots, t_n]$, $t_1 < t_2 < \cdots < t_n$, and each set

$$B = I_1 \times \cdots \times I_n, \qquad I_k = (a_k, b_k),$$

construct the measure $P_\tau(B)$ according to the formula

$$P_\tau(I_1 \times \cdots \times I_n)$$

$$= \int_{I_1} \cdots \int_{I_n} \varphi_{t_1}(a_1|0)\varphi_{t_2 - t_1}(a_2|a_1) \cdots \varphi_{t_n - t_{n-1}}(a_n|a_{n-1})\, da_1 \cdots da_n \qquad (24)$$

(integration in the Riemann sense). Now we define the set function P for each cylinder set $\mathscr{I}_{t_1 \ldots t_n}(I_1 \times \cdots \times I_n) = \{x \in R^T : x_{t_1} \in I_1, \ldots, x_{t_n} \in I_n\}$ by taking

$$\mathsf{P}(\mathscr{I}_{t_1 \ldots t_n}(I_1 \times \cdots \times I_n)) = P_{[t_1 \ldots t_n]}(I_1 \times \cdots \times I_n).$$

The intuitive meaning of this method of assigning a measure to the cylinder set $\mathscr{I}_{t_1 \ldots t_n}(I_1 \times \cdots \times I_n)$ is as follows.

     The set $\mathscr{I}_{t_1 \ldots t_n}(I_1 \times \cdots \times I_n)$ is the set of functions that at times $t_1, \ldots, t_n$ pass through the "windows" $I_1, \ldots, I_n$ (see Figure 24 in §2). We shall interpret

$\varphi_{t_k - t_{k-1}}(a_k | a_{k-1})$ as the probability that a particle, starting at a_{k-1} at time $t_k - t_{k-1}$, arrives in a neighborhood of a_k. Then the product of densities that appears in (24) describes a certain independence of the increments of the displacements of the moving "particle" in the time intervals

$$[0, t_1], [t_1, t_2], \ldots, [t_{n-1}, t_n].$$

The family of measures $\{P_\tau\}$ constructed in this way is easily seen to be consistent, and therefore can be extended to a measure on $(R^{[0, \infty)}, \mathscr{B}(R^{[0, \infty)}))$. The measure so obtained plays an important role in probability theory. It was introduced by N. Wiener and is known as *Wiener measure*.

6. Problems

1. Let $F(x) = P(-\infty, x]$. Verify the following formulas:

$$P(a, b] = F(b) - F(a), \qquad P(a, b) = F(b-) - F(a),$$
$$P[a, b] = F(b) - F(a-), \qquad P[a, b) = F(b-) - F(a-),$$
$$P\{x\} = F(x) - F(x-),$$

where $F(x-) = \lim_{y \uparrow x} F(y)$.

2. Verify (7).

3. Prove Theorem 2.

4. Show that a distribution function $F = F(x)$ on R has at most a countable set of points of discontinuity. Does a corresponding result hold for distribution functions on R^n?

5. Show that each of the functions

$$G(x, y) = \begin{cases} 1, & x + y \geq 0, \\ 0, & x + y < 0, \end{cases}$$

$$G(x, y) = [x + y], \text{ the integral part of } x + y,$$

is continuous on the right, and continuous in each argument, but is not a (generalized) distribution function on R^2.

6. Let μ be the Lebesgue–Stieltjes measure generated by a continuous distribution function. Show that if the set A is at most countable, then $\mu(A) = 0$.

7. Let c be the cardinal number of the continuum. Show that the cardinal number of the collection of Borel sets in R^n is c, whereas that of the collection of Lebesgue measurable sets is 2^c.

8. Let $(\Omega, \mathscr{F}, P)$ be a probability space and $\mathscr{A}$ an algebra of subsets of Ω such that $\sigma(\mathscr{A}) = \mathscr{F}$. Using the principle of appropriate sets, prove that for every $\varepsilon > 0$ and $B \in \mathscr{F}$ there is a set $A \in \mathscr{A}$ such that

$$P(A \triangle B) \leq \varepsilon.$$

9. Let P be a probability measure on $(R^n, \mathscr{B}(R^n))$. Using Problem 8, show that, for every $\varepsilon > 0$ and $B \in \mathscr{B}(R^n)$, there is a compact subset A of $\mathscr{B}(R^n)$ such that $A \subseteq B$ and

$$\mathsf{P}(B \backslash A) \leq \varepsilon.$$

(This was used in the proof of Theorem 1.)

10. Verify the consistency of the measure defined by (21).

§4. Random Variables. I

1. Let $(\Omega, \mathscr{F})$ be a measurable space and let $(R, \mathscr{B}(R))$ be the real line with the system $\mathscr{B}(R)$ of Borel sets.

Definition 1. A real function $\xi = \xi(\omega)$ defined on (Ω, F) is an $\mathscr{F}$-*measurable function*, or a *random variable*, if

$$\{\omega : \xi(\omega) \in B\} \in \mathscr{F} \tag{1}$$

for every $B \in \mathscr{B}(R)$; or, equivalently, if the inverse image

$$\xi^{-1}(B) \equiv \{\omega : \xi(\omega) \in B\}$$

is a measurable set in Ω.

When $(\Omega, \mathscr{F}) = (R^n, \mathscr{B}(R^n))$, the $\mathscr{B}(R^n)$-measurable functions are called *Borel functions*.

The simplest example of a random variable is the indicator $I_A(\omega)$ of an arbitrary (measurable) set $A \in \mathscr{F}$.

A random variable ξ that has a representation

$$\xi(\omega) = \sum_{i=1}^{\infty} x_i I_{A_i}(\omega), \tag{2}$$

where $\sum A_i = \Omega$, $A_i \in \mathscr{F}$, is called *discrete*. If the sum in (2) is finite, the random variable is called *simple*.

With the same interpretation as in §4 of Chapter I, we may say that a random variable is a numerical property of an experiment, with a value depending on "chance." Here the requirement (1) of measurability is fundamental, for the following reason. If a probability measure P is defined on $(\Omega, \mathscr{F})$, it then makes sense to speak of the probability of the event $\{\xi(\omega) \in B\}$ that the value of the random variable belongs to a Borel set B.

We introduce the following definitions.

Definition 2. A probability measure P_ξ on $(R, \mathscr{B}(R))$ with

$$P_\xi(B) = \mathsf{P}\{\omega : \xi(\omega) \in B\}, \qquad B \in \mathscr{B}(R),$$

is called the *probability distribution of* ξ on $(R, \mathscr{B}(R))$.

Definition 3. The function

$$F_\xi(x) = \mathsf{P}(\omega: \xi(\omega) \leq x\}, \qquad x \in R,$$

is called the *distribution function of* ξ.

For a discrete random variable the measure P_ξ is concentrated on an at most countable set and can be represented in the form

$$P_\xi(B) = \sum_{\{k:\, x_k \in B\}} p(x_k), \tag{3}$$

where $p(x_k) = \mathsf{P}\{\xi = x_k\} = \Delta F_\xi(x_k)$.

The converse is evidently true: If P_ξ is represented in the form (3) then ξ is a *discrete* random variable.

A random variable ξ is called *continuous* if its distribution function $F_\xi(x)$ is continuous for $x \in R$.

A random variable ξ is called *absolutely continuous* if there is a nonnegative function $f = f_\xi(x)$, called its density, such that

$$F_\xi(x) = \int_{-\infty}^{x} f_\xi(y)\, dy, \qquad x \in R, \tag{4}$$

(the integral can be taken in the Riemann sense, or more generally in that of Lebesgue; see §6 below).

2. To establish that a function $\xi = \xi(\omega)$ is a random variable, we have to verify property (1) for all sets $B \in \mathscr{F}$. The following lemma shows that the class of such "test" sets can be considerably narrowed.

Lemma 1. *Let $\mathscr{E}$ be a system of sets such that $\sigma(\mathscr{E}) = \mathscr{B}(R)$. A necessary and sufficient condition that a function $\xi = \xi(\omega)$ is $\mathscr{F}$-measurable is that*

$$\{\omega: \xi(\omega) \in E\} \in \mathscr{F} \tag{5}$$

for all $E \in \mathscr{E}$.

PROOF. The necessity is evident. To prove the sufficiency we again use the principle of appropriate sets.

Let $\mathscr{D}$ be the system of those Borel sets D in $\mathscr{B}(R)$ for which $\xi^{-1}(D) \in \mathscr{F}$. The operation "form the inverse image" is easily shown to preserve the set-theoretic operations of union, intersection and complement:

$$\xi^{-1}\left(\bigcup_\alpha B_\alpha\right) = \bigcup_\alpha \xi^{-1}(B_\alpha),$$

$$\xi^{-1}\left(\bigcap_\alpha B_\alpha\right) = \bigcap_\alpha \xi^{-1}(B_\alpha), \tag{6}$$

$$\overline{\xi^{-1}(B_\alpha)} = \xi^{-1}(\overline{B_\alpha}).$$

It follows that $\mathscr{D}$ is a σ-algebra. Therefore

$$\mathscr{E} \subseteq \mathscr{D} \subseteq \mathscr{B}(R)$$

and

$$\sigma(\mathscr{E}) \subseteq \sigma(\mathscr{D}) = \mathscr{D} \subseteq \mathscr{B}(R).$$

But $\sigma(E) = \mathscr{B}(R)$ and consequently $\mathscr{D} = \mathscr{B}(R)$.

Corollary. *A necessary and sufficient condition for $\xi = \xi(\omega)$ to be a random variable is that*

$$\{\omega : \xi(\omega) < x\} \in \mathscr{F}$$

for every $x \in R$, or that

$$\{\omega : \xi(\omega) \leq x\} \in \mathscr{F}$$

for every $x \in R$.

The proof is immediate, since each of the systems

$$\mathscr{E}_1 = \{x : x < c, c \in R\},$$
$$\mathscr{E}_2 = \{x : x \leq c, c \in R\}$$

generates the σ-algebra $\mathscr{B}(R)$: $\sigma(E_1) = \sigma(E_2) = \mathscr{B}(R)$ (see §2).

The following lemma makes it possible to construct random variables as functions of other random variables.

Lemma 2. *Let $\varphi = \varphi(x)$ be a Borel function and $\xi = \xi(\omega)$ a random variable. Then the composition $\eta = \varphi \circ \xi$, i.e. the function $\eta(\omega) = \varphi(\xi(\omega))$, is also a random variable.*

The proof follows from the equations

$$\{\omega : \eta(\omega) \in B\} = \{\omega : \varphi(\xi(\omega)) \in B\} = \{\omega : \xi(\omega) \in \varphi^{-1}(B)\} \in \mathscr{F} \qquad (7)$$

for $B \in \mathscr{B}(R)$, since $\varphi^{-1}(B) \in \mathscr{B}(R)$.

Therefore if ξ is a random variable, so are, for examples, ξ^n, $\xi^+ = \max(\xi, 0)$, $\xi^- = -\min(\xi, 0)$, and $|\xi|$, since the functions x^n, x^+, x^- and $|x|$ are Borel functions (Problem 4).

3. Starting from a given collection of random variables $\{\xi_n\}$, we can construct new functions, for example, $\sum_{k=1}^{\infty} |\xi_k|$, $\overline{\lim} \, \xi_n$, $\underline{\lim} \, \xi_n$, etc. Notice that in general such functions take values on the extended real line $\overline{R} = [-\infty, \infty]$. Hence it is advisable to extend the class of $\mathscr{F}$-measurable functions somewhat by allowing them to take the values $\pm\infty$.

Definition 4. A function $\xi = \xi(\omega)$ defined on $(\Omega, \mathscr{F})$ with values in $\bar{R} = [-\infty, \infty]$ will be called an *extended random variable* if condition (1) is satisfied for every Borel set $B \in \mathscr{B}(R)$.

The following theorem, despite its simplicity, is the key to the construction of the Lebesgue integral (§6).

Theorem 1.

(a) *For every random variable* $\xi = \xi(\omega)$ *(extended ones included) there is a sequence of simple random variables* $\xi_1, \xi_2, \ldots,$ *such that* $|\xi_n| \leq |\xi|$ *and* $\xi_n(\omega) \to \xi(\omega), n \to \infty,$ *for all* $\omega \in \Omega.$
(b) *If also* $\xi(\omega) \geq 0,$ *there is a sequence of simple random variables* $\xi_1, \xi_2, \ldots,$ *such that* $\xi_n(\omega) \uparrow \xi(\omega), n \to \infty,$ *for all* $\omega \in \Omega.$

PROOF. We begin by proving the second statement. For $n = 1, 2, \ldots,$ put

$$\xi_n(\omega) = \sum_{k=1}^{n2^n} \frac{k-1}{2^n} I_{k,n}(\omega) + nI_{\{\xi(\omega) \geq n\}}(\omega),$$

where $I_{k,n}$ is the indicator of the set $\{(k-1)/2^n \leq \xi(\omega) < k/2^n\}$. It is easy to verify that the sequence $\xi_n(\omega)$ so constructed is such that $\xi_n(\omega) \uparrow \xi(\omega)$ for all $\omega \in \Omega$. The first statement follows from this if we merely observe that ξ can be represented in the form $\xi = \xi^+ - \xi^-$. This completes the proof of the theorem.

We next show that the class of extended random variables is closed under pointwise convergence. For this purpose, we note first that if $\xi_1, \xi_2, \ldots$ is a sequence of extended random variables, then $\sup \xi_n$, $\inf \xi_n$, $\overline{\lim} \xi_n$ and $\underline{\lim} \xi_n$ are also random variables (possibly extended). This follows immediately from

$$\{\omega : \sup \xi_n > x\} = \bigcup_n \{\omega : \xi_n > x\} \in \mathscr{F},$$

$$\{\omega : \inf \xi_n < x\} = \bigcup_n \{\omega : \xi_n < x\} \in \mathscr{F},$$

and

$$\overline{\lim} \, \xi_n = \inf_n \sup_{m \geq n} \xi_m, \qquad \underline{\lim} \, \xi_n = \sup_n \sup_{m \geq n} \xi_m.$$

Theorem 2. *Let* $\xi_1, \xi_2, \ldots$ *be a sequence of extended random variables and* $\xi(\omega) = \lim \xi_n(\omega)$. *Then* $\xi(\omega)$ *is also an extended random variable.*

The proof follows immediately from the remark above and the fact that

$$\begin{aligned}
\{\omega : \xi(\omega) < x\} &= \{\omega : \lim \xi_n(\omega) < x\} \\
&= \{\omega : \overline{\lim} \, \xi_n(\omega) = \underline{\lim} \, \xi_n(\omega)\} \cap \{\overline{\lim} \, \xi_n(\omega) < x\} \\
&= \Omega \cap \{\overline{\lim} \, \xi_n(\omega) < x\} = \{\overline{\lim} \, \xi_n(\omega) < x\} \in \mathscr{F}.
\end{aligned}$$

4. We mention a few more properties of the simplest functions of random variables considered on the measurable space $(\Omega, \mathscr{F})$ and possibly taking values on the extended real line $\bar{R} = [-\infty, \infty]$.†

If ξ and η are random variables, $\xi + \eta, \xi - \eta, \xi\eta$, and ξ/η are also random variables (assuming that they are defined, i.e. that no indeterminate forms like $\infty - \infty, \infty/\infty, a/0$ occur.

In fact, let $\{\xi_n\}$ and $\{\eta_n\}$ be sequences of random variables converging to ξ and η (see Theorem 1). Then

$$\xi_n \pm \eta_n \to \xi \pm \eta,$$

$$\xi_n \eta_n \to \xi\eta,$$

$$\frac{\xi_n}{\eta_n + \dfrac{1}{n} I_{\{\eta_n = 0\}}(\omega)} \to \frac{\xi}{\eta}.$$

The functions on the left-hand sides of these relations are simple random variables. Therefore, by Theorem 2, the limit functions $\xi \pm \eta$, $\xi\eta$ and ξ/η are also random variables.

5. Let ξ be a random variable. Let us consider sets from $\mathscr{F}$ of the form $\{\omega : \xi(\omega) \in B\}$, $B \in \mathscr{B}(R)$. It is easily verified that they form a σ-algebra, called the *σ-algebra generated by* ξ, and denoted by $\mathscr{F}_\xi$.

If φ is a Borel function, it follows from Lemma 2 that the function $\eta = \varphi \circ \xi$ is also a random variable, and in fact $\mathscr{F}_\xi$-measurable, i.e. such that

$$\{\omega : \eta(\omega) \in B\} \in \mathscr{F}_\xi, \quad B \in \mathscr{B}(R)$$

(see (7)). It turns out that the converse is also true.

Theorem 3. *Let η be a $\mathscr{F}_\xi$-measurable random variable. Then there is a Borel function φ such that $\eta = \varphi \circ \xi$, i.e. $\eta(\omega) = \varphi(\xi(\omega))$ for every $\omega \in \Omega$.*

PROOF. Let Φ be the class of $\mathscr{F}_\xi$-measurable functions $\eta = \eta(\omega)$ and $\tilde{\Phi}_\xi$ the class of $\mathscr{F}_\xi$-measurable functions representable in the form $\varphi \circ \xi$, where φ is a Borel function. It is clear that $\tilde{\Phi} \subseteq \Phi_\xi$. The conclusion of the theorem is that in fact $\tilde{\Phi}_\xi = \Phi_\xi$.

Let $A \in \mathscr{F}_\xi$ and $\eta(\omega) = I_A(\omega)$. Let us show that $\eta \in \tilde{\Phi}_\xi$. In fact, if $A \in \mathscr{F}_\xi$ there is a $B \in \mathscr{B}(R)$ such that $A = \{\omega : \xi(\omega) \in B\}$. Let

$$\chi_B(x) = \begin{cases} 1, & x \in B, \\ 0, & x \notin B. \end{cases}$$

Then $I_A(\omega) = \chi_B(\xi(\omega)) \in \tilde{\Phi}_\xi$. Hence it follows that every simple $\mathscr{F}_\xi$-measurable function $\sum_{i=1}^n c_i I_{A_i}(\omega)$, $A_i \in \mathscr{F}_\xi$, also belongs to $\tilde{\Phi}_\xi$.

---

† We shall assume the usual conventions about arithmetic operations in $\bar{R}$: if $a \in R$ then $a \pm \infty = \pm\infty, a/\pm\infty = 0; a \cdot \infty = \infty$ if $a > 0$, and $a \cdot \infty = -\infty$ if $a < 0; 0 \cdot (\pm\infty) = 0$, $\infty + \infty = \infty, -\infty - \infty = -\infty$.

Now let η be an arbitrary $\mathscr{F}_\xi$-measurable function. By Theorem 1 there is a sequence of simple $\mathscr{F}_\xi$-measurable functions $\{\eta_n\}$ such that $\eta_n(\omega) \to \eta(\omega)$, $n \to \infty$, $\omega \in \Omega$. As we just showed, there are Borel functions $\varphi_n = \varphi_n(x)$ such that $\eta_n(\omega) = \varphi_n(\xi(\omega))$. Then $\varphi_n(\xi(\omega)) \to \eta(\omega)$, $n \to \infty$, $\omega \in \Omega$.

Let B denote the set $\{x \in R : \lim_n \varphi_n(x) \text{ exists}\}$. This is a Borel set. Therefore

$$\varphi(x) = \begin{cases} \lim_n \varphi_n(x), & x \in B, \\ 0, & x \notin B \end{cases}$$

is also a Borel function (see Problem 7).

But then it is evident that $\eta(\omega) = \lim_n \varphi_n(\xi(\omega)) = \varphi(\xi(\omega))$ for all $\omega \in \Omega$. Consequently $\tilde{\Phi}_\xi = \Phi_\xi$.

6. Let us consider a probability space $(\Omega, \mathscr{F}, P)$, where the σ-algebra $\mathscr{F}$ is generated by a finite or countably infinite decomposition $\mathscr{D} = \{D_1, D_2, \ldots\}$, $\sum D_i = \Omega$, $P(D_i) > 0$. Here we shall suppose that the D_i are atoms with respect to P, i.e. if $A \subseteq D_i$, $A \in \mathscr{F}$, then either $P(A) = 0$ or $P(D_i \backslash A) = 0$.

Lemma 3. *Let ξ be an $\mathscr{F}$-measurable function, where $\mathscr{F} = \sigma(\mathscr{D})$. Then ξ is constant on the atoms of the decomposition, i.e. ξ has the representation*

$$\xi(\omega) = \sum_{k=1}^{\infty} x_k I_{D_k}(\omega) \quad \text{(P-a.s.)}.\dagger \tag{8}$$

(The notation "$\xi = \eta$ (P-a.s.)" means that $P(\xi \neq \eta) = 0$.)

PROOF. Let D be an atom of the decomposition with respect to P. Let us show that ξ is constant (P-a.s.), i.e. $P\{D \cap (\xi \neq \text{const})\} = 0$.

Let $K = \sup\{x \in \bar{R} : P\{D \cap (\xi < x)\} = 0\}$. Then

$$P\{D \cap (\xi < K)\} = P\left[\bigcup_{\substack{r < K \\ \text{rational } r}} \{\omega \in D; \xi(\omega) < r\} \right] = 0,$$

since if $P\{D \cap (\xi < x)\} = 0$, then also $P\{D \cap (\xi < y)\} = 0$ for all $y \leq x$.

Let $x > K$; then $P\{D \cap (\xi < x)\} > 0$ and therefore $P\{D \cap (\xi \geq x)\} = 0$, since D is an atom. Therefore

$$P\{D \cap (\xi > K)\} = P\left[\bigcup_{\substack{r > K \\ \text{rational } r}} \{\omega \in D : \xi \geq r\} \right] = 0.$$

Thus

$$P\{D \cap (\xi > K)\} = P\{D \cap (\xi < K)\} = 0$$

and therefore $P\{D \cap (\xi \neq K)\} = 0$.

Then (8) follows in general since $\sum D_i = \Omega$. This completes the proof of the lemma.

---

† a.s. = almost surely.

7. PROBLEMS

1. Show that the random variable ξ is continuous if and only if $\mathsf{P}(\xi = x) = 0$ for all $x \in R$.

2. If $|\xi|$ is $\mathscr{F}$-measurable, is it true that ξ is also $\mathscr{F}$-measurable?

3. Show that $\xi = \xi(\omega)$ is an extended random variable if and only if $\{\omega: \xi(\omega) \in \bar{B}\} \in \mathscr{F}$ for all $\bar{B} \in \mathscr{B}(\bar{R})$.

4. Prove that x^n, $x^+ = \max(x, 0)$, $x^- = -\min(x, 0)$, and $|x| = x^+ + x^-$ are Borel functions.

5. If ξ and η are $\mathscr{F}$-measurable, then $\{\omega: \xi(\omega) = \eta(\omega)\} \in \mathscr{F}$.

6. Let ξ and η be random variables on $(\Omega, \mathscr{F})$, and $A \in \mathscr{F}$. Then the function

$$\zeta(\omega) = \xi(\omega) \cdot I_A + \eta(\omega) I_{\bar{A}}$$

is also a random variable.

7. Let $\xi_1, \ldots, \xi_n$ be random variables and $\varphi(x_1, \ldots, x_n)$ a Borel function. Show that $\varphi(\xi_1(\omega), \ldots, \xi_n(\omega))$ is also a random variable.

8. Let ξ and η be random variables, both taking the values $1, 2, \ldots, N$. Suppose that $\mathscr{F}_\xi = \mathscr{F}$. Show that there is a permutation $(i_1, i_2, \ldots, i_N)$ of $(1, 2, \ldots, N)$ such that $\{\omega: \xi = j\} = \{\omega: \eta = i_j\}$ for $j = 1, 2, \ldots, N$.

§5. Random Elements

1. In addition to random variables, probability theory and its applications involve random objects of more general kinds, for example random points, vectors, functions, processes, fields, sets, measures, etc. In this connection it is desirable to have the concept of a random object of any kind.

Definition 1. Let $(\Omega, \mathscr{F})$ and $(E, \mathscr{E})$ be measurable spaces. We say that a function $X = X(\omega)$, defined on Ω and taking values in E, is $\mathscr{F}/\mathscr{E}$-measurable, or is a *random element* (with values in E), if

$$\{\omega: X(\omega) \in B\} \in \mathscr{F} \tag{1}$$

for every $B \in \mathscr{E}$. Random elements (with values in E) are sometimes called E-valued random variables.

Let us consider some special cases.

If $(E, \mathscr{E}) = (R, \mathscr{B}(R))$, the definition of a random element is the same as the definition of a random variable (§4).

Let $(E, \mathscr{E}) = (R^n, \mathscr{B}(R^n))$. Then a random element $X(\omega)$ is a "random point" in R^n. If π_k is the projection of R^n on the kth coordinate axis, $X(\omega)$ can be represented in the form

$$X(\omega) = (\xi_1(\omega), \ldots, \xi_n(\omega)), \tag{2}$$

where $\xi_k = \pi_k \circ X$.

It follows from (1) that ξ_k is an ordinary random variable. In fact, for $B \in \mathscr{B}(R)$ we have

$$\{\omega: \xi_k(\omega) \in B\} = \{\omega: \xi_1(\omega) \in R, \ldots, \xi_{k-1} \in R, \xi_k \in B, \xi_{k+1} \in R, \ldots\}$$
$$= \{\omega: X(\omega) \in (R \times \cdots \times R \times B \times R \times \cdots \times R)\} \in \mathscr{F},$$

since $R \times \cdots \times R \times B \times R \times \cdots \times R \in \mathscr{B}(R^n)$.

Definition 2. An ordered set $(\eta_1(\omega), \ldots, \eta_n(\omega))$ of random variables is called an *n-dimensional random vector*.

According to this definition, every random element $X(\omega)$ with values in R^n is an n-dimensional random vector. The converse is also true: every random vector $X(\omega) = (\xi_1(\omega), \ldots, \xi_n(\omega))$ is a random element in R^n. In fact, if $B_k \in \mathscr{B}(R)$, $k = 1, \ldots, n$, then

$$\{\omega: X(\omega) \in (B_1 \times \cdots \times B_n)\} = \prod_{k=1}^{n} \{\omega: \xi_k(\omega) \in B_k\} \in \mathscr{F}.$$

But $\mathscr{B}(R^n)$ is the smallest σ-algebra containing the sets $B_1 \times \cdots \times B_n$. Consequently we find immediately, by an evident generalization of Lemma 1 of §4, that whenever $B \in \mathscr{B}(R^n)$, the set $\{\omega: X(\omega) \in B\}$ belongs to $\mathscr{F}$.

Let $(E, \mathscr{E}) = (\mathbf{Z}, B(\mathbf{Z}))$, where $\mathbf{Z}$ is the set of complex numbers $x + iy$, $x, y \in R$, and $B(\mathbf{Z})$ is the smallest σ-algebra containing the sets $\{z: z = x + iy, a_1 < x \le b_1, a_2 < y \le b_2\}$. It follows from the discussion above that a complex-valued random variable $Z(\omega)$ can be represented as $Z(\omega) = X(\omega) + iY(\omega)$, where $X(\omega)$ and $Y(\omega)$ are random variables. Hence we may also call $Z(\omega)$ a *complex random variable*.

Let $(E, \mathscr{E}) = (R^T, \mathscr{B}(R^T))$, where T is a subset of the real line. In this case every random element $X = X(\omega)$ can evidently be represented as $X = (\xi_t)_{t \in T}$ with $\xi_t = \pi_t \circ X$, and is called a random function with time domain T.

Definition 3. Let T be a subset of the real line. A set of random variables $X = (\xi_t)_{t \in T}$ is called a *random process*† with time domain T.

If $T = \{1, 2, \ldots\}$ we call $X = (\xi_1, \xi_2, \ldots)$ a *random process with discrete time*, or a *random sequence*.

If $T = [0, 1]$, $(-\infty, \infty)$, $[0, \infty), \ldots$, we call $X = (\xi_t)_{t \in T}$ a *random process with continuous time*.

---

† Or stochastic process (Translator).

It is easy to show, by using the structure of the σ-algebra $\mathscr{B}(R^T)$ (§2) that every random process $X = (\xi_t)_{t \in T}$ (in the sense of Definition 3) is also a random function on the space $(R^T, \mathscr{B}(R^T))$.

Definition 4. Let $X = (\xi_t)_{t \in T}$ be a random process. For each given $\omega \in \Omega$ the function $(\xi_t(\omega))_{t \in T}$ is said to be a *realization* or a *trajectory* of the process, corresponding to the outcome ω.

The following definition is a natural generalization of Definition 2 of §4.

Definition 5. Let $X = (\xi_t)_{t \in T}$ be a random process. The probability measure P_X on $(R^T, \mathscr{B}(R^T))$ defined by

$$P_X(B) = \mathsf{P}\{\omega\colon X(\omega) \in B\}, \qquad B \in \mathscr{B}(R^T),$$

is called the *probability distribution of X*. The probabilities

$$P_{t_1,\ldots,t_n}(B) \equiv \mathsf{P}\{\omega\colon (\xi_{t_1},\ldots,\xi_{t_n}) \in B\}$$

with $t_1 < t_2 < \cdots < t_n$, $t_i \in T$, are called finite-dimensional probabilities (or probability distributions). The functions

$$F_{t_1,\ldots,t_n}(x_1,\ldots,x_n) \equiv \mathsf{P}\{\omega\colon \xi_{t_1} \le x_1,\ldots,\xi_{t_n} \le x_n\}$$

with $t_1 < t_2 < \cdots < t_n$, $t_i \in T$, are called finite-dimensional distribution functions.

Let $(E, \mathscr{E}) = (C, \mathscr{B}_0(C))$, where C is the space of continuous functions $x = (x_t)_{t \in T}$ on $T = [0, 1]$ and $\mathscr{B}_0(C)$ is the σ-algebra generated by the open sets (§2). We show that every random element X on $(C, \mathscr{B}_0(C))$ is also a random process with continuous trajectories in the sense of Definition 3.

In fact, according to §2 the set $A = \{x \in C\colon x_t < a\}$ is open in $\mathscr{B}_0(C)$. Therefore

$$\{\omega\colon \xi_t(\omega) < a\} = \{\omega\colon X(\omega) \in A\} \in \mathscr{F}.$$

On the other hand, let $X = (\xi_t(\omega))_{t \in T}$ be a random process (in the sense of Definition 3) whose trajectories are continuous functions for every $\omega \in \Omega$. According to (2.14),

$$\{x \in C\colon x \in S_\rho(x^0)\} = \bigcap_{t_k} \{x \in C\colon |x_{t_k} - x_{t_k}^0| < \rho\},$$

where t_k are the rational points of $[0, 1]$. Therefore

$$\{\omega\colon X(\omega) \in S_\rho(X^0\omega))\} = \bigcap_{t_k} \{\omega\colon |\xi_{t_k}(\omega) - \xi_{t_k}^0(\omega)| < \rho\} \in \mathscr{F},$$

and therefore we also have $\{\omega\colon X(\omega) \in B\} \in \mathscr{F}$ for every $B \in \mathscr{B}_0(C)$.

Similar reasoning will show that every random element of the space $(D, \mathscr{B}_0(D))$ can be considered as a random process with trajectories in the space of functions with no discontinuities of the second kind; and conversely.

2. Let $(\Omega, \mathscr{F}, \mathsf{P})$ be a probability space and $(E_\alpha, \mathscr{E}_\alpha)$ measurable spaces, where α belongs to an (arbitrary) set $\mathfrak{A}$.

Definition 6. We say that the $\mathscr{F}/\mathscr{E}_\alpha$-measurable functions $(X_\alpha(\omega))$, $\alpha \in \mathfrak{A}$, are independent (or collectively independent) if, for every finite set of indices $\alpha_1, \ldots, \alpha_n$ the random elements $X_{\alpha_1}, \ldots, X_{\alpha_n}$ are independent, i.e.

$$\mathsf{P}(X_{\alpha_1} \in B_{\alpha_1}, \ldots, X_{\alpha_n} \in B_{\alpha_n}) = \mathsf{P}(X_{\alpha_1} \in B_{\alpha_1}) \cdots \mathsf{P}(X_{\alpha_n} \in B_{\alpha_n}), \qquad (3)$$

where $B_\alpha \in \mathscr{E}_\alpha$.

Let $\mathfrak{A} = \{1, 2, \ldots, n\}$, let ξ_α be random variables, let $\alpha \in \mathfrak{A}$ and let

$$F_\xi(x_1, \ldots, x_n) = \mathsf{P}(\xi_1 \leq x_1, \ldots, \xi_n \leq x_n)$$

be the n-dimensional distribution function of the random vector $\xi = (\xi_1, \ldots, \xi_n)$. Let $F_{\xi_i}(x_i)$ be the distribution functions of the random variables ξ_i, $i = 1, \ldots, n$.

Theorem. *A necessary and sufficient condition for the random variables $\xi_1, \ldots, \xi_n$ to be independent is that*

$$F_\xi(x_1, \ldots, x_n) = F_{\xi_1}(x_1) \cdots F_{\xi_n}(x_n) \qquad (4)$$

for all $(x_1, \ldots, x_n) \in R^n$.

PROOF. The necessity is evident. To prove the sufficiency we put $a = (a_1, \ldots, a_n), b = (b_1, \ldots, b_n)$,

$$P_\xi(a, b] = \mathsf{P}\{\omega : a_1 < \xi_1 \leq b_1, \ldots, a_n < \xi_n \leq b_n\},$$
$$P_{\xi_i}(a_i, b_i] = \mathsf{P}\{a_i < \xi_i \leq b_i\}.$$

Then

$$P_\xi(a, b] = \prod_{i=1}^n [F_{\xi_i}(b_i) - F_{\xi_i}(a_i)] = \prod_{i=1}^n P_{\xi_i}(a_i, b_i]$$

by (4) and (3.7), and therefore

$$\mathsf{P}\{\xi_1 \in I_1, \ldots, \xi_n \in I_n\} = \prod_{i=1}^n \mathsf{P}\{\xi_i \in I_i\}, \qquad (5)$$

where $I_i = (a_i, b_i]$.

We fix $I_2, \ldots, I_n$ and show that

$$\mathsf{P}\{\xi_1 \in B_1, \xi_2 \in I_2, \ldots, \xi_n \in I_n\} = \mathsf{P}\{\xi_1 \in B_1\} \prod_{i=2}^n \mathsf{P}\{\xi_i \in I_i\} \qquad (6)$$

for all $B_1 \in \mathscr{B}(R)$. Let $\mathscr{M}$ be the collection of sets in $\mathscr{B}(R)$ for which (6) holds. Then $\mathscr{M}$ evidently contains the algebra $\mathscr{A}$ of sets consisting of sums of disjoint intervals of the form $I_1 = (a_1, b_1]$. Hence $\mathscr{A} \subseteq \mathscr{M} \subseteq \mathscr{B}(R)$. From the countable additivity (and therefore continuity) of probability measures it also follows that $\mathcal{M}$ is a monotonic class. Therefore (see Subsection 1 of §2)

$$\mu(\mathcal{A}) \subseteq \mathcal{M} \subseteq \mathcal{B}(R).$$

But $\mu(\mathcal{A}) = \sigma(\mathcal{A}) = \mathcal{B}(R)$ by Theorem 1 of §2. Therefore $\mathcal{M} = \mathcal{B}(R)$.

Thus (6) is established. Now fix $B_1, I_3, \ldots, I_n$; by the same method we can establish (6) with I_2 replaced by the Borel set B_2. Continuing in this way, we can evidently arrive at the required equation,

$$\mathsf{P}(\xi_1 \in B_1, \ldots, \xi_n \in B_n) = \mathsf{P}(\xi_1 \in B_1) \cdots \mathsf{P}(\xi_n \in B_n),$$

where $B_i \in \mathcal{B}(R)$. This completes the proof of the theorem.

3. PROBLEMS

1. Let $\xi_1, \ldots, \xi_n$ be discrete random variables. Show that they are independent if and only if

$$\mathsf{P}(\xi_1 = x_1, \ldots, \xi_n = x_n) = \prod_{i=1}^{n} \mathsf{P}(\xi_i = x_i)$$

for all real $x_1, \ldots, x_n$.

2. Carry out the proof that every random function (in the sense of Definition 1) is a random process (in the sense of Definition 3) and conversely.

3. Let $X_1, \ldots, X_n$ be random elements with values in $(E_1, \mathcal{E}_1), \ldots, (E_n, \mathcal{E}_n)$, respectively. In addition let $(E'_1, \mathcal{E}'_1), \ldots, (E'_n, \mathcal{E}'_n)$ be measurable spaces and let $g_1, \ldots, g_n$ be $\mathcal{E}_1/\mathcal{E}'_1, \ldots, \mathcal{E}_n/\mathcal{E}'_n$-measurable functions, respectively. Show that if $X_1, \ldots, X_n$ are independent, the random elements $g_1 \cdot X_1, \ldots, g_n \cdot X_n$ are also independent.

§6. Lebesgue Integral. Expectation

1. When $(\Omega, \mathcal{F}, \mathsf{P})$ is a finite probability space and $\xi = \xi(\omega)$ is a simple random variable,

$$\xi(\omega) = \sum_{k=1}^{n} x_k I_{A_k}(\omega), \tag{1}$$

the expectation $\mathsf{E}\xi$ was defined in §4 of Chapter I. The same definition of the expectation $\mathsf{E}\xi$ of a simple random variable ξ can be used for any probability space $(\Omega, \mathcal{F}, \mathsf{P})$. That is, we define

$$\mathsf{E}\xi = \sum_{k=1}^{n} x_k \mathsf{P}(A_k). \tag{2}$$

This definition is consistent (in the sense that $E\xi$ is independent of the particular representation of ξ in the form (1)), as can be shown just as for finite probability spaces. The simplest properties of the expectation can be established similarly (see Subsection 5 of §4 of Chapter I).

In the present section we shall define and study the properties of the expectation $E\xi$ of an arbitrary random variable. In the language of analysis, $E\xi$ is merely the Lebesgue integral of the $\mathscr{F}$-measurable function $\xi = \xi(\omega)$ with respect to the measure P. In addition to $E\xi$ we shall use the notation $\int_\Omega \xi(\omega)P(d\omega)$ or $\int_\Omega \xi\, dP$.

Let $\xi = \xi(\omega)$ be a nonnegative random variable. We construct a sequence of simple nonnegative random variables $\{\xi_n\}_{n\geq 1}$ such that $\xi_n(\omega) \uparrow \xi(\omega)$, $n \to \infty$, for each $\omega \in \Omega$ (see Theorem 1 in §4).

Since $E\xi_n \leq E\xi_{n+1}$ (cf. Property 3) of Subsection 5, §4, Chapter I), the limit $\lim_n E\xi_n$ exists, possibly with the value $+\infty$.

Definition 1. The *Lebesgue integral* of the nonnegative random variable, $\xi = \xi(\omega)$, or its *expectation*, is

$$E\xi \equiv \lim_n E\xi_n. \tag{3}$$

To see that this definition is consistent, we need to show that the limit is independent of the choice of the approximating sequence $\{\xi_n\}$. In other words, we need to show that if $\xi_n \uparrow \xi$ and $\eta_m \uparrow \xi$, where $\{\eta_m\}$ is a sequence of simple functions, then

$$\lim_n E\xi_n = \lim_m E\eta_m. \tag{4}$$

Lemma 1. *Let η and ξ_n be simple random variables, $n \geq 1$, and*

$$\xi_n \uparrow \xi \geq \eta.$$

Then

$$\lim_n E\xi_n \geq E\eta. \tag{5}$$

PROOF. Let $\varepsilon > 0$ and

$$A_n = \{\omega: \xi_n \geq \eta - \varepsilon\}.$$

It is clear that $A_n \uparrow \Omega$ and

$$\xi_n = \xi_n I_{A_n} + \xi_n I_{\bar{A}_n} \geq \xi_n I_{A_n} \geq (\eta - \varepsilon)I_{A_n}.$$

Hence by the properties of the expectations of simple random variables we find that

$$E\xi_n \geq E(\eta - \varepsilon)I_{A_n} = E\eta I_{A_n} - \varepsilon P(A_n)$$
$$= E\eta - E\eta I_{\bar{A}_n} - \varepsilon P(A_n) \geq E\eta - CP(\bar{A}_n) - \varepsilon,$$

where $C = \max_\omega \eta(\omega)$. Since ε is arbitrary, the required inequality (5) follows. It follows from this lemma that $\lim_n \mathsf{E}\xi_n \geq \lim_m \mathsf{E}\eta_m$ and by symmetry $\lim_m \mathsf{E}\eta_m \geq \lim_n \mathsf{E}\xi_n$, which proves (4).

The following remark is often useful.

Remark 1. The expectation $\mathsf{E}\xi$ of the nonnegative random variable ξ satisfies

$$\mathsf{E}\xi = \sup_{\{s \in S: s \leq \xi\}} \mathsf{E}s, \tag{6}$$

where $S = \{s\}$ is a set of simple random variables (Problem 1).

Thus the expectation is well defined for nonnegative random variables. We now consider the general case.

Let ξ be a random variable and $\xi^+ = \max(\xi, 0)$, $\xi^- = -\min(\xi, 0)$.

Definition 2. We say that the expectation $\mathsf{E}\xi$ of the random variable ξ *exists*, or *is defined*, if at least one of $\mathsf{E}\xi^+$ and $\mathsf{E}\xi^-$ is finite:

$$\min(\mathsf{E}\xi^+, \mathsf{E}\xi^-) < \infty.$$

In this case we *define*

$$\mathsf{E}\xi \equiv \mathsf{E}\xi^+ - \mathsf{E}\xi^-.$$

The *expectation* $\mathsf{E}\xi$ is also called the *Lebesgue integral* (of the function ξ with respect to the probability measure P).

Definition 3. We say that the *expectation of ξ is finite* if $\mathsf{E}\xi^+ < \infty$ and $\mathsf{E}\xi^- < \infty$.

Since $|\xi| = \xi^+ - \xi^-$, the finiteness of $\mathsf{E}\xi$, or $|\mathsf{E}\xi| < \infty$, is equivalent to $\mathsf{E}|\xi| < \infty$. (In this sense one says that the Lebesgue integral is absolutely convergent.)

Remark 2. In addition to the expectation $\mathsf{E}\xi$, significant numerical characteristics of a random variable ξ are the number $\mathsf{E}\xi^r$ (if defined) and $\mathsf{E}|\xi|^r, r > 0$, which are known as the *moment* of order r (or rth moment) and the *absolute moment* of order r (or absolute rth moment) of ξ.

Remark 3. In the definition of the Lebesgue integral $\int_\Omega \xi(\omega)\mathsf{P}(d\omega)$ given above, we suppose that P was a probability measure ($\mathsf{P}(\Omega) = 1$) and that the $\mathscr{F}$-measurable functions (random variables) ξ had values in $R = (-\infty, \infty)$. Suppose now that μ is any measure defined on a measurable space $(\Omega, \mathscr{F})$ and possibly taking the value $+\infty$, and that $\xi = \xi(\omega)$ is an $\mathscr{F}$-measurable function with values in $\bar{R} = [-\infty, \infty]$ (an extended random variable). In this case the Lebesgue integral $\int_\Omega \xi(\omega)\mu(d\omega)$ is defined in the same way: first, for nonnegative simple ξ (by (2) with P replaced by μ), then for arbitrary nonnegative ξ, and in general by the formula

$$\int_\Omega \xi(\omega)\mu(d\omega) = \int_\Omega \xi^+ \mu(d\omega) - \int_\Omega \xi^- \mu(d\omega),$$

provided that no indeterminacy of the form $\infty - \infty$ arises.

A case that is particularly important for mathematical analysis is that in which $(\Omega, F) = (R, \mathscr{B}(R))$ and μ is Lebesgue measure. In this case the integral $\int_R \xi(x)\mu(dx)$ is written $\int_R \xi(x)\,dx$, or $\int_{-\infty}^{\infty} \xi(x)\,dx$, or (L) $\int_{-\infty}^{\infty} \xi(x)\,dx$ to emphasize its difference from the Riemann integral (R) $\int_{-\infty}^{\infty} \xi(x)\,dx$. If the measure μ (Lebesgue–Stieltjes) corresponds to a generalized distribution function $G = G(x)$, the integral $\int_R \xi(x)\mu(dx)$ is also called a *Lebesgue–Stieltjes integral* and is denoted by (L–S) $\int_R \xi(x)G(dx)$, a notation that distinguishes it from the corresponding Riemann–Stieltjes integral

$$(\text{R–S}) \int_R \xi(x)G(dx)$$

(see Subsection 10 below).

It will be clear from what follows (Property **D**) that if $\mathsf{E}\xi$ is defined then so is the expectation $\mathsf{E}(\xi I_A)$ for every $A \in \mathscr{F}$. The notations $\mathsf{E}(\xi; A)$ or $\int_A \xi\,d\mathsf{P}$ are often used for $\mathsf{E}(\xi I_A)$ or its equivalent, $\int_\Omega \xi I_A\,d\mathsf{P}$. The integral $\int_A \xi\,d\mathsf{P}$ is called the *Lebesgue integral of ξ with respect to P over the set A.*

Similarly, we write $\int_A \xi\,d\mu$ instead of $\int_\Omega \xi \cdot I_A\,d\mu$ for an arbitrary measure μ. In particular, if μ is an n-dimensional Lebesgue–Stieltjes measure, and $A = (a_1, b_1] \times \cdots \times (a_n, b_n]$, we use the notation

$$\int_{a_1}^{b_1} \cdots \int_{a_n}^{b_n} \xi(x_1, \ldots, x_n)\mu(dx_1 \cdots dx_n) \qquad \text{instead of} \qquad \int_A \xi\,d\mu.$$

If μ is Lebesgue measure, we write simply $dx_1 \cdots dx_n$ instead of $\mu(dx_1, \ldots, dx_n)$.

---

2. Properties of the expectation $\mathsf{E}\xi$ of the random variable ξ.

A. *Let c be a constant and let $\mathsf{E}\xi$ exist. Then $\mathsf{E}(c\xi)$ exists and*

$$\mathsf{E}(c\xi) = c\mathsf{E}\xi.$$

B. *Let $\xi \leq \eta$; then*

$$\mathsf{E}\xi \leq \mathsf{E}\eta$$

with the understanding that

$$\text{if} \quad -\infty < \mathsf{E}\xi \quad \text{then} \quad -\infty < \mathsf{E}\eta \quad \text{and} \quad \mathsf{E}\xi \leq \mathsf{E}\eta$$

or

$$\text{if} \quad \mathsf{E}\eta < \infty \quad \text{then} \quad \mathsf{E}\xi < \infty \quad \text{and} \quad \mathsf{E}\xi \leq \mathsf{E}\eta.$$

C. *If* $\mathsf{E}\xi$ *exists then*

$$|\mathsf{E}\xi| \leq \mathsf{E}|\xi|.$$

D. *If* $\mathsf{E}\xi$ *exists then* $\mathsf{E}(\xi I_A)$ *exists for each* $A \in \mathscr{F}$; *if* $\mathsf{E}\xi$ *is finite,* $\mathsf{E}(\xi I_A)$ *is finite.*

E. *If* ξ *and* η *are nonnegative random variables, or such that* $\mathsf{E}|\xi| < \infty$ *and* $\mathsf{E}|\eta| < \infty$, *then*

$$\mathsf{E}(\xi + \eta) = \mathsf{E}\xi + \mathsf{E}\eta.$$

(See Problem 2 for a generalization.)

Let us establish **A–E.**

A. This is obvious for simple random variables. Let $\xi \geq 0$, $\xi_n \uparrow \xi$, where ξ_n are simple random variables and $c \geq 0$. Then $c\xi_n \uparrow c\xi$ and therefore

$$\mathsf{E}(c\xi) = \lim \mathsf{E}(c\xi_n) = c \lim \mathsf{E}\xi_n = c\mathsf{E}\xi.$$

In the general case we need to use the representation $\xi = \xi^+ - \xi^-$ and notice that $(c\xi)^+ = c\xi^+$, $(c\xi)^- = c\xi^-$ when $c \geq 0$, whereas when $c < 0$, $(c\xi)^+ = -c\xi^-$, $(c\xi)^- = -c\xi^+$.

B. If $0 \leq \xi \leq \eta$, then $\mathsf{E}\xi$ and $\mathsf{E}\eta$ are defined and the inequality $\mathsf{E}\xi \leq \mathsf{E}\eta$ follows directly from (6). Now let $\mathsf{E}\xi > -\infty$; then $\mathsf{E}\xi^- < \infty$. If $\xi \leq \eta$, we have $\xi^+ \leq \eta^+$ and $\xi^- \geq \eta^-$. Therefore $\mathsf{E}\eta^- \leq \mathsf{E}\xi^- < \infty$; consequently $\mathsf{E}\eta$ is defined and $\mathsf{E}\xi = \mathsf{E}\xi^+ - \mathsf{E}\xi^- \leq \mathsf{E}\eta^+ - \mathsf{E}\eta^- = \mathsf{E}\eta$. The case when $\mathsf{E}\eta < \infty$ can be discussed similarly.

C. Since $-|\xi| \leq \xi \leq |\xi|$, Properties **A** and **B** imply

$$-\mathsf{E}|\xi| \leq \mathsf{E}\xi \leq \mathsf{E}|\xi|,$$

i.e. $|\mathsf{E}\xi| \leq \mathsf{E}|\xi|$.

D. This follows from **B** and

$$(\xi I_A)^+ = \xi^+ I_A \leq \xi^+, \qquad (\xi I_A)^- = \xi^- I_A \leq \xi^-.$$

E. Let $\xi \geq 0$, $\eta \geq 0$, and let $\{\xi_n\}$ and $\}\eta_n\}$ be sequences of simple functions such that $\xi_n \uparrow \xi$ and $\eta_n \uparrow \eta$. Then $\mathsf{E}(\xi_n + \eta_n) = \mathsf{E}\xi_n + \mathsf{E}\eta_n$ and

$$\mathsf{E}(\xi_n + \eta_n) \uparrow \mathsf{E}(\xi + \eta), \quad \mathsf{E}\xi_n \uparrow \mathsf{E}\xi, \quad \mathsf{E}\eta_n \uparrow \mathsf{E}\eta$$

and therefore $\mathsf{E}(\xi + \eta) = \mathsf{E}\xi + \mathsf{E}\eta$. The case when $\mathsf{E}|\xi| < \infty$ and $\mathsf{E}|\eta| < \infty$ reduces to this if we use the facts that

$$\xi = \xi^+ - \xi^-, \quad \eta = \eta^+ - \eta^-, \quad \xi^+ \leq |\xi|, \quad \xi^- \leq |\xi|,$$

and

$$\eta^+ \leq |\eta|, \qquad \eta^- \leq |\eta|.$$

The following group of statements about expectations involve the notion of "P-almost surely." We say that a property holds "P-*almost surely*" *if there is a set* $\mathcal{N} \in \mathcal{F}$ *with* $P(\mathcal{N}) = 0$ *such that the property holds for every point* ω *of* $\Omega \setminus \mathcal{N}$. Instead of "P-almost surely" we often say "P-almost everywhere" or simply "almost surely" (a.s.) or "almost everywhere" (a.e.).

F. If $\xi = 0$ (a.s.) then $E\xi = 0$.

In fact, if ξ is a simple random variable, $\xi = \sum x_k I_{A_k}(\omega)$ and $x_k \neq 0$, we have $P(A_k) = 0$ by hypothesis and therefore $E\xi = 0$. If $\xi \geq 0$ and $0 \leq s \leq \xi$, where s is a simple random variable, then $s = 0$ (a.s.) and consequently $Es = 0$ and $E\xi = \sup_{\{s \in S: s \leq \xi\}} Es = 0$. The general case follows from this by means of the representation $\xi = \xi^+ - \xi^-$ and the facts that $\xi^+ \leq |\xi|$, $\xi^- \leq |\xi|$, and $|\xi| = 0$ (a.s.).

G. If $\xi = \eta$ (a.s.) and $E|\xi| < \infty$, then $E|\eta| < \infty$ and $E\xi = E\eta$ (see also Problem 3).

In fact, let $\mathcal{N} = \{\omega: \xi \neq \eta\}$. Then $P(\mathcal{N}) = 0$ and $\xi = \xi I_{\mathcal{N}} + \xi I_{\bar{\mathcal{N}}}$, $\eta = \eta I_{\mathcal{N}} + \eta I_{\mathcal{N}} = \eta I_{\mathcal{N}} + \xi I_{\bar{\mathcal{N}}}$. By properties **E** and **F**, we have $E\xi = E\xi I_{\mathcal{N}} + E\xi I_{\bar{\mathcal{N}}} = E\eta I_{\bar{\mathcal{N}}}$. But $E\eta I_{\mathcal{N}} = 0$, and therefore $E\xi = E\eta I_{\bar{\mathcal{N}}} + E\eta I_{\mathcal{N}} = E\eta$, by Property **E**.

H. Let $\xi \geq 0$ and $E\xi = 0$. Then $\xi = 0$ (a.s).

For the proof, let $A = \{\omega: \xi(\omega) > 0\}$, $A_n = \{\omega: \xi(\omega) \geq 1/n\}$. It is clear that $A_n \uparrow A$ and $0 \leq \xi \cdot I_{A_n} \leq \xi \cdot I_A$. Hence, by Property **B**,

$$0 \leq E\xi I_{A_n} \leq E\xi = 0.$$

Consequently

$$0 = E\xi I_{A_n} \geq \frac{1}{n} P(A_n)$$

and therefore $P(A_n) = 0$ for all $n \geq 1$. But $P(A) = \lim P(A_n)$ and therefore $P(A) = 0$.

I. Let ξ and η be such that $E|\xi| < \infty$, $E|\eta| < \infty$ and $E(\xi I_A) \leq E(\eta I_A)$ for all $A \in \mathcal{F}$. Then $\xi \leq \eta$ (a.s.).

In fact, let $B = \{\omega: \xi(\omega) > \eta(\omega)\}$. Then $E(\eta I_B) \leq E(\xi I_B) \leq E(\eta I_B)$ and therefore $E(\xi I_B) = E(\eta I_B)$. By Property **E**, we have $E((\xi - \eta)I_B) = 0$ and by Property **H** we have $(\xi - \eta)I_B = 0$ (a.s.), whence $P(B) = 0$.

J. Let ξ be an extended random variable and $E|\xi| < \infty$. Then $|\xi| < \infty$ (a. s.). In fact, let $A = \{\omega | \xi(\omega)| = \infty\}$ and $P(A) > 0$. Then $E|\xi| \geq E(|\xi| I_A) = \infty \cdot P(A) = \infty$, which contradicts the hypothesis $E|\xi| < \infty$. (See also Problem 4.)

3. Here we consider the fundamental theorems on *taking limits* under the expectation sign (or the Lebesgue integral sign).

Theorem 1 (On Monotone Convergence). *Let* η, ξ, ξ_1, $\xi_2, \ldots$ *be random variables.*

(a) *If* $\xi_n \geq \eta$ *for all* $n \geq 1$, $E\eta > -\infty$, *and* $\xi_n \uparrow \xi$, *then*   *increasing ?*

   or $E(x_1^-) < \infty$

$$E\xi_n \uparrow E\xi.$$

(b) *If* $\xi_n \leq \eta$ *for all* $n \geq 1$, $E\eta < \infty$, *and* $\xi_n \downarrow \xi$, *then*   *decreasing*

   or $E(x_1^+) < \infty$

$$E\xi_n \downarrow E\xi.$$

PROOF. (a) First suppose that $\eta \geq 0$. For each $k \geq 1$ let $\{\xi_k^{(n)}\}_{n \geq 1}$ be a sequence of simple functions such that $\xi_k^{(n)} \uparrow \xi_k$, $n \to \infty$. Put $\xi^{(n)} = \max_{1 \leq k \leq n} \xi_k^{(n)}$. Then

$$\zeta^{(n-1)} \leq \zeta^{(n)} = \max_{1 \leq k \leq n} \xi_k^{(n)} \leq \max_{1 \leq k \leq n} \xi_k = \xi_n.$$

Let $\zeta = \lim_n \zeta^{(n)}$. Since

$$\xi_k^{(n)} \leq \zeta^{(n)} \leq \xi_n$$

for $1 \leq k \leq n$, we find by taking limits as $n \to \infty$ that

$$\xi_k \leq \zeta \leq \xi$$

for every $k \geq 1$ and therefore $\xi = \zeta$.

The random variables $\zeta^{(n)}$ are simple and $\zeta^{(n)} \uparrow \zeta$. Therefore

$$E\xi = E\zeta = \lim E\zeta^{(n)} \leq \lim E\xi_n.$$

On the other hand, it is obvious, since $\xi_n \leq \xi_{n+1} \leq \xi$, that

$$\lim E\xi_n \leq E\xi.$$

Consequently $\lim E\xi_n = E\xi$.

Now let η be any random variable with $E\eta > -\infty$.

If $E\eta = \infty$ then $E\xi_n = E\xi = \infty$ by Property **B**, and our proposition is proved. Let $E\eta < \infty$. Then instead of $E\eta > -\infty$ we find $E|\eta| < \infty$. It is clear that $0 \leq \xi_n - \eta \uparrow \xi - \eta$ for all $\omega \in \Omega$. Therefore by what has been established, $E(\xi_n - \eta) \uparrow E(\xi - \eta)$ and therefore (by Property **E** and Problem 2)

$$E\xi_n - E_\eta \uparrow E\xi - E\eta.$$

But $E|\eta| < \infty$, and therefore $E\xi_n \uparrow E_\xi$, $n \to \infty$.

The proof of (b) follows from (a) if we replace the original variables by their negatives.

Corollary. *Let* $\{\eta_n\}_{n \geq 1}$ *be a sequence of nonnegative random variables. Then*

$$E \sum_{n=1}^{\infty} \eta_n = \sum_{n=1}^{\infty} E\eta_n.$$

The proof follows from Property E (see also Problem 2), the monotone convergence theorem, and the remark that

$$\sum_{n=1}^{k} \eta_n \uparrow \sum_{n=1}^{\infty} \eta_n, \quad k \to \infty.$$

Theorem 2 (Fatou's Lemma). *Let* $\eta, \xi_1, \xi_2, \ldots$ *be random variables.*

(a) *If* $\xi_n \geq \eta$ *for all* $n \geq 1$ *and* $\mathsf{E}\eta > -\infty$, *then*

$$\mathsf{E} \varliminf \xi_n \leq \varliminf \mathsf{E}\xi_n.$$

(b) *If* $\xi_n \leq \eta$ *for all* $n \geq 1$ *and* $\mathsf{E}\eta < \infty$, *then*

$$\varlimsup \mathsf{E}\xi_n \leq \mathsf{E} \varlimsup \xi_n.$$

(c) *If* $|\xi_n| \leq \eta$ *for all* $n \geq 1$ *and* $\mathsf{E}\eta < \infty$, *then*

$$\mathsf{E} \varliminf \xi_n \leq \varliminf \mathsf{E}\xi_n \leq \varlimsup \mathsf{E}\xi_n \leq \mathsf{E} \varlimsup \xi_n. \tag{7}$$

PROOF. (a) Let $\zeta_n = \inf_{m \geq n} \xi_m$; then

$$\varliminf \xi_n = \lim_n \inf_{m \geq n} \xi_m = \lim_n \zeta_n.$$

It is clear that $\zeta_n \uparrow \varliminf \xi_n$ and $\zeta_n \geq \eta$ for all $n \geq 1$. Then by Theorem 1

$$\mathsf{E} \varliminf \xi_n = \mathsf{E} \lim_n \zeta_n = \lim_n \mathsf{E}\zeta_n = \varliminf_n \mathsf{E}\zeta_n \leq \varliminf_n \mathsf{E}\xi_n,$$

which establishes (a). The second conclusion follows from the first. The third is a corollary of the first two.

Theorem 3 (Lebesgue's Theorem on Dominated Convergence). *Let* $\eta, \xi,$ $\xi_1, \xi_2, \ldots$ *be random variables such that* $|\xi_n| \leq \eta$, $\mathsf{E}\eta < \infty$ *and* $\xi_n \to \xi$ *(a.s.).* *Then* $\mathsf{E}|\xi| < \infty$,

$$\mathsf{E}\xi_n \to \mathsf{E}\xi \tag{8}$$

and

$$\mathsf{E}|\xi_n - \xi| \to 0 \tag{9}$$

as $n \to \infty$.

PROOF. Formula (7) is valid by Fatou's lemma. By hypothesis, $\varliminf \xi_n = \varlimsup \xi_n = \xi$ (a.s.). Therefore by Property G,

$$\mathsf{E} \varliminf \xi_n = \varliminf \mathsf{E}\xi_n = \varlimsup \mathsf{E}\xi_n = \mathsf{E} \varlimsup \xi_n = \mathsf{E}\xi,$$

which establishes (8). It is also clear that $|\xi| \leq \eta$. Hence $\mathsf{E}|\xi| < \infty$.

Conclusion (9) can be proved in the same way if we observe that $|\xi_n - \xi| \leq 2\eta$.

Corollary. *Let* η, ξ, $\xi_1, \dots$ *be random variables such that* $|\xi_n| \le \eta$, $\xi_n \to \xi$ *(a.s.) and* $\mathsf{E}\eta^p < \infty$ *for some* $p > 0$. *Then* $\mathsf{E}|\xi|^p < \infty$ *and* $\mathsf{E}|\xi - \xi_n|^p \to 0$, $n \to \infty$.

For the proof, it is sufficient to observe that

$$|\xi| \le \eta, |\xi - \xi_n|^p \le (|\xi| + |\xi_n|)^p \le (2\eta)^p.$$

The condition "$|\xi_n| \le \eta$, $\mathsf{E}\eta < \infty$" that appears in Fatou's lemma and the dominated convergence theorem, and ensures the validity of formulas (7)–(9), can be somewhat weakened. In order to be able to state the corresponding result (Theorem 4), we introduce the following definition.

Definition 4. A family $\{\xi_n\}_{n \ge 1}$ of random variables is said to be *uniformly integrable* if

$$\sup_n \int_{\{|\xi_n| > c\}} |\xi_n| \mathsf{P}(d\omega) \to 0, \qquad c \to \infty, \tag{10}$$

or, in a different notation,

$$\sup_n \mathsf{E}[|\xi_n| I_{\{|\xi_n| > c\}}] \to 0, \qquad c \to \infty. \tag{11}$$

It is clear that if ξ_n, $n \ge 1$, satisfy $|\xi_n| \le \eta$, $\mathsf{E}\eta < \infty$, then the family $\{\xi_n\}_{n \ge 1}$ is uniformly integrable.

Theorem 4. *Let* $\{\xi_n\}_{n \ge 1}$ *be a uniformly integrable family of random variables. Then*

(a) $\mathsf{E} \varliminf \xi_n \le \varliminf \mathsf{E}\xi_n \le \varlimsup \mathsf{E}\xi_n \le \mathsf{E} \varlimsup \xi_n$.
(b) *If in addition* $\xi_n \to \xi$ *(a.s.) then* ξ *is integrable and*

$$\mathsf{E}\xi_n \to \mathsf{E}\xi, \qquad n \to \infty,$$

$$\mathsf{E}|\xi_n - \xi| \to 0, \qquad n \to \infty.$$

PROOF. (a) For every $c > 0$

$$\mathsf{E}\xi_n = \mathsf{E}[\xi_n I_{\{\xi_n < -c\}}] + \mathsf{E}[\xi_n I_{\{\xi_n \ge -c\}}]. \tag{12}$$

By uniform integrability, for every $\varepsilon > 0$ we can take c so large that

$$\sup_n |\mathsf{E}[\xi_n I_{\{\xi_n < -c\}}]| < \varepsilon. \tag{13}$$

By Fatou's lemma,

$$\varliminf \mathsf{E}[\xi_n I_{\{\xi_n \ge -c\}}] \ge \mathsf{E}[\varliminf \xi_n I_{\{\xi_n \ge -c\}}].$$

But $\xi_n I_{\{\xi_n \ge -c\}} \ge \xi_n$ and therefore

$$\varliminf \mathsf{E}[\xi_n I_{\{\xi_n \ge -c\}}] \ge \mathsf{E}[\varliminf \xi_n]. \tag{14}$$

From (12)–(14) we obtain

$$\underline{\lim} \, \mathsf{E}\xi_n \geq \mathsf{E}[\underline{\lim} \, \xi_n] - \varepsilon.$$

Since $\varepsilon > 0$ is arbitrary, it follows that $\underline{\lim} \, \mathsf{E}\xi_n \geq \mathsf{E} \, \underline{\lim} \, \xi_n$. The inequality with upper limits, $\overline{\lim} \, \mathsf{E}\xi_n \leq \mathsf{E} \, \overline{\lim} \, \xi_n$, is proved similarly.

Conclusion (b) can be deduced from (a) as in Theorem 3.

The deeper significance of the concept of uniform integrability is revealed by the following theorem, which gives a necessary and sufficient condition for taking limits under the expectation sign.

Theorem 5. *Let* $0 \leq \xi_n \to \xi$ *and* $\mathsf{E}\xi_n < \infty$. *Then* $\mathsf{E}\xi_n \to \mathsf{E}\xi < \infty$ *if and only if the family* $\{\xi_n\}_{n \geq 1}$ *is uniformly integrable.*

PROOF. The sufficiency follows from conclusion (b) of Theorem 4. For the proof of the necessity we consider the (at most countable) set

$$A = \{a \colon \mathsf{P}(\xi = a) > 0\}.$$

Then we have $\xi_n I_{\{\xi_n < a\}} \to \xi I_{\{\xi < a\}}$ for each $a \notin A$, and the family

$$\{\xi_n I_{\{\xi_n < a\}}\}_{n \geq 1}$$

is uniformly integrable. Hence, by the sufficiency part of the theorem, we have $\mathsf{E}\xi_n I_{\{\xi_n < a\}} \to \mathsf{E}\xi I_{\{\xi < a\}}$, $a \notin A$, and therefore

$$\mathsf{E}\xi_n I_{\{\xi_n \geq a\}} \to \mathsf{E}\xi I_{\{\xi \geq a\}}, \qquad a \notin A, \quad n \to \infty. \tag{15}$$

Take an $\varepsilon > 0$ and choose $a_0 \in A$ so large that $\mathsf{E}\xi I_{\{\xi \geq a_0\}} < \varepsilon/2$; then choose N_0 so large that

$$\mathsf{E}\xi_n I_{\{\xi_n \geq a_0\}} \leq \mathsf{E}\xi I_{\{\xi \geq a_0\}} + \varepsilon/2$$

for all $n \geq N_0$, and consequently $\mathsf{E}\xi_n I_{\{\xi_n \geq a_0\}} \leq \varepsilon$. Then choose $a_1 \geq a_0$ so large that $\mathsf{E}\xi_{\{\xi_n \geq a_1\}} \leq \varepsilon$ for all $n \leq N_0$. Then we have

$$\sup_n \mathsf{E}\xi_n I_{\{\xi_n \geq a_1\}} \leq \varepsilon,$$

which establishes the uniform integrability of the family $\{\xi_n\}_{n \geq 1}$ of random variables.

4. Let us notice some tests for uniform integrability.

We first observe that if $\{\xi_n\}$ is a family of uniformly integrable random variables, then

$$\sup_n \mathsf{E}|\xi_n| < \infty. \tag{16}$$

[handwritten annotation at top:] For every $\varepsilon > 0$, $\exists\, \delta(\varepsilon) > 0$ s.t. $\forall\, A \in \mathscr{F}$
$P(A) < \delta(\varepsilon) \Rightarrow \int_A |x_t|\, d\mathcal{P} < \varepsilon$ $\forall\, t \in T$

In fact, for a given $\varepsilon > 0$ and sufficiently large $c > 0$

$$\sup_n E\,|\xi_n| = \sup_n \left[E(|\xi_n| I_{\{|\xi_n| \geq c\}}) + E(|\xi_n| I_{\{|\xi_n| < c\}}) \right]$$

$$\leq \sup_n E(|\xi_n| I_{\{|\xi_n| \geq c\}}) + \sup_n E(|\xi_n| I_{(|\xi_n| < c)}) \leq \varepsilon + c,$$

which establishes (16).

It turns out that (16) together with a condition of uniform continuity is necessary and sufficient for uniform integrability.

Lemma 2. *A necessary and sufficient condition for a family* $\{\xi_n\}_{n \geq 1}$ *of random variables to be uniformly integrable is that* $E\,|\xi_n|, n \geq 1$, *are uniformly bounded (i.e., (16) holds) and that* $E\{|\xi_n| I_A\}, n \geq 1$, *are uniformly absolutely continuous (i.e.* $\sup E\{|\xi_n| I_A\} \to 0$ *when* $P(A) \to 0$).

PROOF. *Necessity.* Condition (16) was verified above. Moreover,

$$E\{|\xi_n| I_A\} = E\{|\xi_n| I_{A \cap \{|\xi_n| \geq c\}}\} + E\{|\xi_n| I_{A \cap \{|\xi_n| < c\}}\}$$
$$\leq E\{|\xi_n| I_{\{|\xi_n| \geq c\}}\} + cP(A). \tag{17}$$

Take c so large that $\sup_n E\{|\xi| I_{\{|\xi_n| \geq c\}}\} \leq \varepsilon/2$. Then if $P(A) \leq \varepsilon/2c$, we have

$$\sup_n E\{|\xi_n| I_A\} \leq \varepsilon$$

by (17). This establishes the uniform absolute continuity.

Sufficiency. Let $\varepsilon > 0$ and $\delta > 0$ be chosen so that $P(A) < \delta$ implies that $E(|\xi_n| I_A) \leq \varepsilon$, uniformly in n. Since

$$E\,|\xi_n| \geq E|\xi_n| I_{\{|\xi_n| \geq c\}} \geq cP\{|\xi_n| \geq c\}$$

for every $c > 0$ (cf. Chebyshev's inequality), we have

$$\sup_n P\{|\xi_n| \geq c\} \leq \frac{1}{c} \sup E\,|\xi_n| \to 0, \qquad c \to \infty,$$

and therefore, when c is sufficiently large, any set $\{|\xi_n| \geq c\}, n \geq 1$, can be taken as A. Therefore $\sup E(|\xi_n| I_{\{|\xi_n| \geq c\}}) \leq \varepsilon$, which establishes the uniform integrability. This completes the proof of the lemma.

The following proposition provides a simple sufficient condition for uniform integrability.

[handwritten annotation:] take $G(t) = t^{1+\Delta}$

Lemma 3. *Let* $\xi_1, \xi_2, \ldots$ *be a sequence of integrable random variables and* $G = G(t)$ *a nonnegative increasing function, defined for* $t \geq 0$, *such that*

$$\lim_{t \to \infty} \frac{G(t)}{t} = \infty. \tag{18}$$

$$\sup_n E[G(|\xi_n|)] < \infty. \tag{19}$$

Then the family $\{\xi_n\}_{n \geq 1}$ *is uniformly integrable.*

PROOF. Let $\varepsilon > 0$, $M = \sup_n \mathsf{E}[G(|\xi_n|)]$, $a = M/\varepsilon$. Take c so large that $G(t)/t \geq a$ for $t \geq c$. Then

$$\mathsf{E}[|\xi_n|I_{\{|\xi_n| \geq c\}}] \leq \frac{1}{a}\mathsf{E}[G(|\xi_n|) \cdot I_{\{|\xi_n| \geq c\}}] \leq \frac{M}{a} = \varepsilon$$

uniformly for $n \geq 1$.

5. If ξ and η are independent simple random variables, we can show, as in Subsection 5 of §4 of Chapter I, that $\mathsf{E}\xi\eta = \mathsf{E}\xi \cdot \mathsf{E}\eta$. Let us now establish a similar proposition in the general case (see also Problem 5).

Theorem 6. *Let ξ and η be independent random variables with $\mathsf{E}|\xi| < \infty$, $\mathsf{E}|\eta| < \infty$. Then $\mathsf{E}|\xi\eta| < \infty$ and*

$$\mathsf{E}\xi\eta = \mathsf{E}\xi \cdot \mathsf{E}\eta. \tag{20}$$

PROOF. First let $\xi \geq 0$, $\eta \geq 0$. Put

$$\xi_n = \sum_{k=0}^{\infty} \frac{k}{n} I_{\{k/n \leq \xi(\omega) < (k+1)/n\}},$$

$$\eta_n = \sum_{k=0}^{\infty} \frac{k}{n} I_{\{k/n \leq \eta(\omega) < (k+1)/n\}}.$$

Then $\xi_n \leq \xi$, $|\xi_n - \xi| \leq 1/n$ and $\eta_n \leq \eta$, $|\eta_n - \eta| \leq 1/n$. Since $\mathsf{E}\xi < \infty$ and $\mathsf{E}\eta < \infty$, it follows from Lebesgue's dominated convergence theorem that

$$\lim \mathsf{E}\xi_n = \mathsf{E}\xi, \qquad \lim \mathsf{E}\eta_n = \mathsf{E}\eta.$$

Moreover, since ξ and η are independent,

$$\mathsf{E}\xi_n\eta_n = \sum_{k,l \geq 0} \frac{kl}{n^2} \mathsf{E}I_{\{k/n \leq \xi < (k+1)/n\}} I_{\{l/n \leq \eta < (l+1)/n\}}$$

$$= \sum_{k,l \geq 0} \frac{kl}{n^2} \mathsf{E}I_{\{k/n \leq \xi < (k+1)/n\}} \cdot \mathsf{E}I_{\{l/n \leq \eta < (l+1)/n\}} = \mathsf{E}\xi_n \cdot \mathsf{E}\eta_n.$$

Now notice that

$$|\mathsf{E}\xi\eta - \mathsf{E}\xi_n\eta_n| \leq \mathsf{E}|\xi\eta - \xi_n\eta_n| \leq \mathsf{E}[|\xi| \cdot |\eta - \eta_n|]$$

$$+ \mathsf{E}[|\eta_n| \cdot |\xi - \xi_n|] \leq \frac{1}{n}\mathsf{E}\xi + \frac{1}{n}\mathsf{E}\left(\eta + \frac{1}{n}\right) \to 0, \quad n \to \infty.$$

Therefore $\mathsf{E}\xi\eta = \lim_n \mathsf{E}\xi_n\eta_n = \lim \mathsf{E}\xi_n \cdot \lim \mathsf{E}\eta_n = \mathsf{E}\xi \cdot \mathsf{E}\eta$, and $\mathsf{E}\xi\eta < \infty$.

The general case reduces to this one if we use the representations $\xi = \xi^+ - \xi^-$, $\eta = \eta^+ - \eta^-$, $\xi\eta = \xi^+\eta^+ - \xi^-\eta^+ - \xi^+\eta^- + \xi^-\eta^-$. This completes the proof.

6. The inequalities for expectations that we develop in this subsection are regularly used both in probability theory and in analysis.

Chebyshev's Inequality. *Let ξ be a nonnegative random variable. Then for every $\varepsilon > 0$*

$$P(\xi \geq \varepsilon) \leq \frac{E\xi}{\varepsilon}. \tag{21}$$

The proof follows immediately from

$$E\xi \geq E[\xi \cdot I_{(\xi > \varepsilon)}] \geq E I_{(\xi \geq \varepsilon)} = \varepsilon P(\xi \geq \varepsilon).$$

From (21) we can obtain the following variant of Chebyshev's inequality: If ξ is any random variable then

$$P(\xi \geq \varepsilon) \leq \frac{E\xi^2}{\varepsilon^2} \tag{22}$$

and

$$P(|\xi - E\xi| \geq \varepsilon) \leq \frac{V\xi^2}{\varepsilon^2}, \tag{23}$$

where $V\xi = E(\xi - E\xi)^2$ is the variance of ξ.

The Cauchy–Bunyakovskii Inequality. *Let ξ and η satisfy $E\xi^2 < \infty, E\eta^2 < \infty$. Then $E|\xi\eta| < \infty$ and*

$$(E|\xi\eta|)^2 \leq E\xi^2 \cdot E\eta^2. \tag{24}$$

PROOF. Suppose that $E\xi^2 > 0$, $E\eta^2 > 0$. Then, with $\tilde{\xi} = \xi/\sqrt{E\xi^2}$, $\tilde{\eta} = \eta/\sqrt{E\eta^2}$, we find, since $2|\tilde{\xi}\tilde{\eta}| \leq \tilde{\xi}^2 + \tilde{\eta}^2$, that

$$2E|\tilde{\xi}\tilde{\eta}| \leq E\tilde{\xi}^2 + E\tilde{\eta}^2 = 2,$$

i.e. $E|\tilde{\xi}\tilde{\eta}| \leq 1$, which establishes (24).

On the other hand if, say, $E\xi^2 \equiv 0$, then $\xi = 0$ (a.s.) by Property **I**, and then $E\xi\eta = 0$ by Property **F**, i.e. (24) is still satisfied.

Jensen's Inequality. *Let the Borel function $g = g(x)$ be convex downward and $E|\xi| < \infty$. Then*

$$g(E\xi) \leq Eg(\xi). \tag{25}$$

PROOF. If $g = g(x)$ is convex downward, for each $x_0 \in R$ there is a number $\lambda(x_0)$ such that

$$g(x) \geq g(x_0) + (x - x_0) \cdot \lambda(x_0) \tag{26}$$

for all $x \in R$. Putting $x = \xi$ and $x_0 = E\xi$, we find from (26) that

$$g(\xi) \geq g(E\xi) + (\xi - E\xi) \cdot \lambda(E\xi),$$

and consequently $Eg(\xi) \geq g(E\xi)$.

A whole series of useful inequalities can be derived from Jensen's inequality. We obtain the following one as an example.

Lyapunov's Inequality. *If $0 < s < t$,*

$$(E\,|\xi|^s)^{1/s} \le (E\,|\xi|^t)^{1/t}. \tag{27}$$

To prove this, let $r = t/s$. Then, putting $\eta = |\xi|^s$ and applying Jensen's inequality to $g(x) = |x|^r$, we obtain $|E\eta|^r \le E\,|\eta|^r$, i.e.

$$(E\,|\xi|^s)^{t/s} \le E\,|\xi|^t,$$

which establishes (27).

The following chain of inequalities among absolute moments in a consequence of Lyapunov's inequality:

$$E\,|\xi| \le (E\,|\xi|^2)^{1/2} \le \cdots \le (E\,|\xi|^n)^{1/n}. \tag{28}$$

Hölder's Inequality. *Let $1 < p < \infty$, $1 < q < \infty$, and $(1/p) + (1/q) = 1$. If $E\,|\xi|^p < \infty$ and $E\,|\eta|^q < \infty$, then $E\,|\xi\eta| < \infty$ and*

$$E\,|\xi\eta| \le (E\,|\xi|^p)^{1/p}(E\,|\eta|^q)^{1/q}. \tag{29}$$

If $E\,|\xi|^p = 0$ or $E\,|\eta|^q = 0$, (29) follows immediately as for the Cauchy–Bunyakovskii inequality (which is the special case $p = q = 2$ of Hölder's inequality).

Now let $E\,|\xi|^p > 0$, $E\,|\eta|^q > 0$ and

$$\tilde{\xi} = \frac{\xi}{(E\,|\xi|^p)^{1/p}}, \qquad \tilde{\eta} = \frac{\eta}{(E\,|\eta|^q)^{1/q}}.$$

We apply the inequality

$$x^a y^b \le ax + by, \tag{30}$$

which holds for positive x, y, a, b and $a + b = 1$, and follows immediately from the concavity of the logarithm:

$$\ln[ax + by] \ge a \ln x + b \ln y = \ln x^a y^b.$$

Then, putting $x = \tilde{\xi}^p$, $y = \tilde{\eta}^q$, $a = 1/p$, $b = 1/q$, we find that

$$\tilde{\xi}\tilde{\eta} \le \frac{1}{p}\tilde{\xi}^p + \frac{1}{q}\tilde{\eta}^q,$$

whence

$$E\tilde{\xi}\tilde{\eta} \le \frac{1}{p}E\tilde{\xi}^p + \frac{1}{q}E\tilde{\eta}^q = \frac{1}{p} + \frac{1}{q} = 1.$$

This establishes (29).

Minkowski's Inequality. *If* $\mathsf{E}|\xi|^p < \infty$, $\mathsf{E}|\eta|^p < \infty$, $1 \le p < \infty$, *then we have* $\mathsf{E}|\xi + \eta|^p < \infty$ *and*

$$(\mathsf{E}|\xi + \eta|^p)^{1/p} \le (\mathsf{E}|\xi|^p)^{1/p} + (\mathsf{E}|\eta|^p)^{1/p}. \tag{31}$$

We begin by establishing the following inequality: if $a, b > 0$ and $p \ge 1$, then

$$(a + b)^p \le 2^{p-1}(a^p + b^p). \tag{32}$$

In fact, consider the function $F(x) = (a + x)^p - 2^{p-1}(a^p + x^p)$. Then

$$F'(x) = p(a + x)^{p-1} - 2^{p-1}px^{p-1},$$

and since $p \ge 1$, we have $F'(a) = 0$, $F'(x) > 0$ for $x < a$ and $F'(x) < 0$ for $x > a$. Therefore

$$F(b) \le \max F(x) = F(a) = 0,$$

from which (32) follows.

According to this inequality,

$$|\xi + \eta|^p \le (|\xi| + |\eta|)^p \le 2^{p-1}(|\xi|^p + |\eta|^p) \tag{33}$$

and therefore if $\mathsf{E}|\xi|^p < \infty$ and $\mathsf{E}|\eta|^p < \infty$ it follows that $\mathsf{E}|\xi + \eta|^p < \infty$. If $p = 1$, inequality (31) follows from (33).

Now suppose that $p > 1$. Take $q > 1$ so that $(1/p) + (1/q) = 1$. Then

$$|\xi + \eta|^p = |\xi + \eta| \cdot |\xi + \eta|^{p-1} \le |\xi| \cdot |\xi + \eta|^{p-1} + |\eta||\xi + \eta|^{p-1}. \tag{34}$$

Notice that $(p - 1)q = p$. Consequently

$$\mathsf{E}(|\xi + \eta|^{p-1})^q = \mathsf{E}|\xi + \eta|^p < \infty,$$

and therefore by Hölder's inequality

$$\mathsf{E}(|\xi||\xi + \eta|^{p-1}) \le (\mathsf{E}|\xi|^p)^{1/p}(\mathsf{E}|\xi + \eta|^{(p-1)q})^{1/q}$$
$$= (\mathsf{E}|\xi|^p)^{1/p}(\mathsf{E}|\xi + \eta|^p)^{1/q} < \infty.$$

In the same way,

$$\mathsf{E}(|\eta||\xi + \eta|^{p-1}) \le (\mathsf{E}|\eta|^p)^{1/p}(\mathsf{E}|\xi + \eta|^p)^{1/q}.$$

Consequently, by (34),

$$\mathsf{E}|\xi + \eta|^p \le (\mathsf{E}|\xi + \eta|^p)^{1/q}((\mathsf{E}|\xi|^p)^{1/p} + (\mathsf{E}|\eta|^p)^{1/p}). \tag{35}$$

If $\mathsf{E}|\xi + \eta|^p = 0$, the desired inequality (31) is evident. Now let $\mathsf{E}|\xi + \eta|^p > 0$. Then we obtain

$$(\mathsf{E}|\xi + \eta|^p)^{1-(1/q)} \le (\mathsf{E}|\xi|^p)^{1/p} + (\mathsf{E}|\eta|^p)^{1/p}$$

from (35), and (31) follows since $1 - (1/q) = 1/p$.

7. Let ξ be a random variable for which $E\xi$ is defined. Then, by Property **D**, the set function

$$Q(A) \equiv \int_A \xi \, dP, \qquad A \in \mathcal{F}, \tag{36}$$

is well defined. Let us show that this function is countably additive.

First suppose that ξ is nonnegative. If $A_1, A_2, \ldots$ are pairwise disjoint sets from $\mathcal{F}$ and $A = \sum A_n$, the corollary to Theorem 1 implies that

$$Q(A) = E(\xi \cdot I_A) = E(\xi \cdot I_{\sum A_n}) = E(\sum \xi \cdot I_{A_n})$$
$$= \sum E(\xi \cdot I_{A_n}) = \sum Q(A_n).$$

If ξ is an arbitrary random variable for which $E\xi$ is defined, the countable additivity of $Q(A)$ follows from the representation

$$Q(A) = Q^+(A) - Q^-(A), \tag{37}$$

where

$$Q^+(A) = \int_A \xi^+ \, dP, \qquad Q^-(A) = \int_A \xi^- \, dP,$$

together with the countable additivity for nonnegative random variables and the fact that $\min(Q^+(\Omega), Q^-(\Omega)) < \infty$.

Thus if $E\xi$ is defined, the set function $Q = Q(A)$ is a signed measure— a countably additive set function representable as $Q = Q_1 - Q_2$, where at least one of the measures Q_1 and Q_2 is finite.

We now show that $Q = Q(A)$ has the following important property of _absolute continuity_ with respect to P:

$$\text{if} \quad P(A) = 0 \quad \text{then} \quad Q(A) = 0 \quad (A \in \mathcal{F})$$

(this property is denoted by the abbreviation $Q \ll P$).

To prove the sufficiency we consider nonnegative random variables. If $\xi = \sum_{k=1}^n x_k I_{A_k}$ is a simple nonnegative random variable and $P(A) = 0$, then

$$Q(A) = E(\xi \cdot I_A) = \sum_{k=1}^n x_k P(A_k \cap A) = 0.$$

If $\{\xi_n\}_{n \geq 1}$ is a sequence of nonnegative simple functions such that $\xi_n \uparrow \xi \geq 0$, then the theorem on monotone convergence shows that

$$Q(A) = E(\xi \cdot I_A) = \lim E(\xi_n \cdot I_A) = 0,$$

since $E(\xi_n \cdot I_A) = 0$ for all $n \geq 1$ and A with $P(A) = 0$.

Thus the Lebesgue integral $Q(A) = \int_A \xi \, dP$, considered as a function of sets $A \in \mathcal{F}$, is a signed measure that is absolutely continuous with respect to P $(Q \ll P)$. It is quite remarkable that the converse is also valid.

Radon–Nikodým Theorem. *Let $(\Omega, \mathscr{F})$ be a measurable space, μ a σ-finite measure, and λ a signed measure (i.e., $\lambda = \lambda_1 - \lambda_2$, where at least one of the measures λ_1 and λ_2 is finite) which is absolutely continuous with respect to μ. Then there is an $\mathscr{F}$-measurable function $f = f(\omega)$ with values in $\bar{R} = [-\infty, \infty]$ such that*

$$\lambda(A) = \int_A f(\omega)\mu(d\omega), \qquad A \in \mathscr{F}. \tag{38}$$

The function $f(\omega)$ is unique up to sets of μ-measure zero: if $h = h(\omega)$ is another $\mathscr{F}$-measurable function such that $\lambda(A) = \int_A h(\omega)\mu(d\omega)$, $A \in \mathscr{F}$, then $\mu\{\omega: f(\omega) \neq h(\omega)\} = 0$.

If λ is a measure, then $f = f(\omega)$ has its values in $\bar{R}^+ = [0, \infty]$.

Remark. The function $f = f(\omega)$ in the representation (38) is called the *Radon–Nikodým derivative* or the *density* of the measure λ with respect to μ, and denoted by $d\lambda/d\mu$ or $(d\lambda/d\mu)(\omega)$.

The Radon–Nikodým theorem, which we quote without proof, will play a key role in the construction of conditional expectations (§7).

8. If $\xi = \sum_{i=1}^n x_i I_{A_i}$ is a simple random variable,

$$\mathsf{E}g(\xi) = \sum g(x_i)\mathsf{P}(A_i) = \sum g(x_i)\Delta F_\xi(x_i). \tag{39}$$

In other words, in order to calculate the expectation of a function of the (simple) random variable ξ it is unnecessary to know the probability measure P completely; it is enough to know the probability distribution P_ξ or, equivalently, the distribution function F_ξ of ξ.

The following important theorem generalizes this property.

Theorem 7 (Change of Variables in a Lebesgue Integral). *Let $(\Omega, \mathscr{F})$ and $(E, \mathscr{E})$ be measurable spaces and $X = X(\omega)$ an $\mathscr{F}/\mathscr{E}$-measurable function with values in E. Let P be a probability measure on $(\Omega, \mathscr{F})$ and P_X the probability measure on $(E, \mathscr{E})$ induced by $X = X(\omega)$:*

$$P_X(A) = \mathsf{P}\{\omega: X(\omega) \in A\}, \qquad A \in \mathscr{E}. \tag{40}$$

Then

$$\int_A g(x)P_X(dx) = \int_{X^{-1}(A)} g(X(\omega))\mathsf{P}(d\omega), \qquad A \in \mathscr{E}, \tag{41}$$

for every $\mathscr{E}$-measurable function $g = g(x)$, $x \in E$ (in the sense that if one integral exists, the other is well defined, and the two are equal).

Proof. Let $A \in \mathscr{E}$ and $g(x) = I_B(x)$, where $B \in \mathscr{E}$. Then (41) becomes

$$P_X(AB) = \mathsf{P}(X^{-1}(A) \cap X^{-1}(B)), \tag{42}$$

which follows from (40) and the observation that $X^{-1}(A) \cap X^{-1}(B) = X^{-1}(A \cap B)$.

It follows from (42) that (41) is valid for nonnegative simple functions $g = g(x)$, and therefore, by the monotone convergence theorem, also for all nonnegative $\mathscr{E}$-measurable functions.

In the general case we need only represent g as $g^+ - g^-$. Then, since (41) is valid for g^+ and g^-, if (for example) $\int_A g^+(x)P_X(dx) < \infty$, we have

$$\int_{X^{-1}(A)} g^+(X(\omega))P(d\omega) < \infty$$

also, and therefore the existence of $\int_A g(x)P_X(dx)$ implies the existence of $\int_{X^{-1}(A)} g(X(\omega))P(d\omega)$.

Corollary. *Let* $(E, \mathscr{E}) = (R, \mathscr{B}(R))$ *and let* $\xi = \xi(\omega)$ *be a random variable with probability distribution* P_ξ. *Then if* $g = g(x)$ *is a Borel function and either of the integrals* $\int_A g(x)P_\xi(dx)$ *or* $\int_{\xi^{-1}(A)} g(\xi(\omega))P(d\omega)$ *exists, we have*

$$\int_A g(x)P_\xi(dx) = \int_{\xi^{-1}(A)} g(\xi(\omega))P(d\omega).$$

In particular, for $A = R$ we obtain

$$\mathsf{E}g(\xi(\omega)) = \int_\Omega g(\xi(\omega))P(d\omega) = \int_R g(x)P_\xi(dx). \tag{43}$$

The measure P_ξ can be uniquely reconstructed from the distribution function F_ξ (Theorem 1 of §3). Hence the Lebesgue integral $\int_R g(x)P_\xi(dx)$ is often denoted by $\int_R g(x)F_\xi(dx)$ and called a *Lebesgue–Stieltjes integral* (with respect to the measure corresponding to the distribution function $F_\xi(x)$).

Let us consider the case when $F_\xi(x)$ has a density $f_\xi(x)$, i.e. let

$$F_\xi(x) = \int_{-\infty}^x f_\xi(y)\, dy, \tag{44}$$

where $f_\xi = f_\xi(x)$ is a nonnegative Borel function and the integral is a Lebesgue integral with respect to Lebesgue measure on the set $(-\infty, x]$ (see Remark 2 in Subsection 1). With the assumption of (44), formula (43) takes the form

$$\mathsf{E}g(\xi(\omega)) = \int_{-\infty}^\infty g(x)f_\xi(x)\, dx, \tag{45}$$

where the integral is the Lebesgue integral of the function $g(x)f_\xi(x)$ with respect to Lebesgue measure. In fact, if $g(x) = I_B(x)$, $B \in \mathscr{B}(R)$, the formula becomes

$$P_\xi(B) = \int_B f_\xi(x)\, dx, \qquad B \in \mathscr{B}(R); \tag{46}$$

its correctness follows from Theorem 1 of §3 and the formula

$$F_\xi(b) - F_\xi(a) = \int_a^b f_\xi(x)\, dx.$$

In the general case, the proof is the same as for Theorem 7.

9. Let us consider the special case of measurable spaces $(\Omega, \mathscr{F})$ with a measure μ, where $\Omega = \Omega_1 \times \Omega_2$, $\mathscr{F} = \mathscr{F}_1 \otimes \mathscr{F}_2$, and $\mu = \mu_1 \times \mu_2$ is the direct product of measures μ_1 and μ_2 (i.e., the measure on $\mathscr{F}$ such that

$$\mu_1 \times \mu_2(A \times B) = \mu_1(A_1)\mu_2(B), \qquad A \in \mathscr{F}_1, \quad B \in \mathscr{F}_2;$$

the existence of this measure follows from the proof of Theorem 8).

The following theorem plays the same role as the theorem on the reduction of a double Riemann integral to an iterated integral.

Theorem 8 (Fubini's Theorem). *Let $\xi = \xi(\omega_1, \omega_2)$ be an $\mathscr{F}_1 \otimes \mathscr{F}_2$-measurable function, integrable with respect to the measure $\mu_1 \times \mu_2$:*

$$\int_{\Omega_1 \times \Omega_2} |\xi(\omega_1, \omega_2)|\, d(\mu_1 \times \mu_2) < \infty. \qquad (47)$$

Then the integrals $\int_{\Omega_1} \xi(\omega_1, \omega_2)\mu_1(d\omega_1)$ and $\int_{\Omega_2} \xi(\omega_1, \omega_2)\mu_2(d\omega_2)$

(1) *are defined for all ω_1 and ω_2;*
(2) *are respectively $\mathscr{F}_2$- and $\mathscr{F}_1$-measurable functions with*

$$\mu_2\left\{ \omega_2 : \int_{\Omega_1} |\xi(\omega_1, \omega_2)|\mu_1(d\omega_1) = \infty \right\} = 0,$$

$$\mu_1\left\{ \omega_1 : \int_{\Omega_2} |\xi(\omega_1, \omega_2)|\mu_2(d\omega_2) = \infty \right\} = 0 \qquad (48)$$

and (3)

$$\int_{\Omega_1 \times \Omega_2} \xi(\omega_1, \omega_2)\, d(\mu_1 \times \mu_2) = \int_{\Omega_1}\left[\int_{\Omega_2} \xi(\omega_1, \omega_2)\mu_2(d\omega_2) \right]\mu_1(d\omega_1)$$

$$= \int_{\Omega_2}\left[\int_{\Omega_1} \xi(\omega_1, \omega_2)\mu_1(d\omega_1) \right]\mu_2(d\omega_2). \qquad (49)$$

PROOF. We first show that $\xi_{\omega_1}(\omega_2) = \xi(\omega_1, \omega_2)$ is $\mathscr{F}_2$-measurable with respect to ω_2, for each $\omega_1 \in \Omega_1$.

Let $F \in \mathscr{F}_1 \otimes \mathscr{F}_2$ and $\xi(\omega_1, \omega_2) = I_F(\omega_1, \omega_2)$. Let

$$F_{\omega_1} = \{\omega_2 \in \Omega_2 : (\omega_1, \omega_2) \in \mathscr{F}\}$$

be the *cross-section* of F at ω_1, and let $\mathscr{C}_{\omega_1} = \{F \in \mathscr{F}: F_{\omega_1} \in F_2\}$. We must show that $\mathscr{C}_{\omega_1} = \mathscr{F}$ for every ω_1.

If $F = A \times B$, $A \in \mathscr{F}_1$, $B \in \mathscr{F}_2$, then

$$(A \times B)_{\omega_1} = \begin{cases} B & \text{if } \omega_1 \in A, \\ \varnothing & \text{if } \omega_1 \notin A. \end{cases}$$

Hence rectangles with measurable sides belong to $\mathscr{C}_{\omega_1}$. In addition, if $F \in \mathscr{F}$, then $(\bar{F})_{\omega_1} = \overline{F_{\omega_1}}$, and if $\{F^n\}_{n \geq 1}$ are sets in $\mathscr{F}$, then $(\bigcup F^n)_{\omega_1} = \bigcup F^n_{\omega_1}$. It follows that $\mathscr{C}_{\omega_1} = \mathscr{F}$.

Now let $\xi(\omega_1, \omega_2) \geq 0$. Then, since the function $\xi(\omega_1, \omega_2)$ is $\mathscr{F}_2$-measurable for each ω_1, the integral $\int_{\Omega_2} \xi(\omega_1, \omega_2)\mu_2(d\omega_2)$ is defined. Let us show that this integral is an $\mathscr{F}_1$-measurable function and

$$\int_{\Omega_1}\left[\int_{\Omega_2} \xi(\omega_1, \omega_2)\mu_2(d\omega_2)\right]\mu_1(d\omega_1) = \int_{\Omega_1 \times \Omega_2} \xi(\omega_1, \omega_2)\, d(\mu_1 \times \mu_2). \quad (50)$$

Let us suppose that $\xi(\omega_1, \omega_2) = I_{A \times B}(\omega_1, \omega_2)$, $A \in \mathscr{F}_1$, $B \in \mathscr{F}_2$. Then since $I_{A \times B}(\omega_1, \omega_2) = I_A(\omega_1)I_B(\omega_2)$, we have

$$\int_{\Omega_2} I_{A \times B}(\omega_1, \omega_2)\mu_2(d\omega_2) = I_A(\omega_1)\int_{\Omega_2} I_B(\omega_2)\mu_2(d\omega_2) \quad (51)$$

and consequently the integral on the left of (51) is an $\mathscr{F}_1$-measurable function.

Now let $\xi(\omega_1, \omega_2) = I_F(\omega_1, \omega_2)$, $F \in \mathscr{F} = \mathscr{F}_1 \otimes \mathscr{F}_2$. Let us show that the integral $f(\omega_1) = \int_{\Omega_2} I_F(\omega_1, \omega_2)\mu_2(d\omega_2)$ is $\mathscr{F}$-measurable. For this purpose we put $\mathscr{C} = \{F \in \mathscr{F}: f(\omega_1) \text{ is } \mathscr{F}_1\text{-measurable}\}$. According to what has been proved, the set $A \times B$ belongs to $\mathscr{C}$ ($A \in \mathscr{F}_1$, $B \in \mathscr{F}_2$) and therefore the algebra $\mathscr{A}$ consisting of finite sums of disjoint sets of this form also belongs to $\mathscr{C}$. It follows from the monotone convergence theorem that $\mathscr{C}$ is a monotonic class, $\mathscr{C} = \mu(\mathscr{C})$. Therefore, because of the inclusions $\mathscr{A} \subseteq \mathscr{C} \subseteq \mathscr{F}$ and Theorem 1 of §2, we have $\mathscr{F} = \sigma(\mathscr{A}) = \mu(\mathscr{A}) \subseteq \mu(\mathscr{C}) = \mathscr{C} \subseteq \mathscr{F}$, i.e. $\mathscr{C} = \mathscr{F}$.

Finally, if $\xi(\omega_1, \omega_2)$ is an arbitrary nonnegative $\mathscr{F}$-measurable function, the $\mathscr{F}_1$-measurability of the integral $\int_{\Omega_2} \xi(\omega_1, \omega_2)\mu_2(d\omega)$ follows from the monotone convergence theorem and Theorem 2 of §4.

Let us now show that the measure $\mu = \mu_1 \times \mu_2$ defined on $\mathscr{F} = \mathscr{F}_2 \otimes \mathscr{F}_2$, with the property $(\mu_1 \times \mu_2)(A \times B) = \mu_1(A) \cdot \mu_2(B)$, $A \in \mathscr{F}_1$, $B \in \mathscr{F}_2$, actually exists and is unique.

For $F \in \mathscr{F}$ we put

$$\mu(F) = \int_{\Omega_1}\left[\int_{\Omega_2} I_{F_{\omega_1}}(\omega_2)\mu_2(d\omega_2)\right]\mu_1(d\omega_1).$$

As we have shown, the inner integral is an $\mathscr{F}_1$-measurable function, and consequently the set function $\mu(F)$ is actually defined for $F \in \mathscr{F}$. It is clear that if $F = A \times B$, then $\mu(A \times B) = \mu_1(A)\mu_2(B)$. Now let $\{F^n\}$ be disjoint sets from $\mathscr{F}$. Then

$$\mu(\textstyle\sum F^n) = \int_{\Omega_1}\left[\int_{\Omega_2} I_{(\sum F^n)_{\omega_1}}(\omega_2)\mu_2(d\omega_2)\right]\mu_1(d\omega_1)$$

$$= \int_{\Omega_1}\sum_n\left[\int_{\Omega_2} I_{F^n_{\omega_1}}(\omega_2)\mu_2(d\omega_2)\right]\mu_1(d\omega_1)$$

$$= \sum_n\int_{\Omega_1}\left[\int_{\Omega_2} I_{F^n_{\omega_1}}(\omega_2)\mu_2(d\omega_2)\right]\mu_1(d\omega_1) = \sum_n \mu(F^n),$$

i.e. μ is a (σ-finite) measure on $\mathscr{F}$.

It follows from Carathéodory's theorem that this measure μ is the unique measure with the property that $\mu(A \times B) = \mu_1(A)\mu_2(B)$.

We can now establish (50). If $\xi(\omega_1, \omega_2) = I_{A \times B}(\omega_1, \omega_2)$, $A \in \mathscr{F}_1$, $B \in \mathscr{F}_2$, then

$$\int_{\Omega_1 \times \Omega_2} I_{A \times B}(\omega_1, \omega_2)d(\mu_1 \times \mu_2) = (\mu_1 \times \mu_2)(A \times B), \qquad (52)$$

and since $I_{A \times B}(\omega_1, \omega_2) = I_A(\omega_1)I_B(\omega_2)$, we have

$$\int_{\Omega_1}\left[\int_{\Omega_2} I_{A \times B}(\omega_1, \omega_2)\mu_2(d\omega_2)\right]\mu_1(d\omega_1)$$

$$= \int_{\Omega_1}\left[I_A(\omega_1)\int_{\Omega_2} I_B(\omega_1, \omega_2)\mu_2(d\omega_2)\right]\mu_1(d\omega_1) = \mu_1(A)\mu_2(B). \qquad (53)$$

But, by the definition of $\mu_1 \times \mu_2$,

$$(\mu_1 \times \mu_2)(A \times B) = \mu_1(A)\mu_2(B).$$

Hence it follows from (52) and (53) that (50) is valid for $\xi(\omega_1, \omega_2) = I_{A \times B}(\omega_1, \omega_2)$.

Now let $\xi(\omega_1, \omega_2) = I_F(\omega_1, \omega_2)$, $F \in \mathscr{F}$. The set function

$$\lambda(F) = \int_{\Omega_2 \times \Omega_2} I_F(\omega_1, \omega_2)d(\mu_1 \times \mu_2), \qquad F \in \mathscr{F},$$

is evidently a σ-finite measure. It is also easily verified that the set function

$$\nu(F) = \int_{\Omega_1}\left[\int_{\Omega_2} I_F(\omega_1, \omega_2)\mu_2(d\omega_2)\right]\mu_1(d\omega_1)$$

is a σ-finite measure. It will be shown below that λ and ν coincide on sets of the form $F = A \times B$, and therefore on the algebra $\mathscr{F}$. Hence it follows by Carathéodory's theorem that λ and ν coincide for all $F \in \mathscr{F}$.

We turn now to the proof of the full conclusion of Fubini's theorem. By (47),

$$\int_{\Omega_1 \times \Omega_2} \xi^+(\omega_1, \omega_2)\, d(\mu_1 \times \mu_2) < \infty, \qquad \int_{\Omega_1 \times \Omega_2} \xi^-(\omega_1, \omega_2) d(\mu_1 \times \mu_2) < \infty.$$

By what has already been proved, the integral $\int_{\Omega_2} \xi^+(\omega_1, \omega_2)\mu_2(d\omega_2)$ is an $\mathscr{F}_1$-measurable function of ω_1 and

$$\int_{\Omega_1}\left[\int_{\Omega_2} \xi^+(\omega_1, \omega_2)\mu_2(d\omega_2)\right]\mu_1(d\omega_1) = \int_{\Omega_1 \times \Omega_2} \xi^+(\omega_1, \omega_2)\, d(\mu_1 \times \mu_2) < \infty.$$

Consequently by Problem 4 (see also Property **J** in Subsection 2)

$$\int_{\Omega_2} \xi^+(\omega_1, \omega_2)\mu_2(d\omega_2) < \infty \quad (\mu_1\text{-a.s.}).$$

In the same way

$$\int_{\Omega_2} \xi^-(\omega_1, \omega_2)\mu_1(d\omega_1) < \infty \quad (\mu_1\text{-a.s.}),$$

and therefore

$$\int_{\Omega_2} |\xi(\omega_1, \omega_2)|\mu_2(d\omega_2) < \infty \quad (\mu_1\text{-a.s.}).$$

It is clear that, except on a set $\mathscr{N}$ of μ_1-measure zero,

$$\int_{\Omega_2} \xi(\omega_1, \omega_2)\mu_2(d\omega_2) = \int_{\Omega_2} \xi^+(\omega_1, \omega_2)\mu_2(d\omega_2) - \int_{\Omega_2} \xi^-(\omega_1, \omega_2)\mu_2(d\omega_2).$$

$$(54)$$

Taking the integrals to be zero for $\omega_1 \in \mathscr{N}$, we may suppose that (54) holds for all $\omega \in \Omega_1$. Then, integrating (54) with respect to μ_1 and using (50), we obtain

$$\int_{\Omega_1}\left[\int_{\Omega_2} \xi(\omega_1, \omega_2)\mu_2(d\omega_2)\right]\mu_1(d\omega_1) = \int_{\Omega_1}\left[\int_{\Omega_2} \xi^+(\omega_1, \omega_2)\mu_2(d\omega_2)\right]\mu_1(d\omega_1)$$

$$- \int_{\Omega_1}\left[\int_{\Omega_2} \xi^-(\omega_1, \omega_2)\mu_2(d\omega_2)\right]\mu_1(d\omega_1)$$

$$= \int_{\Omega_1 \times \Omega_2} \xi^+(\omega_1, \omega_2)d(\mu_1 \times \mu_2)$$

$$- \int_{\Omega_1 \times \Omega_2} \xi^-(\omega_1, \omega_2)\, d(\mu_1 \times \mu_2)$$

$$= \int_{\Omega_1 \times \Omega_2} \xi(\omega_1, \omega_2)d(\mu_1 \times \mu_2).$$

Similarly we can establish the first equation in (48) and the equation

$$\int_{\Omega_1 \times \Omega_2} \xi(\omega_1, \omega_2)\, d(\mu_1 \times \mu_2) = \int_{\Omega_2}\left[\int_{\Omega_1} \xi(\omega_1, \omega_2)\mu_1(d\omega_1)\right]\mu_2(d\omega_2).$$

This completes the proof of the theorem.

Corollary. *If* $\int_{\Omega_1} [\int_{\Omega_2} |\xi(\omega_1, \omega_2)|\mu_2(d\omega_2)]\mu_1\,(d\omega_1) < \infty$, *the conclusion of Fubini's theorem is still valid.*

In fact, under this hypothesis (47) follows from (50), and consequently the conclusions of Fubini's theorem hold.

EXAMPLE. Let (ξ, η) be a pair of random variables whose distribution has a two-dimensional density $f_{\xi\eta}(x, y)$, i.e.

$$P((\xi, \eta) \in B) = \int_B f_{\xi\eta}(x, y)\, dx\, dy, \qquad B \in \mathscr{B}(R^2),$$

where $f_{\xi\eta}(x, y)$ is a nonnegative $\mathscr{B}(R^2)$-measurable function, and the integral is a Lebesgue integral with respect to two-dimensional Lebesgue measure.

Let us show that the one-dimensional distributions for ξ and η have densities $f_\xi(x)$ and $f_\eta(y)$, and furthermore

$$f_\xi(x) = \int_{-\infty}^{\infty} f_{\xi\eta}(x, y)\, dy$$

and (55)

$$f_\eta(y) = \int_{-\infty}^{\infty} f_{\xi\eta}(x, y)\, dx.$$

In fact, if $A \in \mathscr{B}(R)$, then by Fubini's theorem

$$P(\xi \in A) = P((\xi, \eta) \in A \times R) = \int_{A \times R} f_{\xi\eta}(x, y)\, dx\, dy = \int_A\left[\int_R f_{\xi\eta}(x, y)\, dy\right]dx.$$

This establishes both the existence of a density for the probability distribution of ξ and the first formula in (55). The second formula is established similarly.

According to the theorem in §5, a necessary and sufficient condition that ξ and η are independent is that

$$F_{\xi\eta}(x, y) = F_\xi(x)F_\eta(y), \qquad (x, y) \in R^2.$$

Let us show that when there is a two-dimensional density $f_{\xi\eta}(x, y)$, the variables ξ and η are independent if and only if

$$f_{\xi\eta}(x, y) = f_\xi(x) f_\eta(y) \tag{56}$$

(where the equation is to be understood in the sense of holding almost surely with respect to two-dimensional Lebesgue measure).

In fact, in (56) holds, then by Fubini's theorem

$$F_{\xi\eta}(x, y) = \int_{(-\infty, x] \times (-\infty, y]} f_{\xi\eta}(x, y) \, dx \, dy = \int_{(-\infty, x] \times (-\infty, y]} f_\xi(x) f_\eta(y) \, dx \, dy$$

$$= \int_{(-\infty, x]} f_\xi(x) \, dx \left(\int_{(-\infty, y]} f_\eta(y) \, dy \right) = F_\xi(x) F_\eta(y)$$

and consequently ξ and η are independent.

Conversely, if they are independent and have a density $f_{\xi\eta}(x, y)$, then again by Fubini's theorem

$$\int_{(-\infty, x] \times (-\infty, y]} f_{\xi\eta}(x, y) \, dx \, dy = \left(\int_{(-\infty, x]} f_\xi(x) \, dx \right) \left(\int_{(-\infty, y]} f_\eta(y) \, dy \right)$$

$$= \int_{(-\infty, x] \times (-\infty, y]} f_\xi(x) f_\eta(y) \, dx \, dy.$$

It follows that

$$\int_B f_{\xi\eta}(x, y) \, dx \, dy = \int_B f_\xi(x) f_\eta(y) \, dx \, dy$$

for every $B \in \mathscr{B}(R^2)$, and it is easily deduced from Property I that (56) holds.

10. In this subsection we discuss the relation between the Lebesgue and Riemann integrals.

We first observe that the construction of the Lebesgue integral is independent of the measurable space $(\Omega, \mathscr{F})$ on which the integrands are given. On the other hand, the Riemann integral is not defined on abstract spaces in general, and for $\Omega = R^n$ it is defined sequentially: first for R^1, and then extended, with corresponding changes, to the case $n > 1$.

We emphasize that the constructions of the Riemann and Lebesgue integrals are based on different ideas. The first step in the construction of the Riemann integral is to group the points $x \in R^1$ according to their distances along the x axis. On the other hand, in Lebesgue's construction (for $\Omega = R^1$) the points $x \in R^1$ are grouped according to a different principle: by the distances between the values of the integrand. It is a consequence of these different approaches that the Riemann approximating sums have limits only for "mildly" discontinuous functions, whereas the Lebesgue sums converge to limits for a much wider class of functions.

Let us recall the definition of the Riemann–Stieltjes integral. Let $G = G(x)$ be a generalized distribution function on R (see subsection 2 of §3) and μ its corresponding Lebesgue–Stieltjes measure, and let $g = g(x)$ be a bounded function that vanishes outside $[a, b]$.

Consider a decomposition $\mathscr{P} = \{x_0, \ldots, x_n\}$,

$$a = x_0 < x_1 < \cdots < x_n = b,$$

of $[a, b]$, and form the upper and lower sums

$$\overline{\sum_{\mathscr{P}}} = \sum_{i=1}^{n} \bar{g}_i [G(x_{i+1}) - G(x_i)], \qquad \underline{\sum_{\mathscr{P}}} = \sum_{i=1}^{n} \underline{g}_i [G(x_{i+1}) - G(x_i)]$$

where

$$\bar{g}_i = \sup_{x_{i-1} < y \le x_i} g(y), \qquad \underline{g}_i = \inf_{x_{i-1} < y \le x_i} g(y).$$

Define simple functions $\bar{g}_{\mathscr{P}}(x)$ and $\underline{g}_{\mathscr{P}}(x)$ by taking

$$\bar{g}_{\mathscr{P}}(x) = \bar{g}_i, \qquad \underline{g}_{\mathscr{P}}(x) = \underline{g}_i,$$

on $x_{i-1} < x \le x_i$, and define $\bar{g}_{\mathscr{P}}(a) = \underline{g}_{\mathscr{P}}(a) = g(a)$. It is clear that then

$$\overline{\sum_{\mathscr{P}}} = (\text{L-S}) \int_a^b \bar{g}_{\mathscr{P}}(x) G(dx)$$

and

$$\underline{\sum_{\mathscr{P}}} = (\text{L-S}) \int_a^b \underline{g}_{\mathscr{P}}(x) G(dx).$$

Now let $\{\mathscr{P}_k\}$ be a sequence of decompositions such that $\mathscr{P}_k \subseteq \mathscr{P}_{k+1}$. Then

$$\bar{g}_{\mathscr{P}_1} \ge \bar{g}_{\mathscr{P}_2} \ge \cdots \ge g \ge \cdots \ge \underline{g}_{\mathscr{P}_2} \ge \underline{g}_{\mathscr{P}_1},$$

and if $|g(x)| \le C$ we have, by the dominated convergence theorem,

$$\lim_{k \to \infty} \overline{\sum_{\mathscr{P}_k}} = (\text{L-S}) \int_a^b \bar{g}(x) G(dx),$$

$$\lim_{k \to \infty} \underline{\sum_{\mathscr{P}_k}} = (\text{L-S}) \int_a^b \underline{g}(x) G(dx),$$

(57)

where $\bar{g}(x) = \lim_k \bar{g}_{\mathscr{P}_k}(x)$, $\underline{g}(x) = \lim_k \underline{g}_{\mathscr{P}_k}(x)$.

If the limits $\lim_k \overline{\sum_{\mathscr{P}_k}}$ and $\lim_k \underline{\sum_{\mathscr{P}_k}}$ are *finite and equal, and their common value is independent of the sequence of decompositions* $\{\mathscr{P}_k\}$, we say that $g = g(x)$ is *Riemann–Stieltjes integrable*, and the common value of the limits is denoted by

$$(\text{R-S}) \int_a^b g(x) G(dx). \qquad (58)$$

When $G(x) = x$, the integral is called a Riemann integral and denoted by

$$(\text{R}) \int_a^b g(x) \, dx.$$

Now let (L-S) $\int_a^b g(x)G(dx)$ be the corresponding Lebesgue–Stieltjes integral (see Remark 2 in Subsection 2).

Theorem 9. *If $g = g(x)$ is continuous on $[a, b]$, it is Riemann–Stieltjes integrable and*

$$\text{(R-S)} \int_a^b g(x)G(dx) = \text{(L-S)} \int_a^b g(x)G(dx). \tag{59}$$

PROOF. Since $g(x)$ is continuous, we have $\bar{g}(x) = g(x) = \underline{g}(x)$. Hence by (57) $\lim_{k\to\infty} \overline{\sum}_{\mathscr{P}_k} = \lim_{k\to\infty} \underline{\sum}_{\mathscr{P}_k}$. Consequently $g = g(x)$ is Riemann–Stieltjes integral (again by (57)).

Let us consider in more detail the question of the correspondence between the Riemann and Lebesgue integrals for the case of Lebesgue measure on the line R.

Theorem 10. *Let $g(x)$ be a bounded function on $[a, b]$.*

(a) *The function $g = g(x)$ is Riemann integrable on $[a, b]$ if and only if it is continuous almost everywhere (with respect to Lebesgue measure λ on $\overline{\mathscr{B}}([a, b])$).*

(b) *If $g = g(x)$ is Riemann integrable, it is Lebesgue integrable and*

$$\text{(R)} \int_a^b g(x)\, dx = \text{(L)} \int_a^b g(x)\bar{\lambda}(dx). \tag{60}$$

PROOF. (a) Let $g = g(x)$ be Riemann integrable. Then, by (57),

$$\text{(L)} \int_a^b \bar{g}(x)\bar{\lambda}(dx) = \text{(L)} \int_a^b \underline{g}(x)\bar{\lambda}(dx).$$

But $\underline{g}(x) \le g(x) \le \bar{g}(x)$, and hence by Property **H**

$$\underline{g}(x) = g(x) = \bar{g}(x) \quad (\bar{\lambda}\text{-a.s.}), \tag{61}$$

from which it is easy to see that $g(x)$ is continuous almost everywhere (with respect to $\bar{\lambda}$).

Conversely, let $g = g(x)$ be continuous almost everywhere (with respect to $\bar{\lambda}$). Then (61) is satisfied and consequently $g(x)$ differs from the (Borel) measurable function $\bar{g}(x)$ only on a set $\mathscr{N}$ with $\bar{\lambda}(\mathscr{N}) = 0$. But then

$$\{x : g(x) \le c\} = \{x : g(x) \le c\} \cap \overline{\mathscr{N}} + \{x : g(x) \le c\} \cap \mathscr{N}$$
$$= \{x : \bar{g}(x) \le c\} \cap \overline{\mathscr{N}} + \{x : g(x) \le c\} \cap \mathscr{N}$$

It is clear that the set $\{x : \bar{g}(x) \le c\} \cap \overline{\mathscr{N}} \in \overline{\mathscr{B}}([a, b])$, and that

$$\{x : g(x) \le c\} \cap \mathscr{N}$$

is a subset of $\mathcal{N}$ having Lebesgue measure $\bar{\lambda}$ equal to zero and therefore also belonging to $\overline{\mathscr{B}}([a, b])$. Therefore $g(x)$ is $\overline{\mathscr{B}}([a, b])$-measurable and, as a bounded function, is Lebesgue integrable. Therefore by Property **G**,

$$(\mathrm{L}) \int_a^b \bar{g}(x)\bar{\lambda}(dx) = (\mathrm{L}) \int_a^b \underline{g}(x)\bar{\lambda}(dx) = (\mathrm{L}) \int_a^b g(x)\bar{\lambda}(dx),$$

which completes the proof of (a).

(b) If $g = g(x)$ is Riemann integrable, then according to (a) it is continuous ($\bar{\lambda}$-a.s.). It was shown above than then $g(x)$ is Lebesgue integrable and its Riemann and Lebesgue integrals are equal.

This completes the proof of the theorem.

Remark. Let μ be a Lebesgue–Stieltjes measure on $\mathscr{B}([a, b])$. Let $\overline{\mathscr{B}}_\mu([a, b])$ be the system consisting of those subsets $\Lambda \subseteq [a, b]$ for which there are sets A and B in $\mathscr{B}([a, b])$ such that $A \subseteq \Lambda \subseteq B$ and $\mu(B\backslash A) = 0$. Let $\bar{\mu}$ be an *extension* of μ to $\overline{\mathscr{B}}_\mu([a, b])$ ($\bar{\mu}(\Lambda) = \mu(A)$ for Λ such that $A \subseteq \Lambda \subseteq B$ and $\mu(B\backslash A) = 0$). Then the conclusion of the theorem remains valid if we consider $\bar{\mu}$ instead of Lebesgue measure $\bar{\lambda}$, and the Riemann–Stieltjes and Lebesgue–Stieltjes measures with respect to $\bar{\mu}$ instead of the Riemann and Lebesgue integrals.

11. In this part we present a useful theorem on integration by parts for the Lebesgue–Stieltjes integral.

Let two generalized distribution functions $F = F(x)$ and $G = G(x)$ be given on $(R, \mathscr{B}(R))$.

Theorem 11. *The following formulas are valid for all real a and b, $a < b$:*

$$F(b)G(b) - F(a)G(a) = \int_a^b F(s-)dG(s) + \int_a^b G(s)\,dF(s), \qquad (62)$$

or equivalently

$$F(b)G(b) - F(a)G(a) = \int_a^b F(s-)dG(s) + \int_a^b G(s-)\,dF(s)$$
$$+ \sum_{a < s \leq b} \Delta F(s) \cdot \Delta G(s), \qquad (63)$$

where $F(s-) = \lim_{t \uparrow s} F(t)$, $\Delta F(s) = F(s) - F(s-)$.

Remark 1. Formula (62) can be written symbolically in "differential" form

$$d(FG) = F_- \, dG + G \, dF. \qquad (64)$$

Remark 2. The conclusion of the theorem remains valid for functions F and G of bounded variation on $[a, b]$. (Every such function that is continuous on the right and has limits on the left can be represented as the difference of two monotone nondecreasing functions.)

PROOF. We first recall that in accordance with Subsection 1 an integral $\int_a^b (\cdot)$ means $\int_{(a, b]} (\cdot)$. Then (see formula (2) in §3)

$$(F(b) - F(a))(G(b) - G(a)) = \int_a^b dF(s) \cdot \int_a^b dG(t).$$

Let $F \times G$ denote the direct product of the measures corresponding to F and G. Then by Fubini's theorem

$$(F(b) - F(a))(G(b) - G(a)) = \int_{(a, b] \times (a, b]} d(F \times G)(s, t)$$

$$= \int_{(a, b] \times (a, b]} I_{\{s \geq t\}}(s, t) \, d(F \times G)(s, t) + \int_{(a, b] \times (a, b]} I_{\{s \leq t\}}(s, t) \, d(F \times G)(s, t)$$

$$= \int_{(a, b]} (G(s) - G(a)) \, dF(s) + \int_{(a, b]} (F(t-) - F(a)) \, dG(t)$$

$$= \int_a^b G(s) \, dF(s) + \int_a^b F(s-) \, dG(s) - G(a)(F(b) - F(a)) - F(a)(G(b) - G(a)),$$

$$\tag{65}$$

where I_A is the indicator of the set A.

Formula (62) follows immediately from (65). In turn, (63) follows from (62) if we observe that

$$\int_a^b (G(s) - G(s-)) \, dF(s) = \sum_{a < s \leq b} \Delta G(s) \cdot \Delta F(s). \tag{66}$$

Corollary 1. *If $F(x)$ and $G(x)$ are distribution functions, then*

$$F(x)G(x) = \int_{-\infty}^x F(s-) \, dG(s) + \int_{-\infty}^x G(s) \, dF(s). \tag{67}$$

If also

$$F(x) = \int_{-\infty}^x f(s) \, ds,$$

then

$$F(x)G(x) = \int_{-\infty}^x F(s) \, dG(s) + \int_{-\infty}^x G(s) f(s) \, ds. \tag{68}$$

Corollary 2. *Let ξ be a random variable with distribution function $F(x)$ and* $E|\xi|^n < \infty$. *Then*

$$\int_0^\infty x^n \, dF(x) = n \int_0^\infty x^{n-1}[1 - F(x)] \, dx, \tag{69}$$

$$\int_{-\infty}^0 |x|^n \, dF(x) = - \int_0^\infty x^n \, dF(-x) = n \int_0^\infty x^{n-1} F(-x) \, dx \tag{70}$$

and

$$E|\xi|^n = \int_{-\infty}^\infty |x|^n \, dF(x) = n \int_0^\infty x^{n-1}[1 - F(x) + F(-x)] \, dx. \tag{71}$$

To prove (69) we observe that

$$\int^\infty x^n \, dF(x) = - \int_0^b x^n \, d(1 - F(x))$$

$$= - b^n(1 - F(b)) + n \int_0^b x^{n-1}(1 - F(x)) \, dx. \tag{72}$$

Let us show that since $E|\xi|^n < \infty$,

$$b^n(1 - F(b) + F(-b)) \le b^n P(|\xi| \ge b) \to 0. \tag{73}$$

In fact,

$$E|\xi|^n = \sum_{k=1}^\infty \int_{k-1}^k |x|^n \, dF(x) < \infty$$

and therefore

$$\sum_{k \ge b+1} \int_{k-1}^k |x|^n \, dF(x) \to 0, \qquad n \to \infty.$$

But

$$\sum_{k \ge b+1} \int_{k-1}^k |x|^n \, dF(x) \ge b^n P(|\xi| \ge b),$$

which establishes (73).

Taking the limit as $b \to \infty$ in (72), we obtain (69).
Formula (70) is proved similarly, and (71) follows from (69) and (70).

12. Let $A(t), t \ge 0$, be a function of locally bounded variation (i.e., of bounded variation on each finite interval $[a, b]$), which is continuous on the right and has limits on the left. Consider the equation

$$Z_t = 1 + \int_0^t Z_{s-} \, dA(s), \tag{74}$$

which can be written in differential form as

$$dZ = Z_- \, dA, \qquad Z_0 = 1. \tag{75}$$

The formula that we have proved for integration by parts lets us solve (74) explicitly in the class of functions of bounded variation.

We introduce the function

$$\mathscr{E}_t(A) = e^{A(t) - A(0)} \prod_{0 \le s \le t} (1 + \Delta A(s)) e^{-\Delta A(s)}, \tag{76}$$

where $\Delta A(s) = A(s) - A(s-)$ for $s > 0$, and $\Delta A(0) = 0$.

The function $A(s)$, $0 \le s \le t$, has bounded variation and therefore has at most a countable number of discontinuities, and so the series $\sum_{0 \le s \le t} |\Delta A(s)|$ converges. It follows that

$$\prod_{0 \le s \le t} (1 + \Delta A(s)) e^{-\Delta A(s)}$$

is a function of locally bounded variation.

If $A^c(t) = A(t) - \sum_{0 \le s \le t} \Delta A(s)$ is the continuous component of $A(t)$, we can rewrite (76) in the form

$$\mathscr{E}_t(A) = e^{A^c(t) - A^c(0)} \prod_{0 \le s \le t} (1 + \Delta A(s)). \tag{77}$$

Let us write

$$F(t) = e^{A^c(t) - A^c(0)}, \qquad G(t) = \prod_{0 \le s \le t} (1 + \Delta A(s)).$$

Then by (62)

$$\mathscr{E}_t(A) = F(t)G(t) = 1 + \int_0^t F(s) \, dG(s) + \int_0^t G(s-) \, dF(s)$$

$$= 1 + \sum_{0 \le s \le t} F(s)G(s-)\Delta A(s) + \int_0^t G(s-)F(s) \, dA^c(s)$$

$$= 1 + \int_0^t \mathscr{E}_{s-}(A) \, dA(s).$$

Therefore $\mathscr{E}_t(A)$, $t \ge 0$, is a (locally bounded) solution of (74). Let us show that this is the only locally bounded solution.

Suppose that there are two such solutions and let $Y = Y(t)$, $t \ge 0$, be their difference. Then

$$Y(t) = \int_0^t Y(s-) \, dA(s).$$

Put

$$T = \inf\{t \ge 0 : Y(t) \ne 0\},$$

where we take $T = \infty$ if $Y(t) = 0$ for $t \ge 0$.

Since $A(t)$ is a function of locally bounded variation, there are two generalized distribution functions $A_1(t)$ and $A_2(t)$ such that $A(t) = A_1(t) - A_2(t)$. If we suppose that $T < \infty$, we can find a finite T' such that

$$[A_1(T') + A_2(T')] - [A_1(T) + A_2(T)] \leq \tfrac{1}{2}.$$

Then it follows from the equation

$$Y(t) = \int_T^t Y(s-)\, dA(s), \qquad t \geq T,$$

that

$$\sup_{t \leq t'} |Y(t)| \leq \tfrac{1}{2} \sup_{t \leq T'} |Y(t)|$$

and since $\sup |Y(t)| < \infty$, we have $Y(t) = 0$ for $T < t \leq T'$, contradicting the assumption that $T < \infty$.

Thus we have proved the following theorem.

Theorem 12. *There is a unique locally bounded solution of* (74), *and it is given by* (76).

13. PROBLEMS

1. Establish the representation (6).

2. Prove the following extension of Property E. Let ξ and η be random variables for which $E\xi$ and $E\eta$ are defined and the sum $E\xi + E\eta$ is meaningful (does not have the form $\infty - \infty$ or $-\infty + \infty$). Then

$$E(\xi + \eta) = E\xi + E\eta.$$

3. Generalize Property G by showing that if $\xi = \eta$ (a.s.) and $E\xi$ exists, then $E\eta$ exists and $E\xi = E\eta$.

4. Let ξ be an extended random variable, μ a σ-finite measure, and $\int_\Omega |\xi|\, d\mu < \infty$. Show that $|\xi| < \infty$ (μ-a.s.) (cf. Property J).

5. Let μ be a σ-finite measure, ξ and η extended random variables for which $E\xi$ and $E\eta$ are defined. If $\int_A \xi\, dP \leq \int_A \eta\, dP$ for all $A \in \mathscr{F}$, then $\xi \leq \eta$ (μ-a.s.). (Cf. Property I.)

6. Let ξ and η be independent nonnegative random variables. Show that $E\xi\eta = E\xi \cdot E\eta$.

7. Using Fatou's lemma, show that

$$P(\varliminf A_n) \leq \varliminf P(A_n), \qquad P(\varlimsup A_n) \geq \varlimsup P(A_n).$$

8. Find an example to show that in general it is impossible to weaken the hypothesis "$|\xi_n| \leq \eta, E\eta < \infty$" in the dominated convergence theorem.

9. Find an example to show that in general the hypothesis "$\xi_n \leq \eta$, $E\eta > -\infty$" in Fatou's lemma cannot be omitted.

10. Prove the following variants of Fatou's lemma. Let the family $\{\xi_n^+\}_{n \geq 1}$ of random variables be uniformly integrable and let $E \varlimsup \xi_n$ exist. Then

$$\varlimsup E\xi_n \leq E \varlimsup \xi_n.$$

Let $\xi_n \leq \eta_n$, $n \geq 1$, where the family $\{\xi_n^+\}_{n \geq 1}$ is uniformly integrable and η_n converges a.s. (or only in probability—see §10 below) to a random variable η. Then $\varlimsup E\xi_n \leq E \varlimsup \xi_n$.

11. Dirichlet's function

$$d(x) = \begin{cases} 1, & x \text{ irrational,} \\ 0, & x \text{ rational,} \end{cases}$$

is defined on $[0, 1]$, Lebesgue integrable, but not Riemann integrable. Why?

12. Find an example of a sequence of Riemann integrable functions $\{f_n\}_{n \geq 1}$, defined on $[0, 1]$, such that $|f_n| \leq 1$, $f_n \to f$ almost everywhere (with Lebesgue measure), but f is not Riemann integrable.

13. Let $(a_{i, j}; i, j \geq 1)$ be a sequence of real numbers such that $\sum_{i, j} |a_{i, j}| < \infty$. Deduce from Fubini's theorem that

$$\sum_{(i, j)} a_{ij} = \sum_i \left(\sum_j a_{ij} \right) = \sum_j \left(\sum_i a_{ij} \right). \tag{78}$$

14. Find an example of a sequence $(a_{ij}; i, j \geq 1)$ for which $\sum_{i, j} |a_{ij}| = \infty$ and the equation in (78) does not hold.

15. Starting from simple functions and using the theorem on taking limits under the Lebesgue integral sign, prove the following result on *integration by substitution*.
    Let $h = h(y)$ be a nondecreasing continuously differentiable function on $[a, b]$, and let $f(x)$ be (Lebesgue) integrable on $[h(a), h(b)]$. Then the function $f(h(y))h'(y)$ is integrable on $[a, b]$ and

$$\int_{h(a)}^{h(b)} f(x)\, dx = \int_a^b f(h(y))h'(y)\, dy.$$

16. Prove formula (70).

17. Let $\xi, \xi_1, \xi_2, \ldots$ be nonnegative integrable random variables such that $E\xi_n \to E\xi$ and $P(\xi - \xi_n > \varepsilon) \to 0$ for every $\varepsilon > 0$. Show that then $E|\xi_n - \xi| \to 0$, $n \to \infty$.

18. Let ξ, η, ζ and $\xi_n, \eta_n, \zeta_n, n \geq 1$, be random variables such that

$$\xi_n \xrightarrow{P} \xi, \qquad \eta_n \xrightarrow{P} \eta, \qquad \zeta_n \xrightarrow{P} \zeta, \qquad \eta_n \leq \xi_n \leq \zeta_n, \quad n \geq 1,$$
$$E\zeta_n \to E\zeta, \qquad E\eta_n \to E\eta,$$

and the expectations $E\xi, E\eta, E\zeta$ are finite. Show that then $E\xi_n \to E\xi$ (*Pratt's lemma*).
    If also $\eta_n \leq 0 \leq \zeta_n$ then $E|\xi_n - \xi| \to 0$,
    Deduce that if $\xi_n \xrightarrow{P} \xi$, $E|\xi_n| \to E|\xi|$ and $E|\xi| < \infty$, then $E|\xi_n - \xi| \to 0$.

§7. Conditional Probabilities and Conditional Expectations with Respect to a σ-Algebra

1. Let $(\Omega, \mathscr{F}, \mathsf{P})$ be a probability space, and let $A \in \mathscr{F}$ be an event such that $\mathsf{P}(A) > 0$. As for finite probability spaces, the *conditional probability of B with respect to A* (denoted by $\mathsf{P}(B|A)$) means $\mathsf{P}(BA)/\mathsf{P}(A)$, and the *conditional probability of B with respect to the finite or countable decomposition* $\mathscr{D} = \{D_1, D_2 \ldots\}$ with $\mathsf{P}(D_i) > 0, i \geq 1$ (denoted by $\mathsf{P}(B|\mathscr{D})$) is the random variable equal to $\mathsf{P}(B|D_i)$ for $\omega \in D_i, i \geq 1$:

$$\mathsf{P}(B|\mathscr{D}) = \sum_{i \geq 1} \mathsf{P}(B|D_i) I_{D_i}(\omega).$$

In a similar way, if ξ is a random variable for which $\mathsf{E}\xi$ is defined, the *conditional expectation of ξ with respect to the event A* with $\mathsf{P}(A) > 0$ (denoted by $\mathsf{E}(\xi|A)$) is $\mathsf{E}(\xi I_A)/\mathsf{P}(A)$ (cf. (I.8.10)).

The random variable $\mathsf{P}(B|\mathscr{D})$ is evidently measurable with respect to the σ-algebra $\mathscr{G} = \sigma(\mathscr{D})$, and is consequently also denoted by $\mathsf{P}(B|\mathscr{G})$ (see §8 of Chapter I).

However, in probability theory we may have to consider conditional probabilities with respect to events whose probabilities are *zero*.

Consider, for example, the following experiment. Let ξ be a random variable that is uniformly distributed on $[0, 1]$. If $\xi = x$, toss a coin for which the probability of head is x, and the probability of tail is $1 - x$. Let ν be the number of heads in n independent tosses of this coin. What is the "conditional probability $\mathsf{P}(\nu = k | \xi = x)$"? Since $\mathsf{P}(\xi = x) = 0$, the conditional probability $\mathsf{P}(\nu = k | \xi = x)$ is undefined, although it is intuitively plausible that "it ought to be $C_n^k x^k (1 - x)^{n-k}$."

Let us now give a general definition of conditional expectation (and, in particular, of conditional probability) with respect to a σ-algebra $\mathscr{G}, \mathscr{G} \subseteq \mathscr{F}$, and compare it with the definition given in §8 of Chapter I for finite probability spaces.

2. Let $(\Omega, \mathscr{F}, \mathsf{P})$ be a probability space, $\mathscr{G}$ a σ-algebra, $\mathscr{G} \subseteq \mathscr{F}$ ($\mathscr{G}$ is a σ-*subalgebra* of $\mathscr{F}$), and $\xi = \xi(\omega)$ a random variable. Recall that, according to §6, the expectation $\mathsf{E}\xi$ was defined in two stages: first for a nonnegative random variable ξ, then in the general case by

$$\mathsf{E}\xi = \mathsf{E}\xi^+ - \mathsf{E}\xi^-,$$

and only under the assumption that

$$\min(\mathsf{E}\xi^-, \mathsf{E}\xi^+) < \infty.$$

A similar two-stage construction is also used to define conditional expectations $\mathsf{E}(\xi|\mathscr{G})$.

Definition 1.

(1) The *conditional expectation of a nonnegative* random variable ξ *with respect to the σ-algebra* $\mathscr{G}$ is a nonnegative extended random variable, denoted by $\mathsf{E}(\xi|\mathscr{G})$ or $\mathsf{E}(\xi|\mathscr{G})(\omega)$, such that

(a) $\mathsf{E}(\xi|\mathscr{G})$ is $\mathscr{G}$-measurable;
(b) for every $A \in \mathscr{G}$

$$\int_A \xi \, d\mathsf{P} = \int_A \mathsf{E}(\xi|\mathscr{G}) \, d\mathsf{P}. \tag{1}$$

(2) *The conditional expectation* $\mathsf{E}(\xi|\mathscr{G})$, or $\mathsf{E}(\xi|\mathscr{G})(\omega)$, *of any* random variable ξ *with respect to the σ-algebra* $\mathscr{G}$, is considered to be defined if

$$\min(\mathsf{E}(\xi^+|\mathscr{G}), \mathsf{E}(\xi^-|\mathscr{G})) < \infty,$$

P-a.s., and it is given by the formula

$$\mathsf{E}(\xi|\mathscr{G}) \equiv \mathsf{E}(\xi^+|\mathscr{G}) - \mathsf{E}(\xi^-|\mathscr{G}),$$

where, on the set (of probability zero) of sample points for which $\mathsf{E}(\xi^+|\mathscr{G}) = \mathsf{E}(\xi^-|\mathscr{G}) = \infty$, the difference $\mathsf{E}(\xi^+|\mathscr{G}) - \mathsf{E}(\xi^-|\mathscr{G})$ is given an arbitrary value, for example zero.

We begin by showing that, for nonnegative random variables, $\mathsf{E}(\xi|\mathscr{G})$ actually exists. By (6.36) the set function

$$Q(A) = \int_A \xi \, d\mathsf{P}, \qquad A \in \mathscr{G}, \tag{2}$$

is a measure on $(\Omega, \mathscr{G})$, and is absolutely continuous with respect to P (considered on $(\Omega, \mathscr{G})$, $\mathscr{G} \subseteq \mathscr{F}$). Therefore (by the Radon–Nikodým theorem) there is a nonnegative $\mathscr{G}$-measurable extended random variable $\mathsf{E}(\xi|\mathscr{G})$ such that

$$Q(A) = \int_A \mathsf{E}(\xi|\mathscr{G}) \, d\mathsf{P}. \tag{3}$$

Then (1) follows from (2) and (3).

Remark 1. In accordance with the Radon–Nikodým theorem, the conditional expectation $\mathsf{E}(\xi|\mathscr{G})$ is defined only up to sets of P-measure zero. In other words, $\mathsf{E}(\xi|\mathscr{G})$ can be taken to be any $\mathscr{G}$-measurable function $f(\omega)$ for which $Q(A) = \int_A f(\omega) \, d\mathsf{P}$, $A \in \mathscr{G}$ (a "variant" of the conditional expectation).

Let us observe that, in accordance with the remark on the Radon–Nikodým theorem,

$$\mathsf{E}(\xi|\mathscr{G}) \equiv \frac{dQ}{d\mathsf{P}}(\omega), \tag{4}$$

i.e. the conditional expectation is just the derivative of the Radon–Nikodým measure Q with respect to P (considered on $(\Omega, \mathcal{G})$).

Remark 2. In connection with (1), we observe that we cannot in general put $E(\xi|\mathcal{G}) = \xi$, since ξ is *not necessarily* $\mathcal{G}$-measurable.

Remark 3. Suppose that ξ is a random variable for which $E\xi$ does not exist. Then $E(\xi|\mathcal{G})$ may be definable as a $\mathcal{G}$-measurable function for which (1) holds. This is usually just what happens. Our definition $E(\xi|\mathcal{G}) \equiv E(\xi^+|\mathcal{G}) - E(\xi^-|\mathcal{G})$ has the advantage that for the trivial σ-algebra $\mathcal{G} = \{\varnothing, \Omega\}$ it reduces to the definition of $E\xi$ but does not presuppose the existence of $E\xi$. (For example, if ξ is a random variable with $E\xi^+ = \infty, E\xi^- = \infty$, and $\mathcal{G} = \mathcal{F}$, then $E\xi$ is not defined, but in terms of Definition 1, $E(\xi|\mathcal{G})$ exists and is simply $\xi = \xi^+ - \xi^-$.

Remark 4. Let the random variable ξ have a conditional expectation $E(\xi|\mathcal{G})$ with respect to the σ-algebra $\mathcal{G}$. The *conditional variance* (denoted by $V(\xi|\mathcal{G})$ or $V(\xi|\mathcal{G})(\alpha)$) of ξ is the random variable

$$V(\xi|\mathcal{G}) \equiv E[(\xi - E(\xi|\mathcal{G}))^2 | \mathcal{G}].$$

(Cf. the definition of the conditional variance $V(\xi|\mathcal{D})$ of ξ with respect to a decomposition $\mathcal{D}$, as given in Problem 2, §8, Chapter I.)

Definition 2. Let $B \in \mathcal{F}$. The conditional expectation $E(I_B|\mathcal{G})$ is denoted by $P(B|\mathcal{G})$, or $P(B|\mathcal{G})(\omega)$, and is called the *conditional probability of the event B with respect to the σ-algebra $\mathcal{G}$, $\mathcal{G} \subseteq \mathcal{F}$.*

It follows from Definitions 1 and 2 that, for a given $B \in \mathcal{F}$, $P(B|\mathcal{G})$ is a random variable such that

(a) $P(B|\mathcal{G})$ is $\mathcal{G}$-measurable,

(b) $$P(A \cap B) = \int_A P(B|\mathcal{G})dP \tag{5}$$

for every $A \in \mathcal{G}$.

Definition 3. Let ξ be a random variable and $\mathcal{G}_\eta$ the σ-algebra generated by a random element η. Then $E(\xi|\mathcal{G}_\eta)$, if defined, means $E(\xi|\eta$ or $E(\xi|\eta)(\omega)$, and is called the *conditional expectation of ξ with respect to η.*

The conditional probability $P(B|\mathcal{G}_\eta)$ is denoted by $P(B|\eta)$ or $P(B|\eta)(\omega)$, and is called the *conditional probability of B with respect to η.*

3. Let us show that the definition of $E(\xi|\mathcal{G})$ given here agrees with the definition of conditional expectation in §8 of Chapter I.

Let $\mathcal{D} = \{D_1, D_2, \ldots\}$ be a finite or countable decomposition with atoms D_i with respect to the probability P (i.e. $\mathsf{P}(D_i) > 0$, and if $A \subseteq D_i$, then either $\mathsf{P}(A) = 0$ or $\mathsf{P}(D_i \backslash A) = 0$).

Theorem 1. *If $\mathcal{G} = \sigma(\mathcal{D})$ and ξ is a random variable for which $\mathsf{E}\xi$ is defined, then*

$$\mathsf{E}(\xi|\mathcal{G}) = \mathsf{E}(\xi|D_i) \quad (\text{P-a.s. on } D_i) \tag{6}$$

or equivalently

$$\mathsf{E}(\xi|\mathcal{G}) = \frac{\mathsf{E}(\xi I_{D_i})}{\mathsf{P}(D_i)} \quad (\text{P-a.s. on } D_i).$$

(The notation "$\xi = \eta$ (P-a.s. on A)," or

"$\xi = \eta (A; \text{P-a.s.})$" means that $\mathsf{P}(A \cap \{\xi \neq \eta\}) = 0$.)

PROOF. According to Lemma 3 of §4, $\mathsf{E}(\xi|\mathcal{G}) = K_i$ on D_i, where K_i are constants. But

$$\int_{D_i} \xi \, d\mathsf{P} = \int_{D_i} \mathsf{E}(\xi|\mathcal{G}) \, d\mathsf{P} = K_i \mathsf{P}(D_i),$$

whence

$$K_i = \frac{1}{\mathsf{P}(D_i)} \int_{D_i} \xi \, d\mathsf{P} = \frac{\mathsf{E}(\xi I_{D_i})}{\mathsf{P}(D_i)} = \mathsf{E}(\xi|D_i).$$

This completes the proof of the theorem.

Consequently the concept of the conditional expectation $\mathsf{E}(\xi|\mathcal{D})$ with respect to a finite decomposition $\mathcal{D} = \{D_1, \ldots, D_n\}$, as introduced in Chapter I, is a special case of the concept of conditional expectation with respect to the σ-algebra $\mathcal{G} = \sigma(D)$.

4. Properties of conditional expectations. (We shall suppose that the expectations are defined for all the random variables that we consider and that $\mathcal{G} \subseteq \mathcal{F}$.)

A*. *If C is a constant and $\xi = C$ (a.s.), then $\mathsf{E}(\xi|\mathcal{G}) = C$ (a.s.).*

B*. *If $\xi \leq \eta$ (a.s.) then $\mathsf{E}(\xi|\mathcal{G}) \leq \mathsf{E}(\eta|\mathcal{G})$ (a.s.).*

C*. *$|\mathsf{E}(\xi|\mathcal{G})| \leq \mathsf{E}(|\xi||\mathcal{G})$ (a.s.).*

D*. *If a, b are constants and $a\mathsf{E}\xi + b\mathsf{E}\eta$ is defined, then*

$$\mathsf{E}(a\xi + b\eta|\mathcal{G}) = a\mathsf{E}(\xi|\mathcal{G}) + b\mathsf{E}(\eta|\mathcal{G}) \quad (\text{a.s.}).$$

E*. *Let $\mathcal{F}_* = \{\varphi, \Omega\}$ be the trivial σ-algebra. Then*

$$\mathsf{E}(\xi|\mathcal{F}_*) = \mathsf{E}\xi \quad (\text{a.s.}).$$

F*. $E(\xi|\mathscr{F}) = \xi$ (a.s.).
G*. $E(E(\xi|\mathscr{G})) = E\xi$.
H*. If $\mathscr{G}_1 \subseteq \mathscr{G}_2$ then

$$E[E(\xi|\mathscr{G}_2)|\mathscr{G}_1] = E(\xi|\mathscr{G}_1) \quad (a.s.).$$

I*. If $\mathscr{G}_1 \supseteq \mathscr{G}_2$ then

$$E[E(\xi|\mathscr{G}_2)|\mathscr{G}_1) = E(\xi|\mathscr{G}_2) \quad (a.s.).$$

J*. Let a random variable ξ for which $E\xi$ is defined be independent of the σ-algebra $\mathscr{G}$ (i.e., independent of I_B, $B \in \mathscr{G}$). Then

$$E(\xi|\mathscr{G}) = E\xi \quad (a.s.).$$

K*. Let η be a $\mathscr{G}$-measurable random variable, $E|\eta| < \infty$ and $E|\xi\eta| < \infty$. Then

$$E(\xi\eta|\mathscr{G}) = \eta E(\xi|\mathscr{G}) \quad (a.s.).$$

Let us establish these properties.

A*. A constant function is measurable with respect to $\mathscr{G}$. Therefore we need only verify that

$$\int_A \xi dP = \int_A C\, dP, \quad A \in \mathscr{G}.$$

But, by the hypothesis $\xi = C$ (a.s.) and Property **G** of §6, this equation is obviously satisfied.

B*. If $\xi \leq \eta$ (a.s.), then by Property **B** of §6

$$\int_A \xi\, dP \leq \int_A \eta\, dP, \quad A \in \mathscr{G},$$

and therefore

$$\int_A E(\xi|\mathscr{G})\, dP \leq \int_A E(\eta|\mathscr{G})\, dP, \quad A \in \mathscr{G}.$$

The required inequality now follows from Property **I** (§6).

C*. This follows from the preceding property if we observe that $-|\xi| \leq \xi \leq |\xi|$.

D*. If $A \in \mathscr{G}$ then by Problem 2 of §6,

$$\int_A (a\xi + b\eta)\, dP = \int_A a\xi\, dP + \int_A b\eta\, dP = \int_A aE(\xi|\mathscr{G})\, dP$$

$$+ \int_A bE(\eta|\mathscr{G})\, dP = \int_A [aE(\xi|\mathscr{G}) + bE(\eta|\mathscr{G})]\, dP,$$

which establishes **D***.

E*. This property follows from the remark that $\mathsf{E}\xi$ is an $\mathscr{F}_*$-measurable function and the evident fact that if $A = \Omega$ or $A = \emptyset$ then

$$\int_A \xi \, d\mathsf{P} = \int_A \mathsf{E}\xi \, d\mathsf{P}.$$

F*. Since ξ if $\mathscr{F}$-measurable and

$$\int_A \xi \, d\mathsf{P} = \int_A \xi \, d\mathsf{P}, \qquad A \in \mathscr{F},$$

we have $\mathsf{E}(\xi \,|\, F) = \xi$ (a.s.).

G*. This follows from **E*** and **H*** by taking $\mathscr{G}_1 = \{\emptyset, \Omega\}$ and $\mathscr{G}_2 = \mathscr{G}$.

H*. Let $A \in \mathscr{G}_1$; then

$$\int_A \mathsf{E}(\xi \,|\, \mathscr{G}_1) \, d\mathsf{P} = \int_A \xi \, d\mathsf{P}.$$

Since $\mathscr{G}_1 \subseteq \mathscr{G}_2$, we have $A \in \mathscr{G}_2$ and therefore

$$\int_A \mathsf{E}[\mathsf{E}(\xi \,|\, \mathscr{G}_2) \,|\, \mathscr{G}_1] \, d\mathsf{P} = \int_A \mathsf{E}(\xi \,|\, \mathscr{G}_2) \, d\mathsf{P} = \int_A \xi \, d\mathsf{P}.$$

Consequently, when $A \in \mathscr{G}_1$,

$$\int_A \mathsf{E}(\xi \,|\, \mathscr{G}_1) \, d\mathsf{P} = \int_A \mathsf{E}[\mathsf{E}(\xi \,|\, \mathscr{G}_2) \,|\, \mathscr{G}_1] \, d\mathsf{P}$$

and by Property I (§6) and Problem 5 (§6)

$$\mathsf{E}(\xi \,|\, \mathscr{G}_1) = \mathsf{E}[\mathsf{E}(\xi \,|\, \mathscr{G}_2) \,|\, \mathscr{G}_1] \quad \text{(a.s.).}$$

I*. If $A \in \mathscr{G}_1$, then by the definition of $\mathsf{E}[\mathsf{E}(\xi \,|\, \mathscr{G}_2) \,|\, \mathscr{G}_1]$

$$\int_A \mathsf{E}[\mathsf{E}(\xi \,|\, \mathscr{G}_2) \,|\, \mathscr{G}_1] d\mathsf{P} = \int_A \mathsf{E}(\xi \,|\, \mathscr{G}_2) \, d\mathsf{P}.$$

The function $\mathsf{E}(\xi \,|\, \mathscr{G}_2)$ is $\mathscr{G}_2$-measurable and, since $\mathscr{G}_2 \subseteq \mathscr{G}_1$, also $\mathscr{G}_1$-measurable. It follows that $\mathsf{E}(\xi \,|\, \mathscr{G}_2)$ is a variant of the expectation $\mathsf{E}[\mathsf{E}(\xi \,|\, \mathscr{G}_2) \,|\, \mathscr{G}_1]$, which proves Property **I***.

J*. Since $\mathsf{E}\xi$ is a $\mathscr{G}$-measurable function, we have only to verify that

$$\int_B d\mathsf{P} = \int_B \mathsf{E}\xi \, d\mathsf{P},$$

i.e. that $\mathsf{E}[\xi \cdot I_B] = \mathsf{E}\xi \cdot \mathsf{E}I_B$. If $\mathsf{E}|\xi| < \infty$, this follows immediately from Theorem 6 of §6. The general case can be reduced to this by applying Problem 6 of §6.

The proof of Property **K*** will be given a little later; it depends on conclusion (a) of the following theorem.

Theorem 2 (On Taking Limits Under the Expectation Sign). *Let $\{\xi_n\}_{n\geq 1}$ be a sequence of extended random variables.*

(a) *If $|\xi_n| \leq \eta, E\eta < \infty$ and $\xi_n \to \xi$ (a.s.), then*

$$E(\xi_n|\mathscr{G}) \to E(\xi|\mathscr{G}) \quad (a.s.)$$

and

$$E(|\xi_n - \xi||\mathscr{G}) \to 0 \quad (a.s.).$$

(b) *If $\xi_n \geq \eta, E\eta > -\infty$ and $\xi_n \uparrow \xi$ (a.s.), then*

$$E(\xi_n|\mathscr{G}) \uparrow E(\xi|\mathscr{G}) \quad (a.s.).$$

(c) *If $\xi_n \leq \eta, E\eta < \infty$, and $\xi_n \downarrow \xi$ (a.s.), then*

$$E(\xi_n|\mathscr{G}) \downarrow E(\xi|\mathscr{G}) \quad (a.s.).$$

(d) *If $\xi_n \geq \eta, E\eta > -\infty$, then*

$$E(\underline{\lim}\, \xi_n|\mathscr{G}) \leq \underline{\lim}\, E(\xi_n|\mathscr{G}) \quad (a.s.).$$

(e) *If $\xi_n \leq \eta, E\eta < \infty$, then*

$$\overline{\lim}\, E(\xi_n|\mathscr{G}) \leq E(\overline{\lim}\, \xi_n|\mathscr{G}) \quad (a.s.).$$

(f) *If $\xi_n \geq 0$ then*

$$E(\textstyle\sum \xi_n|\mathscr{G}) = \sum E(\xi_n|\mathscr{G}) \quad (a.s.).$$

PROOF. (a) Let $\zeta_n = \sup_{m\geq n} |\xi_m - \xi|$. Since $\xi_n \to \xi$ (a.s.), we have $\zeta_n \downarrow 0$ (a.s.). The expectations $E\xi_n$ and $E\xi$ are finite; therefore by Properties D^* and C^* (a.s.)

$$|E(\xi_n|\mathscr{G}) - E(\xi|\mathscr{G})| = |E(\xi_n - \xi|\mathscr{G})| \leq E(|\xi_n - \xi||\mathscr{G}) \leq E(\zeta_n|\mathscr{G}).$$

Since $E(\zeta_{n+1}|\mathscr{G}) \leq E(\zeta_n|\mathscr{G})$ (a.s.), the limit $h = \lim_n E(\zeta_n|\mathscr{G})$ exists (a.s.). Then

$$0 \leq \int_\Omega h\, dP \leq \int_\Omega E(\zeta_n|\mathscr{G})\, dP = \int_\Omega \zeta_n\, dP \to 0, \quad n \to \infty,$$

where the last statement follows from the dominated convergence theorem, since $0 \leq \zeta_n \leq 2\eta$, $E\eta < \infty$. Consequently $\int_\Omega h\, dP = 0$ and then $h = 0$ (a.s.) by Property **H**.

(b) First let $\eta \equiv 0$. Since $E(\xi_n|\mathscr{G}) \leq E(\xi_{n+1}|\mathscr{G})$ (a.s.) the limit $\zeta(\omega) = \lim_n E(\xi_n|\mathscr{G})$ exists (a.s.). Then by the equation

$$\int_A \xi_n\, dP = \int_A E(\xi_n|\mathscr{G})\, dP, \quad A \in \mathscr{G},$$

and the theorem on monotone convergence,

$$\int_A \xi\, dP = \int_A \zeta\, dP, \quad A \in \mathscr{G}.$$

Consequently $\xi = \zeta$ (a.s.) by Property **I** and Problem 5 of §6.

For the proof in the general case, we observe that $0 \le \xi_n^+ \uparrow \xi^+$, and by what has been proved,

$$\mathsf{E}(\xi_n^+ | \mathcal{G}) \uparrow \mathsf{E}(\xi^+ | \mathcal{G}) \quad \text{(a.s.)}. \tag{7}$$

But $0 \le \xi_n^- \le \xi^-$, $\mathsf{E}\xi^- < \infty$, and therefore by (a)

$$\mathsf{E}(\xi_n^- | \mathcal{G}) \to \mathsf{E}(\xi^- | \mathcal{G}),$$

which, with (7), proves (b).

Conclusion (c) follows from (b).

(d) Let $\zeta_n = \inf_{m \ge n} \xi_m$; then $\zeta_n \uparrow \zeta$, where $\zeta = \underline{\lim}\, \xi_n$. According to (b), $\mathsf{E}(\zeta_n | \mathcal{G}) \uparrow \mathsf{E}(\zeta | \mathcal{G})$ (a.s.). Therefore (a.s.) $\mathsf{E}(\underline{\lim}\, \xi_n | \mathcal{G}) = \mathsf{E}(\zeta | \mathcal{G}) = \lim_n \mathsf{E}(\zeta_n | \mathcal{G}) = \underline{\lim}\, \mathsf{E}(\zeta_n | \mathcal{G}) \le \underline{\lim}\, \mathsf{E}(\xi_n | \mathcal{G})$.

Conclusion (e) follows from (d).

(f) If $\xi_n \ge 0$, by Property **D*** we have

$$\mathsf{E}\left(\sum_{k=1}^n \xi_k | \mathcal{G}\right) = \sum_{k=1}^n \mathsf{E}(\xi_k | \mathcal{G}) \quad \text{(a.s.)}$$

which, with (b), establishes the required result.

This completes the proof of the theorem.

We can now establish Property **K***. Let $\eta = I_B$, $B \in \mathcal{G}$. Then, for every $A \in \mathcal{G}$,

$$\int_A \xi \eta \, d\mathsf{P} = \int_{A \cap B} \xi \, d\mathsf{P} = \int_{A \cap B} \mathsf{E}(\xi | \mathcal{G}) \, d\mathsf{P} = \int_A I_B \mathsf{E}(\xi | \mathcal{G}) \, d\mathsf{P} = \int_A \eta \mathsf{E}(\xi | \mathcal{G}) \, d\mathsf{P}.$$

By the additivity of the Lebesgue integral, the equation

$$\int_A \xi \eta \, d\mathsf{P} = \int_A \eta \mathsf{E}(\xi | \mathcal{G}) \, d\mathsf{P}, \qquad A \in \mathcal{G}, \tag{8}$$

remains valid for the simple random variables $\eta = \sum_{k=1}^n y_k I_{B_k}$, $B_k \in \mathcal{G}$. Therefore, by Property **I** (§6), we have

$$\mathsf{E}(\xi \eta | \mathcal{G}) = \eta \mathsf{E}(\xi | \mathcal{G}) \quad \text{(a.s.)} \tag{9}$$

for these random variables.

Now let η be any $\mathcal{G}$-measurable random variable with $\mathsf{E}|\eta| < \infty$, and let $\{\eta_n\}_{n \ge 1}$ be a sequence of simple $\mathcal{G}$-measurable random variables such that $|\eta_n| \le \eta$ and $\eta_n \to \eta$. Then by (9)

$$\mathsf{E}(\xi \eta_n | \mathcal{G}) = \eta_n \mathsf{E}(\xi | \mathcal{G}) \quad \text{(a.s.)}.$$

It is clear that $|\xi \eta_n| \le |\xi \eta|$, where $\mathsf{E}|\xi_n| < \infty$. Therefore $\mathsf{E}(\xi \eta_n | \mathcal{G}) \to \mathsf{E}(\xi \eta | \mathcal{G})$ (a.s.) by Property (a). In addition, since $\mathsf{E}|\xi| < \infty$, we have $\mathsf{E}(\xi | \mathcal{G})$ finite (a.s.) (see Property **C*** and Property **J** of §6). Therefore $\eta_n \mathsf{E}(\xi | \mathcal{G}) \to \eta \mathsf{E}(\xi | \mathcal{G})$ (a.s.). (The hypothesis that $\mathsf{E}(\xi | \mathcal{G})$ is finite, almost surely, is essential, since, according to the footnote on p. 172, $0 \cdot \infty = 0$, but if $\eta_n = 1/n$, $\eta \equiv 0$, we have $1/n \cdot \infty \not\to 0 \cdot \infty = 0$.)

5. Here we consider the more detailed structure of conditional expectations $E(\xi|\mathscr{G}_\eta)$, which we also denote, as usual, by $E(\xi|\eta)$.

Since $E(\xi|\eta)$ is a $\mathscr{G}_\eta$-measurable function, then by Theorem 3 of §4 (more precisely, by its obvious modification for extended random variables) there is a Borel function $m = m(y)$ from $\bar{R}$ to $\bar{R}$ such that

$$m(\eta(\omega)) = E(\xi|\eta)(\omega) \tag{10}$$

for all $\omega \in \Omega$. We denote this function $m(y)$ by $E(\xi|\eta = y)$ and call it the *conditional expectation of ξ with respect to the event $\{\eta = y\}$, or the conditional expectation of ξ under the condition that $\eta = y$.*

Correspondingly we define

$$\int_A \xi \, dP = \int_A E(\xi|\eta) \, dP = \int_A m(\eta) \, dP, \qquad A \in \mathscr{G}_\eta. \tag{11}$$

Therefore by Theorem 7 of §6 (on change of variable under the Lebesgue integral sign)

$$\int_{\{\omega: \eta \in B\}} m(\eta) \, dP = \int_B m(y)P_\eta(dy), \qquad B \in \mathscr{B}(\bar{R}), \tag{12}$$

where P_η is the probability distribution of η. Consequently $m = m(y)$ is a Borel function such that

$$\int_{\{\omega: \eta \in B\}} \xi \, dP = \int_B m(y) \, dP_\eta. \tag{13}$$

for every $B \in \mathscr{B}(R)$.

This remark shows that we can give a different definition of the conditional expectation $E(\xi|\eta = y)$.

Definition 4. Let ξ and η be random variables (possible, extended) and let $E\xi$ be defined. The conditional expectation of the random variable ξ under the condition that $\eta = y$ is any $\mathscr{B}(\bar{R})$-measurable function $m = m(y)$ for which

$$\int_{\{\omega: \eta \in B\}} \xi \, dP = \int_B m(y)P_\eta(dy), \qquad B \in \mathscr{B}(\bar{R}). \tag{14}$$

That such a function exists follows again from the Radon–Nikodým theorem if we observe that the set function

$$Q(B) = \int_{\{\omega: \eta \in B\}} \xi \, dP$$

is a signed measure absolutely continuous with respect to the measure P_η.

Now suppose that $m(y)$ is a conditional expectation in the sense of Definition 4. Then if we again apply the theorem on change of variable under the Lebesgue integral sign, we obtain

$$\int_{\{\omega:\,\eta\in B\}} \xi\, d\mathsf{P} = \int_B m(y)P_\eta(dy) = \int_{\{\omega:\,\eta\in B\}} m(\eta)P_\eta(dy), \qquad B\in\mathscr{B}(\overline{R}).$$

The function $m(\eta)$ is $\mathscr{G}_\eta$-measurable, and the sets $\{\omega:\eta\in B\}$, $B\in\mathscr{B}(\overline{R})$, exhaust the subsets of $\mathscr{G}_\eta$.

Hence it follows that $m(\eta)$ is the expectation $\mathsf{E}(\xi|\eta)$. Consequently if we know $\mathsf{E}(\xi|\eta=y)$ we can reconstruct $\mathsf{E}(\xi|\eta)$, and conversely from $\mathsf{E}(\xi|\eta)$ we can find $\mathsf{E}(\xi|\eta=y)$.

From an intuitive point of view, the conditional expectation $\mathsf{E}(\xi|\eta=y)$ is simpler and more natural than $\mathsf{E}(\xi|\eta)$. However, $\mathsf{E}(\xi|\eta)$, considered as a $\mathscr{G}_\eta$-measurable random variable, is more convenient to work with.

Observe that Properties **A*–K*** above and the conclusions of Theorem 2 can easily be transferred to $\mathsf{E}(\xi|\eta=y)$ (replacing "almost surely" by "P_η-almost surely"). Thus, for example, Property **K*** transforms as follows: if $\mathsf{E}|\xi|<\infty$ and $\mathsf{E}|\xi f(\eta)|<\infty$, where $f=f(y)$ is a $\mathscr{B}(\overline{R})$ measurable function, then

$$\mathsf{E}(\xi f(\eta)|\eta=y) = f(y)\mathsf{E}(\xi|\eta=y) \quad (P_\eta\text{-a.s.}). \tag{15}$$

In addition (cf. Property **J***), if ξ and η are independent, then

$$\mathsf{E}(\xi|\eta=y) = \mathsf{E}\xi \quad (P_\eta\text{-a.s.}).$$

We also observe that if $B\in\mathscr{B}(R^2)$ and ξ and η are independent, then

$$\mathsf{E}[I_B(\xi,\eta)|\eta=y] = \mathsf{E}I_B(\xi,y) \quad (P_\eta\text{-a.s.}), \tag{16}$$

and if $\varphi=\varphi(x,y)$ is a $\mathscr{B}(R^2)$-measurable function such that $\mathsf{E}|\varphi(\xi,\eta)|<\infty$, then

$$\mathsf{E}[\varphi(\xi,\eta)|\eta=y] = \mathsf{E}[\varphi(\xi,y)] \quad (P_\eta\text{-a.s.}).$$

To prove (16) we make the following observation. If $B=B_1\times B_2$, the validity of (16) will follow from

$$\int_{\{\omega:\,\eta\in A\}} I_{B_1\times B_2}(\xi,\eta)\mathsf{P}(d\omega) = \int_{(y\in A)} \mathsf{E}I_{B_1\times B_2}(\xi,y)P_\eta(dy).$$

But the left-hand side is $\mathsf{P}\{\xi\in B_1,\eta\in A\cap B_2\}$, and the right-hand side is $\mathsf{P}(\xi\in B_1)\mathsf{P}(\eta\in A\cap B_2)$; their equality follows from the independence of ξ and η. In the general case the proof depends on an application of Theorem 1, §2, on monotone classes (cf. the corresponding part of the proof of Fubini's theorem).

Definition 5. The conditional probability of the event $A\in\mathscr{F}$ under the condition that $\eta=y$ (notation: $\mathsf{P}(A|\eta=y)$) is $\mathsf{E}(I_A|\eta=y)$.

It is clear that $P(A | \eta = y)$ can be defined as the $\mathscr{B}(\bar{R})$-measurable function such that

$$P(A \cap \{\eta \in B\}) = \int_B P(A | \eta = y) P_\eta(dy), \qquad B \in \mathscr{B}(\bar{R}). \qquad (17)$$

6. Let us calculate some examples of conditional probabilities and conditional expectations.

EXAMPLE 1. Let η be a discrete random variable with $P(\eta = y_k) > 0$, $\sum_{k=1}^\infty P(\eta = y_k) = 1$. Then

$$P(A | \eta = y_k) = \frac{P(A \cap \{\eta = y_k\})}{P(\eta = y_k)}, \qquad k \geq 1.$$

For $y \notin \{y_1, y_2, \ldots\}$ the conditional probability $P(A | \eta = y)$ can be defined in any way, for example as zero.

If ξ is a random variable for which $E\xi$ exists, then

$$E(\xi | \eta = y_k) = \frac{1}{P(\eta = y_k)} \int_{\{\omega : \eta = y_k\}} \xi \, dP.$$

When $y \notin \{y_1, y_2, \ldots\}$ the conditional expectation $E(\xi | \eta = y)$ can be defined in any way (for example, as zero).

EXAMPLE 2. Let (ξ, η) be a pair of random variables whose distribution has a density $f_{\xi\eta}(x, y)$:

$$P\{(\xi, \eta) \in B\} = \int_B f_{\xi\eta}(x, y) \, dx \, dy, \qquad B \in \mathscr{B}(R^2).$$

Let $f_\xi(x)$ and $f_\eta(y)$ be the densities of the probability distribution of ξ and η (see (6.46), (6.55) and (6.56)).

Let us put

$$f_{\xi|\eta}(x | y) = \frac{f_{\xi\eta}(x, y)}{f_\eta(y)}, \qquad (18)$$

taking $f_{\xi|\eta}(x | y) = 0$ if $f_\eta(y) = 0$.

Then

$$P(\xi \in C | \eta = y) = \int_C f_{\xi|\eta}(x | y) \, dx, \qquad C \in \mathscr{B}(R), \qquad (19)$$

i.e. $f_{\xi|\eta}(x | y)$ is the density of a conditional probability distribution.

In fact, in order to prove (19) it is enough to verify (17) for $B \in \mathcal{B}(R)$, $A = \{\xi \in C\}$. By (6.43), (6.45) and Fubini's theorem,

$$\int_B \left[\int_C f_{\xi|\eta}(x|y) \, dx \right] P_\eta(dy) = \int_B \left[\int_C f_{\xi|\eta}(x|y) \, dx \right] f_\eta(y) \, dy$$

$$= \int_{C \times B} f_{\xi|\eta}(x|y) f_\eta(y) \, dx \, dy$$

$$= \int_{C \times B} f_{\xi\eta}(x, y) \, dx \, dy$$

$$= P\{(\xi, \eta) \in C \times B\} = P\{(\xi \in C) \cap (\eta \in B)\},$$

which proves (17).

In a similar way we can show that if $E\xi$ exists, then

$$E(\xi|\eta = y) = \int_{-\infty}^{\infty} x f_{\xi|\eta}(x|y) \, dx. \tag{20}$$

EXAMPLE 3. Let the length of time that a piece of apparatus will continue to operate be described by a nonnegative random variable $\eta = \eta(\omega)$ whose distribution $F_\eta(y)$ has a density $f_\eta(y)$ (naturally, $F_\eta(y) = f_\eta(y) = 0$ for $y < 0$). Find the conditional expectation $E(\eta - a|\eta \geq a)$, i.e. the average time for which the apparatus will continue to operate on the hypothesis that it has already been operating for time a.

Let $P(\eta \geq a) > 0$. Then according to the definition (see Subsection 1) and (6.45),

$$E(\eta - a|\eta \geq a) = \frac{E[(\eta - a)I_{\{\eta \geq a\}}]}{P(\eta \geq a)} = \frac{\int_\Omega (\eta - a)I_{\{\eta \geq a\}} P(d\omega)}{P(\eta \geq a)}$$

$$= \frac{\int_a^\infty (y - a) f_\eta(y) \, dy}{\int_a^\infty f_\eta(y) \, dy}.$$

It is interesting to observe that if η is exponentially distributed, i.e.

$$f_\eta(y) = \begin{cases} \lambda e^{-\lambda y}, & y \geq 0, \\ 0 & y < 0, \end{cases} \tag{21}$$

then $E\eta = E(\eta|\eta \geq 0) = 1/\lambda$ and $E(\eta - a|\eta \geq a) = 1/\lambda$ for every $a > 0$. In other words, in this case the average time for which the apparatus continues to operate, assuming that it has already operated for time a, is independent of a and simply equals the average time $E\eta$.

Under the assumption (21) we can find the conditional distribution $P(\eta - a \leq x|\eta \geq a)$.

We have

$$P(\eta - a \leq x | \eta \geq a) = \frac{P(a \leq \eta \leq a + x)}{P(\eta \geq a)}$$

$$= \frac{F_\eta(a + x) - F_\eta(a) + P(\eta = a)}{1 - F_\eta(a) + P(\eta = a)}$$

$$= \frac{[1 - e^{-\lambda(a+x)}] - [1 - e^{-\lambda a}]}{1 - [1 - e^{-\lambda a}]}$$

$$= \frac{e^{-\lambda a}[1 - e^{-\lambda x}]}{e^{-\lambda a}} = 1 - e^{-\lambda x}.$$

Therefore the conditional distribution $P(\eta - a \leq x | \eta \geq a)$ is the same as the unconditional distribution $P(\eta \leq x)$. This remarkable property is unique to the exponential distribution: there are no other distributions that have densities and possess the property $P(\eta - a \leq x | \eta \geq a) = P(\eta \leq x)$, $a \geq 0, 0 \leq x < \infty$.

EXAMPLE 4 (Buffon's needle). Suppose that we toss a needle of unit length "at random" onto a pair of parallel straight lines, a unit distance apart, in a plane. What is the probability that the needle will intersect at least one of the lines?

To solve this problem we must first define what it means to toss the needle "at random." Let ξ be the distance from the midpoint of the needle to the left-hand line. We shall suppose that ξ is uniformly distributed on $[0, 1]$, and (see Figure 29) that the angle θ is uniformly distributed on $[-\pi/2, \pi/2]$. In addition, we shall assume that ξ and θ are independent.

Let A be the event that the needle intersects one of the lines. It is easy to see that if

$$B = \{(a, x): |a| \leq \frac{\pi}{2}, \quad x \in [0, \tfrac{1}{2}\cos a] \cup [1 - \tfrac{1}{2}\cos a, 1]\},$$

then $A = \{\omega: (\theta, \xi) \in B\}$, and therefore the probability in question is

$$P(A) = EI_A(\omega) = EI_B(\theta(\omega), \xi(\omega)).$$

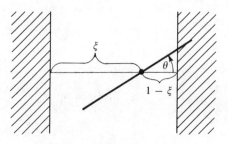

Figure 29

By Property **G*** and formula (16),

$$EI_B(\theta(\omega), \xi(\omega)) = E(E[I_B(\theta(\omega), \xi(\omega))|\theta(\omega)])$$

$$= \int_\Omega E[I_B(\theta(\omega), \xi(\omega))|\theta(\omega)]P(d\omega)$$

$$= \int_{-\pi/2}^{\pi/2} E[I_B(\theta(\omega), \xi(\omega))|\theta(\omega) = \alpha]P_\theta(da)$$

$$= \frac{1}{\pi}\int_{-\pi/2}^{\pi/2} EI_B(a, \xi(\omega))\, da = \frac{1}{\pi}\int_{-\pi/2}^{\pi/2} \cos a\, da = \frac{2}{\pi},$$

where we have used the fact that

$$EI_B(a, \xi(\omega)) = P\{\xi \in [0, \tfrac{1}{2}\cos a] \cup [1 - \tfrac{1}{2}\cos a]\} = \cos a.$$

Thus the probability that a "random" toss of the needle intersects one of the lines is $2/\pi$. This result could be used as the basis for an experimental evaluation of π. In fact, let the needle be tossed N times independently. Define ξ_i to be 1 if the needle intersects a line on the ith toss, and 0 otherwise. Then by the law of large numbers (see, for example, (I.5.6))

$$P\left\{\left|\frac{\xi_1 + \cdots + \xi_N}{N} - P(A)\right| > \varepsilon\right\} \to 0, \qquad N \to \infty.$$

for every $\varepsilon > 0$.

In this sense the frequency satisfies

$$\frac{\xi_1 + \cdots + \xi_N}{N} \approx P(A) = \frac{2}{\pi}$$

and therefore

$$\frac{2N}{\xi_1 + \cdots + \xi_N} \approx \pi.$$

This formula has actually been used for a statistical evaluation of π. In 1850, R. Wolf (an astronomer in Zurich) threw a needle 5000 times and obtained the value 3.1596 for π. Apparently this problem was one of the first applications (now known as Monte Carlo methods) of probabilistic-statistical regularities to numerical analysis.

7. If $\{\xi_n\}_{n \geq 1}$ is a sequence of nonnegative random variables, then according to conclusion (f) of Theorem 2,

$$E(\sum \xi_n|\mathscr{G}) = \sum E(\xi_n|\mathscr{G}) \quad \text{(a.s.)}$$

In particular, if $B_1, B_2, \ldots$ is a sequence of pairwise disjoint sets,

$$P(\sum B_n|\mathscr{G}) = \sum P(B_n|\mathscr{G}) \quad \text{(a.s.)} \tag{22}$$

It must be emphasized that this equation is satisfied only almost surely and that consequently the conditional probability $P(B|\mathcal{G})(\omega)$ cannot be considered as a measure on B for given ω. One might suppose that, except for a set $\mathcal{N}$ of measure zero, $P(\cdot|\mathcal{G})(\omega)$ would still be a measure for $\omega \in \mathcal{N}$. However, in general this is not the case, for the following reason. Let $\mathcal{N}(B_1, B_2, \ldots)$ be the set of sample points ω such that the countable additivity property (22) fails for these $B_1, B_2, \ldots$. Then the excluded set $\mathcal{N}$ is

$$\mathcal{N} = \bigcup \mathcal{N}(B_1, B_2, \ldots), \tag{23}$$

where the union is taken over all $B_1, B_2, \ldots$ in $\mathcal{F}$. Although the P-measure of each set $\mathcal{N}(B_1, B_2, \ldots)$ is zero, the P-measure of $\mathcal{N}$ can be different from zero (because of an uncountable union in (23)). (Recall that the Lebesgue measure of a single point is zero, but the measure of the set $\mathcal{N} = [0, 1]$, which is an uncountable sum of the individual points $\{x\}$, is 1).

However, it would be convenient if the conditional probability $P(\cdot|\mathcal{G})(\omega)$ were a measure for each $\omega \in \Omega$, since then, for example, the calculation of conditional probabilities $E(\xi|\mathcal{G})$ could be carried out (see Theorem 3 below) in a simple way by averaging with respect to the measure $P(\cdot|\mathcal{G})(\omega)$:

$$E(\xi|\mathcal{G}) = \int_\Omega \xi(\omega)P(d\omega|\mathcal{G}) \quad \text{(a.s.)}$$

(cf. (I.8.10)).

We introduce the following definition.

Definition 6. A function $P(\omega; B)$, defined for all $\omega \in \Omega$ and $B \in \mathcal{F}$, is a *regular* conditional probability with respect to $\mathcal{G}$ if

(a) $P(\omega; \cdot)$ is a probability measure on $\mathcal{F}$ for every $\omega \in \Omega$;
(b) For each $B \in \mathcal{F}$ the function $P(\omega; B)$, as a function of ω, is a variant of the conditional probability $P(B|\mathcal{G})(\omega)$, i.e. $P(\omega: B) = P(B|\mathcal{G})(\omega)$ (a.s.).

Theorem 3. *Let $P(\omega; B)$ be a regular conditional probability with respect to $\mathcal{G}$ and let ξ be an integrable random variable. Then*

$$E(\xi|\mathcal{G})(\omega) = \int_\Omega \xi(\tilde{\omega})P(\omega; d\tilde{\omega}) \quad \text{(a.s.)}. \tag{24}$$

PROOF. If $\xi = I_B$, $B \in \mathcal{F}$, the required formula (24) becomes

$$P(B|\mathcal{G})(\omega) = P(\omega; B) \quad \text{(a.s.)},$$

which holds by Definition 6(b). Consequently (24) holds for simple functions.

Now let $\xi \geq 0$ and $\xi_n \uparrow \xi$, where ξ_n are simple functions. Then by (b) of Theorem 2 we have $E(\xi|\mathscr{G})(\omega) = \lim_n E(\xi_n|\mathscr{G})(\omega)$ (a.s.). But since $P(\omega;\cdot)$ is a measure for every $\omega \in \Omega$, we have

$$\lim_n E(\xi_n|\mathscr{G})(\omega) = \lim_n \int_\Omega \xi_n(\tilde{\omega})P(\omega; d\tilde{\omega}) = \int_\Omega \xi(\tilde{\omega})P(\omega; d\tilde{\omega})$$

by the monotone convergence theorem.

The general case reduces to this one if we use the representation $\xi = \xi^+ - \xi^-$.

This completes the proof.

Corollary. *Let $\mathscr{G} = \mathscr{G}_\eta$, where η is a random variable, and let the pair (ξ, η) have a probability distribution with density $f_{\xi\eta}(x, y)$. Let $E|g(\xi)| < \infty$. Then*

$$E(g(\xi)|\eta = y) = \int_{-\infty}^\infty g(x)f_{\xi|\eta}(x|y)\, dx,$$

where $f_{\xi|\eta}(x|y)$ is the density of the conditional distribution (see (18)).

In order to be able to state the basic result on the existence of regular conditional probabilities, we need the following definitions.

Definition 7. Let $(E, \mathscr{E})$ be a measurable space, $X = X(\omega)$ a random element with values in E, and $\mathscr{G}$ a σ-subalgebra of $\mathscr{F}$. A function $Q(\omega; B)$, defined for $\omega \in \Omega$ and $B \in \mathscr{E}$ is a *regular conditional distribution of X with respect to $\mathscr{G}$* if

(a) for each $\omega \in \Omega$ the function $Q(\omega; B)$ is a probability measure on $(E, \mathscr{E})$;
(b) for each $B \in \mathscr{E}$ the function $Q(\omega; B)$, as a function of ω, is a variant of the conditional probability $P(X \in B|\mathscr{G})(\omega)$, i.e.

$$Q(\omega; B) = P(X \in B|\mathscr{G})(\omega) \quad \text{(a.s.)}.$$

Definition 8. Let ξ be a random variable. A function $F = F(\omega; x)$, $\omega \in \Omega$, $x \in R$, is a *regular distribution function for ξ with respect to $\mathscr{G}$* if :

(a) $F(\omega; x)$ is, for each $\omega \in \Omega$, a distribution function on R;
(b) $F(\omega; x) = P(\xi \leq x|\mathscr{G})(\omega)$ (a.s.), for each $x \in R$.

Theorem 4. *A regular distribution function and a regular conditional distribution function always exist for the random variable ξ with respect to $\mathscr{G}$.*

PROOF. For each rational number $r \in R$, define $F_r(\omega) = P(\xi \leq r|\mathcal{G})(\omega)$, where $P(\xi \leq r|\mathcal{G})(\omega) = E(I_{\{\xi \leq r\}}|\mathcal{G})(\omega)$ is any variant of the conditional probability, with respect to $\mathcal{G}$, of the event $\{\xi \leq r\}$. Let $\{r_i\}$ be the set of rational numbers in R. If $r_i < r_j$, Property **B*** implies that $P(\xi \leq r_i|\mathcal{G}) \leq P(\xi \leq r_j|\mathcal{G})$ (a.s.), and therefore if $A_{ij} = \{\omega: F_{r_j}(\omega) < F_{r_i}(\omega)\}$, $A = \bigcup A_{ij}$, we have $P(A) = 0$. In other words, the set of points ω at which the distribution function $F_r(\omega)$, $r \in \{r_i\}$, fails to be monotonic has measure zero.

Now let

$$B_i = \left\{\omega: \lim_{n \to \infty} F_{r_i + (1/n)}(\omega) \neq F_{r_i}(\omega)\right\}, \qquad B = \bigcup_{i=1}^{\infty} B_i.$$

It is clear that $I_{\{\xi \leq r_i + (1/n)\}} \downarrow I_{\{\xi \leq r_i\}}$, $n \to \infty$. Therefore, by (a) of Theorem 2, $F_{r_i + (1/n)}(\omega) \to F_{r_i}(\omega)$ (a.s.), and therefore the set B on which continuity on the right fails (with respect to the rational numbers) also has measure zero, $P(B) = 0$.

In addition, let

$$C = \left\{\omega: \lim_{n \to \infty} F_n(\omega) \neq 1\right\} \cup \left\{\omega: \lim_{n \to -\infty} F_n(\omega) > 0\right\}.$$

Then, since $\{\xi \leq n\} \uparrow \Omega$, $n \to \infty$, and $\{\xi \leq n\} \downarrow \varnothing$, $n \to -\infty$, we have $P(C) = 0$.

Now put

$$F(\omega; x) = \begin{cases} \lim_{r \downarrow x} F_r(\omega), & \omega \notin A \cup B \cup C, \\ G(x), & \omega \in A \cup B \cup C, \end{cases}$$

where $G(x)$ is any distribution function on R; we show that $F(\omega; x)$ satisfies the conditions of Definition 8.

Let $\omega \notin A \cup B \cup C$. Then it is clear that $F(\omega; x)$ is a nondecreasing function of x. If $x < x' \leq r$, then $F(\omega; x) \leq F(\omega; x') \leq F(\omega; r) = F_r(\omega) \downarrow F(\omega, x)$ when $r \downarrow x$. Consequently $F(\omega; x)$ is continuous on the right. Similarly $\lim_{x \to \infty} F(\omega; x) = 1$, $\lim_{x \to -\infty} F(\omega; x) = 0$. Since $F(\omega; x) = G(x)$ when $\omega \in A \cup B \cup C$, it follows that $F(\omega; x)$ is a distribution function on R for every $\omega \in \Omega$, i.e. condition (a) of Definition 8 is satisfied.

By construction, $P(\xi \leq r)|\mathcal{G})(\omega) = F_r(\omega) = F(\omega; r)$. If $r \downarrow x$, we have $F(\omega; r) \downarrow F(\omega; x)$ for all $\omega \in \Omega$ by the continuity on the right that we just established. But by conclusion (a) of Theorem 2, we have $P(\xi \leq r|\mathcal{G})(\omega) \to P(\xi \leq x|\mathcal{G})(\omega)$ (a.s.). Therefore $F(\omega; x) = P(\xi \leq x|G)(\omega)$ (a.s.), which establishes condition (b) of Definition 8.

We now turn to the proof of the existence of a regular conditional distribution of ξ with respect to $\mathcal{G}$.

Let $F(\omega; x)$ be the function constructed above. Put

$$Q(\omega; B) = \int_B F(\omega; dx),$$

where the integral is a Lebesgue–Stieltjes integral. From the properties of the integral (see §6, Subsection 7), it follows that $Q(\omega; B)$ is a measure on B for each given $\omega \in \Omega$. To establish that $Q(\omega; B)$ is a variant of the conditional probability $\mathsf{P}(\xi \in B | \mathscr{G})(\omega)$, we use the principle of appropriate sets.

Let $\mathscr{C}$ be the collection of sets B in $\mathscr{B}(R)$ for which $Q(\omega; B) = \mathsf{P}(\xi \in B | \mathscr{G})(\omega)$ (a.s.). Since $F(\omega; x) = \mathsf{P}(\xi \leq x | \mathscr{G})(\omega)$ (a.s.), the system $\mathscr{C}$ contains the sets B of the form $B = (-\infty, x]$, $x \in R$. Therefore $\mathscr{C}$ also contains the intervals of the form $(a, b]$, and the algebra $\mathscr{A}$ consisting of finite sums of disjoint sets of the form $(a, b]$. Then it follows from the continuity properties of $Q(\omega; B)$ (ω fixed) and from conclusion (b) of Theorem 2 that $\mathscr{C}$ is a monotone class, and since $\mathscr{A} \subseteq \mathscr{C} \subseteq \mathscr{B}(R)$, we have, from Theorem 1 of §2,

$$\mathscr{B}(R) = \sigma(\mathscr{A}) \subseteq \sigma(\mathscr{C}) = \mu(\mathscr{C}) = \mathscr{C} \subseteq \mathscr{B}(R),$$

whence $\mathscr{C} = \mathscr{B}(R)$.

This completes the proof of the theorem.

By using topological considerations we can extend the conclusion of Theorem 4 on the existence of a regular conditional distribution to random elements with values in what are known as Borel spaces. We need the following definition.

Definition 9. A measurable space $(E, \mathscr{E})$ is a *Borel space* if it is Borel equivalent to a Borel subset of the real line, i.e. there is a one-to-one mapping $\varphi = \varphi(e)$: $(E, \mathscr{E}) \rightarrow (R, \mathscr{B}(R))$ such that

(1) $\varphi(E) \equiv \{\varphi(e): e \in E\}$ is a set in $\mathscr{B}(R)$;
(2) φ is $\mathscr{E}$-measurable ($\varphi^{-1}(A) \in \mathscr{E}$, $A \in \varphi(E) \cap \mathscr{B}(R)$),
(3) φ^{-1} is $\mathscr{B}(R)/\mathscr{E}$-measurable ($\varphi(B) \in \varphi(E) \cap \mathscr{B}(R)$, $B \in \mathscr{E}$).

Theorem 5. *Let $X = X(\omega)$ be a random element with values in the Borel space $(E, \mathscr{E})$. Then there is a regular conditional distribution of X with respect to $\mathscr{G}$.*

PROOF. Let $\varphi = \varphi(e)$ be the function in Definition 9. By (2), $\varphi(X(\omega))$ is a random variable. Hence, by Theorem 4, we can define the conditional distribution $Q(\omega; A)$ of $\varphi(X(\omega))$ with respect to $\mathscr{G}$, $A \in \varphi(E) \cap \mathscr{B}(R)$.

We introduce the function $\tilde{Q}(\omega; B) = Q(\omega; \varphi(B))$, $B \in \mathscr{E}$. By (3) of Definition 9, $\varphi(B) \in \varphi(E) \cap \mathscr{B}(R)$ and consequently $\tilde{Q}(\omega; B)$ is defined. Evidently $\tilde{Q}(\omega; B)$ is a measure on $B \in \mathscr{E}$ for every ω. Now fix $B \in \mathscr{E}$. By the one-to-one character of the mapping $\varphi = \varphi(e)$,

$$\tilde{Q}(\omega; B) = Q(\omega; \varphi(B)) = \mathsf{P}\{\varphi(X) \in \varphi(B) | \mathscr{G}\} = \mathsf{P}\{X \in B | \mathscr{G}\} \quad \text{(a.s.)}.$$

Therefore $\tilde{Q}(\omega; B)$ is a regular conditional distribution of X with respect to $\mathscr{G}$.

This completes the proof of the theorem.

Corollary. *Let $X = X(\omega)$ be a random element with values in a complete separable metric space $(E, \mathcal{E})$. Then there is a regular conditional distribution of X with respect to $\mathcal{G}$. In particular, such a distribution exists for the spaces $(R^n, \mathcal{B}(R^n))$ and $(R^\infty, \mathcal{B}(R^\infty))$.*

The proof follows from Theorem 5 and the well known topological result that such spaces are Borel spaces.

8. The theory of conditional expectations developed above makes it possible to give a generalization of Bayes's theorem; this has applications in statistics.

Recall that if $\mathcal{D} = \{A_1, \ldots, A_n\}$ is a partition of the space Ω with $P(A_i) > 0$, Bayes's theorem (I.3.9) states that

$$P(A_i | B) = \frac{P(A_i)P(B|A_i)}{\sum_{j=1}^n P(A_j)P(B|A_j)}. \tag{25}$$

for every B with $P(B) > 0$. Therefore if $\theta = \sum_{i=1}^n a_i I_{A_i}$ is a discrete random variable then, according to (I.8.10),

$$E[g(\theta)|B] = \frac{\sum_{i=1}^n g(a_i)P(A_i)P(B|A_i)}{\sum_{j=1}^n P(A_j)P(B|A_j)}, \tag{26}$$

or

$$E[g(\theta)|B] = \frac{\int_{-\infty}^\infty g(a)P(B|\theta = a)P_\theta(da)}{\int_{-\infty}^\infty P(B|\theta = a)P_\theta(da)}. \tag{27}$$

On the basis of the definition of $E[g(\theta)|B]$ given at the beginning of this section, it is easy to establish that (27) holds for all events B with $P(B) > 0$, random variables θ and functions $g = g(a)$ with $E|g(\theta)| < \infty$.

We now consider an analog of (27) for conditional expectations $E[g(\theta)|\mathcal{G}]$ with respect to a σ-algebra $\mathcal{G}$, $\mathcal{G} \subseteq \mathcal{F}$.

Let

$$Q(B) = \int_B g(\theta)P(d\omega), \qquad B \in \mathcal{G}. \tag{28}$$

Then by (4)

$$E[g(\theta)|\mathcal{G}] = \frac{dQ}{dP}(\omega). \tag{29}$$

We also consider the σ-algebra $\mathcal{G}_\theta$. Then, by (5),

$$P(B) = \int_\Omega P(B|\mathcal{G}_\theta)\,dP \tag{30}$$

or, by the formula for change of variable in Lebesgue integrals,

$$P(B) = \int_{-\infty}^\infty P(B|\theta = a)P_0(da). \tag{31}$$

Since

$$Q(B) = E[g(\theta)I_B] = E[g(\theta) \cdot E(I_B|\mathscr{G}_\theta)],$$

we have

$$Q(B) = \int_{-\infty}^{\infty} g(a)P(B|\theta = a)P_\theta(da). \tag{32}$$

Now suppose that the conditional probability $P(B|\theta = a)$ is regular and admits the representation

$$P(B|\theta = a) = \int_B \rho(\omega; a)\lambda(d\omega), \tag{33}$$

where $\rho = \rho(\omega; a)$ is nonnegative and measurable in the two variables jointly, and λ is a σ-finite measure on $(\Omega, \mathscr{G})$.

Let $E|g(\theta)| < \infty$. Let us show that (P-a.s.)

$$E[g(\theta)|\mathscr{G}] = \frac{\int_{-\infty}^{\infty} g(a)\rho(\omega; a)P_\theta(da)}{\int_{-\infty}^{\infty} \rho(\omega; a)P_\theta(da)} \tag{34}$$

(*generalized Bayes theorem*).

In proving (34) we shall need the following lemma.

Lemma. *Let (Ω, F) be a measurable space.*

(a) *Let μ and λ be σ-finite measures, and $f = f(\omega)$ an $\mathscr{F}$-measurable function. Then*

$$\int_\Omega f \, d\mu = \int_\Omega f \frac{d\mu}{d\lambda} \cdot d\lambda \tag{35}$$

(in the sense that if either integral exists, the other exists and they are equal).

(b) *If ν is a signed measure and μ, λ are σ-finite measures $\nu \ll \mu$, $\mu \ll \lambda$, then*

$$\frac{d\nu}{d\lambda} = \frac{d\nu}{d\mu} \cdot \frac{d\mu}{d\lambda} \quad (\lambda\text{-a.s.}) \tag{36}$$

and

$$\frac{d\nu}{d\mu} = \frac{d\nu}{d\lambda} \bigg/ \frac{d\mu}{d\lambda} \quad (\mu\text{-a.s.}) \tag{37}$$

PROOF. (a) Since

$$\mu(A) = \int_A \left(\frac{d\mu}{d\lambda}\right) d\lambda, \qquad A \in \mathscr{F},$$

(35) is evidently satisfied for simple functions $f = \sum f_i I_{A_i}$. The general case follows from the representation $f = f^+ - f^-$ and the monotone convergence theorem.

(b) From (a) with $f = dv/d\mu$ we obtain

$$v(A) = \int_A \left(\frac{dv}{d\mu}\right) d\mu = \int_A \left(\frac{dv}{d\mu}\right) \cdot \left(\frac{d\mu}{d\lambda}\right) \cdot d\lambda.$$

Then $v \ll \lambda$ and therefore

$$v(A) = \int_A \frac{dv}{d\lambda} d\lambda,$$

whence (36) follows since A is arbitrary, by Property I (§6).

Property (37) follows from (36) and the remark that

$$\mu\left\{\omega: \frac{d\mu}{d\lambda} = 0\right\} = \int_{\{\omega: d\mu/d\lambda = 0\}} \frac{d\mu}{d\lambda} d\lambda = 0$$

(on the set $\{\omega: d\mu/d\lambda = 0\}$ the right-hand side of (37) can be defined arbitrarily, for example as zero). This completes the proof of the lemma.

To prove (34) we observe that by Fubini's theorem and (33),

$$Q(B) = \int_B \left[\int_{-\infty}^{\infty} g(a)\rho(\omega; a)P_\theta(da)\right]\lambda(d\omega), \qquad (38)$$

$$P(B) = \int_B \left[\int_{-\infty}^{\infty} \rho(\omega; a)P_\theta(da)\right]\lambda(d\omega). \qquad (39)$$

Then by the lemma

$$\frac{dQ}{dP} = \frac{dQ/d\lambda}{dP/d\lambda} \quad \text{(P-a.s.)}.$$

Taking account of (38), (39) and (29), we have (34).

Remark. Formula (34) remains valid if we replace θ by a random element with values in some measurable space $(E, \mathscr{E})$ (and replace integration over R by integration over E).

Let us consider some special cases of (34).

Let the σ-algebra $\mathscr{G}$ be generated by the random variable ξ, $\mathscr{G} = \mathscr{G}_\xi$. Suppose that

$$P(\xi \in A | \theta = a) = \int_A q(x; a)\lambda(dx), \qquad A \in \mathscr{B}(R), \qquad (40)$$

where $q = q(x; a)$ is a nonnegative function, measurable with respect to both variables jointly, and λ is a σ-finite measure on $(R, \mathscr{B}(R))$. Then we obtain

$$E[g(\theta)|\xi = x] = \frac{\int_{-\infty}^{\infty} g(a)q(x; a)P_\theta(da)}{\int_{-\infty}^{\infty} q(x; a)P_\theta(da)}. \qquad (41)$$

In particular, let (θ, ξ) be a pair of discrete random variables, $\theta = \sum a_i I_{A_i}$, $\xi = \sum x_j I_{B_j}$. Then, taking λ to be the *counting* measure $(\lambda(\{x_i\}) = 1, i = 1, 2, \ldots)$ we find from (40) that

$$E[g(\theta)|\xi = x_j] = \frac{\sum_i g(a_i)P(\xi = x_j|\theta = a_i)P(\theta = a_i)}{\sum_i P(\xi = x_j|\theta = a_i)P(\theta = a_i)}. \qquad (42)$$

(Compare (26).)

Now let (θ, ξ) be a pair of absolutely continuous measures with density $f_{\theta, \xi}(a, x)$. Then by (19) the representation (40) applies with $q(x; a) = f_{\xi|\theta}(x|a)$ and Lebesgue measure λ. Therefore

$$E[g(\theta)|\xi = x] = \frac{\int_{-\infty}^{\infty} g(a) f_{\xi|\theta}(x|a) f_\theta(a) \, da}{\int_{-\infty}^{\infty} f_{\xi|\theta}(x|a) f_\theta(a) \, da}. \qquad (43)$$

9. PROBLEMS

1. Let ξ and η be independent identically distributed random variables with $E\xi$ defined. Show that

$$E(\xi|\xi + \eta) = E(\eta|\xi + \eta) = \frac{\xi + \eta}{2} \quad \text{(a.s.)}.$$

2. Let $\xi_1, \xi_2, \ldots$ be independent identically distributed random variables with $E|\xi_i| < \infty$. Show that

$$E(\xi_1 | S_n, S_{n+1}, \ldots) = \frac{S_n}{n} \quad \text{(a.s.)},$$

where $S_n = \xi_1 + \cdots + \xi_n$.

3. Suppose that the random elements (X, Y) are such that there is a regular distribution $P_x(B) = P(Y \in B | X = x)$. Show that if $E|g(X, Y)| < \infty$ then

$$E[g(X, Y)|X = x] = \int g(x, y) P_x(dy) \quad (P_x\text{-a.s.}).$$

4. Let ξ be a random variable with distribution function $F_\xi(x)$. Show that

$$E(\xi|\alpha < \xi \le b) = \frac{\int_a^b x \, dF_\xi(x)}{F_\xi(b) - F_\xi(a)}$$

(assuming that $F_\xi(b) - F_\xi(a) > 0$).

5. Let $g = g(x)$ be a convex Borel function with $E|g(\xi)| < \infty$. Show that Jensen's inequality

$$g(E(\xi|\mathscr{G})) \le E(g(\xi)|\mathscr{G})$$

holds for the conditional expectations.

6. Show that a necessary and sufficient condition for the random variable ξ and the σ-algebra $\mathcal{G}$ to be independent (i.e., the random variables ξ and $I_B(\omega)$ are independent for every $B \in \mathcal{G}$) is that $\mathsf{E}(g(\xi)|\mathcal{G}) = \mathsf{E}g(\xi)$ for every Borel function $g(x)$ with $\mathsf{E}|g(\xi)| < \infty$.

7. Let ξ be a nonnegative random variable and $\mathcal{G}$ a σ-algebra, $\mathcal{G} \subseteq \mathcal{F}$. Show that $\mathsf{E}(\xi|\mathcal{G}) < \infty$ (a.s.) if and only if the measure Q, defined on sets $A \in \mathcal{G}$ by $\mathsf{Q}(A) = \int_A \xi \, d\mathsf{P}$, is σ-finite.

§8. Random Variables. II

1. In the first chapter we introduced characteristics of simple random variables, such as the variance, covariance, and correlation coefficient. These extend similarly to the general case. Let $(\Omega, \mathcal{F}, \mathsf{P})$ be a probability space and $\xi = \xi(\omega)$ a random variable for which $\mathsf{E}\xi$ is defined.

The variance of ξ is

$$\mathsf{V}\xi = \mathsf{E}(\xi - \mathsf{E}\xi)^2.$$

The number $\sigma = +\sqrt{\mathsf{V}\xi}$ is the *standard deviation*.

If ξ is a random variable with a Gaussian (normal) density

$$f_\xi(x) = \frac{1}{\sqrt{2\pi}\sigma} e^{-[(x-m)^2]/2\sigma^2}, \qquad \sigma > 0, \quad -\infty < m < \infty, \tag{1}$$

the parameters m and σ in (1) are very simple:

$$m = \mathsf{E}\xi, \qquad \sigma^2 = \mathsf{V}\xi.$$

Hence the probability distribution of this random variable ξ, which we call *Gaussian*, or *normally distributed*, is completely determined by its mean value m and variance σ^2. (It is often convenient to write $\xi \sim \mathcal{N}(m, \sigma^2)$.)

Now let (ξ, η) be a pair of random variables. Their covariance is

$$\mathrm{cov}(\xi, \eta) = \mathsf{E}(\xi - \mathsf{E}\xi)(\eta - \mathsf{E}\eta) \tag{2}$$

(assuming that the expectations are defined).

If $\mathrm{cov}(\xi, \eta) = 0$ we say that ξ and η are *uncorrelated*.

If $\mathsf{V}\xi > 0$ and $\mathsf{V}\eta > 0$, the number

$$\rho(\xi, \eta) \equiv \frac{\mathrm{cov}(\xi, \eta)}{\sqrt{\mathsf{D}\xi \cdot \mathsf{D}\eta}} \tag{3}$$

is the *correlation coefficient* of ξ and η.

The properties of variance, covariance, and correlation coefficient were investigated in §4 of Chapter I for simple random variables. In the general case these properties can be stated in a completely analogous way.

Let $\xi = (\xi_1, \ldots, \xi_n)$ be a random vector whose components have finite second moments. The *covariance matrix* of ξ is the $n \times n$ matrix $\mathbb{R} = \|R_{ij}\|$, where $R_{ij} = \text{cov}(\xi_i, \xi_j)$. It is clear that $\mathbb{R}$ is *symmetric*. Moreover, it is *nonnegative definite*, i.e.

$$\sum_{i,j=1}^{n} R_{ij}\lambda_i\lambda_j \geq 0$$

for all $\lambda_i \in R, i = 1, \ldots, n$, since

$$\sum_{i,j}^{n} R_{ij}\lambda_i\lambda_j = \mathsf{E}\left[\sum_{i=1}^{n} (\xi_i - \mathsf{E}\xi_i)\lambda_i\right]^2 \geq 0.$$

The following lemma shows that the converse is also true.

Lemma. *A necessary and sufficient condition that an $n \times n$ matrix $\mathbb{R}$ is the covariance matrix of a vector $\xi = (\xi_1, \ldots, \xi_n)$ is that the matrix is symmetric and nonnegative definite, or, equivalently, that there is an $n \times k$ matrix A $(1 \leq k \leq n)$ such that*

$$\mathbb{R} = AA^{\mathsf{T}},$$

where T *denotes the transpose.*

PROOF. We showed above that every covariance matrix is symmetric and nonnegative definite.

Conversely, let $\mathbb{R}$ be a matrix with these properties. We know from matrix theory that corresponding to every symmetric nonnegative definite matrix $\mathbb{R}$ there is an orthogonal matrix $\mathcal{O}$ (i.e., $\mathcal{O}\mathcal{O}^{\mathsf{T}} = E$, the unit matrix) such that

$$\mathcal{O}^{\mathsf{T}}\mathbb{R}\mathcal{O} = D,$$

where

$$D = \begin{pmatrix} d_1 & & 0 \\ & \ddots & \\ 0 & & d_n \end{pmatrix}$$

is a diagonal matrix with nonnegative elements $d_i, i = 1, \ldots, n$.

It follows that

$$\mathbb{R} = \mathcal{O}D\mathcal{O}^{\mathsf{T}} = (\mathcal{O}B)(B^{\mathsf{T}}\mathcal{O}^{\mathsf{T}}),$$

where B is the diagonal matrix with elements $b_i = +\sqrt{d_i}, i = 1, \ldots, n$. Consequently if we put $A = \mathcal{O}B$ we have the required representation $\mathbb{R} = AA^{\mathsf{T}}$ for $\mathbb{R}$.

It is clear that every matrix AA^{T} is symmetric and nonnegative definite. Consequently we have only to show that $\mathbb{R}$ is the covariance matrix of some random vector.

Let $\eta_1, \eta_2, \ldots, \eta_n$ be a sequence of independent normally distributed random variables, $\mathcal{N}(0, 1)$. (The existence of such a sequence follows, for example, from Corollary 1 of Theorem 1, §9, and in principle could easily be derived from Theorem 2 of §3.) Then the random vector $\xi = A\eta$ (vectors are thought of as column vectors) has the required properties. In fact,

$$\mathsf{E}\xi\xi^{\mathsf{T}} = \mathsf{E}(A\eta)(A\eta)^{\mathsf{T}} = A \cdot \mathsf{E}\eta\eta^{\mathsf{T}} \cdot A^{\mathsf{T}} = A\mathsf{E}A^{\mathsf{T}} = AA^{\mathsf{T}}.$$

(If $\zeta = \|\zeta_{ij}\|$ is a matrix whose elements are random variables, $\mathsf{E}\zeta$ means the matrix $\|\mathsf{E}\zeta_{ij}\|$).

This completes the proof of the lemma.

We now turn our attention to the two-dimensional Gaussian (normal) density

$$f_{\xi\eta}(x, y) = \frac{1}{2\pi\sigma_1\sigma_2\sqrt{1 - \rho^2}} \exp\left\{ -\frac{1}{2(1 - \rho^2)} \left[\frac{(x - m_1)^2}{\sigma_1^2} \right.\right.$$
$$\left.\left. - 2\rho\frac{(x - m_1)(y - m_2)}{\sigma_1\sigma_2} + \frac{(y - m_2)^2}{\sigma_2^2} \right]\right\}, \tag{4}$$

characterized by the five parameters $m_1, m_2, \sigma_1, \sigma_2$ and ρ (cf. (3.14)), where $|m_1| < \infty, |m_2| < \infty, \sigma_1 > 0, \sigma_2 > 0, |\rho| < 1$. An easy calculation identifies these parameters:

$$m_1 = \mathsf{E}\xi, \quad \sigma_1^2 = \mathsf{V}\xi,$$
$$m_2 = \mathsf{E}\eta, \quad \sigma_2^2 = \mathsf{V}\eta,$$
$$\rho = \rho(\xi, \eta).$$

In §4 of Chapter I we explained that if ξ and η are uncorrelated ($\rho(\xi, \eta) = 0$), it does not follow that they are independent. However, if the pair (ξ, η) is Gaussian, it does follow that if ξ and η are uncorrelated then they are independent.

In fact, if $\rho = 0$ in (4), then

$$f_{\xi\eta}(x, y) = \frac{1}{2\pi\sigma_1\sigma_2} e^{-[(x - m_1)2]/2\sigma_1^2} \cdot e^{-[(y - m_1)^2]/2\sigma_2^2}.$$

But by (6.55) and (4),

$$f_\xi(x) = \int_{-\infty}^\infty f_{\xi\eta}(x, y)\, dy = \frac{1}{\sqrt{2\pi}\sigma_1} e^{-[(x - m_1)^2]/2\sigma_1^2},$$
$$f_\eta(y) = \int_{-\infty}^\infty f_{\xi\eta}(x, y)\, dx = \frac{1}{\sqrt{2\pi}\sigma_2} e^{-[(y - m_2)^2]/2\sigma_2^2}.$$

Consequently

$$f_{\xi\eta}(x, y) = f_\xi(x) \cdot f_\eta(y),$$

from which it follows that ξ and η are independent (see the end of Subsection 8 of §6).

2. A striking example of the utility of the concept of conditional expectation (introduced in §7) is its application to the solution of the following problem which is connected with *estimation theory* (cf. Subsection 8 of §4 of Chapter I).

Let (ξ, η) be a pair of random variables such that ξ is observable but η is not. We ask how the unobservable component η can be "estimated" from the knowledge of observations of ξ.

To state the problem more precisely, we need to define the concept of an *estimator*. Let $\varphi = \varphi(x)$ be a Borel function. We call the random variable $\varphi(\xi)$ an estimator of η in terms of ξ, and $E[\eta - \varphi(\xi)]^2$ the (mean square) error of this estimator. An estimator $\varphi^*(\xi)$ is called *optimal* (in the mean-square sense) if

$$\Delta \equiv E[\eta - \varphi^*(\xi)]^2 = \inf_{\varphi} E[\eta - \varphi(\xi)]^2, \tag{5}$$

where inf is taken over all Borel functions $\varphi = \varphi(x)$.

Theorem 1. *Let* $E\eta^2 < \infty$. *Then there is an optimal estimator* $\varphi^* = \varphi^*(\xi)$ *and* $\varphi^*(x)$ *can be taken to be the function*

$$\varphi^*(x) = E(\eta \mid \xi = x). \tag{6}$$

PROOF. Without loss of generality we may consider only estimators $\varphi(\xi)$ for which $E\varphi^2(\xi) < \infty$. Then if $\varphi(\xi)$ is such an estimator, and $\varphi^*(\xi) = E(\eta \mid \xi)$, we have

$$\begin{aligned}
E[\eta - \varphi(\xi)]^2 &= E[(\eta - \varphi^*(\xi)) + (\varphi^*(\xi) - \varphi(\xi))]^2 \\
&= E[\eta - \varphi^*(\xi)]^2 + E[\varphi^*(\xi) - \varphi(\xi)]^2 \\
&\quad + 2E[(\eta - \varphi^*(\xi))(\varphi^*(\xi) - \varphi(\xi))] \geq E[\eta - \varphi^*(\xi)]^2,
\end{aligned}$$

since $E[\varphi^*(\xi) - \varphi(\xi)]^2 \geq 0$ and, by the properties of conditional expectations,

$$\begin{aligned}
E[(\eta - \varphi^*(\xi))(\varphi^*(\xi) - \varphi(\xi))] &= E\{E[(\eta - \varphi^*(\xi))(\varphi^*(\xi) - \varphi(\xi))] \mid \xi]\} \\
&= E\{(\varphi^*(\xi) - \varphi(\xi))E(\eta - \varphi^*(\xi) \mid \xi)\} = 0.
\end{aligned}$$

This completes the proof of the theorem.

Remark. It is clear from the proof that the conclusion of the theorem is still valid when ξ is not merely a random variable but any random element with values in a measurable space $(E, \mathscr{E})$. We would then assume that $\varphi = \varphi(x)$ is an $\mathscr{E}/\mathscr{B}(R)$-measurable function.

Let us consider the form of $\varphi^*(x)$ on the hypothesis that (ξ, η) is a Gaussian pair with density given by (4).

From (1), (4) and (7.10) we find that the density $f_{\eta|\xi}(y|x)$ of the conditional probability distribution is given by

$$f_{\eta|\xi}(y|x) = \frac{1}{\sqrt{2\pi(1-\rho^2)}\sigma_2}\, e^{[(y-m(x))^2]/[2\sigma_2^2(1-\rho^2)]}, \tag{7}$$

where

$$m(x) = m_2 + \frac{\sigma_2}{\sigma_1}\rho\cdot(x - m_1). \tag{8}$$

Then by the Corollary of Theorem 3, §7,

$$E(\eta|\xi = x) = \int_{-\infty}^{\infty} y f_{\eta|\xi}(y|x)\, dy = m(x) \tag{9}$$

and

$$V(\eta|\xi = x) \equiv E[(\eta - E(\eta|\xi = x))^2|\xi = x]$$
$$= \int_{-\infty}^{\infty} (y - m(x))^2 f_{\eta|\xi}(y|x)\, dy$$
$$= \sigma_2^2(1 - \rho^2). \tag{10}$$

Notice that the conditional variance $V(\eta|\xi = x)$ is independent of x and therefore

$$\Delta = E[\eta - E(\eta|\xi = x)]^2 = \sigma_2^2(1 - \rho^2). \tag{11}$$

Formulas (9) and (11) were obtained under the assumption that $V\xi > 0$ and $V\eta > 0$. However, if $V\xi > 0$ and $V\eta = 0$ they are still evidently valid. Hence we have the following result (cf. (I.4.16) and (I.4.17)).

Theorem 2. Let (ξ, η) be a Gaussian vector with $V\xi > 0$. Then the optimal estimator of η in terms of ξ is

$$E(\eta|\xi) = E\eta + \frac{\text{cov}(\xi, \eta)}{E\xi}(\xi - E\xi), \tag{12}$$

and its error is

$$\Delta \equiv E[\eta - E(\eta|\xi)]^2 = V\eta - \frac{\text{cov}^2(\xi, \eta)}{V\xi}. \tag{13}$$

Remark. The curve $y(x) = E(\eta|\xi = x)$ is the *curve of regression* of η on ξ or *of η with respect to ξ*. In the Gaussian case $E(\eta|\xi = x) = a + bx$ and consequently the regression of η and ξ is linear. Hence it is not surprising that the right-hand sides of (12) and (13) agree with the corresponding parts of (I.4.6) and (I.4.17) for the optimal linear estimator and its error.

Corollary. *Let ε_1 and ε_2 be independent Gaussian random variables with mean zero and unit variance, and*

$$\xi = a_1\varepsilon_1 + a_2\varepsilon_2, \qquad \eta = b_1\varepsilon_1 + b_2\varepsilon_2.$$

Then $\mathsf{E}\xi = \mathsf{E}\eta = 0$, $\mathsf{V}\xi = a_1^2 + a_2^2$, $\mathsf{V}\eta = b_1^2 + b_2^2$, $\mathrm{cov}(\xi, \eta) = a_1b_1 + a_2b_2$, and if $a_1^2 + a_2^2 > 0$, then

$$\mathsf{E}(\eta|\xi) = \frac{a_1b_1 + a_2b_2}{a_1^2 + a_2^2}\, \xi, \tag{14}$$

$$\Delta = \frac{(a_1b_2 - a_2b_1)^2}{a_1^2 + a_2^2}. \tag{15}$$

3. Let us consider the problem of determining the distribution functions of random variables that are functions of other random variables.

Let ξ be a random variable with distribution function $F_\xi(x)$ (and density $f_\xi(x)$, if it exists), let $\varphi = \varphi(x)$ be a Borel function and $\eta = \varphi(\xi)$. Letting $I_y = (-\infty, y)$, we obtain

$$F_\eta(y) = \mathsf{P}(\eta \le y) = \mathsf{P}(\varphi(\xi) \in I_y) = \mathsf{P}(\xi \in \varphi^{-1}(I_y)) = \int_{\varphi^{-1}(I_y)} F_\xi(dx), \tag{16}$$

which expresses the distribution function $F_\eta(y)$ in terms of $F_\xi(x)$ and φ.

For example, if $\eta = a\xi + b$, $a > 0$, we have

$$F_\eta(y) = \mathsf{P}\left(\xi \le \frac{y-b}{a}\right) = F_\xi\left(\frac{y-b}{a}\right). \tag{17}$$

If $\eta = \xi^2$, it is evident that $F_\eta(y) = 0$ for $y < 0$, while for $y \ge 0$

$$F_\eta(y) = \mathsf{P}(\xi^2 \le y) = \mathsf{P}(-\sqrt{y} \le \xi \le \sqrt{y})$$
$$= F_\xi(\sqrt{y}) - F_\xi(-\sqrt{y}) + \mathsf{P}(\xi = -\sqrt{y}). \tag{18}$$

We now turn to the problem of determining $f_\eta(y)$.

Let us suppose that the range of ξ is a (finite or infinite) open interval $I = (a, b)$, and that the function $\varphi = \varphi(x)$, with domain (a, b), is continuously differentiable and either strictly increasing or strictly decreasing. We also suppose that $\varphi'(x) \ne 0$, $x \in I$. Let us write $h(y) = \varphi^{-1}(y)$ and suppose for definiteness that $\varphi(x)$ is strictly increasing. Then when $y \in \varphi(I)$,

$$F_\eta(y) = \mathsf{P}(\eta \le y) = \mathsf{P}(\varphi(\xi) \le y) = \mathsf{P}(\xi \le \varphi^{-1}(y))$$
$$= \mathsf{P}(\xi \le h(y)) = \int_{-\infty}^{h(y)} f_\xi(x)\, dx. \tag{19}$$

By Problem 15 of §6,

$$\int_{-\infty}^{h(y)} f_\xi(x) \, dx = \int_{-\infty}^{y} f_\xi(h(z))h'(z) \, dz \tag{20}$$

and therefore

$$f_\eta(y) = f_\xi(h(y))h'(y). \tag{21}$$

Similarly, if $\varphi(x)$ is strictly decreasing,

$$f_\eta(y) = f_\xi(h(y))((-h'(y))).$$

Hence in either case

$$f_\eta(y) = f_\xi(h(y))|h'(y)|. \tag{22}$$

For example, if $\eta = a\xi + b$, $a \neq 0$, we have

$$h(y) = \frac{y - b}{a} \quad \text{and} \quad f_\eta(y) = \frac{1}{|a|} f_\xi\left(\frac{y - b}{a}\right).$$

If $\xi \sim \mathcal{N}(m, \sigma^2)$ and $\eta = e^\xi$, we find from (22) that

$$f_\eta(y) = \begin{cases} \dfrac{1}{\sqrt{2\pi}\,\sigma y} \exp\left[-\dfrac{\ln(y/M)^2}{2\sigma^2}\right], & y > 0, \\ 0 & y \leq 0, \end{cases} \tag{23}$$

with $M = e^m$.

A probability distribution with the density (23) is said to be *lognormal* (logarithmically normal).

If $\varphi = \varphi(x)$ is neither strictly increasing nor strictly decreasing, formula (22) is inapplicable. However, the following generalization suffices for many applications.

Let $\varphi = \varphi(x)$ be defined on the set $\sum_{k=1}^{n} [a_k, b_k]$, continuously differentiable and either strictly increasing or strictly decreasing on each open interval $I_k = (a_k, b_k)$, and with $\varphi'(x) \neq 0$ for $x \in I_k$. Let $h_k = h_k(y)$ be the inverse of $\varphi(x)$ for $x \in I_k$. Then we have the following generalization of (22):

$$f_\eta(y) = \sum_{k=1}^{n} f_\xi(h_k(y))|h_k'(y)| \cdot I_{D_k}(y), \tag{24}$$

where D_k is the domain of $h_k(y)$.

For example, if $\eta = \xi^2$ we can take $I_1 = (-\infty, 0)$, $I_2 = (0, \infty)$, and find that $h_1(y) = -\sqrt{y}$, $h_2(y) = \sqrt{y}$, and therefore

$$f_\eta(y) = \begin{cases} \dfrac{1}{2\sqrt{y}} [f_\xi(\sqrt{y}) + f_\xi(-\sqrt{y})], & y > 0, \\ 0, & y \leq 0. \end{cases} \tag{25}$$

We can observe that this result also follows from (18), since $P(\xi = -\sqrt{y}) = 0$. In particular, if $\xi \sim \mathcal{N}(0, 1)$,

$$f_{\xi^2}(y) = \begin{cases} \dfrac{1}{\sqrt{2\pi y}}\, e^{-y/2}, & y > 0, \\ 0, & y \le 0. \end{cases} \tag{26}$$

A straightforward calculation shows that

$$f_{|\xi|}(y) = \begin{cases} f_\xi(y) + f_\xi(-y), & y > 0, \\ 0, & y \le 0. \end{cases} \tag{27}$$

$$f_{+\sqrt{|\xi|}}(y) = \begin{cases} 2y(f_\xi(y^2) + f_\xi(-y^2)), & y > 0, \\ 0, & y \le 0. \end{cases} \tag{28}$$

4. We now consider functions of several random variables.

If ξ and η are random variables with joint distribution $F_{\xi\eta}(x, y)$, and $\varphi = \varphi(x, y)$ is a Borel function, then if we put $\zeta = \varphi(\xi, \eta)$ we see at once that

$$F_\zeta(z) = \int_{\{x, y:\, \varphi(x, y) \le z\}} dF_{\xi\eta}(x, y). \tag{29}$$

For example, if $\varphi(x, y) = x + y$, and ξ and η are independent (and therefore $F_{\xi\eta}(x, y) = F_\xi(x) \cdot F_\eta(y)$) then Fubini's theorem shows that

$$F_\zeta(z) = \int_{\{x, y:\, x+y \le z\}} dF_\xi(x) \cdot dF_\eta(y)$$

$$= \int_{R^2} I_{\{x+y \le z\}}(x, y)\, dF_\xi(x)\, dF_\eta(y)$$

$$= \int_{-\infty}^{\infty} dF_\xi(x)\left\{\int_{-\infty}^{\infty} I_{\{x+y \le z\}}(x, y)\, dF_\eta(y)\right\} = \int_{-\infty}^{\infty} F_\eta(z - x)\, dF_\xi(x) \tag{30}$$

and similarly

$$F_\zeta(z) = \int_{-\infty}^{\infty} F_\xi(z - y)\, dF_\eta(y). \tag{31}$$

If F and G are distribution functions, the function

$$H(z) = \int_{-\infty}^{\infty} F(z - x)\, dG(x)$$

is denoted by $F * G$ and called the *convolution* of F and G.

Thus *the distribution function F_ζ of the sum of two independent random variables ξ and η is the convolution of their distribution functions F_ξ and F_η*:

$$F_\zeta = F_\xi * F_\eta.$$

It is clear that $F_\xi * F_\eta = F_\eta * F_\xi$.

Now suppose that the independent random variables ξ and η have densities f_ξ and f_η. Then we find from (31), with another application of Fubini's theorem, that

$$F_\zeta(z) = \int_{-\infty}^{\infty} \left[\int_{-\infty}^{z-y} f_\xi(u)\, du \right] f_\eta(y)\, dy$$

$$= \int_{-\infty}^{\infty} \left[\int_{-\infty}^{z} f_\xi(u-y)\, du \right] f_\eta(y)\, dy = \int_{-\infty}^{z} \left[\int_{-\infty}^{\infty} f_\xi(u-y) f_\eta(y)\, dy \right] du,$$

whence

$$f_\zeta(z) = \int_{-\infty}^{\infty} f_\xi(z-y) f_\eta(y)\, dy, \tag{32}$$

and similarly

$$f_\zeta(z) = \int_{-\infty}^{\infty} f_\eta(z-x) f_\xi(x)\, dx. \tag{33}$$

Let us see some examples of the use of these formulas.

Let $\xi_1, \xi_2, \ldots, \xi_n$ be a sequence of independent identically distributed random variables with the uniform density on $[-1, 1]$:

$$f(x) = \begin{cases} \frac{1}{2}, & |x| \leq 1, \\ 0, & |x| > 1. \end{cases}$$

Then by (32) we have

$$f_{\xi_1+\xi_2}(x) = \begin{cases} \dfrac{2-|x|}{4}, & |x| \leq 2, \\[2mm] 0, & |x| > 2, \end{cases}$$

$$f_{\xi_1+\xi_2+\xi_3}(x) = \begin{cases} \dfrac{(3-|x|)^2}{16}, & 1 \leq |x| \leq 3, \\[2mm] \dfrac{3-x^2}{8}, & 0 \leq |x| \leq 1, \\[2mm] 0, & |x| > 3, \end{cases}$$

and by induction

$$f_{\xi_1+\cdots+\xi_n}(x) = \begin{cases} \dfrac{1}{2^n(n-1)!} \displaystyle\sum_{k=0}^{[(n+x)/2]} (-1)^k C_n^k (n+x-2k)^{n-1}, & |x| \leq n, \\[2mm] 0, & |x| > n. \end{cases}$$

Now let $\xi \sim \mathcal{N}(m_1, \sigma_1^2)$ and $\eta \sim \mathcal{N}(m_2, \sigma_2^2)$. If we write

$$\varphi(x) = \frac{1}{\sqrt{2\pi}}\, e^{-x^2/2},$$

then

$$f_\xi(x) = \frac{1}{\sigma_1} \varphi\left(\frac{x - m_1}{\sigma_1}\right), \qquad f_\eta(x) = \frac{1}{\sigma_2} \varphi\left(\frac{x - m_2}{\sigma_2}\right),$$

and the formula

$$f_{\xi+\eta}(x) = \frac{1}{\sqrt{\sigma_1^2 + \sigma_2^2}} \varphi\left(\frac{x - (m_1 + m_2)}{\sqrt{\sigma_1^2 + \sigma_2^2}}\right)$$

follows easily from (32).

Therefore the *sum of two independent Gaussian random variables is again a Gaussian random variable with mean* $m_1 + m_2$ *and variance* $\sigma_1^2 + \sigma_2^2$.

Let $\xi_1, \ldots, \xi_n$ be independent random variables each of which is normally distributed with mean 0 and variance 1. Then it follows easily from (26) (by induction) that

$$f_{\xi_1^2 + \cdots + \xi_n^2}(x) = \begin{cases} \dfrac{1}{2^{n/2}\Gamma(n/2)} x^{(n/2)-1} e^{-x/2}, & x > 0, \\ 0, & x \le 0. \end{cases} \tag{34}$$

The variable $\xi_1^2 + \cdots + \xi_n^2$ is usually denoted by χ_n^2, and its distribution (with density (30)) is the χ^2-*distribution* ("chi-square distribution") with n degrees of freedom (cf. Table 2 in §3).

If we write $\chi_n = +\sqrt{\chi_n^2}$, it follows from (28) and (34) that

$$f_{\chi_n}(x) = \begin{cases} \dfrac{2x^{n-1} e^{-x^2/2}}{2^{n/2}\Gamma(n/2)}, & x \ge 0, \\ 0, & x < 0. \end{cases} \tag{35}$$

The probability distribution with this density is the χ-distribution (chi-distribution) with n degrees of freedom.

Again let ξ and η be independent random variables with densities f_ξ and f_η. Then

$$F_{\xi\eta}(z) = \iint\limits_{\{x, y: xy \le z\}} f_\xi(x) f_\eta(y) \, dx \, dy,$$

$$F_{\xi/\eta}(z) = \iint\limits_{\{x, y: x/y \le z\}} f_\xi(x) f_\eta(y) \, dx \, dy.$$

Hence we easily obtain

$$f_{\xi\eta}(z) = \int_{-\infty}^{\infty} f_\xi\left(\frac{z}{y}\right) f_\eta(y) \frac{dy}{|y|} = \int_{-\infty}^{\infty} f_\eta\left(\frac{z}{x}\right) f_\xi(x) \frac{dx}{|x|} \tag{36}$$

and

$$f_{\xi/\eta}(z) = \int_{-\infty}^{\infty} f_\xi(zy) f(y) |y| \, dy. \tag{37}$$

Putting $\xi = \xi_0$ and $\eta = \sqrt{(\xi_1^2 + \cdots + \xi_n^2)/n}$, in (37), where $\xi_0, \xi_1, \ldots, \xi_n$ are independent Gaussian random variables with mean 0 and variance $\sigma^2 > 0$, and using (35), we find that

$$f_{\xi_0/[\sqrt{(1/n)(\xi_1^2 + \cdots + \xi_n^2)}]}(x) = \frac{1}{\sqrt{\pi n}} \frac{\Gamma\left(\dfrac{n+1}{2}\right)}{\Gamma\left(\dfrac{n}{2}\right)} \frac{1}{\left(1 + \dfrac{x^2}{n}\right)^{(n+1)/2}}. \tag{38}$$

The variable $\xi_0/[\sqrt{(1/n)(\xi_1^2 + \cdots + \xi_n^2)}]$ is denoted by t, and its distribution is the *t-distribution*, or *Student's distribution*, with n degrees of freedom (cf. Table 2 in §3). Observe that this distribution is independent of σ.

5. PROBLEMS

1. Verify formulas (9), (10), (24), (27), (28), and (34)–(38).

2. Let $\xi_1, \ldots, \xi_n$, $n \geq 2$, be independent identically distributed random variables with distribution function $F(x)$ (and density $f(x)$, if it exists), and let $\bar\xi = \max(\xi_1, \ldots, \xi_n)$, $\underline\xi = \min(\xi_1, \ldots, \xi_n)$, $\rho = \bar\xi - \underline\xi$. Show that

$$F_{\bar\xi, \underline\xi}(y, x) = \begin{cases} (F(y))^n - (F(y) - F(x))^n, & y > x, \\ (F(y))^n, & y \leq x, \end{cases}$$

$$f_{\bar\xi, \underline\xi}(y, x) = \begin{cases} n(n-1)[F(y) - F(x)]^{n-2} f(x) f(y), & y > x, \\ 0, & y < x, \end{cases}$$

$$F_\rho(x) = \begin{cases} n \int_{-\infty}^{\infty} [F(y) - F(y - x)]^{n-1} f(y)\, dy, & x \geq 0, \\ 0, & x < 0, \end{cases}$$

$$f_\rho(x) = \begin{cases} n(n-1) \int_{-\infty}^{\infty} [F(y) - F(y - x)]^{n-2} f(y - x) f(y)\, dy, & x > 0, \\ 0, & x < 0. \end{cases}$$

3. Let ξ_1 and ξ_2 be independent Poisson random variables with respective parameters λ_1 and λ_2. Show that $\xi_1 + \xi_2$ has a Poisson distribution with parameter $\lambda_1 + \lambda_2$.

4. Let $m_1 = m_2 = 0$ in (4). Show that

$$f_{\xi/\eta}(z) = \frac{\sigma_1 \sigma_2 \sqrt{1 - \rho^2}}{\pi(\sigma_2^2 z^2 - 2\rho\sigma_1\sigma_2 z + \sigma_1^2)}.$$

5. The *maximal correlation coefficient* of ξ and η is $\rho^*(\xi, \eta) = \sup_{u, v} \rho(u(\xi), v(\xi))$, where the supremum is taken over the Borel functions $u = u(x)$ and $v = v(x)$ for which the correlation coefficient $\rho(u(\xi), v(\xi))$ is defined. Show that ξ and η are independent if and only if $\rho^*(\xi, \eta) = 0$.

6. Let $\tau_1, \tau_2, \ldots, \tau_n$ be independent nonnegative identically distributed random variables with the exponential density

$$f(t) = \lambda e^{-\lambda t}, \qquad t \geq 0.$$

Show that the distribution of $\tau_1 + \cdots + \tau_k$ has the density

$$\frac{\lambda^k t^{k-1} e^{-\lambda t}}{(k-1)!}, \qquad t \geq 0, \quad 1 \leq k \leq n,$$

and that

$$P(\tau_1 + \cdots + \tau_k > t) = \sum_{i=0}^{k-1} e^{-\lambda t} \frac{(\lambda t)^i}{i!}.$$

7. Let $\xi \sim \mathcal{N}(0, \sigma^2)$. Show that, for every $p \geq 1$,

$$E|\xi|^p = C_p \sigma^p,$$

where

$$C_p = \frac{2^{p/2}}{\pi^{1/2}} \Gamma\left(\frac{p+1}{2}\right)$$

and $\Gamma(s) = \int_0^\infty e^{-x} x^{s-1} \, dx$ is the gamma function. In particular, for each integer $n \geq 1$,

$$E\xi^{2n} = (2n-1)!! \, \sigma^{2n}.$$

§9. Construction of a Process with Given Finite-Dimensional Distribution

1. Let $\xi = \xi(\omega)$ be a random variable defined on the probability space $(\Omega, \mathscr{F}, P)$, and let

$$F_\xi(x) = P\{\omega : \xi(\omega) \leq x\}$$

be its distribution function. It is clear that $F_\xi(x)$ is a distribution function on the real line in the sense of Definition 1 of §3.

We now ask the following question. Let $F = F(x)$ be a distribution function on R. Does there exist a random variable whose distribution function is $F(x)$?

One reason for asking this question is as follows. Many statements in probability theory begin, "Let ξ be a random variable with the distribution function $F(x)$; then ...". Consequently if a statement of this kind is to be meaningful we need to be certain that the object under consideration actually exists. Since to know a random variable we first have to know its domain $(\Omega, \mathscr{F})$, and in order to speak of its distribution we need to have a probability measure P on $(\Omega, \mathscr{F})$, a correct way of phrasing the question of the existence of a random variable with a given distribution function $F(x)$ is this:

Do there exist a probability space $(\Omega, \mathscr{F}, P)$ and a random variable $\xi = \xi(\omega)$ on it, such that

$$P\{\omega : \xi(\omega) \leq x\} = F(x)?$$

Let us show that the answer is positive, and essentially contained in Theorem 1 of §1.

In fact, let us put

$$\Omega = R, \qquad \mathscr{F} = \mathscr{B}(R).$$

It follows from Theorem 1 of §1 that there is a probability measure P (and only one) on $(R, \mathscr{B}(R))$ for which $P(a, b)] = F(b) - F(a), a < b$.

Put $\xi(\omega) \equiv \omega$. Then

$$P\{\omega: \xi(\omega) \leq x\} = P\{\omega: \omega \leq x\} = P(-\infty, x] = F(x).$$

Consequently we have constructed the required probability space and the random variable on it.

2. Let us now ask a similar question for random processes.

Let $X = (\xi_t)_{t \in T}$ be a random process (in the sense of Definition 3, §5) defined on the probability space $(\Omega, \mathscr{F}, P)$, with $t \in T \subseteq R$.

From a physical point of view, the most fundamental characteristic of a random process is the set $\{F_{t_1, \ldots, t_n}(x_1, \ldots, x_n)\}$ of its *finite-dimensional distribution functions*

$$F_{t_1, \ldots, t_n}(x_1, \ldots, x_n) = P\{\omega: \xi_{t_1} \leq x_1, \ldots, \xi_{t_n} \leq x_n\}, \qquad (1)$$

defined for all sets $t_1, \ldots, t_n$ with $t_1 < t_2 < \cdots < t_n$.

We see from (1) that, for each set $t_1, \ldots, t_n$ with $t_1 < t_2 < \cdots < t_n$ the functions $F_{t_1, \ldots, t_n}(x_1, \ldots, x_n)$ are n-dimensional distribution functions (in the sense of Definition 2, §3) and that the collection $\{F_{t_1, \ldots, t_n}(x_1, \ldots, x_n)\}$ has the following *consistency* property:

$$\lim_{x_k \uparrow \infty} F_{t_1, \ldots, t_n}(x_1, \ldots, x_n) = F_{t_1, \ldots, \hat{t}_k, \ldots, t_n}(x_1, \ldots, \hat{x}_k, \ldots, x_n) \qquad (2)$$

where ˆ indicates an omitted coordinate.

Now it is natural to ask the following question: under what conditions can a given family $\{F_{t_1, \ldots, t_n}(x_1, \ldots, x_n)\}$ of distribution functions $F_{t_1, \ldots, t_n}(x_1, \ldots, x_n)$ (in the sense of Definition 2, §3) be the family of finite-dimensional distribution functions of a random process? It is quite remarkable that all such conditions are covered by the consistency condition (2).

Theorem 1 (Kolmogorov's Theorem on the Existence of a Process). *Let* $\{F_{t_1, \ldots, t_n}(x_1, \ldots, x_n)\}$, *with* $t_i \in T \subseteq R$, $t_1 < t_2 < \cdots < t_n$, $n \geq 1$, *be a given family of finite-dimensional distribution functions, satisfying the consistency condition* (2). *Then there are a probability space* $(\Omega, \mathscr{F}, P)$ *and a random process* $X = (\xi_t)_{t \in T}$ *such that*

$$P\{\omega: \xi_{t_1} \leq x_1, \ldots, \xi_{t_n} \leq x_n\} = F_{t_1 \cdots t_n}(x_1 \cdots x_n). \qquad (3)$$

PROOF. Put

$$\Omega = R^T, \qquad \mathscr{F} = \mathscr{B}(R^T),$$

i.e. take Ω to be the space of real functions $\omega = (\omega_t)_{t \in T}$ with the σ-algebra generated by the cylindrical sets.

Let $\tau = [t_1, \ldots, t_n], t_1 < t_2 < \cdots < t_n$. Then by Theorem 2 of §3 we can construct on the space $(R^n, \mathscr{B}(R^n))$ a unique probability measure P_τ such that

$$P_\tau\{(\omega_{t_1}, \ldots, \omega_{t_n}): \omega_{t_1} \leq x_1, \ldots, \omega_{t_n} \leq x_n\} = F_{t_1 \cdots t_n}(x_1, \ldots, x_n). \qquad (4)$$

It follows from the consistency condition (2) that the family $\{P_\tau\}$ is also consistent (see (3.20)). According to Theorem 4 of §3 there is a probability measure P on $(R^T, \mathscr{B}(R^T))$ such that

$$P\{\omega: (\omega_{t_1}, \ldots, \omega_{t_n}) \in B\} = P_\tau(B)$$

for every set $\tau = [t_1, \ldots, t_n], t_1 < \cdots < t_n$.

From this, it also follows that (4) is satisfied. Therefore the required random process $X = (\xi_t(\omega))_{t \in T}$ can be taken to be the process defined by

$$\xi_t(\omega) = \omega_t, \qquad t \in T. \qquad (5)$$

This completes the proof of the theorem.

Remark 1. The probability space $(R^T, \mathscr{B}(R^T), P)$ that we have constructed is called *canonical*, and the construction given by (5) is called the *coordinate method* of constructing the process.

Remark 2. Let $(E_\alpha, \mathscr{E}_\alpha)$ be complete separable metric spaces, where α belongs to some set $\mathfrak{A}$ of indices. Let $\{P_\tau\}$ be a set of consistent finite-dimensional distribution functions $P_\tau, \tau = [\alpha_1, \ldots, \alpha_n]$ on

$$(E_{\alpha_1} \times \cdots \times E_{\alpha_n}, \mathscr{E}_{\alpha_1} \otimes \cdots \otimes \mathscr{E}_{\alpha_n}).$$

Then there are a probability space $(\Omega, \mathscr{F}, P)$ and a family of $\mathscr{F}/\mathscr{E}_\alpha$-measurable functions $(X_\alpha(\omega))_{\alpha \in \mathfrak{A}}$ such that

$$P\{(X_{\alpha_1}, \ldots, X_{\alpha_n}) \in B\} = P_\tau(B)$$

for all $\tau = [\alpha_1, \ldots, \alpha_n]$ and $B \in \mathscr{E}_\alpha \otimes \cdots \otimes \mathscr{E}_{\alpha_n}$.

This result, which generalizes Theorem 1, follows from Theorem 4 of §3 if we put $\Omega = \prod_\alpha E_\alpha, \mathscr{F} = \bigotimes_\alpha \mathscr{E}_\alpha$ and $X_\alpha(\omega) = \omega_\alpha$ for each $\omega = \omega(\omega_\alpha), \alpha \in \mathfrak{A}$.

Corollary 1. *Let $F_1(x), F_2(x), \ldots$ be a sequence of one-dimensional distribution functions. Then there exist a probability space $(\Omega, \mathscr{F}, P)$ and a sequence of independent random variables $\xi_1, \xi_2, \ldots$ such that*

$$P\{\omega: \xi_i(\omega) \leq x\} = F_i(x). \qquad (6)$$

In particular, there is a probability space $(\Omega, \mathscr{F}, \mathsf{P})$ on which an infinite sequence of Bernoulli random variables is defined (in this connection see Subsection 2 of §5 of Chapter I). Notice that Ω can be taken to be the space

$$\Omega = \{\omega: \omega = (a_1, a_2, \ldots), a_i = 0, 1\}$$

(cf. also Theorem 2).

To establish the corollary it is enough to put $F_{1,\ldots,n}(x_1, \ldots, x_n) = F_1(x_1) \cdots F_n(x_n)$ and apply Theorem 1.

Corollary 2. *Let* $T = [0, \infty)$ *and let* $\{p(s, x; t, B\}$ *be a family of nonnegative functions defined for* $s, t \in T, t > s, x \in R, B \in \mathscr{B}(R)$, *and satisfying the following conditions*:

(a) $p(s, x; t, B)$ *is a probability measure on* B *for given* s, x *and* t;
(b) *for given* s, t *and* B, *the function* $p(s, x; t, B)$ *is a Borel function of* x;
(c) *for* $0 \le s < t < \tau$ *and* $B \in \mathscr{B}(R)$, *the* Kolmogorov–Chapman *equation*

$$p(s, x; \tau, B) = \int_R p(s, x; t, dy)p(t, y; \tau, B) \tag{7}$$

is satisfied.

Also let $\pi = \pi(B)$ be a probability measure on $(R, \mathscr{B}(R))$. Then there are a probability space $(\Omega, \mathscr{F}, \mathsf{P})$ and a random process $X = (\xi_t)_{t \ge 0}$ defined on it, such that

$$P\{\xi_{t_0} \le x_0, \xi_{t_1} \le x_1, \ldots, \xi_{t_n} \le x_n\} = \int_{-\infty}^{x_0} \pi(dy_0) \int_{-\infty}^{x_1} p(0, y_0; t_1, dy_1)$$

$$\cdots \int_{-\infty}^{x_n} p(t_{n-1}, y_{n-1}; t_n, dy_n) \tag{8}$$

for $0 = t_0 < t_1 < \cdots < t_n$.

The process X so constructed is a *Markov process* with initial distribution π and transition probabilities $\{p(s, x; t, B\}$.

Corollary 3. *Let* $T = \{0, 1, 2, \ldots\}$ *and let* $\{P_k(x; B)\}$ *be a family of nonnegative functions defined for* $k \ge 1$, $x \in R$, $B \in \mathscr{B}(R)$, *and such that* $p_k(x; B)$ *is a probability measure on* B *(for given* k *and* x*) and measurable in* x *(for given* k *and* B*). In addition, let* $\pi = \pi(B)$ *be a probability measure on* $(R, \mathscr{B}(R))$.

Then there is a probability space $(\Omega, \mathscr{F}, \mathsf{P})$ with a family of random variables $X = \{\xi_0, \xi_1, \ldots\}$ defined on it, such that

$$\mathsf{P}\{\xi_{t_0} \le x_0, \xi_{t_1} \le x_1, \ldots, \xi_n \le x_n\} = \int_{-\infty}^{x_0} \pi(dy_0) \int_{-\infty}^{x_1} p(0, y_0; t_1, dy_1)$$

$$\cdots \int_{-\infty}^{x_n} p(t_{n-1}, y_{n-1}; t_n, dy_n)$$

3. In the situation of Corollary 1, there is a sequence of independent random variables $\xi_1, \xi_2, \ldots$ whose one-dimensional distribution functions are $F_1, F_2, \ldots$, respectively.

Now let $(E_1, \mathscr{E}_1), (E_2, \mathscr{E}_2), \ldots$ be complete separable metric spaces and let $P_1, P_2, \ldots$ be probability measures on them. Then it follows from Remark 2 that there are a probability space $(\Omega, \mathscr{F}, \mathsf{P})$ and a sequence of independent elements $X_1, X_2, \ldots$ such that X_n is $\mathscr{F}/\mathscr{E}_n$-measurable and $\mathsf{P}(X_n \in B) = P_n(B)$, $B \in \mathscr{E}_n$.

It turns out that this result remains valid when the spaces $(E_n, \mathscr{E}_n)$ are *arbitrary measurable spaces.*

Theorem 2 (Ionescu Tulcea's Theorem on Extending a Measure and the Existence of a Random Sequence). *Let $(\Omega_n, \mathscr{F}_n)$, $n = 1, 2, \ldots$, be arbitrary measurable spaces and $\Omega = \prod \Omega_n$, $\mathscr{F} = \bigotimes \mathscr{F}_n$. Suppose that a probability measure P_1 is given on $(\Omega_1, \mathscr{F}_1)$ and that, for every set $(\omega_1, \ldots, \omega_n) \in \Omega_1 \times \cdots \times \Omega_n, n \ge 1$, probability measures $P(\omega_1, \ldots, \omega_n; \cdot)$ are given on $(\Omega_{n+1}, \mathscr{F}_{n+1})$. Suppose that for every $B \in \mathscr{F}_{n+1}$ the functions $P(\omega_1, \ldots, \omega_n; B)$ are Borel functions on $(\omega_1, \ldots, \omega_n)$ and let*

$$P_n(A_1 \times \cdots \times A_n) = \int_{A_1} P_1(d\omega_1) \int_{A_2} P(\omega_1; d\omega_2)$$

$$\cdots \int_{A_n} P(\omega_1, \ldots, \omega_{n-1}; d\omega_n) \qquad A_i \in \mathscr{F}_i, \qquad n \ge 1. \quad (9)$$

Then there is a unique probability measure P on $(\Omega, \mathscr{F})$ such that

$$\mathsf{P}\{\omega: \omega_1 \in A_1, \ldots, \omega_n \in A_n\} = P_n(A_1 \times \cdots \times A_n) \quad (10)$$

for every $n \ge 1$, and there is a random sequence $X = (X_1(\omega), X_2(\omega), \ldots)$ such that

$$\mathsf{P}\{\omega: X_1(\omega) \in A_1, \ldots, X_n(\omega) \in A_n\} = P_n(A_1 \times \cdots \times A_n), \quad (11)$$

where $A_i \in \mathscr{E}_i$.

PROOF. The first step is to establish that for each $n > 1$ the set function P_n defined by (9) on the rectangle $A_1 \times \cdots \times A_n$ can be extended to the σ-algebra $\mathscr{F}_1 \otimes \cdots \otimes \mathscr{F}_n$.

For each $n \ge 2$ and $B \in \mathscr{F}_1 \otimes \cdots \otimes \mathscr{F}_n$ we put

$$P_n(B) = \int_{\Omega_1} P_1(d\omega_1) \int_{\Omega_2} P(\omega_1; d\omega_2) \int_{\Omega_{n-1}} P(\omega_1, \ldots, \omega_{n-2}; d\omega_{n-1})$$

$$\times \int_{\Omega_n} I_B(\omega_1, \ldots, \omega_n) P(\omega_1, \ldots, \omega_{n-1}; d\omega_n). \quad (12)$$

It is easily seen that when $B = A_1 \times \cdots \times A_n$ the right-hand side of (12) is the same as the right-hand side of (9). Moreover, when $n = 2$ it can be shown, just as in Theorem 8 of §6, that P_2 is a measure. Consequently it is easily established by induction that P_n is a measure for all $n \geq 2$.

The next step is the same as in Kolmogorov's theorem on the extension of a measure in $(R^\infty, \mathscr{B}(R^\infty))$ (Theorem 3, §3). Thus for every cylindrical set $J_n(B) = \{\omega \in \Omega : (\omega_1, \ldots, \omega_n) \in B\}$, $B \in \mathscr{F}_1 \otimes \cdots \otimes \mathscr{F}_n$, we define the set function P by

$$P(J_n(B)) = P_n(B). \tag{13}$$

If we use (12) and the fact that $P(\omega_1, \ldots, \omega_k; \cdot)$ are measures, it is easy to establish that the definition (13) is consistent, in the sense that the value of $P(J_n(B))$ is independent of the representation of the cylindrical set.

It follows that the set function P defined in (13) for cylindrical sets, and in an obvious way on the algebra that contains all the cylindrical sets, is a finitely additive measure on this algebra. It remains to verify its countable additivity and apply Carathéodory's theorem.

In Theorem 3 of §3 the corresponding verification was based on the property of $(R^n, \mathscr{B}(R^n))$ that for every Borel set B there is a compact set $A \subseteq B$ whose probability measure is arbitrarily close to the measure of B. In the present case this part of the proof needs to be modified in the following way.

As in Theorem 3 of §3, let $\{\hat{B}_n\}_{n \geq 1}$ be a sequence of cylindrical sets

$$\hat{B}_n = \{\omega : (\omega_1, \ldots, \omega_n) \in B_n\},$$

that decrease to the empty set $\varnothing$, but have

$$\lim_{n \to \infty} P(\hat{B}_n) > 0. \tag{14}$$

For $n > 1$, we have from (12)

$$P(\hat{B}_n) = \int_{\Omega_1} f_n^{(1)}(\omega_1) P_1(d\omega_1),$$

where

$$f_n^{(1)}(\omega_1) = \int_{\Omega_2} P(\omega_1; d\omega_2) \cdots \int_{\Omega_n} I_{B_n}(\omega_1, \ldots, \omega_n) P(\omega_2, \ldots, \omega_{n-1}; d\omega_n).$$

Since $\hat{B}_{n+1} \subseteq \hat{B}_n$, we have $B_{n+1} \subseteq B_n \times \Omega_{n+1}$ and therefore

$$I_{B_{n+1}}(\omega_1, \ldots, \omega_{n+1}) \leq I_{B_n}(\omega_1, \ldots, \omega_n) I_{\Omega_{n+1}}(\omega_{n+1}).$$

Hence the sequence $\{f_n^{(1)}(\omega_1)\}_{n \geq 1}$ decreases. Let $f^{(1)}(\omega_1) = \lim_n f_n^{(1)}(\omega_1)$. By the dominated convergence theorem

$$\lim_n P(\hat{B}_n) = \lim_n \int_{\Omega_1} f_n^{(1)}(\omega_1) P_1(d\omega_1) = \int_{\Omega_1} f^{(1)}(\omega_1) P_1(d\omega_1).$$

By hypothesis, $\lim_n P(\hat{B}_n) > 0$. It follows that there is an $\omega_1^0 \in B$ such that $f^{(1)}(\omega_1^0) > 0$, since if $\omega_1 \notin B_1$ then $f_n^{(1)}(\omega_1) = 0$ for $n \geq 1$.

Moreover, for $n > 2$,

$$f_n^{(1)}(\omega_1^0) = \int_{\Omega_2} f_n^{(2)}(\omega_2)P(\omega_1^0; d\omega_2), \tag{15}$$

where

$$f_n^{(2)}(\omega_2) = \int_{\Omega} P(\omega_1^0, \omega_2; d\omega_3)$$

$$\cdots \int_{\Omega_n} I_{B_n}(\omega_1^0, \omega_2, \ldots, \omega_n)P(\omega_1^0, \omega_2, \ldots, \omega_{n-1}, d\omega_n).$$

We can establish, as for $\{f_n^{(1)}(\omega_1)\}$, that $\{f_n^{(2)}(\omega_2)\}$ is decreasing. Let $f^{(2)}(\omega_2) = \lim_{n\to\infty} f_n^{(2)}(\omega_2)$. Then it follows from (15) that

$$0 < f^{(1)}(\omega_1^0) = \int_{\Omega_2} f^{(2)}(\omega_2)P(\omega_1^0; d\omega_2),$$

and there is a point $\omega_2^0 \in \Omega_2$ such that $f^{(2)}(\omega_2^0) > 0$. Then $(\omega_1^0, \omega_2^0) \in B_2$. Continuing this process, we find a point $(\omega_1^0, \ldots, \omega_n^0) \in B_n$ for each n. Consequently $(\omega_1^0, \ldots, \omega_n^0, \ldots) \in \bigcap \hat{B}_n$, but by hypothesis we have $\bigcap \hat{B}_n = \varnothing$. This contradiction shows that $\lim_n P(\hat{B}_n) = 0$.

Thus we have proved the part of the theorem about the existence of the probability measure P. The other part follows from this by putting $X_n(\omega) = \omega_n, n \geq 1$.

Corollary 1. *Let $(E_n, \mathscr{E}_n)_{n\geq 1}$ be any measurable spaces and $(P_n)_{n\geq 1}$, measures on them. Then there are a probability space $(\Omega, \mathscr{F}, P)$ and a family of independent random elements $X_1, X_2, \ldots$ with values in $(E_1, \mathscr{E}_1), (E_2, \mathscr{E}_2), \ldots$, respectively, such that*

$$P\{\omega: X_n(\omega) \in B\} = P_n(B), \qquad B \in \mathscr{E}_n, n \geq 1.$$

Corollary 2. *Let $E = \{1, 2, \ldots\}$, and let $\{p_k(x, y)\}$ be a family of nonnegative functions, $k \geq 1$, $x, y \in E$, such that $\sum_{y \in E} p_k(x; y) = 1$, $x \in E$, $k \geq 1$. Also let $\pi = \pi(x)$ be a probability distribution on E (that is, $\pi(x) \geq 0, \sum_{x \in E} \pi(x) = 1$).*

Then there are a probability space $(\Omega, \mathscr{F}, P)$ and a family $X = \{\xi_0, \xi_1, \ldots\}$ of random variables on it, such that

$$P\{\xi_0 = x_0, \xi_1 = x_1, \ldots, \xi_n = x_n\} = \pi(x_0)p_1(x_0, x_1) \cdots p_n(x_{n-1}, x_n) \tag{16}$$

(cf. (I.12.4)) for all $x_i \in E$ and $n \geq 1$. We may take Ω to be the space

$$\Omega = \{\omega: \omega = (x_0, x_1, \ldots), x_i \in E\}.$$

A sequence $X = \{\xi_0, \xi_1, \ldots\}$ of random variables satisfying (16) is a *Markov chain* with a countable set E of states, transition matrix $\{p_k(x, y)\}$ and initial probability distribution π. (Cf. the definition in §12 of Chapter I.)

4. PROBLEMS

1. Let $\Omega = [0, 1]$, let $\mathscr{F}$ be the class of Borel subsets of $[0, 1]$, and let P be Lebesgue measure on $[0, 1]$. Show that the space $(\Omega, \mathscr{F}, P)$ is universal in the following sense. For every distribution function $F(x)$ on $(\Omega, \mathscr{F}, P)$ there is a random variable $\xi = \xi(\omega)$ such that its distribution function $F_\xi(x) = P(\xi \leq x)$ coincides with $F(x)$. (Hint. $\xi(\omega) = F^{-1}(\omega)$, $0 < \omega < 1$, where $F^{-1}(\omega) = \sup\{x: F(x) < \omega\}$, when $0 < \omega < 1$, and $\xi(0)$, $\xi(1)$ can be chosen arbitrarily.)

2. Verify the consistency of the families of distributions in the corollaries to Theorems 1 and 2.

3. Deduce Corollary 2, Theorem 2, from Theorem 1.

§10. Various Kinds of Convergence of Sequences of Random Variables

1. Just as in analysis, in probability theory we need to use various kinds of convergence of random variables. Four of these are particularly important: *in probability, with probability one, in mean of order p, in distribution.*

First some definitions. Let $\xi, \xi_1, \xi_2, \ldots$ be random variables defined on a probability space $(\Omega, \mathscr{F}, P)$.

Definition 1. The sequence $\xi_1, \xi_2, \ldots$ of random variables converges *in probability* to the random variable ξ (notation: $\xi_n \xrightarrow{P} \xi$) if for every $\varepsilon > 0$

$$P\{|\xi_n - \xi| > \varepsilon\} \to 0, \qquad n \to \infty. \tag{1}$$

We have already encountered this convergence in connection with the law of large numbers for a Bernoulli scheme, which stated that

$$P\left(\left|\frac{S_n}{n} - p\right| > \varepsilon\right) \to 0, \qquad n \to \infty$$

(see §5 of Chapter I). In analysis this is known as *convergence in measure.*

Definition 2. The sequence $\xi_1, \xi_2, \ldots$ of random variables converges *with probability one* (*almost surely, almost everywhere*) to the random variable ξ if

$$P\{\omega: \xi_n \not\to \xi\} = 0, \tag{2}$$

i.e. if the set of sample points ω for which $\xi_n(\omega)$ does not converge to ξ has probability zero.

This convergence is denoted by $\xi_n \to \xi$ (P-a.s.), or $\xi_n \xrightarrow{\text{a.s.}} \xi$ or $\xi_n \xrightarrow{\text{a.e.}} \xi$.

Definition 3. The sequence $\xi_1, \xi_2, \dots$ of random variables converges *in mean of order p*, $0 < p < \infty$, to the random variable ξ if

$$\mathsf{E}\,|\xi_n - \xi|^p \to 0, \qquad n \to \infty. \tag{3}$$

In analysis this is known as *convergence in* L^p, and denoted by $\xi_n \xrightarrow{L^p} \xi$. In the special case $p = 2$ it is called *mean square convergence* and denoted by $\xi = \text{l.i.m.}\ \xi_n$ (for "limit in the mean").

Definition 4. The sequence $\xi_1, \xi_2, \dots$ of random variables *converges in distribution* to the random variable ξ (notation: $\xi_n \xrightarrow{d} \xi$) if

$$\mathsf{E}f(\xi_n) \to \mathsf{E}f(\xi), \qquad n \to \infty, \tag{4}$$

for every bounded continuous function $f = f(x)$. The reason for the terminology is that, according to what will be proved in Chapter III, §1, condition (4) is equivalent to the convergence of the distribution $F_{\xi_n}(x)$ to $F_\xi(x)$ at each *point x of continuity* of $F_\xi(x)$. This convergence is denoted by $F_{\xi_n} \Rightarrow F_\xi$.

We emphasize that the convergence of random variables in distribution is defined only in terms of the convergence of their distribution functions. Therefore it makes sense to discuss this mode of convergence even when the random variables are defined on different probability spaces. This convergence will be studied in detail in Chapter III, where, in particular, we shall explain why in the definition of $F_{\xi_n} \Rightarrow F_\xi$ we require only convergence at points of continuity of $F_\xi(x)$ and not at all x.

2. In solving problems of analysis on the convergence (in one sense or another) of a given sequence of functions, it is useful to have the concept of a fundamental sequence (or Cauchy sequence). We can introduce a similar concept for each of the first three kinds of convergence of a sequence of random variables.

Let us say that a sequence $\{\xi_n\}_{n \geq 1}$ of random variables is *fundamental in probability*, or *with probability* 1, or *in mean of order*, p, $0 < p < \infty$, if the corresponding one of the following properties is satisfied: $P\{|\xi_n - \xi| > \varepsilon\} \to 0$, as $m, n \to \infty$ for every $\varepsilon > 0$; the sequence $\{\xi_n(\omega)\}_{n \geq 1}$ is fundamental for almost all $\omega \in \Omega$; the sequence $\{\xi_n(\omega)\}_{n \geq 1}$ is fundamental in L^p, i.e. $\mathsf{E}\,|\xi_n - \xi_m|^p \to 0$ as $n, m \to \infty$.

3. Theorem 1.

(a) *A necessary and sufficient condition that* $\xi_n \to \xi$ (P-a.s.) *is that*

$$P\left\{\sup_{k \geq n}|\xi_k - \xi| \geq \varepsilon\right\} \to 0, \qquad n \to \infty. \tag{5}$$

for every $\varepsilon > 0$.

(b) *The sequence* $\{\xi_n\}_{n\geq 1}$ *is fundamental with probability* 1 *if and only if*

$$\mathsf{P}\left\{\sup_{\substack{k\geq n \\ l\geq n}} |\xi_k - \xi_l| \geq \varepsilon\right\} \to 0, \qquad n \to \infty, \tag{6}$$

for every $\varepsilon > 0$; *or equivalently*

$$\mathsf{P}\left\{\sup_{k\geq 0} |\xi_{n+k} - \xi_n| \geq \varepsilon\right\} \to 0, \qquad n \to \infty. \tag{7}$$

PROOF. (a) Let $A_n^\varepsilon = \{\omega: |\xi_n - \xi| \geq \varepsilon\}$, $A^\varepsilon = \overline{\lim} A_n^\varepsilon \equiv \bigcap_{n=1}^\infty \bigcup_{k\geq n} A_k^\varepsilon$. Then

$$\{\omega: \xi_n \nrightarrow \xi\} = \bigcup_{\varepsilon \geq 0} A^\varepsilon = \bigcup_{m=1}^\infty A^{1/m}.$$

But

$$\mathsf{P}(A^\varepsilon) = \lim_n \mathsf{P}\left(\bigcup_{k\geq n} A_k^\varepsilon\right),$$

Hence (a) follows from the following chain of implications:

$$0 = \mathsf{P}\{\omega: \xi_n \nrightarrow \xi\} = \mathsf{P}\left(\bigcup_{\varepsilon > 0} A^\varepsilon\right) \Leftrightarrow \mathsf{P}\left(\bigcup_{m=1}^\infty A^{1/m}\right) = 0$$

$$\Leftrightarrow \mathsf{P}(A^{1/m}) = 0, \quad m \geq 1 \Leftrightarrow \mathsf{P}(A^\varepsilon) = 0, \quad \varepsilon > 0,$$

$$\Leftrightarrow \mathsf{P}\left(\bigcup_{k\geq n} A_k^\varepsilon\right) \to 0, \quad n \to \infty \Leftrightarrow \mathsf{P}\left(\sup_{k\geq n} |\xi_k - \xi| \geq \varepsilon\right) \to 0,$$

$$n \to \infty.$$

(b) Let

$$B_{k,l}^\varepsilon = \{\omega: |\xi_k - \xi_l| \geq \varepsilon\}, \qquad B^\varepsilon = \bigcap_{n=1}^\infty \bigcup_{\substack{k\geq n \\ l\geq n}} B_{k,l}^\varepsilon.$$

Then $\{\omega: \{\xi_n(\omega)\}_{n\geq 1}$ *is not fundamental*$\} = \bigcup_{\varepsilon \geq 0} B^\varepsilon$, and it can be shown as in (a) that $\mathsf{P}\{\omega: \{\xi_n(\omega)\}_{n\geq 1}$ is not fundamental$\} = 0 \Leftrightarrow (6)$. The equivalence of (6) and (7) follows from the obvious inequalities

$$\sup_{k\geq 0} |\xi_{n+k} - \xi_n| \leq \sup_{\substack{k\geq 0 \\ l\geq 0}} |\xi_{n+k} - \xi_{n+l}| \leq 2 \sup_{k\geq 0} |\xi_{n+k} - \xi_n|.$$

This completes the proof of the theorem.

Corollary. *Since*

$$\mathsf{P}\left\{\sup_{k\geq n} |\xi_k - \xi| \geq \varepsilon\right\} = \mathsf{P}\left\{\bigcup_{k\geq n} (|\xi_k - \xi| \geq \varepsilon)\right\} \leq \sum_{k\geq n} \mathsf{P}\{|\xi_k - \xi| \geq \varepsilon\},$$

a sufficient condition for $\xi_n \overset{\text{a.s.}}{\to} \xi$ *is that*

$$\sum_{k=1}^{\infty} P\{|\xi_k - \xi| \geq \varepsilon\} < \infty \tag{8}$$

is satisfied for every $\varepsilon > 0$.

It is appropriate to observe at this point that the reasoning used in obtaining (8) lets us establish the following simple but important result which is essential in studying properties that are satisfied with probability 1.

Let $A_1, A_2, \ldots$ be a sequence of events in F. Let (see the table in §1) $\{A_n \text{ i.o.}\}$ denote the event $\overline{\lim} A_n$ that consists in the realization of infinitely many of $A_1, A_2, \ldots$.

Borel–Cantelli Lemma.

(a) *If* $\sum P(A_n) < \infty$ *then* $P\{A_n \text{ i.o.}\} = 0$.
(b) *If* $\sum P(A_n) = \infty$ *and* $A_1, A_2, \ldots$ *are independent, then* $P\{A_n \text{ i.o.}\} = 1$.

PROOF. (a) By definition

$$\{A_n \text{ i.o.}\} = \overline{\lim} A_n = \bigcap_{n=1}^{\infty} \bigcup_{k \geq n} A_k.$$

Consequently

$$P\{A_n \text{ i.o.}\} = P\left\{\bigcap_{n=1}^{\infty} \bigcup_{k \geq n} A_k\right\} = \lim P\left(\bigcup_{k \geq n} A_k\right) \leq \lim \sum_{k \geq n} P(A_k),$$

and (a) follows.

(b) If $A_1, A_2, \ldots$ are independent, so are $\bar{A}_1, \bar{A}_2, \ldots$. Hence for $N \geq n$ we have

$$P\left(\bigcap_{k=n}^{N} A_k\right) = \prod_{k=n}^{N} P(\bar{A}_k),$$

and it is then easy to deduce that

$$P\left(\bigcap_{k=n}^{\infty} \bar{A}_k\right) = \prod_{k=n}^{\infty} P(\bar{A}_k). \tag{9}$$

Since $\log(1 - x) \leq -x, 0 \leq x < 1$,

$$\log \prod_{k=n}^{\infty} [1 - P(A_k)] = \sum_{k=n}^{\infty} \log[1 - P(A_k)] \leq - \sum_{k=n}^{\infty} P(A_k) = -\infty.$$

Consequently

$$P\left(\bigcap_{k=n}^{\infty} \bar{A}_k\right) = 0$$

for all n, and therefore $P(A_n \text{ i.o.}) = 1$.

This completes the proof of the lemma.

Corollary 1. If $A_n^\varepsilon = \{\omega: |\xi_n - \xi| \ge \varepsilon\}$ then (8) shows that $\sum_{n=1}^\infty P(A_n) < \infty$, $\varepsilon > 0$, and then by the Borel–Cantelli lemma we have $P(A^\varepsilon) = 0$, $\varepsilon > 0$, where $A^\varepsilon = \overline{\lim} A_n^\varepsilon$. Therefore

$$\sum P\{|\xi_k - \xi| \ge \varepsilon\} < \infty, \varepsilon > 0 \Rightarrow P(A^\varepsilon) = 0, \varepsilon > 0$$
$$\Rightarrow P\{\omega: \xi_n \nrightarrow \xi)\} = 0,$$

as we already observed above.

Corollary 2. Let $(\varepsilon_n)_{n \ge 1}$ be a sequence of positive numbers such that $\varepsilon_n \downarrow 0$, $n \to \infty$. If

$$\sum_{n=1}^\infty P\{|\xi_n - \xi| \ge \varepsilon_n\} < \infty, \tag{10}$$

then $\xi_n \xrightarrow{a.s.} \xi$.

In fact, let $A_n = \{|\xi_n - \xi| \ge \varepsilon_n\}$. Then $P(A_n \text{ i.o.}) = 0$ by the Borel–Cantelli lemma. This means that, for almost every $\omega \in \Omega$, there is an $N = N(\omega)$ such that $|\xi_n(\omega) - \xi(\omega)| \le \varepsilon_n$ for $n \ge N(\omega)$. But $\varepsilon_n \downarrow 0$, and therefore $\xi_n(\omega) \to \xi(\omega)$ for almost every $\omega \in \Omega$.

4. Theorem 2. We have the following implications:

$$\xi_n \xrightarrow{a.s.} \xi \Rightarrow \xi_n \xrightarrow{P} \xi, \tag{11}$$
$$\xi_n \xrightarrow{L^p} \xi \Rightarrow \xi_n \xrightarrow{P} \xi, \quad p > 0, \tag{12}$$
$$\xi_n \xrightarrow{P} \xi \Rightarrow \xi_n \xrightarrow{d} \xi. \tag{13}$$

PROOF. Statement (11) follows from comparing the definition of convergence in probability with (5), and (12) follows from Chebyshev's inequality.

To prove (13), let $f(x)$ be a continuous function, let $|f(x)| \le c$, let $\varepsilon > 0$, and let N be such that $P(|\xi| > N) \le \varepsilon/4c$. Take δ so that $|f(x) - f(y)| \le \varepsilon/2c$ for $|x| < N$ and $|x - y| \le \delta$. Then (cf. the proof of Weierstrass's theorem in Subsection 5, §5, Chapter I)

$$E|f(\xi_n) - f(\xi)| = E(|f(\xi_n) - f(\xi)|; |\xi_n - \xi| \le \delta, |\xi| \le N)$$
$$+ E(|f(\xi_n) - f(\xi)|; |\xi_n - \xi| \le \delta, |\xi| > N)$$
$$+ E(|f(\xi_n) - f(\xi)|; |\xi_n - \xi| > \delta)$$
$$\le \varepsilon/2 + \varepsilon/2 + 2cP\{|\xi_n - \xi| > \delta\}$$
$$= \varepsilon + 2cP\{|\xi_n - \xi| > \delta\}.$$

But $P\{|\xi_n - \xi| > \delta\} \to 0$, and hence $E|f(\xi_n) - f(\xi)| \le 2\varepsilon$ for sufficiently large n; since $\varepsilon > 0$ is arbitrary, this establishes (13).

This completes the proof of the theorem.

We now present a number of examples which show, in particular, that the converses of (11) and (12) are false in general.

EXAMPLE 1 ($\xi_n \overset{P}{\to} \xi \not\Rightarrow \xi_n \overset{\text{a.s.}}{\to} \xi$; $\xi_n \overset{L^p}{\to} \xi \not\Rightarrow \xi_n \overset{\text{a.s.}}{\to} \xi$). Let $\Omega = [0, 1]$, $\mathscr{F} = \mathscr{B}([0, 1])$, $\mathsf{P} =$ Lebesgue measure. Put

$$A_n^i = \left[\frac{i-1}{n}, \frac{i}{n}\right], \qquad \xi_n^i = I_{A_n^i}(\omega), \qquad i = 1, 2, \ldots, n; n \geq 1.$$

Then the sequence

$$\{\xi_1^1; \xi_2^1, \xi_2^2; \xi_3^1, \xi_3^2, \xi_3^3; \cdots\}$$

of random variables converges both in probability and in mean of order $p > 0$, but does not converge at any point $\omega \in [0, 1]$.

EXAMPLE 2 ($\xi_n \overset{\text{a.s.}}{\to} \xi \Rightarrow \xi_n \overset{P}{\to} \xi \not\Rightarrow \xi_n \overset{L^p}{\to} \xi$, $p > 0$). Again let $\Omega = [0, 1]$, $\mathscr{F} = \mathscr{B}[0, 1]$, $\mathsf{P} =$ Lebesgue measure, and let

$$\xi_n(\omega) = \begin{cases} e^n, & 0 \leq \omega \leq 1/n, \\ 0, & \omega > 1/n. \end{cases}$$

Then $\{\xi_n\}$ converges with probability 1 (and therefore in probability) to zero, but

$$\mathsf{E}|\xi_n|^p = \frac{e^{np}}{n} \to \infty, \qquad n \to \infty,$$

for every $p > 0$.

EXAMPLE 3 ($\xi_n \overset{L^p}{\to} \xi \not\Rightarrow \xi_n \overset{\text{a.s.}}{\to} \xi$). Let $\{\xi_n\}$ be a sequence of independent random variables with

$$\mathsf{P}(\xi_n = 1) = p_n, \qquad \mathsf{P}(\xi_n = 0) = 1 - p_n.$$

Then it is easy to show that

$$\xi_n \overset{P}{\to} 0 \Leftrightarrow p_n \to 0, \qquad n \to \infty, \tag{14}$$

$$\xi_n \overset{L^p}{\to} 0 \Leftrightarrow p_n \to 0, \qquad n \to \infty, \tag{15}$$

$$\xi_n \overset{\text{a.s.}}{\to} 0 \Rightarrow \sum_{n=1}^{\infty} p_n < \infty. \tag{16}$$

In particular, if $p_n = 1/n$ then $\xi_n \overset{L^p}{\to} 0$ for every $p > 0$, but $\xi_n \overset{\text{a.s.}}{\not\to} 0$.

The following theorem singles out an interesting case when almost sure convergence implies convergence in L^1.

Theorem 3. *Let* (ξ_n) *be a sequence of nonnegative random variables such that* $\xi_n \overset{\text{a.s.}}{\to} \xi$ *and* $\mathsf{E}\xi_n \to \mathsf{E}\xi < \infty$. *Then*

$$\mathsf{E}|\xi_n - \xi| \to 0, \qquad n \to \infty. \tag{17}$$

PROOF. We have $\mathsf{E}\xi_n < \infty$ for sufficiently large n, and therefore for such n we have

$$\mathsf{E}|\xi - \xi_n| = \mathsf{E}(\xi - \xi_n)I_{\{\xi \geq \xi_n\}} + \mathsf{E}(\xi_n - \xi)I_{\{\xi_n > \xi\}}$$
$$= 2\mathsf{E}(\xi - \xi_n)I_{\{\xi \geq \xi_n\}} + \mathsf{E}(\xi_n - \xi).$$

But $0 \leq (\xi - \xi_n)I_{\{\xi \geq \xi_n\}} \leq \xi$. Therefore, by the dominated convergence theorem, $\lim_n \mathsf{E}(\xi - \xi_n)I_{\{\xi \geq \xi_n\}} = 0$, which together with $\mathsf{E}\xi_n \to \mathsf{E}\xi$ proves (17).

Remark. The dominated convergence theorem also holds when almost sure convergence is replaced by convergence in probability (see Problem 1). Hence in Theorem 3 we may replace "$\xi_n \overset{\text{a.s.}}{\to} \xi$" by "$\xi_n \overset{P}{\to} \xi$."

5. It is shown in analysis that every fundamental sequence (x_n), $x_n \in R$, is convergent (Cauchy criterion). Let us give a similar result for the convergence of a sequence of random variables.

Theorem 4 (Cauchy Criterion for Almost Sure Convergence). *A necessary and sufficient condition for the sequence $(\xi_n)_{n \geq 1}$ of random variables to converge with probability 1 (to a random variable ξ) is that it is fundamental with probability 1.*

PROOF. If $\xi_n \overset{\text{a.s.}}{\to} \xi$ then

$$\sup_{\substack{k \geq n \\ l \geq n}}|\xi_k - \xi_l| \leq \sup_{k \geq n}|\xi_k - \xi| + \sup_{l \geq n}|\xi_l - \xi|,$$

whence the necessity follows.

Now let $(\xi_n)_{n \geq 1}$ be fundamental with probability 1. Let $\mathcal{N} = \{\omega : (\xi_n(\omega))$ is not fundamental$\}$. Then whenever $\omega \in \Omega \setminus \mathcal{N}$ the sequence of numbers $(\xi_n(\omega))_{n \geq 1}$ is fundamental and, by Cauchy's criterion for sequences of numbers, $\lim \xi_n(\omega)$ exists. Let

$$\xi(\omega) = \begin{cases} \lim \xi_n(\omega), & \omega \in \Omega \setminus \mathcal{N}, \\ 0, & \omega \in \mathcal{N}. \end{cases} \tag{18}$$

The function so defined is a random variable, and evidently $\xi_n \overset{\text{a.s.}}{\to} \xi$.
This completes the proof.

Before considering the case of convergence in probability, let us establish the following useful result.

Theorem 5. *If the sequence (ξ_n) is fundamental (or convergent) in probability, it contains a subsequence (ξ_{n_k}) that is fundamental (or convergent) with probability 1.*

PROOF. Let (ξ_n) be fundamental in probability. By Theorem 4, it is enough to show that it contains a subsequence that converges almost surely.

Take $n_1 = 1$ and define n_k inductively as the smallest $n > n_{k-1}$ for which

$$P\{|\xi_t - \xi_s| > 2^{-k}\} < 2^{-k}.$$

for all $s \geq n, t \geq n$. Then

$$\sum_k P\{|\xi_{n_{k+1}} - \xi_{n_k}| > 2^{-k}\} < \sum 2^{-k} < \infty$$

and by the Borel–Cantelli lemma

$$P\{|\xi_{n_{k+1}} - \xi_{n_k}| > 2^{-k} \text{ i.o.}\} = 0.$$

Hence

$$\sum_{k=1}^{\infty} |\xi_{n_{k+1}} - \xi_{n_k}| < \infty$$

with probability 1.

Let $\mathcal{N} = \{\omega: \sum |\xi_{n_{k+1}} - \xi_{n_k}| = \infty\}$. Then if we put

$$\xi(\omega) = \begin{cases} \xi_{n_1}(\omega) + \sum_{k=1}^{\infty} (\xi_{n_{k+1}}^{(\omega)} - \xi_{n_k}(\omega)), & \omega \in \Omega\setminus\mathcal{N}, \\ 0, & \omega \in \mathcal{N}, \end{cases}$$

we obtain $\xi_{n_k} \xrightarrow{\text{a.s.}} \xi$.

If the original sequence converges in probability, then it is fundamental in probability (see also (19)), and consequently this case reduces to the one already considered.

This completes the proof of the theorem.

Theorem 6 (Cauchy Criterion for Convergence in Probability). *A necessary and sufficient condition for a sequence $(\xi_n)_{n \geq 1}$ of random variables to converge in probability is that it is fundamental in probability.*

PROOF. If $\xi_n \xrightarrow{P} \xi$ then

$$P\{|\xi_n - \xi_m| \geq \varepsilon\} \leq P\{|\xi_n - \xi| \geq \varepsilon/2\} + P\{|\xi_m - \xi| \geq \varepsilon/2\} \quad (19)$$

and consequently (ξ_n) is fundamental in probability.

Conversely, if (ξ_n) is fundamental in probability, by Theorem 5 there are a subsequence (ξ_{n_k}) and a random variable ξ such that $\xi_{n_k} \xrightarrow{\text{a.s.}} \xi$. But then

$$P\{|\xi_n - \xi| \geq \varepsilon\} \leq P\{|\xi_n - \xi_{n_k}| \geq \varepsilon/2\} + P\{|\xi_{n_k} - \xi| \geq \varepsilon/2\},$$

from which it is clear that $\xi_n \xrightarrow{P} \xi$. This completes the proof.

Before discussing convergence in mean of order p, we make some observations about L^p spaces.

We denote by $L^p = L^p(\Omega, \mathscr{F}, \mathsf{P})$ the space of random variables $\xi = \xi(\omega)$ with $\mathsf{E}|\xi|^p \equiv \int_\Omega |\xi|^p \, d\mathsf{P} < \infty$. Suppose that $p \geq 1$ and put

$$\|\xi\|_p = (\mathsf{E}|\xi|^p)^{1/p}.$$

It is clear that

$$\|\xi\|_p \geq 0, \tag{20}$$

$$\|c\xi\|_p = |c|\,\|\xi\|_p, \quad c \text{ constant}, \tag{21}$$

and by Minkowski's inequality (6.31)

$$\|\xi + \eta\|_p \leq \|\xi\|_p + \|\eta\|_p. \tag{22}$$

Hence, in accordance with the usual terminology of functional analysis, the function $\|\cdot\|_p$, defined on L^p and satisfying (20)–(22), is (for $p \geq 1$) a *seminorm*.

For it to be a *norm*, it must also satisfy

$$\|\xi\|_p = 0 \Rightarrow \xi = 0. \tag{23}$$

This property is, of course, not satisfied, since according to Property **H** (§6) we can only say that $\xi = 0$ almost surely. However, if L^p means the space whose elements are not random variables ξ with $\mathsf{E}|\xi|^p < \infty$, but equivalence classes of random variables (ξ is equivalent to η if $\xi = \eta$ almost surely), then $\|\cdot\|$ becomes a norm, so that L^p is a normed linear space. If we select from each equivalence class of random variables a single element, taking the identically zero function as the representative of the class equivalent to it, we obtain a space (also denoted by L^p) which is actually a normed linear space of functions (rather than of equivalence classes).

It is a basic result of functional analysis that the spaces L^p, $p \geq 1$, are complete, i.e. that every fundamental sequence has a limit. Let us state and prove this in probabilistic language.

Theorem 7 (Cauchy Test for Convergence in Mean pth Power). *A necessary and sufficient condition that a sequence $(\xi_n)_{n\geq 1}$ of random variables in L^p convergences in mean of order p to a random variable in L^p is that the sequence is fundamental in mean of order p.*

PROOF. The necessity follows from Minkowski's inequality. Let (ξ_n) be fundamental ($\|\xi_n - \xi_m\|_p \to 0$, $n, m \to \infty$). As in the proof of Theorem 5, we select a subsequence (ξ_{n_k}) such that $\xi_{n_k} \xrightarrow{\text{a.s.}} \xi$, where ξ is a random variable with $\|\xi\|_p < \infty$.

Let $n_1 = 1$ and define n_k inductively as the smallest $n > n_{k-1}$ for which

$$\|\xi_t - \xi_s\|_p < 2^{-2k}$$

for all $s \geq n, t \geq n$. Let

$$A_k = \{\omega: |\xi_{n_{k+1}} - \xi_{n_k}| \geq 2^{-k}\}.$$

Then by Chebyshev's inequality

$$P(A_k) \le \frac{E|\xi_{n_{k+1}} - \xi_{n_k}|^r}{2^{-kr}} \le \frac{2^{-2kr}}{2^{-kr}} = 2^{-kr} \le 2^{-k}.$$

As in Theorem 5, we deduce that there is a random variable ξ such that $\xi_{n_k} \xrightarrow{\text{a.s.}} \xi$.

We now deduce that $\|\xi_n - \xi\|_p \to 0$ as $n \to \infty$. To do this, we fix $\varepsilon > 0$ and choose $N = N(\varepsilon)$ so that $\|\xi_n - \xi_m\|_p^p < \varepsilon$ for all $n \ge N, m \ge N$. Then for any fixed $n \ge N$, by Fatou's lemma,

$$E|\xi_n - \xi|^p = E\left\{ \lim_{n_k \to \infty} |\xi_n - \xi_{n_k}|^p \right\} = E\left\{ \varliminf_{n_k \to \infty} |\xi_n - \xi_{n_k}|^p \right\}$$

$$\le \varliminf_{n_k \to \infty} E|\xi_n - \xi_{n_k}|^p = \varliminf_{n_k \to \infty} \|\xi_n - \xi_{n_k}\|_p^p \le \varepsilon.$$

Consequently $E|\xi_n - \xi|^p \to 0, n \to \infty$. It is also clear that since $\xi = (\xi - \xi_n) + \xi_n$ we have $E|\xi|^p < \infty$ by Minkowski's inequality.

This completes the proof of the theorem.

Remark 1. In the terminology of functional analysis a complete normed linear space is called a *Banach space*. Thus $L^p, p \ge 1$, is a Banach space.

Remark 2. If $0 < p < 1$, the function $\|\xi\|_p = (E|\xi|^p)^{1/p}$ does not satisfy the triangle inequality (22) and consequently is not a norm. Nevertheless the space (of equivalence classes) $L^p, 0 < p < 1$, is complete in the metric $d(\xi, \eta) \equiv E|\xi - \eta|^p$.

Remark 3. Let $L^\infty = L^\infty(\Omega, \mathscr{F}, P)$ be the space (of equivalence classes of) random variables $\xi = \xi(\omega)$ for which $\|\xi\|_\infty < \infty$, where $\|\xi\|_\infty$, the *essential supremum* of ξ, is defined by

$$\|\xi\|_\infty \equiv \text{ess sup}|\xi| \equiv \inf\{0 \le c \le \infty : P(|\xi| > c) = 0\}.$$

The function $\|\cdot\|_\infty$ is a norm, and L^∞ is complete in this norm.

6. PROBLEMS

1. Use Theorem 5 to show that almost sure convergence can be replaced by convergence in probability in Theorems 3 and 4 of §6.

2. Prove that L^∞ is complete.

3. Show that if $\xi_n \xrightarrow{P} \xi$ and also $\xi_n \xrightarrow{P} \eta$ then ξ and η are equivalent ($P(\xi \ne \eta) = 0$).

4. Let $\xi_n \xrightarrow{P} \xi, \eta_n \xrightarrow{P} \eta$, and let ξ and η be equivalent. Show that

$$P\{|\xi_n - \eta_n| \ge \varepsilon\} \to 0, \qquad n \to \infty,$$

for every $\varepsilon > 0$.

5. Let $\xi_n \xrightarrow{P} \xi$, $\eta_n \xrightarrow{P} \eta$. Show that $a\xi_n + b\eta_n \xrightarrow{P} a\xi + b\eta$ (a, b constants), $|\xi_n| \xrightarrow{P} |\xi|$, $\xi_n \eta_n \xrightarrow{P} \xi\eta$.

6. Let $(\xi_n - \xi)^2 \to 0$. Show that $\xi_n^2 \to \xi^2$.

7. Show that if $\xi_n \xrightarrow{d} C$, where C is a constant, then this sequence converges in probability:
$$\xi_n \xrightarrow{d} C \Rightarrow \xi_n \xrightarrow{P} C.$$

8. Let $(\xi_n)_{n \geq 1}$ have the property that $\sum_{n=1}^{\infty} E|\xi_n|^p < \infty$ for some $p > 0$. Show that $\xi_n \to 0$ (P-a.s.).

9. Let $(\xi_n)_{n \geq 1}$ be a sequence of independent identically distributed random variables. Show that
$$E|\xi_1| < \infty \Leftrightarrow \sum_{n=1}^{\infty} P\{|\xi_1| > \varepsilon \cdot n\} < \infty$$
$$\Leftrightarrow \sum_{n=1}^{\infty} P\left\{ \left| \frac{\xi_n}{n} \right| > \varepsilon \right\} < \infty \Rightarrow \frac{\xi_n}{n} \to 0 \quad \text{(P-a.s.)}.$$

10. Let $(\xi_n)_{n \geq 1}$ be a sequence of random variables. Suppose that there are a random variable ξ and a sequence $\{n_k\}$ such that $\xi_{n_k} \to \xi$ (P-a.s.) and $\max_{n_{k-1} < l \leq n_k} |\xi_l - \xi_{n_{k-1}}| \to 0$ (P-a.s.) as $k \to \infty$. Show that then $\xi_n \to \xi$ (P-a.s.).

11. Let the d-metric on the set of random variables be defined by
$$d(\xi, \eta) = E \frac{|\xi - \eta|}{1 + |\xi - \eta|}$$
and identify random variables that coincide almost surely. Show that convergence in probability is equivalent to convergence in the d-metric.

12. Show that there is no metric on the set of random variables such that convergence in that metric is equivalent to almost sure convergence.

§11. The Hilbert Space of Random Variables with Finite Second Moment

1. An important role among the Banach spaces L^p, $p \geq 1$, is played by the space $L^2 = L^2(\Omega, \mathscr{F}, P)$, the space of (equivalence classes of) random variables with finite second moments.

If ξ and $\eta \in L^2$, we put
$$(\xi, \eta) \equiv E\xi\eta. \tag{1}$$

It is clear that if ξ, η, $\zeta \in L^2$ then
$$(a\xi + b\eta, \zeta) = a(\xi, \zeta) + b(\eta, \zeta), \qquad a, b \in R,$$
$$(\xi, \xi) \geq 0$$
and
$$(\xi, \xi) = 0 \Leftrightarrow \xi = 0.$$

Consequently (ξ, η) is a *scalar product*. The space L^2 is *complete* with respect to the norm

$$\|\xi\| = (\xi, \xi)^{1/2} \tag{2}$$

induced by this scalar product (as was shown in §10). In accordance with the terminology of functional analysis, a space with the scalar product (1) is a *Hilbert space*.

Hilbert space methods are extensively used in probability theory to study properties that depend only on the first two moments of random variables ("L^2-theory"). Here we shall introduce the basic concepts and facts that will be needed for an exposition of L^2-theory (Chapter VI).

2. Two random variables ξ and η in L^2 are said to be orthogonal ($\xi \perp \eta$) if $(\xi, \eta) \equiv \mathsf{E}\xi\eta = 0$. According to §8, ξ and η are uncorrelated if $\mathrm{cov}(\xi, \eta) = 0$, i.e. if

$$\mathsf{E}\xi\eta = \mathsf{E}\xi\mathsf{E}\eta.$$

It follows that the properties of being orthogonal and of being uncorrelated coincide for random variables with zero mean values.

A set $M \subseteq L^2$ is a *system of orthogonal random variables* if $\xi \perp \eta$ for every $\xi, \eta \in M$ ($\xi \neq \eta$).

If also $\|\xi\| = 1$ for every $\xi \in M$, then M is an *orthonormal system*.

3. Let $M = \{\eta_1, \ldots, \eta_n\}$ be an orthonormal system and ξ any random variable in L^2. Let us find, in the class of linear estimators $\sum_{i=1}^n a_i\eta_i$, the best mean-square estimator for ξ (cf. Subsection 2, §8).

A simple computation shows that

$$\mathsf{E}\left|\xi - \sum_{i=1}^n \alpha_i\eta_i\right|^2 \equiv \left\|\xi - \sum_{i=1}^n a_i\eta_i\right\|^2 = \left(\xi - \sum_{i=1}^n a_i\eta_i, \xi - \sum_{i=1}^n a_i\eta_i\right)$$

$$= \|\xi\|^2 - 2\sum_{i=1}^n a_i(\xi, \eta_i) + \left(\sum_{i=1}^n a_i\eta_i, \sum_{i=1}^n a_i\eta_i\right)$$

$$= \|\xi\|^2 - 2\sum_{i=1}^n a_i(\xi, \eta_i) + \sum_{i=1}^n a_i^2$$

$$= \|\xi\|^2 - \sum_{i=1}^n |(\xi, \eta_i)|^2 + \sum_{i=1}^n |a_i - (\xi, \eta_i)|^2$$

$$\geq \|\xi\|^2 - \sum_{i=1}^n |(\xi, \eta_i)|^2, \tag{3}$$

where we used the equation

$$a_i^2 - 2a_i(\xi, \eta_i) = |\alpha_i - (\xi, \eta_i)|^2 - |(\xi, \eta_i)|^2.$$

It is now clear that the infimum of $E|\xi - \sum_{i=1}^{n} a_i \eta_i|^2$ over all real $a_1, \ldots, a_n$ is attained for $a_i = (\xi, \eta_i), i = 1, \ldots, n$.

Consequently the best (in the mean-square sense) estimator for ξ in terms of $\eta_1, \ldots, \eta_n$ is

$$\hat{\xi} = \sum_{i=1}^{n} (\xi, \eta_i)\eta_i. \tag{4}$$

Here

$$\Delta \equiv \inf E\left|\xi - \sum_{i=1}^{n} a_i \eta_i\right|^2 = E|\xi - \hat{\xi}|^2 = \|\xi\|^2 - \sum_{i=1}^{n} |(\xi, \eta_i)|^2 \tag{5}$$

(compare (I.4.17) and (8.13)).

Inequality (3) also implies *Bessel's inequality*: if $M = \{\eta_1, \eta_2, \ldots\}$ is an orthonormal system and $\xi \in L^2$, then

$$\sum_{i=1}^{\infty} |(\xi, \eta_i)|^2 \leq \|\xi\|^2; \tag{6}$$

and equality is attained if and only if

$$\xi = \text{l.i.m.}_n \sum_{i=1}^{n} (\xi, \eta_i)\eta_i. \tag{7}$$

The *best linear estimator* of ξ is often denoted by $\hat{E}(\xi|\eta_1, \ldots, \eta_n)$ and called the *conditional expectation* (of ξ with respect to $\eta_1, \ldots, \eta_n$) in the *wide sense*.

The reason for the terminology is as follows. If we consider all estimators $\varphi = \varphi(\eta_1, \ldots, \eta_n)$ of ξ in terms of $\eta_1, \ldots, \eta_n$ (where φ is a Borel function), the best estimator will be $\varphi^* = E(\xi|\eta_1, \ldots, \eta_n)$, i.e. the conditional expectation of ξ with respect to $\eta_1, \ldots, \eta_n$ (cf. Theorem 1, §8). Hence the best linear estimator is, by analogy, denoted by $\hat{E}(\xi|\eta_1, \ldots, \eta_n)$ and called the conditional expectation in the wide sense. We note that if $\eta_1, \ldots, \eta_n$ form a Gaussian system (see §13 below), then $E(\xi|\eta_1, \ldots, \eta_n)$ and $\hat{E}(\xi|\eta_1, \ldots, \eta_n)$ are the same.

Let us discuss the *geometric meaning* of $\hat{\xi} = \hat{E}(\xi|\eta_1, \ldots, \eta_n)$.

Let $\mathscr{L} = \mathscr{L}\{\eta_1, \ldots, \eta_n\}$ denote the *linear manifold* spanned by the orthonormal system of random variables $\eta_1, \ldots, \eta_n$ (i.e., the set of random variables of the form $\sum_{i=1}^{n} a_i \eta_i, a_i \in R$).

Then it follows from the preceding discussion that ξ admits the "orthogonal decomposition"

$$\xi = \hat{\xi} + (\xi - \hat{\xi}), \tag{8}$$

where $\hat{\xi} \in \mathscr{L}$ and $\xi - \hat{\xi} \perp \mathscr{L}$ in the sense that $\xi - \hat{\xi} \perp \lambda$ for every $\lambda \in \mathscr{L}$. It is natural to call $\hat{\xi}$ the *projection of* ξ on $\mathscr{L}$ (the element of $\mathscr{L}$ "closest" to ξ), and to say that $\xi - \hat{\xi}$ is *perpendicular* to $\mathscr{L}$.

4. The concept of orthonormality of the random variables $\eta_1, \ldots, \eta_n$ makes it easy to find the best linear estimator (the projection) $\hat{\xi}$ of ξ in terms of

$\eta_1, \ldots, \eta_n$. The situation becomes complicated if we give up the hypothesis of orthonormality. However, the case of arbitrary $\eta_1, \ldots, \eta_n$ can in a certain sense be reduced to the case of orthonormal random variables, as will be shown below. We shall suppose for the sake of simplicity that all our random variables have zero mean values.

We shall say that the random variables $\eta_1, \ldots, \eta_n$ are *linearly independent* if the equation

$$\sum_{i=1}^{n} a_i \eta_i = 0 \quad \text{(P-a.s.)}$$

is satisfied only when all a_i are zero.

Consider the covariance matrix

$$\mathbb{R} = \mathsf{E}\eta\eta^{\mathsf{T}}$$

of the vector $\eta = (\eta_1, \ldots, \eta_n)$. It is symmetric and nonnegative definite, and as noticed in §8, can be diagonalized by an orthogonal matrix $\mathcal{O}$:

$$\mathcal{O}^{\mathsf{T}} \mathbb{R} \mathcal{O} = D,$$

where

$$D = \begin{pmatrix} d_1 & & 0 \\ & \ddots & \\ 0 & & d_n \end{pmatrix}$$

has nonnegative elements d_i, the eigenvalues of $\mathbb{R}$, i.e. the zeros λ of the characteristic equation $\det(\mathbb{R} - \lambda E) = 0$.

If $\eta_1, \ldots, \eta_n$ are linearly independent, the Gram determinant $(\det \mathbb{R})$ is not zero and therefore $d_i > 0$. Let

$$B = \begin{pmatrix} \sqrt{d_1} & & 0 \\ & \ddots & \\ 0 & & \sqrt{d_n} \end{pmatrix}$$

and

$$\beta = B^{-1}\mathcal{O}^{\mathsf{T}}\eta. \tag{9}$$

Then the covariance matrix of β is

$$\mathsf{E}\beta\beta^{\mathsf{T}} = B^{-1}\mathcal{O}^{\mathsf{T}}\mathsf{E}\eta\eta^{\mathsf{T}}\mathcal{O}B^{-1} = B^{-1}\mathcal{O}^{\mathsf{T}}\mathbb{R}\mathcal{O}B^{-1} = E,$$

and therefore $\beta = (\beta_1, \ldots, \beta_n)$ consists of uncorrelated random variables. It is also clear that

$$\eta = (\mathcal{O}B)\beta. \tag{10}$$

Consequently if $\eta_1, \ldots, \eta_n$ are linearly independent there is an orthonormal system such that (9) and (10) hold. Here

$$\mathscr{L}\{\eta_1, \ldots, \eta_n\} = \mathscr{L}\{\beta_1, \ldots, \beta_n\}.$$

This method of constructing an orthonormal system $\beta_1, \ldots, \beta_n$ is frequently inconvenient. The reason is that if we think of η_i as the value of the random sequence $(\eta_1, \ldots, \eta_n)$ at the instant i, the value β_i constructed above depends not only on the "past," $(\eta_1, \ldots, \eta_i)$, but also on the "future," $(\eta_{i+1}, \ldots, \eta_n)$. The *Gram–Schmidt orthogonalization process*, described below, does not have this defect, and moreover has the advantage that it can be applied to an infinite sequence of *linearly independent* random variables (i.e. to a sequence in which every finite set of the variables are linearly independent).

Let $\eta_1, \eta_2, \ldots$ be a sequence of linearly independent random variables in L^2. We construct a sequence $\varepsilon_1, \varepsilon_2, \ldots$ as follows. Let $\varepsilon_1 = \eta_1 / \|\eta_1\|$. If $\varepsilon_1, \ldots, \varepsilon_{n-1}$ have been selected so that they are orthonormal, then

$$\varepsilon_n = \frac{\eta_n - \hat{\eta}_n}{\|\eta_n - \hat{\eta}_n\|}, \tag{11}$$

where $\hat{\eta}_n$ is the projection of η_n on the linear manifold $\mathscr{L}(\varepsilon_1, \ldots, \varepsilon_{n-1})$ generated by

$$\hat{\eta}_n = \sum_{k=1}^{n-1} (\eta_n, \varepsilon_k)\varepsilon_k. \tag{12}$$

Since $\eta_1, \ldots, \eta_n$ are linearly independent and $\mathscr{L}\{\eta_1, \ldots, \eta_{n-1}\} = \mathscr{L}\{\varepsilon_1, \ldots, \varepsilon_{n-1}\}$, we have $\|\eta_n - \hat{\eta}_n\| > 0$ and consequently ε_n is well defined.

By construction, $\|\varepsilon_n\| = 1$ for $n \geq 1$, and it is clear that $(\varepsilon_n, \varepsilon_k) = 0$ for $k < n$. Hence the sequence $\varepsilon_1, \varepsilon_2, \ldots$ is orthonormal. Moreover, by (11),

$$\eta_n = \hat{\eta}_n + b_n \varepsilon_n,$$

where $b_n = \|\eta_n - \hat{\eta}_n\|$ and $\hat{\eta}_n$ is defined by (12).

Now let $\eta_1, \ldots, \eta_n$ be any set of random variables (not necessarily linearly independent). Let $\det \mathbb{R} = 0$, where $\mathbb{R} \equiv \|r_{ij}\|$ is the covariance matrix of $(\eta_1, \ldots, \eta_n)$, and let

$$\text{rank } \mathbb{R} = r < n.$$

Then, from linear algebra, the quadratic form

$$Q(a) = \sum_{i,j=1}^{n} r_{ij} a_i a_j, \qquad a = (a_1, \ldots, a_n),$$

has the property that there are $n - r$ linearly independent vectors $a^{(1)}, \ldots, a^{(n-r)}$ such that $Q(a^{(i)}) = 0$, $i = 1, \ldots, n - r$.

But

$$Q(a) = \mathsf{E}\left(\sum_{k=1}^{n} a_k \eta_k\right)^2.$$

Consequently

$$\sum_{k=1}^{n} a_k^{(i)} \eta_k = 0, \qquad i = 1, \ldots, n - r,$$

with probability 1.

In other words, there are $n - r$ linear relations among the variables $\eta_1, \ldots, \eta_n$. Therefore if, for example, $\eta_1, \ldots, \eta_r$ are linearly independent, the other variables $\eta_{r+1}, \ldots, \eta_n$ can be expressed linearly in terms of them, and consequently $\mathscr{L}\{\eta_1, \ldots, \eta_n\} = \mathscr{L}\{\varepsilon_1, \ldots, \varepsilon_r\}$. Hence it is clear that we can find r orthonormal random variables $\varepsilon_1, \ldots, \varepsilon_r$ such that $\eta_1, \ldots, \eta_n$ can be expressed linearly in terms of them and $\mathscr{L}\{\eta_1, \ldots, \eta_n\} = \mathscr{L}\{\varepsilon_1, \ldots, \varepsilon_r\}$.

5. Let $\eta_1, \eta_2, \ldots$ be a sequence of random variables in L^2. Let $\mathscr{L} = \mathscr{L}\{\eta_1, \eta_2, \ldots\}$ be the *linear manifold* spanned by $\eta_1, \eta_2, \ldots$, i.e. the set of random variables of the form $\sum_{i=1}^{n} a_i \eta_i$, $n \geq 1$, $a_i \in R$. Then $\overline{\mathscr{L}} = \overline{\mathscr{L}}\{\eta_1, \eta_2, \ldots\}$ denotes the *closed linear manifold* spanned by $\eta_1, \eta_2, \ldots$, i.e. the set of random variables in $\mathscr{L}$ together with their mean-square limits.

We say that a set $\eta_1, \eta_2, \ldots$ is a *countable orthonormal basis* (or a *complete orthonormal system*) if:

(a) $\eta_1, \eta_2, \ldots$ is an orthonormal system,
(b) $\overline{\mathscr{L}}\{\eta_1, \eta_2, \ldots\} = L^2$.

A Hilbert space with a countable orthonormal basis is said to be *separable*.

By (b), for every $\xi \in L^2$ and a given $\varepsilon > 0$ there are numbers $a_1, \ldots, a_n$ such that

$$\left\| \xi - \sum_{i=1}^{n} a_i \eta_i \right\| \leq \varepsilon.$$

Then by (3)

$$\left\| \xi - \sum_{i=1}^{n} (\xi, \eta_i) \eta_i \right\| \leq \varepsilon.$$

Consequently every element of a separable Hilbert space L^2 can be represented as

$$\xi = \sum_{i=1}^{\infty} (\xi, \eta_i) \cdot \eta_i, \tag{13}$$

or more precisely as

$$\xi = \underset{n}{\text{l.i.m.}} \sum_{i=1}^{n} (\xi, \eta_i) \eta_i.$$

We infer from this and (3) that *Parseval's equation* holds:

$$\|\xi\|^2 = \sum_{i=1}^{\infty} |(\xi, \eta_i)|^2, \qquad \xi \in L^2. \tag{14}$$

It is easy to show that the converse is also valid: if $\eta_1, \eta_2, \ldots$ is an orthonormal system and either (13) or (14) is satisfied, then the system is a basis. We now give some examples of separable Hilbert spaces and their bases.

EXAMPLE 1. Let $\Omega = R$, $\mathscr{F} = \mathscr{B}(R)$, and let P be the Gaussian measure,

$$P(-\infty, a] = \int_{-\infty}^{a} \varphi(x)\, dx, \qquad \varphi(x) = \frac{1}{\sqrt{2\pi}} e^{-x^2/2}.$$

Let $D = d/dx$ and

$$H_n(x) = \frac{(-1)^n D^n \varphi(x)}{\varphi(x)}, \qquad n \geq 0. \tag{15}$$

We find easily that

$$D\varphi(x) = -x\varphi(x),$$
$$D^2\varphi(x) = (x^2 - 1)\varphi(x), \tag{16}$$
$$D^3\varphi(x) = (3x - x^3)\varphi(x),$$
$$\cdots\cdots\cdots\cdots\cdots\cdots\cdots$$

It follows that $H_n(x)$ are polynomials (the *Hermite polynomials*). From (15) and (16) we find that

$$H_0(x) = 1,$$
$$H_1(x) = x,$$
$$H_2(x) = x^2 - 1,$$
$$H_3(x) = x^3 - 3x,$$
$$\cdots\cdots\cdots\cdots\cdots$$

A simple calculation shows that

$$(H_m, H_n) = \int_{-\infty}^{\infty} H_m(x) H_n(x)\, d\mathbf{P}$$
$$= \int_{-\infty}^{\infty} H_m(x) H_n(x) \varphi(x)\, dx = n!\, \delta_{mn},$$

where δ_{mn} is the Kronecker delta (0, if $m \neq n$, and 1 if $m = n$). Hence if we put

$$h_n(x) = \frac{H_n(x)}{\sqrt{n}},$$

the system of *normalized Hermite polynomials* $\{h_n(x)\}_{n\geq 0}$ will be an orthonormal system. We know from functional analysis that if

$$\lim_{c \downarrow 0} \int_{-\infty}^{\infty} e^{c|x|}\, \mathbf{P}(dx) < \infty, \tag{17}$$

the system $\{1, x, x^2, \ldots\}$ is complete in L^2, i.e. every function $\xi = \xi(x)$ in L^2 can be represented either as $\sum_{i=1}^{n} a_i \eta_i(x)$, where $\eta_i(x) = x^i$, or as a limit of these functions (in the mean-square sense). If we apply the Gram–Schmidt orthogonalization process to the sequence $\eta_1(x), \eta_2(x), \ldots$, with $\eta_i(x) = x^i$, the resulting orthonormal system will be precisely the system of normalized Hermite polynomials. In the present case, (17) is satisfied. Hence $\{h_n(x)\}_{n\geq 0}$ is a basis and therefore every random variable $\xi = \xi(x)$ on this probability space can be represented in the form

$$\xi(x) = \underset{n}{\text{l.i.m.}} \sum_{i=0}^{n} (\xi, h_i)h_i(x). \tag{18}$$

EXAMPLE 2. Let $\Omega = \{0, 1, 2, \ldots\}$ and let $P = \{P_1, P_2, \ldots\}$ be the Poisson distribution

$$P_x = \frac{e^{-\lambda}\lambda^x}{x!}, \qquad x = 0, 1, \ldots; \quad \lambda > 0.$$

Put $\Delta f(x) = f(x) - f(x-1)$ $(f(x) = 0, x < 0)$, and by analogy with (15) define the *Poisson–Charlier polynomials*

$$\Pi_n(x) = \frac{(-1)^n \Delta^n P_x}{P_x}, \qquad n \geq 1, \quad \Pi_0 = 1. \tag{19}$$

Since

$$(\Pi_m, \Pi_n) = \sum_{x=0}^{\infty} \Pi_m(x)\Pi_n(x)P_x = c_n \delta_{mn},$$

where c_n are positive constants, the system of *normalized Poisson–Charlier polynomials* $\{\pi_n(x)\}_{n\geq 0}$, $\pi_n(x) = \Pi_n(x)/\sqrt{c_n}$, is an orthonormal system, which is a basis since it satisfies (17).

EXAMPLE 3. In this example we describe the Rademacher and Haar systems, which are of interest in function theory as well as in probability theory.

Let $\Omega = [0, 1]$, $\mathscr{F} = \mathscr{B}([0, 1])$, and let P be Lebesgue measure. As we mentioned in §1, every $x \in [0, 1]$ has a unique binary expansion

$$x = \frac{x_1}{2} + \frac{x_2}{2^2} + \cdots,$$

where $x_i = 0$ or 1. To ensure uniqueness of the expansion, we agree to consider only expansions containing an infinite number of zeros. Thus we choose the first of the two expansions

$$\frac{1}{2} = \frac{1}{2} + \frac{0}{2^2} + \frac{0}{2^3} + \cdots = \frac{0}{2} + \frac{1}{2^2} + \frac{1}{2^3} + \cdots.$$

We define random variables $\xi_1(x), \xi_2(x), \ldots$ by putting

$$\xi_n(x) = x_n.$$

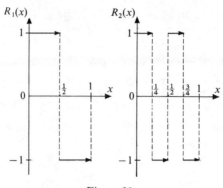

Figure 30

Then for any numbers a_i, equal to 0 or 1,

$$\mathsf{P}\{x\colon \xi_1 = a_1, \ldots, \xi_n = a_n\}$$

$$= \mathsf{P}\left\{x\colon \frac{a_1}{2} + \frac{a_2}{2^2} + \cdots + \frac{a_n}{2^n} \le x < \frac{a_1}{2} + \frac{a_2}{2^2} + \cdots + \frac{a_n}{2^n} + \frac{1}{2^n}\right\}$$

$$= \mathsf{P}\left\{x\colon x \in \left[\frac{a_1}{2} + \cdots + \frac{a_n}{2^n}, \frac{a_1}{2} + \cdots + \frac{a_n}{2^n} + \frac{1}{2^n}\right]\right\} = \frac{1}{2^n}.$$

It follows immediately that $\xi_1, \xi_2, \ldots$ form a *sequence of independent Bernoulli random variables* (Figure 30 shows the construction of $\xi_1 = \xi_1(x)$ and $\xi_2 = \xi_2(x)$).

If we now set $R_n(x) = 1 - 2\xi_n(x)$, $n \ge 1$, it is easily verified that $\{R_n\}$ (the *Rademacher functions*, Figure 31) are orthonormal:

$$\mathsf{E}R_n R_m = \int_0^1 R_n(x) R_m(x)\, dx = \delta_{nm}. \qquad \cdot$$

Notice that $(1, R_n) \equiv \mathsf{E}R_n = 0$. It follows that this system is not complete.

However, the Rademacher system can be used to construct the *Haar system*, which also has a simple structure and is both *orthonormal* and *complete*.

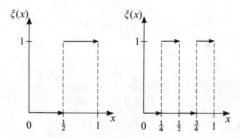

Figure 31. Rademacher functions.

Again let $\Omega = [0, 1)$ and $\mathscr{F} = \mathscr{B}([0, 1))$. Put

$H_1(x) = 1,$

$H_2(x) = R_1(x),$

....

$$H_n(x) = \begin{cases} 2^{j/2} R_j(x) & \text{if } \dfrac{k-1}{2^j} \leq x < \dfrac{k}{2^j}, \quad n = 2^j + k, \quad 1 \leq k \leq 2^j, j \geq 1, \\ 0, & \text{otherwise.} \end{cases}$$

It is easy to see that $H_n(x)$ can also be written in the form

$$H_{2^m+1}(x) = \begin{cases} 2^{m/2}, & 0 \leq x < 2^{-(m+1)}, \\ -2^{m/2}, & 2^{-(m+1)} \leq x < 2^{-m}, \quad m = 1, 2, \dots, \\ 0, & \text{otherwise,} \end{cases}$$

$$H_{2^m+j}(x) = H_{2^m+1}\left(x - \dfrac{j-1}{2^m}\right), \quad j = 1, \dots, 2^m.$$

Figure 32 shows graphs of the first eight functions, to give an idea of the structure of the Haar functions.

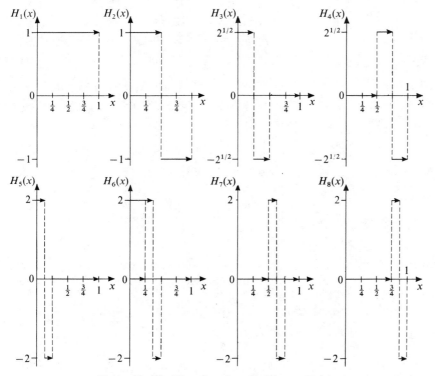

Figure 32. The Haar functions $H_1(x), \dots, H_8(x)$.

It is easy to see that the Haar system is orthonormal. Moreover, it is complete both in L^1 and in L^2, i.e. if $f = f(x) \in L^p$ for $p = 1$ or 2, then

$$\int_0^1 |f(x) - \sum_{k=1}^n (f, H_k)H_k(x)|^p \, dx \to 0, \qquad n \to \infty.$$

The system also has the property that

$$\sum_{k=1}^n (f, H_k)H_k(x) \to f(x), \qquad n \to \infty,$$

with probability 1 (with respect to Lebesgue measure).

In §4, Chapter VII, we shall prove these facts by deriving them from general theorems on the convergence of martingales. This will, in particular, provide a good illustration of the application of martingale methods to the theory of functions.

6. If $\eta_1, \ldots, \eta_n$ is a finite orthonormal system then, as was shown above, for every random variable $\xi \in L^2$ there is a random variable $\hat{\xi}$ in the linear manifold $\mathscr{L} = \mathscr{L}\{\eta_1, \ldots, \eta_n\}$, namely the projection of ξ on $\mathscr{L}$, such that

$$\|\xi - \hat{\xi}\| = \inf\{\|\xi - \zeta\| : \zeta \in \mathscr{L}\{\eta_1, \ldots, \eta_n\}\}.$$

Here $\hat{\xi} = \sum_{i=1}^n (\xi, \eta_i)\eta_i$. This result has a natural generalization to the case when $\eta_1, \eta_2, \ldots$ is a countable orthonormal system (not necessarily a basis). In fact, we have the following result.

Theorem. *Let $\eta_1, \eta_2, \ldots$ be an orthonormal system of random variables, and $\bar{L} = \bar{L}\{\eta_1, \eta_2, \ldots\}$ the closed linear manifold spanned by the system. Then there is a unique element $\hat{\xi} \in \bar{L}$ such that*

$$\|\xi - \hat{\xi}\| = \inf\{\|\xi - \zeta\| : \zeta \in \mathscr{L}\}. \tag{20}$$

Moreover,

$$\hat{\xi} = \operatorname*{l.i.m.}_n \sum_{i=1}^n (\xi, \eta_i)\eta_i \tag{21}$$

and $\xi - \hat{\xi} \perp \zeta, \zeta \in \bar{L}$.

PROOF. Let $d = \inf\{\|\xi - \zeta\| : \zeta \in \mathscr{L}\}$ and choose a sequence $\zeta_1, \zeta_2, \ldots$ such that $\|\xi - \zeta_n\| \to d$. Let us show that this sequence is fundamental. A simple calculation shows that

$$\|\zeta_n - \zeta_m\|^2 = 2\|\zeta_n - \xi\|^2 + 2\|\zeta_m - \xi\|^2 - 4\left\|\frac{\zeta_n + \zeta_m}{2} - \xi\right\|^2.$$

It is clear that $(\zeta_n + \zeta_m)/2 \in \mathscr{L}$; consequently $\|[(\zeta_n + \zeta_m)/2] - \xi\|^2 \geq d^2$ and therefore $\|\zeta_n - \zeta_m\|^2 \to 0$, $n, m \to \infty$.

The space L^2 is complete (Theorem 7, §10). Hence there is an element $\hat{\xi}$ such that $\|\zeta_n - \hat{\xi}\| \to 0$. But $\mathscr{L}$ is closed, so $\hat{\xi} \in \mathscr{L}$. Moreover, $\|\zeta_n - \xi\| \to d$, and consequently $\|\xi - \hat{\xi}\| = d$, which establishes the existence of the required element.

Let us show that $\hat{\xi}$ is the only element of $\mathscr{L}$ with the required property. Let $\tilde{\xi} \in \mathscr{L}$ and let

$$\|\xi - \hat{\xi}\| = \|\xi - \tilde{\xi}\| = d.$$

Then (by Problem 3)

$$\|\hat{\xi} + \tilde{\xi} - 2\xi\|^2 + \|\hat{\xi} - \tilde{\xi}\|^2 = 2\|\hat{\xi} - \xi\|^2 + 2\|\tilde{\xi} - \xi\|^2 = 4d^2.$$

But

$$\|\hat{\xi} + \tilde{\xi} - 2\xi\|^2 = 4\|\tfrac{1}{2}(\hat{\xi} + \tilde{\xi}) - \xi\|^2 \geq 4d^2.$$

Consequently $\|\hat{\xi} - \tilde{\xi}\|^2 = 0$. This establishes the uniqueness of the element of $\mathscr{L}$ that is closest to ξ.

Now let us show that $\xi - \hat{\xi} \perp \zeta, \zeta \in \mathscr{L}$. By (20),

$$\|\xi - \hat{\xi} - c\zeta\| \geq \|\xi - \hat{\xi}\|$$

for every $c \in R$. But

$$\|\xi - \hat{\xi} - c\zeta\|^2 = \|\xi - \hat{\xi}\|^2 + c^2\|\zeta\|^2 - 2(\xi - \hat{\xi}, c\zeta).$$

Therefore

$$c^2\|\zeta\|^2 \geq 2(\xi - \hat{\xi}, c\zeta). \tag{22}$$

Take $c = \lambda(\xi - \hat{\xi}, \zeta), \lambda \in R$. Then we find from (22) that

$$(\xi - \hat{\xi}, \zeta)^2[\lambda^2\|\zeta\|^2 - 2\lambda] \geq 0.$$

We have $\lambda^2\|\zeta\|^2 - 2\lambda < 0$ if λ is a sufficiently small positive number. Consequently $(\xi - \hat{\xi}, \zeta) = 0, \zeta \in \bar{L}$.

It remains only to prove (21).

The set $\mathscr{L} = \mathscr{L}\{\eta_1, \eta_2, \ldots\}$ is a closed subspace of L^2 and therefore a Hilbert space (with the same scalar product). Now the system $\eta_1, \eta_2, \ldots$ is a basis for $\mathscr{L}$ (Problem 4), and consequently

$$\hat{\xi} = \operatorname*{l.i.m.}_{n} \sum_{k=1}^{n} (\hat{\xi}, \eta_k)\eta_k. \tag{23}$$

But $\xi - \hat{\xi} \perp \eta_k, k \geq 1$, and therefore $(\hat{\xi}, \eta_k) = (\xi, \eta_k), k \geq 0$. This, with (23) establishes (21).

This completes the proof of the theorem.

Remark. As in the finite-dimensional case, we say that $\hat{\xi}$ is the projection of ξ on $\bar{L} = \bar{L}\{\eta_1, \eta_2, \ldots\}$, that $\xi - \hat{\xi}$ is perpendicular to $\bar{L}$, and that the representation

$$\xi = \hat{\xi} + (\xi - \hat{\xi})$$

is the orthogonal decomposition of ξ.

We also denote $\hat{\xi}$ by $\hat{E}(\xi|\eta_1, \eta_2, \ldots)$ and call it the *conditional expectation in the wide sense* (of ξ with respect to $\eta_1, \eta_2, \ldots$). From the point of view of estimating ξ in terms of $\eta_1, \eta_2, \ldots$, the variable $\hat{\xi}$ is the optimal linear estimator, with error

$$\Delta \equiv E|\xi - \hat{\xi}|^2 \equiv \|\xi - \hat{\xi}\|^2 = \|\xi\|^2 - \sum_{i=1}^{\infty} |(\xi, \eta_i)|^2,$$

which follows from (5) and (23).

7. Problems

1. Show that if $\xi = \text{l.i.m. } \xi_n$ then $\|\xi_n\| \to \|\xi\|$.

2. Show that if $\xi = \text{l.i.m. } \xi_n$ and $\eta = \text{l.i.m. } \eta_n$ then $(\xi_n, \eta_n) \to (\xi, \eta)$.

3. Show that the norm $\|\cdot\|$ has the *parallelogram* property
$$\|\xi + \eta\|^2 + \|\xi - \eta\|^2 = 2(\|\xi\|^2 + \|\eta\|^2).$$

4. Let $(\xi_1, \ldots, \xi_n)$ be a family of orthogonal random variables. Show that they have the *Pythagorean property*,
$$\left\|\sum_{i=1}^{n} \xi_i\right\|^2 = \sum_{i=1}^{n} \|\xi_i\|^2.$$

5. Let $\eta_1, \eta_2, \ldots$ be an orthonormal system and $\mathscr{L} = \mathscr{L}\{\eta_1, \eta_2, \ldots\}$ the closed linear manifold spanned by $\eta_1, \eta_2, \ldots$. Show that the system is a basis for the (Hilbert) space $\mathscr{L}$.

6. Let $\xi_1, \xi_2, \ldots$ be a sequence of orthogonal random variables and $S_n = \xi_1 + \cdots + \xi_n$. Show that if $\sum_{n=1}^{\infty} E\xi_n^2 < \infty$ there is a random variable S with $ES^2 < \infty$ such that l.i.m. $S_n = S$, i.e. $\|S_n - S\|^2 = E|S_n - S|^2 \to 0$, $n \to \infty$.

7. Show that in the space $L^2 = L^2([-\pi, \pi], \mathscr{B}([-\pi, \pi]))$ with Lebesgue measure μ the system $\{(1/\sqrt{2\pi})e^{i\lambda n}, n = 0, \pm 1, \ldots\}$ is an orthonormal basis.

§12. Characteristic Functions

1. The method of characteristic functions is one of the main tools of the analytic theory of probability. This will appear very clearly in Chapter III in the proofs of limit theorems and, in particular, in the proof of the central limit theorem, which generalizes the De Moivre–Laplace theorem. In the present section we merely define characteristic functions and present their basic properties.

First we make some general remarks.

Besides random variables which take real values, the theory of characteristic functions requires random variables that take complex values (see Subsection 1 of §5).

Many definitions and properties involving random variables can easily be carried over to the complex case. For example, the expectation $E\zeta$ of a complex random variable $\zeta = \xi + i\eta$ will exist if the expectations $E\xi$ and $E\eta$ exist. In this case we define $E\zeta = E\xi + iE\eta$. It is easy to deduce from the definition of the independence of random elements (Definition 6, §5) that the complex random variables $\zeta_1 = \xi_1 + i\eta_1$ and $\zeta_2 = \xi_2 + i\eta_2$ are independent if and only if the pairs (ξ_1, η_1) and (ξ_2, η_2) are independent; or, equivalently, the σ-algebras $\mathcal{L}_{\xi_1, \eta_1}$ and $\mathcal{L}_{\xi_2, \eta_2}$ are independent.

Besides the space L^2 of real random variables with finite second moment, we shall consider the Hilbert space of complex random variables $\zeta = \xi + i\eta$ with $E|\zeta|^2 < \infty$, where $|\zeta|^2 = \xi^2 + \eta^2$ and the scalar product (ζ_1, ζ_2) is defined by $E\zeta_1\bar{\zeta}_2$, where $\bar{\zeta}_2$ is the complex conjugate of ζ. The term "random variable" will now be used for both real and complex random variables, with a comment (when necessary) on which is intended.

Let us introduce some notation.

We consider a vector $a \in R^n$ to be a column vector,

$$a = \begin{pmatrix} a_1 \\ \vdots \\ a_n \end{pmatrix},$$

and a^T to be a row vector, $a^T = (a_1, \ldots, a_n)$. If a and $b \in R^n$ their scalar product (a, b) is $\sum_{i=1}^n a_i b_i$. Clearly $(a, b) = a^T b$.

If $a \in R^n$ and $\mathbb{R} = \|r_{ij}\|$ is an n by n matrix,

$$(\mathbb{R}a, a) = a^T \mathbb{R}a = \sum_{i, j=1}^n r_{ij} a_i a_j. \tag{1}$$

2. Definition 1. Let $F = F(x_1, \ldots, x_n)$ be an n-dimensional distribution function in $(R^n, \mathcal{B}(R^n))$. Its *characteristic function* is

$$\varphi(t) = \int_{R^n} e^{i(t, x)} \, dF(x), \qquad t \in R^n. \tag{2}$$

Definition 2. If $\xi = (\xi_1, \ldots, \xi_n)$ is a random vector defined on the probability space $(\Omega, \mathcal{F}, P)$ with values in R^n, its *characteristic function* is

$$\varphi_\xi(t) = \int_{R^n} e^{i(t, x)} \, dF_\xi(x), \qquad t \in R^n, \tag{3}$$

where $F_\xi = F_\xi(x_1, \ldots, x_n)$ is the distribution function of the vector $\xi = (\xi_1, \ldots, \xi_n)$.

If $F(x)$ has a density $f = f(x)$ then

$$\varphi(t) = \int_{R^n} e^{i(t, x)} f(x) \, dx.$$

In other words, in this case the characteristic function is just the Fourier transform of $f(x)$.

It follows from (3) and Theorem 6.7 (on change of variable in a Lebesgue integral) that the characteristic function $\varphi_\xi(t)$ of a random vector can also be defined by

$$\varphi_\xi(t) = \mathsf{E}e^{i(t,\,\xi)}, \qquad t \in R^n. \tag{4}$$

We now present some basic properties of characteristic functions, stated and proved for $n = 1$. Further important results for the general case will be given as problems.

Let $\xi = \xi(\omega)$ be a random variable, $F_\xi = F_\xi(x)$ its distribution function, and

$$\varphi_\xi(t) = \mathsf{E}e^{it\xi}$$

its characteristic function.

We see at once that if $\eta = a\xi + b$ then

$$\varphi_\eta(t) = \mathsf{E}e^{it\eta} = \mathsf{E}e^{it(a\xi+b)} = e^{itb}\mathsf{E}e^{iat\xi}.$$

Therefore

$$\varphi_\eta(t) = e^{itb}\varphi_\xi(at). \tag{5}$$

Moreover, if $\xi_1, \xi_2, \ldots, \xi_n$ are independent random variables and $S_n = \xi_1 + \cdots + \xi_n$, then

$$\varphi_{S_n}(t) = \prod_{i=1}^{n} \varphi_{\xi_j}(t). \tag{6}$$

In fact,

$$\varphi_{S_n} = \mathsf{E}e^{it(\xi_1 + \cdots + \xi_n)} = \mathsf{E}e^{it\xi_1} \cdots e^{it\xi_n}$$

$$= \mathsf{E}e^{it\xi_1} \cdots \mathsf{E}e^{it\xi_n} = \prod_{j=1}^{n} \varphi_{\xi_j}(t),$$

where we have used the property that the expectation of a product of independent (bounded) random variables (either real or complex; see Theorem 6 of §6, and Problem 1) is equal to the product of their expectations.

Property (6) is the key to the proofs of limit theorems for sums of independent random variables by the method of characteristic functions (see §3, Chapter III). In this connection we note that the distribution function F_{S_n} is expressed in terms of the distribution functions of the individual terms in a rather complicated way, namely $F_{S_n} = F_{\xi_1} * \cdots * F_{\xi_n}$ where $*$ denotes convolution (see §8, Subsection 4).

Here are some examples of characteristic functions.

EXAMPLE 1. Let ξ be a Bernoulli random variable with $\mathsf{P}(\xi = 1) = p$, $\mathsf{P}(\xi = 0) = q, p + q = 1, 1 > p > 0$; then

$$\varphi_\xi(t) = pe^{it} + q.$$

If $\xi_1, \ldots, \xi_n$ are independent identically distributed random variables like ξ, then, writing $T_n = (S_n - np)/\sqrt{npq}$, we have

$$\varphi_{T_n}(t) = \mathsf{E}e^{iT_n t} = e^{-it\sqrt{np/q}}[pe^{it/\sqrt{npq}} + q]^n$$
$$= [pe^{it\sqrt{q/(np)}} + qe^{-it\sqrt{p/(nq)}}]^n. \quad (7)$$

Notice that it follows that as $n \to \infty$

$$\varphi_{T_n}(t) \to e^{-t^2/2}, \qquad T_n = \frac{S_n - np}{\sqrt{npq}}. \quad (8)$$

EXAMPLE 2. Let $\xi \sim \mathcal{N}(m, \sigma^2)$, $|m| < \infty$, $\sigma^2 > 0$. Let us show that

$$\varphi_\xi(t) = e^{itm - t^2\sigma^2/2} \quad (9)$$

Let $\eta = (\xi - m)/\sigma$. Then $\eta \sim \mathcal{N}(0, 1)$ and, since

$$\varphi_\xi(t) = e^{itm}\varphi_\eta(\sigma t)$$

by (5), it is enough to show that

$$\varphi_\eta(t) = e^{-t^2/2}. \quad (10)$$

We have

$$\varphi_\eta(t) = \mathsf{E}e^{it\eta} = \frac{1}{\sqrt{2\pi}} \int_{-\infty}^{\infty} e^{itx}e^{-x^2/2}\, dx$$

$$= \frac{1}{\sqrt{2\pi}} \int_{-\infty}^{\infty} \sum_{n=0}^{\infty} \frac{(itx)^n}{n!} e^{-x^2/2}\, dx = \sum_{n=0}^{\infty} \frac{(it)^n}{n!} \frac{1}{\sqrt{2\pi}} \int_{-\infty}^{\infty} x^n e^{-x^2/2}\, dx$$

$$= \sum_{n=0}^{\infty} \frac{(it)^{2n}}{(2n)!}(2n-1)!! = \sum_{n=0}^{\infty} \frac{(it)^{2n}}{(2n)!} \frac{(2n)!}{2^n n!}$$

$$= \sum_{n=0}^{\infty} \left(-\frac{t^2}{2}\right)^n \cdot \frac{1}{n!} = e^{-t^2/2},$$

where we have used the formula (see Problem 7 in §8)

$$\frac{1}{\sqrt{2\pi}} \int_{-\infty}^{\infty} x^{2n} e^{-x^2/2}\, dx \equiv \mathsf{E}\eta^{2n} = (2n-1)!!.$$

EXAMPLE 3. Let ξ be a Poisson random variable,

$$\mathsf{P}(\xi = k) = \frac{e^{-\lambda}\lambda^k}{k!}, \qquad k = 0, 1, \ldots.$$

Then

$$\mathsf{E}e^{it\xi} = \sum_{k=0}^{\infty} e^{itk} \frac{e^{-\lambda}\lambda^k}{k!} = e^{-\lambda} \sum_{k=0}^{\infty} \frac{(\lambda e^{it})^k}{k!} = \exp\{\lambda(e^{it} - 1)\}. \quad (11)$$

3. As we observed in §9, Subsection 1, with every distribution function in $(R, \mathscr{B}(R))$ we can associate a random variable of which it is the distribution function. Hence in discussing the properties of characteristic functions (in the sense either of Definition 1 or Definition 2), we may consider only characteristic functions $\varphi(t) = \varphi_\xi(t)$ of random variables $\xi = \xi(\omega)$.

Theorem 1. *Let ξ be a random variable with distribution function $F = F(x)$ and*

$$\varphi(t) = \mathsf{E}e^{it\xi}$$

its characteristic function. Then φ has the following properties:

(1) $|\varphi(t)| \le \varphi(0) = 1$;
(2) $\varphi(t)$ *is uniformly continuous for* $t \in R$;
(3) $\varphi(t) = \overline{\varphi(-t)}$;
(4) $\varphi(t)$ *is real-valued if and only if F is symmetric* $(\int_B dF(x) = \int_{-B} dF(x))$, $B \in \mathscr{B}(R)$, $-B = \{-x: x \in B\}$;
(5) *if* $\mathsf{E}|\xi|^n < \infty$ *for some* $n \ge 1$, *then* $\varphi^{(r)}(t)$ *exists for every* $r \le n$, *and*

$$\varphi^{(r)}(t) = \int_R (ix)^r e^{itx} \, dF(x), \tag{12}$$

$$\mathsf{E}\xi^r = \frac{\varphi^{(r)}(0)}{i^r}, \tag{13}$$

$$\varphi(t) = \sum_{r=0}^n \frac{(it)^2}{r!} \mathsf{E}\xi^r + \frac{(it)^n}{n!} \varepsilon_n(t), \tag{14}$$

where $|\varepsilon_n(t)| \le 3\mathsf{E}|\xi|^n$ *and* $\varepsilon_n(t) \to 0$, $t \to 0$;
(6) *if* $\varphi^{(2n)}(0)$ *exists and is finite then* $\mathsf{E}\xi^{2n} < \infty$;
(7) *if* $\mathsf{E}|\xi|^n < \infty$ *for all* $n \ge 1$ *and*

$$\varlimsup_n \frac{(\mathsf{E}|\xi|^n)^{1/n}}{n} = \frac{1}{R} < \infty,$$

then

$$\varphi(t) = \sum_{n=0}^\infty \frac{(it)^n}{n!} \mathsf{E}\xi^n. \tag{15}$$

for all $|t| < R$.

PROOF. Properties (1) and (3) are evident. Property (2) follows from the inequality

$$|\varphi(t + h) - \varphi(t)| = |\mathsf{E}e^{it\xi}(e^{ih\xi} - 1)| \le \mathsf{E}|e^{ih\xi} - 1|$$

and the dominated convergence theorem, according to which $\mathsf{E}|e^{ih\xi} - 1| \to 0$, $h \to 0$.

Property (4). Let F be symmetric. Then if $g(x)$ is a bounded odd Borel function, we have $\int_R g(x) \, dF(x) = 0$ (observe that for simple odd functions this follows directly from the definition of the symmetry of F). Consequently $\int_R \sin tx \, dF(x) = 0$ and therefore

$$\varphi(t) = \mathsf{E} \cos t\xi.$$

Conversely, let $\varphi_\xi(t)$ be a real function. Then by (3)

$$\varphi_{-\xi}(t) = \varphi_\xi(-t) = \overline{\varphi_\xi(t)} = \varphi_\xi(t), \qquad t \in R.$$

Hence (as will be shown below in Theorem 2) the distribution functions $F_{-\xi}$ and F_ξ of the random variables $-\xi$ and ξ are the same, and therefore (by Theorem 3.1)

$$\mathsf{P}(\xi \in B) = \mathsf{P}(-\xi \in B) = \mathsf{P}(\xi \in -B)$$

for every $B \in \mathscr{B}(R)$.

Property (5). If $\mathsf{E}|\xi|^n < \infty$, we have $\mathsf{E}|\xi|^r < \infty$ for $r \leq n$, by Lyapunov's inequality (6.28).

Consider the difference quotient

$$\frac{\varphi(t+h) - \varphi(t)}{h} = \mathsf{E}e^{it\xi}\left(\frac{e^{ih\xi} - 1}{h}\right).$$

Since

$$\left|\frac{e^{ihx} - 1}{h}\right| \leq |x|,$$

and $\mathsf{E}|\xi| < \infty$, it follows from the dominated convergence theorem that the limit

$$\lim_{h \to 0} \mathsf{E}e^{it\xi}\left(\frac{e^{ih\xi} - 1}{h}\right)$$

exists and equals

$$\mathsf{E}e^{it\xi} \lim_{h \to 0}\left(\frac{e^{ih\xi} - 1}{h}\right) = i\mathsf{E}(\xi e^{it\xi}) = i\int_{-\infty}^{\infty} xe^{itx} \, dF(x). \qquad (16)$$

Hence $\varphi'(t)$ exists and

$$\varphi'(t) = i(\mathsf{E}\xi e^{it\xi}) = i\int_{-\infty}^{\infty} xe^{itx} \, dF(x).$$

The existence of the derivatives $\varphi^{(r)}(t)$, $1 < r \leq n$, and the validity of (12), follow by induction.

Formula (13) follows immediately from (12). Let us now establish (14). Since

$$e^{iy} = \cos y + i \sin y = \sum_{k=0}^{n-1} \frac{(iy)^k}{k!} + \frac{(iy)^n}{n!}[\cos \theta_1 y + i \sin \theta_2 y]$$

for real y, with $|\theta_1| \leq 1$ and $|\theta_2| \leq 1$, we have

$$e^{it\xi} = \sum_{k=0}^{n-1} \frac{(it\xi)^k}{k!} + \frac{(it\xi)^n}{n!} [\cos \theta_1(\omega)t\xi + i \sin \theta_2(\omega)t\xi] \tag{17}$$

and

$$\mathsf{E}e^{it\xi} = \sum_{k=0}^{n-1} \frac{(it)^k}{k!} \mathsf{E}\xi^k + \frac{(it)^n}{n!} [\mathsf{E}\xi^n + \varepsilon_n(t)], \tag{18}$$

where

$$\varepsilon_n(t) = \mathsf{P}[\xi^n(\cos \theta_1(\omega)t\xi + i \sin \theta_2(\omega)t\xi - 1)].$$

It is clear that $|\delta_n(t)| \leq 3\mathsf{E}|\xi^n|$. The theorem on dominated convergence shows that $\varepsilon_n(t) \to 0$, $t \to 0$.

Property (6). We give a proof by induction. Suppose first that $\varphi''(0)$ exists and is finite. Let us show that in that case $\mathsf{E}\xi^2 < \infty$. By L'Hôpital's rule and Fatou's lemma,

$$\varphi''(0) = \lim_{h \to 0} \frac{1}{2} \left[\frac{\varphi'(2h) - \varphi'(0)}{2h} + \frac{\varphi'(0) - \varphi'(-2h)}{2h} \right]$$

$$= \lim_{h \to 0} \frac{2\varphi'(2h) - 2\varphi'(-2h)}{8h} = \lim_{h \to 0} \frac{1}{4h^2} [\varphi(2h) - 2\varphi(0) + \varphi(-2h)]$$

$$= \lim_{h \to 0} \int_{-\infty}^{\infty} \left(\frac{e^{ihx} - e^{-ihx}}{2h} \right)^2 dF(x)$$

$$= -\lim_{h \to 0} \int_{-\infty}^{\infty} \left(\frac{\sin hx}{hx} \right)^2 x^2 \, dF(x) \leq -\int_{-\infty}^{\infty} \lim_{h \to 0} \left(\frac{\sin hx}{hx} \right)^2 x^2 \, dF(x)$$

$$= -\int_{-\infty}^{\infty} x^2 \, dF(x).$$

Therefore

$$\int_{-\infty}^{\infty} x^2 \, dF(x) \leq -\varphi''(0) < \infty.$$

Now let $\varphi^{(2k+2)}(0)$ exist, finite, and let $\int_{-\infty}^{+\infty} x^{2k} \, dF(x) < \infty$. If $\int_{-\infty}^{\infty} x^{2k} \, dF(x) = 0$, then $\int_{-\infty}^{\infty} x^{2k+2} \, dF(x) = 0$ also. Hence we may suppose that $\int_{-\infty}^{\infty} x^{2k} \, dF(x) > 0$. Then, by Property (5),

$$\varphi^{(2k)}(t) = \int_{-\infty}^{\infty} (ix)^{2k} e^{itx} \, dF(x)$$

and therefore

$$(-1)^k \varphi^{(2k)}(t) = \int_{-\infty}^{\infty} e^{itx} \, dG(x),$$

where $G(x) = \int_{-\infty}^{x} u^{2k} \, dF(u)$.

Consequently the function $(-1)^k \varphi^{(2k)}(t) G^{-1}(\infty)$ is the characteristic function of the probability distribution $G(x) \cdot G^{-1}(\infty)$ and by what we have proved,

$$G^{-1}(\infty) \int_{-\infty}^{\infty} x^2 \, dG(x) < \infty.$$

But $G^{-1}(\infty) > 0$, and therefore

$$\int_{-\infty}^{\infty} x^{2k+2} \, dF(x) = \int_{-\infty}^{\infty} x^2 \, dG(x) < \infty.$$

Property (7). Let $0 < t_0 < R$. Then, by Stirling's formula we find that

$$\overline{\lim} \frac{(\mathbf{E} |\xi|^n)^{1/n}}{n} < \frac{1}{t_0} \Rightarrow \overline{\lim} \frac{(\mathbf{E} |\xi|^n t_0^n)^{1/n}}{n} < 1 \Rightarrow \lim \left(\frac{\mathbf{E} |\xi|^n t_0^n}{n!} \right)^{1/n} < 1.$$

Consequently the series $\sum [\mathbf{E} |\xi|^n t_0^n / n!]$ converges by Cauchy's test, and therefore the series $\sum_{r=0}^{\infty} [(it)^r / r!] \mathbf{E} \xi^r$ converges for $|t| \le t_0$. But by (14), for $n \ge 1$,

$$\varphi(t) = \sum_{r=0}^{n} \frac{(it)^r}{r!} \mathbf{E} \xi^r + R_n(t),$$

where $|R_n(t)| \le 3(|t|^n / n!) \mathbf{E} |\xi|^n$. Therefore

$$\varphi(t) = \sum_{r=0}^{\infty} \frac{(it)^r}{r!} \mathbf{E} \xi^r$$

for all $|t| < R$. This completes the proof of the theorem.

Remark 1. By a method similar to that used for (14), we can establish that if $\mathbf{E} |\xi|^n < \infty$ for some $n \ge 1$, then

$$\varphi(t) = \sum_{k=0}^{n} \frac{i^k (t-s)^k}{k!} \int_{-\infty}^{\infty} x^k e^{isx} \, dF(x) + \frac{i^n (t-s)^n}{n!} \varepsilon_n(t-s), \quad (19)$$

where $|\varepsilon_n(t-s)| \le 3 \mathbf{E} |\xi^n|$, and $\varepsilon_n(t-s) \to 0$ as $t - s \to 0$.

Remark 2. With reference to the condition that appears in Property (7), see also Subsection 9, below, on the "uniqueness of the solution of the moment problem."

4. The following theorem shows that the characteristic function is uniquely determined by the distribution function.

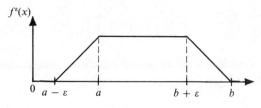

Figure 33

Theorem 2 (Uniqueness). *Let F and G be distribution functions with the same characteristic function, i.e.*

$$\int_{-\infty}^{\infty} e^{itx}\, dF(x) = \int_{-\infty}^{\infty} e^{itx}\, dG(x) \tag{20}$$

for all $t \in R$. Then $F(x) \equiv G(x)$.

PROOF. Choose a and $b \in R$, and $\varepsilon > 0$, and consider the function $f^{\varepsilon} = f^{\varepsilon}(x)$ shown in Figure 33. We show that

$$\int_{-\infty}^{\infty} f^{\varepsilon}(x)\, dF(x) = \int_{-\infty}^{\infty} f^{\varepsilon}(x)\, dG(x). \tag{21}$$

Let $n \geq 0$ be large enough so that $[a - \varepsilon, b + \varepsilon] \subseteq [-n, n]$, and let the sequence $\{\delta_n\}$ be such that $1 \geq \delta_n \downarrow 0, n \to \infty$. Like every continuous function on $[-n, n]$ that has equal values at the endpoints, $f^{\varepsilon} = f^{\varepsilon}(x)$ can be uniformly approximated by trigonometric polynomials (Weierstrass's theorem), i.e. there is a *finite* sum

$$f_n^{\varepsilon}(x) = \sum_k a_k \exp\left(i\pi x \frac{k}{n}\right) \tag{22}$$

such that

$$\sup_{-n \leq x \leq n} |f^{\varepsilon}(x) - f_n^{\varepsilon}(x)| \leq \delta_n. \tag{23}$$

Let us extend the periodic function $f_n(x)$ to all of R, and observe that

$$\sup_x |f_n^{\varepsilon}(x)| \leq 2.$$

Then, since by (20)

$$\int_{-\infty}^{\infty} f_n^{\varepsilon}(x)\, dF(x) = \int_{-\infty}^{\infty} f_n^{\varepsilon}(x)\, dG(x),$$

we have

$$\left| \int_{-\infty}^{\infty} f^{\varepsilon}(x) \, dF(x) - \int_{-\infty}^{\infty} f^{\varepsilon}(x) \, dG(x) \right| = \left| \int_{-n}^{n} f^{\varepsilon} \, dF - \int_{-n}^{n} f^{\varepsilon} \, dG \right|$$

$$\leq \left| \int_{-n}^{n} f_n^{\varepsilon} \, dF - \int_{-n}^{n} f_n^{\varepsilon} \, dG \right| + 2\delta_n$$

$$\leq \left| \int_{-\infty}^{\infty} f_n^{\varepsilon} \, dF - \int_{-\infty}^{\infty} f_n^{\varepsilon} \, dG \right| + 2\delta_n$$

$$+ 2F(\overline{[-n, n]}) + 2G(\overline{[-n, n]}),$$
(24)

where $F(A) = \int_A dF(x)$, $G(A) = \int_A dG(x)$. As $n \to \infty$, the right-hand side of (24) tends to zero, and this establishes (21).

As $\varepsilon \to 0$, we have $f^{\varepsilon}(x) \to I_{(a, b]}(x)$. It follows from (21) by the theorem on distribution functions' being the same.

$$\int_{-\infty}^{\infty} I_{(a, b]}(x) \, dF(x) = \int_{-\infty}^{\infty} I_{(a, b]}(x) \, dG(x),$$

i.e. $F(b) - F(a) = G(b) - G(a)$. Since a and b are arbitrary, it follows that $F(x) = G(x)$ for all $x \in R$.

This completes the proof of the theorem.

5. The preceding theorem says that a distribution function $F = F(x)$ is uniquely determined by its characteristic function $\varphi = \varphi(t)$. The next theorem gives an explicit representation of F in terms of φ.

Theorem 3 (Inversion Formula). *Let $F = F(x)$ be a distribution function and*

$$\varphi(t) = \int_{-\infty}^{\infty} e^{itx} \, dF(x)$$

its characteristic function.

(a) *For pairs of points a and b ($a < b$) at which $F = F(x)$ is continuous,*

$$F(b) - F(a) = \lim_{c \to \infty} \frac{1}{2\pi} \int_{-c}^{c} \frac{e^{-ita} - e^{-itb}}{it} \varphi(t) \, dt;$$
(25)

(b) *If $\int_{-\infty}^{\infty} |\varphi(t)| \, dt < \infty$, the distribution function $F(x)$ has a density $f(x)$,*

$$F(x) = \int_{-\infty}^{x} f(y) \, dy$$
(26)

and

$$f(x) = \frac{1}{2\pi} \int_{-\infty}^{\infty} e^{-itx} \varphi(t) \, dt.$$
(27)

PROOF. We first observe that if $F(x)$ has density $f(x)$ then

$$\varphi(t) = \int_{-\infty}^{\infty} e^{itx} f(x) \, dx, \qquad (28)$$

and (27) is just the Fourier transform of the (integrable) function $\varphi(t)$. Integrating both sides of (27) and applying Fubini's theorem, we obtain

$$F(b) - F(a) = \int_a^b f(x) \, dx = \frac{1}{2\pi} \int_a^b \left[\int_{-\infty}^{\infty} e^{-itx} \varphi(t) \, dt \right] dx$$

$$= \frac{1}{2\pi} \int_{-\infty}^{\infty} \varphi(t) \left[\int_a^b e^{-itx} \, dx \right] dt$$

$$= \frac{1}{2\pi} \int_{-\infty}^{\infty} \varphi(t) \frac{e^{-ita} - e^{-itb}}{it} \, dt.$$

After these remarks, which to some extent clarify (25), we turn to the proof.

(a) We have

$$\Phi_c \equiv \frac{1}{2\pi} \int_{-c}^{c} \frac{e^{-ita} - e^{-itb}}{it} \varphi(t) \, dt$$

$$= \frac{1}{2\pi} \int_{-c}^{c} \frac{e^{-ita} - e^{-itb}}{it} \left[\int_{-\infty}^{\infty} e^{itx} \, dF(x) \right] dt$$

$$= \frac{1}{2\pi} \int_{-\infty}^{\infty} \left[\int_{-c}^{c} \frac{e^{-ita} - e^{-itb}}{it} e^{itx} \, dt \right] dF(x)$$

$$= \int_{-\infty}^{\infty} \Psi_c(x) \, dF(x), \qquad (29)$$

where we have put

$$\Psi_c(x) = \frac{1}{2\pi} \int_{-c}^{c} \frac{e^{-ita} - e^{-itb}}{it} e^{itx} \, dt$$

and applied Fubini's theorem, which is applicable in this case because

$$\left| \frac{e^{-ita} - e^{-itb}}{it} \cdot e^{itx} \right| = \left| \frac{e^{-ita} - e^{-itb}}{it} \right| = \left| \int_a^b e^{-itx} \, dx \right| \le b - a$$

and

$$\int_{-c}^{c} \int_{-\infty}^{\infty} (b - a) \, dF(x) \le 2c(b - a) < \infty.$$

In addition,

$$\Psi_c(x) = \frac{1}{2\pi} \int_{-c}^{c} \frac{\sin t(x - a) - \sin t(x - b)}{t} dt$$

$$= \frac{1}{2\pi} \int_{-c(x-a)}^{c(x-a)} \frac{\sin v}{v} dv - \frac{1}{2\pi} \int_{-c(x-b)}^{c(x-b)} \frac{\sin u}{u} du. \tag{30}$$

The function

$$g(s, t) = \int_{s}^{t} \frac{\sin v}{v} dv$$

is uniformly continuous in s and t, and

$$g(s, t) \to \pi \tag{31}$$

as $s \downarrow -\infty$ and $t \uparrow \infty$. Hence there is a constant C such that $|\Psi_c(x)| < C < \infty$ for all c and x. Moreover, it follows from (30) and (31) that

$$\Psi_c(x) \to \Psi(x), \qquad c \to \infty,$$

where

$$\Psi(x) = \begin{cases} 0, & x < a, x > b, \\ \frac{1}{2}, & x = a, x = b, \\ 1, & a < x < b. \end{cases}$$

Let μ be a measure on $(R, \mathcal{B}(R))$ such that $\mu(a, b] = F(b) - F(a)$. Then if we apply the dominated convergence theorem and use the formulas of Problem 1 of §3, we find that, as $c \to \infty$,

$$\Phi_c = \int_{-\infty}^{\infty} \Psi_c(x) \, dF(x) \to \int_{-\infty}^{\infty} \Psi(x) \, dF(x)$$

$$= \mu(a, b) + \frac{1}{2}\mu\{a\} + \frac{1}{2}\mu\{b\}$$

$$= F(b-) - F(a) + \frac{1}{2}[F(a) - F(a-) + F(b) - F(b-)]$$

$$= \frac{F(b) + F(b-)}{2} - \frac{F(a) + F(a-)}{2} = F(b) - F(a),$$

where the last equation holds for all points a and b of continuity of $F(x)$.
    Hence (25) is established.
    (b) Let $\int_{-\infty}^{\infty} |\varphi(t)| \, dt < \infty$. Write

$$f(x) = \frac{1}{2\pi} \int_{-\infty}^{\infty} e^{-itx} \varphi(t) \, dt.$$

It follows from the dominated convergence theorem that this is a continuous function of x and therefore is integrable on $[a, b]$. Consequently we find, applying Fubini's theorem again, that

$$\int_a^b f(x)\, dx = \int_a^b \frac{1}{2\pi} \left(\int_{-\infty}^{\infty} e^{-itx} \varphi(t)\, dt \right) dx$$

$$= \frac{1}{2\pi} \int_{-\infty}^{\infty} \varphi(t) \left[\int_a^b e^{-itx}\, dx \right] dt = \lim_{c \to \infty} \frac{1}{2\pi} \int_{-c}^{c} \varphi(t) \left[\int_a^b e^{-itx}\, dx \right] dt$$

$$= \lim_{c \to \infty} \frac{1}{2\pi} \int_{-c}^{c} \frac{e^{-ita} - e^{-itb}}{it} \varphi(t)\, dt = F(b) - F(a)$$

for all points a and b of continuity of $F(x)$.

Hence it follows that

$$F(x) = \int_{-\infty}^{x} f(y)\, dy, \qquad x \in R,$$

and since $f(x)$ is continuous and $F(x)$ is nondecreasing, $f(x)$ is the density of $F(x)$.

This completes the proof of the theorem.

Corollary. *The inversion formula* (25) *provides a second proof of Theorem 2.*

Theorem 4. *A necessary and sufficient condition for the components of the random vector* $\xi = (\xi_1, \ldots, \xi_n)$ *to be independent is that its characteristic function is the product of the characteristic functions of the components:*

$$\mathsf{E} e^{i(t_1 \xi_1 + \cdots + t_n \xi_n)} = \prod_{k=1}^{n} \mathsf{E} e^{i t_k \xi_k}, \qquad (t_1, \ldots, t_n) \in R^n.$$

PROOF. The necessity follows from Problem 1. To prove the sufficiency we let $F(x_1, \ldots, x_n)$ be the distribution function of the vector $\xi = (\xi_1, \ldots, \xi_n)$ and $F_k(x)$, the distribution functions of the ξ_k, $1 \le k \le n$. Put $G = G(x_1, \ldots, x_n)$ $= F_1(x_1) \cdots F_n(x_n)$. Then, by Fubini's theorem, for all $(t_1, \ldots, t_n) \in R^n$,

$$\int_{R^n} e^{i(t_1 x_1 + \cdots + t_n x_n)}\, dG(x_1 \cdots x_n) = \prod_{k=1}^{n} \int_R e^{i t_k x_k}\, dF_k(x)$$

$$= \prod_{k=1}^{n} \mathsf{E} e^{i t_k \xi_k} = \mathsf{E} e^{i(t_1 \xi_1 + \cdots + t_k \xi_k)}$$

$$= \int_{R^n} e^{i(t_1 x_1 + \cdots + t_n x_n)}\, dF(x_1 \cdots x_n).$$

Therefore by Theorem 2 (or rather, by its multidimensional analog; see Problem 3) we have $F = G$, and consequently, by the theorem of §5, the random variables $\xi_1, \ldots, \xi_n$ are independent.

6. Theorem 1 gives us necessary conditions for a function to be a characteristic function. Hence if $\varphi = \varphi(t)$ fails to satisfy, for example, one of the first three conclusions of the theorem, that function cannot be a characteristic function. We quote without proof some results in the same direction.

Bochner–Khinchin Theorem. *Let $\varphi(t)$ be continuous, $t \in R$, with $\varphi(0) = 1$. A necessary and sufficient condition that $\varphi(t)$ is a characteristic function is that it is positive semi-definite, i.e. that for all real $t_1, \ldots, t_n$ and all complex $\lambda_1, \ldots, \lambda_n$, $n = 1, 2, \ldots,$*

$$\sum_{i, j=1}^{n} \varphi(t_i - t_j)\lambda_i \bar{\lambda}_j \geq 0. \tag{32}$$

The necessity of (32) is evident since if $\varphi(t) = \int_{-\infty}^{\infty} e^{itx} \, dF(x)$ then

$$\sum_{i, j=1}^{n} \varphi(t_i - t_j)\lambda_i \bar{\lambda}_j = \int_{-\infty}^{\infty} \left| \sum_{k=1}^{n} \lambda_k e^{it_k x} \right|^2 dF(x) \geq 0.$$

The proof of the sufficiency of (32) is more difficult.

Pólya's Theorem. *Let a continuous even function $\varphi(t)$ satisfy $\varphi(t) \geq 0$, $\varphi(0) = 1$, $\varphi(t) \to 0$ as $t \to \infty$ and let $\varphi(t)$ be convex on $0 \leq t < \infty$. Then $\varphi(t)$ is a characteristic function.*

This theorem provides a very convenient method of constructing characteristic functions. Examples are

$$\varphi_1(t) = e^{-|t|},$$

$$\varphi_2(t) = \begin{cases} 1 - |t|, & |t| \leq 1, \\ 0, & |t| > 1. \end{cases}$$

Another is the function $\varphi_3(t)$ drawn in Figure 34. On $[-a, a]$, the function $\varphi_3(t)$ coincides with $\varphi_2(t)$. However, the corresponding distribution functions F_2 and F_3 are evidently different. This example shows that in general two characteristic functions can be the same on a finite interval without their distribution functions' being the same.

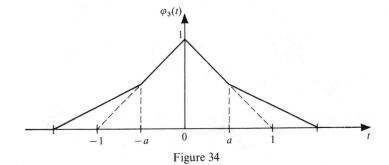

Figure 34

Marcinkiewicz's Theorem. *If a characteristic function $\varphi(t)$ is of the form* $\exp \mathscr{P}(t)$, *where $\mathscr{P}(t)$ is a polynomial, then this polynomial is of degree at most 2.*

It follows, for example, that e^{-t^4} is not a characteristic function.

7. The following theorem shows that a property of the characteristic function of a random variable can lead to a nontrivial conclusion about the nature of the random variable.

Theorem 5. *Let $\varphi_\xi(t)$ be the characteristic function of the random variable ξ.*

(a) *If $|\varphi_\xi(t_0)| = 1$ for some $t_0 \neq 0$, then ξ is concentrated at the points $a + nh$, $h = 2\pi/t_0$, for some a, that is,*

$$\sum_{n=-\infty}^{\infty} \mathsf{P}\{\xi = a + nh\} = 1, \qquad (33)$$

where a is a constant.

(b) *If $|\varphi_\xi(t)| = |\varphi_\xi(\alpha t)| = 1$ for two different points t and αt, where α is irrational, then ξ is degenerate:*

$$\mathsf{P}\{\xi = a\} = 1,$$

where a is some number.

(c) *If $|\varphi_\xi(t)| \equiv 1$, then ξ is degenerate.*

PROOF. (a) If $|\varphi_\xi(t_0)| = 1$, $t_0 \neq 0$, there is a number a such that $\varphi(t_0) = e^{it_0 a}$. Then

$$e^{it_0 a} = \int_{-\infty}^{\infty} e^{it_0 x}\, dF(x) \Rightarrow 1 = \int_{-\infty}^{\infty} e^{it_0(x-a)}\, dF(x) \Rightarrow$$

$$1 = \int_{-\infty}^{\infty} \cos t_0(x-a)\, dF(x) \Rightarrow \int_{-\infty}^{\infty} [1 - \cos t_0(x-a)]\, dF(x) = 0.$$

Since $1 - \cos t_0(x - a) \geq 0$, it follows from property **H** (Subsection 2 of §6) that

$$1 = \cos t_0(\xi - a) \quad \text{(P-a.s.)},$$

which is equivalent to (33).

(b) It follows from $|\varphi_\xi(t)| = |\varphi_\xi(\alpha t)| = 1$ and from (33) that

$$\sum_{n=-\infty}^{\infty} \mathsf{P}\left\{\xi = a + \frac{2\pi}{t}n\right\} = \sum_{m=-\infty}^{\infty} \mathsf{P}\left\{\xi = b + \frac{2\pi}{\alpha t}m\right\} = 1.$$

If ξ is not degenerate, there must be at least two pairs of common points:

$$a + \frac{2\pi}{t}n_1 = b + \frac{2\pi}{\alpha t}m_1, \qquad a + \frac{2\pi}{y}n_2 = b + \frac{2\pi}{\alpha t}m_2,$$

in the sets

$$\left\{a + \frac{2\pi}{t} n, n = 0, \pm 1, \ldots\right\} \quad \text{and} \quad \left\{b + \frac{2\pi}{\alpha t} m, m = 0, \pm 1, \ldots\right\},$$

whence

$$\frac{2\pi}{t}(n_1 - n_2) = \frac{2\pi}{\alpha t}(m_1 - m_2),$$

and this contradicts the assumption that α is irrational. Conclusion (c) follows from (b).

This completes the proof of the theorem.

8. Let $\xi = (\xi_1, \ldots, \xi_k)$ be a random vector,

$$\varphi_\xi(t) = \mathsf{E}e^{i(t, \xi)}, \qquad t = (t_1, \ldots, t_k),$$

its characteristic function. Let us suppose that $\mathsf{E}|\xi_i|^n < \infty$ for some $n \geq 1$, $i = 1, \ldots, k$. From the inequalities of Hölder (6.29) and Lyapunov (6.27) it follows that the (mixed) moments $\mathsf{E}(\xi_1^{v_1} \cdots \xi_k^{v_k})$ exist for all nonnegative $v_1, \ldots, v_k$ such that $v_1 + \cdots + v_k \leq n$.

As in Theorem 1, this implies the existence and continuity of the partial derivatives

$$\frac{\partial^{v_1 + \cdots + v_k}}{\partial t_1^{v_1} \cdots \partial t_k^{v_k}} \varphi_\xi(t_1, \ldots, t_k)$$

for $v_1 + \cdots + v_k \leq n$. Then if we expand $\varphi_\xi(t_1, \ldots, t_k)$ in a Taylor series, we see that

$$\varphi_\xi(t_1, \ldots, t_k) = \sum_{v_1 + \cdots + v_k \leq n} \frac{i^{v_1 + \cdots + v_k}}{v_1! \cdots v_k!} m_\xi^{(v_1, \ldots, v_k)} t_1^{v_1} \cdots t_k^{v_k} + o(|t|^n), \quad (34)$$

where $|t| = |t_1| + \cdots + |t_k|$ and

$$m_\xi^{(v_1, \ldots, v_k)} = \mathsf{E}\xi_1^{v_1} \cdots \xi_k^{v_k}$$

is the *mixed moment of order* $v = (v_1, \ldots, v_k)$.

Now $\varphi_\xi(t_1, \ldots, t_k)$ is continuous, $\varphi_\xi(0, \ldots, 0) = 1$, and consequently this function is different from zero in some neighborhood $|t| < \delta$ of zero. In this neighborhood the partial derivative

$$\frac{\partial^{v_1 + \cdots + v_k}}{\partial t_1^{v_1} \cdots \partial t_k^{v_k}} \ln \varphi_\xi(t_1, \ldots, t_k)$$

exists and is continuous, where $\ln z$ denotes the principal value of the logarithm (if $z = re^{i\theta}$, we take $\ln z$ to be $\ln r + i\theta$). Hence we can expand $\ln \varphi_\xi(t_1, \ldots, t_k)$ by Taylor's formula,

$$\ln \varphi_\xi(t_1 \cdots t_k) = \sum_{v_1 + \cdots + v_k \leq n} \frac{i^{v_1 + \cdots + v_k}}{v_1! \cdots v_k!} s_\xi^{(v_1, \ldots, v_k)} t_1^{v_1} \cdots t_k^{v_k} + o(|t|^n), \quad (35)$$

where the coefficients $s_\xi^{(v_1, \ldots, v_k)}$ are the (*mixed*) *semi-invariants* or *cumulants* of order $v = v(v_1, \ldots, v_k)$ of $\xi = \xi_1, \ldots, \xi_k$.

Observe that if ξ and η are independent, then

$$\ln \varphi_{\xi+\eta}(t) = \ln \varphi_\xi(t) + \ln \varphi_\eta(t), \qquad (36)$$

and therefore

$$s_{\xi+\eta}^{(v_1, \ldots, v_k)} = s_\xi^{(v_1, \ldots, v_k)} + s_\eta^{(v_1, \ldots, v_k)}. \qquad (37)$$

(It is this property that gives rise to the term "semi-invariant" for $s_\xi^{(v_1, \ldots, v_k)}$.)

To simply the formulas and make (34) and (35) look "one-dimensional," we introduce the following notation.

If $v = (v_1, \ldots, v_k)$ is a vector whose components are nonnegative integers, we put

$$v! = v_1! \cdots v_k!, \qquad |v| = v_1 + \cdots + v_k, \qquad t^v = t_1^{v_1} \cdots t_k^{v_k}.$$

We also put $s_\xi^{(v)} = s_\xi^{(v_1, \ldots, v_k)}$, $m_\xi^{(v)} = m_\xi^{(v_1, \ldots, v_k)}$.

Then (34) and (35) can be written

$$\varphi_\xi(t) = \sum_{|v| \le n} \frac{i^{|v|}}{v!} m_\xi^{(v)} t^v + o(|t|^n), \qquad (38)$$

$$\ln \varphi_\xi(t) = \sum_{|v| \le n} \frac{i^{|v|}}{v!} s_\xi^{(v)} t^v + o(|t|^n). \qquad (39)$$

The following theorem and its corollaries give *formulas that connect moments and semi-invariants*.

Theorem 6. Let $\xi = (\xi_1, \ldots, \xi_k)$ be a random vector with $\mathsf{E}|\xi_i|^n < \infty$, $i = 1, \ldots, k, n \ge 1$. Then for $v = (v_1, \ldots, v_k)$ such that $|v| \le n$

$$m_\xi^{(v)} = \sum_{\lambda^{(1)} + \cdots + \lambda^{(q)} = v} \frac{1}{q!} \frac{v!}{\lambda^{(1)}! \cdots \lambda^{(q)}!} \prod_{p=1}^q s^{(\lambda^{(p)})}, \qquad (40)$$

$$s_\xi^{(v)} = \sum_{\lambda^{(1)} + \cdots + \lambda^{(q)} = v} \frac{(-1)^{q-1}}{q} \frac{v!}{\lambda^{(1)}! \cdots \lambda^{(q)}!} \prod_{p=1}^q m_\xi^{(\lambda^{(p)})}, \qquad (41)$$

where $\sum_{\lambda^{(1)} + \cdots + \lambda^{(q)} = v}$ indicates summation over all ordered sets of nonnegative integral vectors $\lambda^{(p)}, |\lambda^{(p)}| > 0$, whose sum is v.

PROOF. Since

$$\varphi_\xi(t) = \exp(\ln \varphi_\xi(t)),$$

if we expand the function exp by Taylor's formula and use (39), we obtain

$$\varphi_\xi(t) = 1 + \sum_{q=1}^n \frac{1}{q!} \left(\sum_{1 \le |\lambda| \le n} \frac{i^{|\lambda|}}{\lambda!} s_\xi^{(\lambda)} t^\lambda \right)^q + o(|t|^n). \qquad (42)$$

Comparing terms in t^λ on the right-hand sides of (38) and (42), and using $|\lambda^{(1)}| + \cdots + |\lambda^{(q)}| = |\lambda^{(1)} + \cdots + \lambda^{(q)}|$, we obtain (40).

Moreover,

$$\ln \varphi_\xi(t) = \ln\left[1 + \sum_{1 \le |\lambda| \le n} \frac{i^{|\lambda|}}{\lambda!} m_\xi^{(\lambda)} t^\lambda + o(|t|^n)\right]. \tag{43}$$

For small z we have the expansion

$$\ln(1 + z) = \sum_{q=1}^{n} \frac{(-1)^{q-1}}{q} z^q + o(z^q).$$

Using this in (43) and then comparing the coefficients of t^λ with the corresponding coefficients on the right-hand side of (38), we obtain (41).

Corollary 1. *The following formulas connect moments and semi-invariants*:

$$m_\xi^{(v)} = \sum_{\{r_1\lambda^{(1)} + \cdots + r_x\lambda^{(x)} = v\}} \frac{1}{r_1! \cdots r_x!} \frac{v!}{(\lambda^{(1)}!)^{r_1} \cdots (\lambda^{(x)}!)^{r_x}} \prod_{j=1}^{x} [s_\xi^{(\lambda^{(j)})}]^{r_j}, \tag{44}$$

$$s_\xi^{(v)} = \sum_{\{r_1\lambda^{(1)} + \cdots + r_x\lambda^{(x)} = v\}} \frac{(-1)^{q-1}(q-1)!}{r_1! \cdots r_x!} \frac{v!}{(\lambda^{(1)}!)^{r_1} \cdots (\lambda^{(x)}!)^{r_x}} \prod_{j=1}^{x} [m_\xi^{(\lambda^{(j)})}]^{r_j}, \tag{45}$$

where $\sum_{\{r_1\lambda^{(1)} + \cdots + r_x\lambda^{(x)} = v\}}$ *denotes summation over all unordered sets of different nonnegative integral vectors* $\lambda^{(j)}, |\lambda^{(j)}| > 0$, *and over all ordered sets of positive integral numbers* r_j *such that* $r_1\lambda^{(1)} + \cdots + r_x\lambda^{(x)} = v$.

To establish (44) we suppose that among all the vectors $\lambda^{(1)}, \ldots, \lambda^{(q)}$ that occur in (40), there are r_1 equal to $\lambda^{(i_1)}, \ldots, r_x$ equal to $\lambda^{(i_x)}$ ($r_j > 0$, $r_1 + \cdots + r_x = q$), where all the $\lambda^{(i_s)}$ are different. There are $q!/(r_1! \ldots r_x!)$ different sets of vectors, corresponding (except for order) with the set $\{\lambda^{(1)}, \ldots \lambda^{(q)}\}$). But if two sets, say, $\{\lambda^{(1)}, \ldots, \lambda^{(q)}\}$ and $\{\overline{\lambda}^{(1)}, \ldots, \overline{\lambda}^{(q)}\}$ differ only in order, then $\prod_{p=1}^{q} s_\xi^{(\lambda^{(p)})} = \prod_{p=1}^{q} s_\xi^{(\overline{\lambda}^{(p)})}$. Hence if we identify sets that differ only in order, we obtain (44) from (40).

Formula (45) can be deduced from (41) in a similar way.

Corollary 2. *Let us consider the special case when* $v = (1, \ldots, 1)$. *In this case the moments* $m_\xi^{(v)} \equiv \mathsf{E}\xi_1 \cdots \xi_k$, *and the corresponding semi-invariants, are called* simple.

Formulas connecting simple moments and simple semi-invariants can be read off from the formulas given above. However, it is useful to have them written in a different way.

For this purpose, we introduce the following notation.

Let $\xi = (\xi_1, \ldots, \xi_k)$ be a vector, and $I_\xi = \{1, 2, \ldots, k\}$ its set of indices. If $I \subseteq I_\xi$, let ξ_I denote the vector consisting of the components of ξ whose indices belong to I. Let $\chi(I)$ be the vector $\{\chi_1, \ldots, \chi_n\}$ for which $\chi_i = 1$ if $i \in I$, and $\chi_i = 0$ if $i \notin I$. These vectors are in one-to-one correspondence with the sets $I \subseteq I_\xi$. Hence we can write

$$m_\xi(I) = m_\xi^{(\chi)(I)}, \qquad s_\xi(I) = s_\xi^{(\chi(I))}.$$

In other words, $m_\xi(I)$ and $s_\xi(I)$ are simple moments and semi-invariants of the subvector ξ_I of ξ.

In accordance with the definition given on p. 12, a *decomposition* of a set I is an unordered collection of disjoint nonempty sets I_p such that $\sum_p I_p = I$.

In terms of these definitions, we have the formulas

$$m_\xi(I) = \sum_{\sum_{p=1}^q I_p = I} \prod_{p=1}^q s_\xi(I_p), \tag{46}$$

$$s_\xi(I) = \sum_{\sum_{p=1}^q I_p = I} (-1)^{q-1}(q-1)! \prod_{p=1}^q m_\xi(I_p). \tag{47}$$

where $\sum_{\sum_{p=1}^q I_p = I}$ denotes summation over all decompositions of I, $1 \leq q \leq N(I)$.

We shall derive (46) from (44). If $v = \chi(I)$ and $\lambda^{(1)} + \cdots + \lambda^{(q)} = v$, then $\lambda^{(p)} = \chi(I_p)$, $I_p \subseteq I$, where the $\lambda^{(p)}$ are all different, $\lambda^{(p)}! = v! = 1$, and every unordered set $\{\chi(I_1), \ldots, \chi(I_q)\}$ is in one-to-one correspondence with the decomposition $I = \sum_{p=1}^q I_p$. Consequently (46) follows from (44).

In a similar way, (47) follows from (35).

EXAMPLE 1. Let ξ be a random variable $(k = 1)$ and $m_n = m_\xi^{(n)} = \mathsf{E}\xi^n$, $s_n = s_\xi^{(n)}$. Then (40) and (41) imply the following formulas:

$$m_1 = s_1,$$
$$m_2 = s_2 + s_1^2,$$
$$m_3 = s_3 + 3s_1 s_2 + s_1^3,$$
$$m_4 = s_4 + 3s_2^2 + 4s_1 s_3 + 6s_1^2 s_2 + s_1^4, \tag{48}$$
$$\cdots\cdots\cdots\cdots\cdots\cdots$$

and

$$s_1 = m_1 = \mathsf{E}\xi,$$
$$s_2 = m_2 - m_1^2 = \mathsf{V}\xi,$$
$$s_3 = m_3 - 3m_1 m_2 + 2m_1^3,$$
$$s_4 = m_4 - 3m_3^2 - 4m_1 m_3 + 12m_1^2 m_2 - 6m_1^4, \tag{49}$$
$$\cdots\cdots\cdots\cdots\cdots\cdots$$

EXAMPLE 2. Let $\xi \sim \mathcal{N}(m, \sigma^2)$. Since, by (9),

$$\ln \varphi_\xi(t) = itm - \frac{t^2\sigma^2}{2},$$

we have $s_1 = m$, $s_2 = \sigma^2$ by (39), and all the semi-invariants, from the third on, are zero: $s_n = 0$, $n \geq 3$.

We may observe that by Marcinkiewicz's theorem a function $\exp \mathscr{P}(t)$, where $\mathscr{P}$ is a polynomial, can be a characteristic function only when the degree of that polynomial is at most 2. It follows, in particular, that the Gaussian distribution is the only distribution with the property that all its semi-invariants s_n are zero from a certain index onward.

EXAMPLE 3. If ξ is a Poisson random variable with parameter $\lambda > 0$, then by (11)

$$\ln \varphi_\xi(t) = \lambda(e^{it} - 1).$$

It follows that

$$s_n = \lambda \tag{50}$$

for all $n \geq 1$.

EXAMPLE 4. Let $\xi = (\xi_1, \ldots, \xi_n)$ be a random vector. Then

$$m_\xi(1) = s_\xi(1),$$
$$m_\xi(1, 2) = s_\xi(1, 2) + s_\xi(1)s_\xi(2),$$
$$m_\xi(1, 2, 3) = s_\xi(1, 2, 3) + s_\xi(1, 2)s_\xi(3) + \tag{51}$$
$$+ s_\xi(1, 3)s_\xi(2) +$$
$$+ s_\xi(2, 3)s_\xi(1) + s_\xi(1)s_\xi(2)s_\xi(3)$$

. . . .

These formulas show that the simple moments can be expressed in terms of the simple semi-invariants in a very *symmetric* way. If we put $\xi_1 \equiv \xi_2 \equiv \cdots \equiv \xi_k$, we then, of course, obtain (48).

The group-theoretical origin of the coefficients in (48) becomes clear from (51). It also follows from (51) that

$$s_\xi(1, 2) = m_\xi(1, 2) - m_\xi(1)m_\xi(2) = \mathsf{E}\xi_1\xi_2 - \mathsf{E}\xi_1\mathsf{E}\xi_2, \tag{52}$$

i.e., $s_\xi(1, 2)$ is just the *covariance* of ξ_1 and ξ_2.

9. Let ξ be a random variable with distribution function $F = F(x)$ and characteristic function $\varphi(t)$. Let us suppose that all the moments $m_n = \mathsf{E}\xi^n$, $n \geq 1$, exist.

It follows from Theorem 2 that a characteristic function uniquely determines a probability distribution. Let us now ask the following question (uniqueness for the moment problem): Do the moments $\{m_n\}_{n \geq 1}$ determine the *probability distribution*?

More precisely, let F and G be distribution functions with the same moments, i.e.

$$\int_{-\infty}^{\infty} x^n \, dF(x) = \int_{-\infty}^{\infty} x^n \, dG(x) \tag{53}$$

for all integers $n \geq 0$. The question is whether F and G must be the same.

In general, the answer is "no." To see this, consider the distribution F with density

$$f(x) = \begin{cases} ke^{-\alpha x^\lambda}, & x > 0, \\ 0, & x \leq 0, \end{cases}$$

where $\alpha > 0, 0 < \lambda < \frac{1}{2}$, and k is determined by the condition $\int_0^\infty f(x) \, dx = 1$. Write $\beta = \alpha \tan \lambda\pi$ and let $g(x) = 0$ for $x \leq 0$ and

$$g(x) = ke^{-\alpha x^\lambda}[1 + \varepsilon \sin(\beta x^\lambda)], \qquad |\varepsilon| < 1, \quad x > 0.$$

It is evident that $g(x) \geq 0$. Let us show that

$$\int_0^\infty x^n e^{-\alpha x^\lambda} \sin \beta x^\lambda \, dx = 0 \tag{54}$$

for all integers $n \geq 0$.

For $p > 0$ and complex q with $\operatorname{Re} q > 0$, we have

$$\int_0^\infty t^{p-1} e^{-qt} \, dt = \frac{\Gamma(p)}{q^p}.$$

Take $p = (n + 1)/\lambda, q = \alpha + i\beta, t = x^\lambda$. Then

$$\int_0^\infty x^{\lambda\{[(n+1)/\lambda]-1\}} e^{-(\alpha+i\beta)x^\lambda} \lambda x^{\lambda-1} \, dx = \lambda \int_0^\infty x^n e^{-(\alpha+i\beta)x^\lambda} \, dx$$

$$= \lambda \int_0^\infty x^n e^{-\alpha x^\lambda} \cos\beta x^\alpha \, dx - i\lambda \int_0^\infty x^n e^{-\alpha x^\lambda} \sin \beta x^\lambda \, dx$$

$$= \frac{\Gamma\left(\dfrac{n + 1}{\lambda}\right)}{\alpha^{(n+1)/\lambda}(1 + i \tan \lambda\pi)^{(n+1)/\lambda}}. \tag{55}$$

But

$$(1 + i \tan \lambda\pi)^{(n+1)/\lambda} = (\cos \lambda\pi + i \sin \lambda\pi)^{(n+1)/\lambda}(\cos \lambda\pi)^{-(n+1)/\lambda}$$

$$= e^{i\pi(n+1)}(\cos \lambda\pi)^{-(n+1)/\lambda}$$

$$= \cos \pi(n + 1) \cdot \cos(\lambda\pi)^{-(n+1)/\lambda},$$

since $\sin \pi(n + 1) = 0$.

Hence right-hand side of (55) is real and therefore (54) is valid for all integral $n \geq 0$. Now let $G(x)$ be the distribution function with density $g(x)$. It follows from (54) that the distribution functions F and G have equal moments, i.e. (53) holds for all integers $n \geq 0$.

We now give some conditions that guarantee the uniqueness of the solution of the moment problem.

Theorem 7. *Let* $F = F(x)$ *be a distribution function and* $\mu_n = \int_{-\infty}^{\infty} |x|^n \, dF(x)$. *If*

$$\overline{\lim_{n \to \infty}} \frac{\mu_n^{1/n}}{n} < \infty, \tag{56}$$

the moments $\{m_n\}_{n \geq 1}$, *where* $m_n = \int_{-\infty}^{\infty} x^n \, dF(x)$, *determine the distribution* $F = F(x)$ *uniquely.*

PROOF. It follows from (56) and conclusion (7) of Theorem 1 that there is a $t_0 > 0$ such that, for all $|t| \leq t_0$, the characteristic function

$$\varphi(t) = \int_{-\infty}^{\infty} e^{itx} \, dF(x)$$

can be represented in the form

$$\varphi(t) = \sum_{k=0}^{\infty} \frac{(it)^k}{k!} m_k$$

and consequently the moments $\{m_n\}_{n \geq 1}$ uniquely determine the characteristic function $\varphi(t)$ for $|t| \leq t_0$.

Take a point s with $|s| \leq t_0/2$. Then, as in the proof of (15), we deduce from (56) that

$$\varphi(t) = \sum_{k=0}^{\infty} \frac{i^k(t-s)^k}{k!} \varphi^{(k)}(s)$$

for $|t - s| \leq t_0$, where

$$\varphi^{(k)}(s) = i^k \int_{-\infty}^{\infty} x^k e^{isx} \, dF(x)$$

is uniquely determined by the moments $\{m_n\}_{n \geq 1}$. Consequently the moments determine $\varphi(t)$ uniquely for $|t| \leq \frac{3}{2}t_0$. Continuing this process, we see that $\{m_n\}_{n \geq 1}$ determines $\varphi(t)$ uniquely for all t, and therefore also determines $F(x)$.

This completes the proof of the theorem.

Corollary 1. *The moments completely determine the probability distribution if it is concentrated on a finite interval.*

Corollary 2. *A sufficient condition for the moment problem to have a unique solution is that*

$$\varlimsup_{n \to \infty} \frac{(m_{2n})^{1/2n}}{2n} < \infty. \tag{57}$$

For the proof it is enough to observe that the odd moments can be estimated in terms of the even ones, and then use (56).

EXAMPLE. Let $F(x)$ be the normal distribution function,

$$F(x) = \frac{1}{\sqrt{2\pi\sigma^2}} \int_{-\infty}^{x} e^{-t^2/2\sigma^2}\, dt.$$

Then $m_{2n+1} = 0, m_{2n} = [(2n)!/2^n n!]\sigma^{2n}$, and it follows from (57) that these are the moments only of the normal distribution.

Finally we state, without proof:

Carleman's test for the uniqueness of the moment problem.

(a) *Let* $\{m_n\}_{n \geq 1}$ *be the moments of a probability distribution, and let*

$$\sum_{n=0}^{\infty} \frac{1}{(m_{2n})^{1/2n}} = \infty.$$

Then they determine the probability distribution uniquely.

(b) *If* $\{m_n\}_{n \geq 1}$ *are the moments of a distribution that is concentrated on* $[0, \infty)$, *then the solution will be unique if we require only that*

$$\sum_{n=0}^{\infty} \frac{1}{(m_n)^{1/2n}} = \infty.$$

10. Let $F = F(x)$ and $G = G(x)$ be distribution functions with characteristic functions $f = f(t)$ and $g = g(t)$, respectively. The following theorem, which we give without proof, makes it possible to estimate how close F and G are to each other (in the uniform metric) in terms of the closeness of f and g.

Theorem (Esseen's Inequality). *Let* $G(x)$ *have derivative* $G'(x)$ *with* $\sup|G'(x)| \leq C$. *Then for every* $T > 0$

$$\sup_x |F(x) - G(x)| \leq \frac{2}{\pi} \int_0^T \left| \frac{f(t) - g(t)}{t} \right| dt + \frac{24}{\pi T} \sup_x |G'(x)|. \tag{58}$$

(This will be used in §6 of Chapter III to prove a theorem on the rapidity of convergence in the central limit theorem.)

11. PROBLEMS

1. Let ξ and η be independent random variables, $f(x) = f_1(x) + if_2(x)$, $g(x) = g_1(x) + ig_2(x)$, where $f_k(x)$ and $g_k(x)$ are Borel functions, $k = 1, 2$. Show that if $E|f(\xi)| < \infty$ and $E|g(\eta)| < \infty$, then

$$E|f(\xi)g(\eta)| < \infty$$

and

$$Ef(\xi)g(\eta) = Ef(\xi) \cdot Eg(\eta).$$

2. Let $\xi = (\xi_1, \ldots, \xi_n)$ and $E\|\xi\|^n < \infty$, where $\|\xi\| = +\sqrt{\sum \xi_i^2}$. Show that

$$\varphi_\xi(t) = \sum_{k=0}^{n} \frac{i^k}{k!} E(t, \xi)^k + \varepsilon_n(t)\|t\|^n,$$

where $t = (t_1, \ldots, t_n)$ and $\varepsilon_n(t) \to 0$, $t \to 0$.

3. Prove Theorem 2 for n-dimensional distribution functions $F = F_n(x_1, \ldots, x_n)$ and $G_n(x_1, \ldots, x_n)$.

4. Let $F = F(x_1, \ldots, x_n)$ be an n-dimensional distribution function and $\varphi = \varphi(t_1, \ldots, t_n)$ its characteristic function. Using the notation of (3.12), establish the inversion formula

$$P(a, b] = \lim_{c \to \infty} \frac{1}{(2\pi)^n} \int_{-c}^{c} \prod_{k=1}^{n} \frac{e^{it_k a_k} - e^{it_k b_k}}{it_k} \varphi(t_1, \ldots, t_k) \, dt_1 \cdots dt_k.$$

(We are to suppose that $(a, b]$ is an interval of continuity of $P(a, b]$, i.e. for $k = 1, \ldots, n$ the points a_k, b_k are points of continuity of the marginal distribution functions $F_k(x_k)$ which are obtained from $F(x_1, \ldots, x_n)$ by taking all the variables except x_k equal to $+\infty$.)

5. Let $\varphi_k(t)$, $k \geq 1$, be a characteristic function, and let the nonnegative numbers λ_k, $k \geq 1$, satisfy $\sum \lambda_k = 1$. Show that $\sum \lambda_k \varphi_k(t)$ is a characteristic function.

6. If $\varphi(t)$ is a characteristic function, are $\operatorname{Re} \varphi(t)$ and $\operatorname{Im} \varphi(t)$ characteristic functions?

7. Let φ_1, φ_2 and φ_3 be characteristic functions, and $\varphi_1\varphi_2 = \varphi_1\varphi_3$. Does it follow that $\varphi_2 = \varphi_3$?

8. Construct the characteristic functions of the distributions given in Tables 1 and 2 of §3.

9. Let ξ be an integral-valued random variable and $\varphi_\xi(t)$ its characteristic function. Show that

$$P(\xi = k) = \frac{1}{2\pi} \int_{-\pi}^{\pi} e^{-ikt}\varphi_\xi(t) \, dt, \qquad k = 0, \pm 1, \pm 2 \ldots.$$

§13. Gaussian Systems

1. Gaussian, or normal, distributions, random variables, processes, and systems play an extremely important role in probability theory and in mathematical statistics. This is explained in the first instance by the central limit theorem (§4 of Chapter III and §8 of Chapter VII), of which the De Moivre–Laplace limit theorem is a special case (§6, Chapter I). According to this theorem, the normal distribution is universal in the sense that the distribution of the sum of a large number of random variables or random vectors, subject to some not very restrictive conditions, is closely approximated by this distribution.

This is what provides a theoretical explanation of the "law of errors" of applied statistics, which says that errors of measurement that result from large numbers of independent "elementary" errors obey the normal distribution.

A multidimensional Gaussian distribution is specified by a small number of parameters; this is a definite advantage in using it in the construction of simple probabilistic models. Gaussian random variables have finite second moments, and consequently they can be studied by Hilbert space methods. Here it is important that in the Gaussian case "uncorrelated" is equivalent to "independent," so that the results of L^2-theory can be significantly strengthened.

2. Let us recall that (see §8) a random variable $\xi = \xi(\omega)$ is Gaussian, or normally distributed, with parameters m and σ^2 ($\xi \sim \mathcal{N}(m, \sigma^2)$), $|m| < \infty$, $\sigma^2 > 0$, if its density $f_\xi(x)$ has the form

$$f_\xi(x) = \frac{1}{\sqrt{2\pi}\,\sigma}\, e^{-(x-m)^2/2\sigma^2}, \tag{1}$$

where $\sigma = +\sqrt{\sigma^2}$.

As $\sigma \downarrow 0$, the density $f_\xi(x)$ "converges to the δ-function supported at $x = m$." It is natural to say that ξ is normally distributed with mean m and $\sigma^2 = 0$ ($\xi \sim \mathcal{N}(m, 0)$) if ξ has the property that $P(\xi = m) = 1$.

We can, however, give a definition that applies both to the *nondegenerate* ($\sigma^2 > 0$) and the *degenerate* ($\sigma^2 = 0$) cases. Let us consider the characteristic function $\varphi_\xi(t) \equiv \mathsf{E}e^{it\xi}$, $t \in R$.

If $P(\xi = m) = 1$, then evidently

$$\varphi_\xi(t) = e^{itm}, \tag{2}$$

whereas if $\xi \sim \mathcal{N}(m, \sigma^2)$, $\sigma^2 > 0$,

$$\varphi_\xi(t) = e^{itm - (1/2)t^2\sigma^2}. \tag{3}$$

It is obvious that when $\sigma^2 = 0$ the right-hand sides of (2) and (3) are the same. It follows, by Theorem 1 of §12, that the Gaussian random variable with parameters m and σ^2 ($|m| < \infty, \sigma^2 \geq 0$) must be the same as the random variable whose characteristic function is given by (3). This is an illustration of the "attraction of characteristic functions," a very useful technique in the multidimensional case.

Let $\xi = (\xi_1, \ldots, \xi_n)$ be a random vector and

$$\varphi_\xi(t) = \mathsf{E}e^{i(t, \xi)}, \qquad t = (t_1, \ldots, t_n) \in R^n, \qquad (4)$$

its characteristic function (see Definition 2, §12).

Definition 1. A random vector $\xi = (\xi_1, \ldots, \xi_n)$ is *Gaussian*, or *normally distributed*, if its characteristic function has the form

$$\varphi_\xi(t) = e^{i(t, m) - (1/2)(\mathbb{R}t, t)}, \qquad (5)$$

where $m = (m_1, \ldots, m_n)$, $|m_k| < \infty$ and $\mathbb{R} = \|r_{kl}\|$ is a symmetric nonnegative definite $n \times n$ matrix; we use the abbreviation $\xi \sim \mathcal{N}(m, \mathbb{R})$.

This definition immediately makes us ask whether (5) is in fact a characteristic function. Let us show that it is.

First suppose that $\mathbb{R}$ is nonsingular. Then we can define the inverse $A = \mathbb{R}^{-1}$ and the function

$$f(x) = \frac{|A|^{1/2}}{(2\pi)^{n/2}} \exp\{-\tfrac{1}{2}(A(x - m), (x - m))\}, \qquad (6)$$

where $x = (x_1, \ldots, x_n)$ and $|A| = \det A$. This function is nonnegative. Let us show that

$$\int_{R^n} e^{i(t, x)} f(x)\, dx = e^{i(t, m) - (1/2)(\mathbb{R}t, t)},$$

or equivalently that

$$I_n \equiv \int_{R^n} e^{i(t, x - m)} \frac{|A|^{1/2}}{(2\pi)^{n/2}} e^{-(1/2)(A(x - m), (x - m))}\, dx = e^{-(1/2)(\mathbb{R}t, t)}. \qquad (7)$$

Let us make the change of variable

$$x - m = \mathcal{O}u, \qquad t = \mathcal{O}v,$$

where $\mathcal{O}$ is an orthogonal matrix such that

$$\mathcal{O}^{\mathsf{T}}\mathbb{R}\mathcal{O} = D,$$

and

$$D = \begin{pmatrix} d_1 & & 0 \\ & \ddots & \\ 0 & & d_n \end{pmatrix}$$

is a diagonal matrix with $d_i \geq 0$ (see the proof of the lemma in §8). Since $|\mathbb{R}| = \det \mathbb{R} \neq 0$, we have $d_i > 0$, $i = 1, \ldots, n$. Therefore

$$|A| = |\mathbb{R}^{-1}| = d_1^{-1} \cdots d_n^{-1}. \qquad (8)$$

Moreover (for notation, see Subsection 1, §12)

$$i(t, x - m) - \tfrac{1}{2}(A(x - m), x - m)) = i(\mathcal{O}v, \mathcal{O}u) - \tfrac{1}{2}(A\mathcal{O}u, \mathcal{O}u)$$
$$= i(\mathcal{O}v)^{\mathsf{T}}\mathcal{O}u - \tfrac{1}{2}(\mathcal{O}u)^{\mathsf{T}}A(\mathcal{O}u)$$
$$= iv^{\mathsf{T}}u - \tfrac{1}{2}u^{\mathsf{T}}\mathcal{O}^{\mathsf{T}}A\mathcal{O}u$$
$$= iv^{\mathsf{T}}u - \tfrac{1}{2}u^{\mathsf{T}}D^{-1}u.$$

Together with (8) and (12.9), this yields

$$I_n = (2\pi)^{-n/2}(d_1 \cdots d_n)^{-1/2} \int_{R^n} \exp(iv^{\mathsf{T}}u - \tfrac{1}{2}u^{\mathsf{T}}D^{-1}u) \, du$$

$$= \prod_{k=1}^{n} (2\pi d_k)^{-1/2} \int_{-\infty}^{\infty} \exp\left(iv_k u_k - \frac{u_k^2}{2d_k}\right) du_k = \prod_{k=1}^{n} \exp(-\tfrac{1}{2}v_k^2 d_k)$$

$$= \exp(-\tfrac{1}{2}v^{\mathsf{T}}Dv) = \exp(-\tfrac{1}{2}v^{\mathsf{T}}\mathcal{O}^{\mathsf{T}}\mathbb{R}\mathcal{O}v) = \exp(-\tfrac{1}{2}t^{\mathsf{T}}\mathbb{R}t) = \exp(-\tfrac{1}{2}(\mathbb{R}t, t)).$$

It also follows from (6) that

$$\int_{R^n} f(x) \, dx = 1. \tag{9}$$

Therefore (5) is the characteristic function of a nondegenerate n-dimensional Gaussian distribution (see Subsection 3, §3).

Now let $\mathbb{R}$ be singular. Take $\varepsilon > 0$ and consider the positive definite symmetric matrix $\mathbb{R}^\varepsilon \equiv \mathbb{R} + \varepsilon E$. Then by what has been proved,

$$\varphi^\varepsilon(t) = \exp\{i(t, m) - \tfrac{1}{2}(\mathbb{R}^\varepsilon t, t)\}$$

is a characteristic function:

$$\varphi^\varepsilon(t) = \int_{R^n} e^{i(t, x)} \, dF_\varepsilon(x),$$

where $F_\varepsilon(x) = F_\varepsilon(x_1, \ldots, x_n)$ is an n-dimensional distribution function.
As $\varepsilon \to 0$,

$$\varphi^\varepsilon(t) \to \varphi(t) = \exp\{i(t, m) - \tfrac{1}{2}(\mathbb{R}^\varepsilon t, t)\}.$$

The limit function $\varphi(t)$ is continuous at $(0, \ldots, 0)$. Hence, by Theorem 1 and Problem 1 of §3 of Chapter III, it is a characteristic function.

We have therefore established Theorem 1.

3. Let us now discuss the significance of the vector m and the matrix $\mathbb{R} = \|r_{kl}\|$ that appear in (5).

Since

$$\ln \varphi_\xi(t) = i(t, m) - \tfrac{1}{2}(\mathbb{R}t, t) = i \sum_{k=1}^{n} t_k m_k - \frac{1}{2} \sum_{k,l=1}^{n} r_{kl} t_k t_l, \tag{10}$$

we find from (12.35) and the formulas that connect the moments and the semi-invariants that

$$m_1 = s_\xi^{(1,0,...,0)} = \mathsf{E}\xi_1, \ldots, m_k = s_\xi^{(0,...,0,1)} = \mathsf{E}\xi_k.$$

Similarly

$$r_{11} = s_\xi^{(2,0,...,0)} = \mathsf{V}\xi_1, \quad r_{12} = s_\xi^{(1,1,0,...)} = \mathsf{cov}(\xi_1, \xi_2),$$

and generally

$$r_{kl} = \mathsf{cov}(\xi_k, \xi_l).$$

Consequently m is the *mean-value vector* of ξ and $\mathbb{R}$ is its covariance matrix.

If $\mathbb{R}$ is nonsingular, we can obtain this result in a different way. In fact, in this case ξ has a density $f(x)$ given by (6).

A direct calculation shows that

$$\mathsf{E}\xi_k \equiv \int x_k f(x)\, dx = m_k, \tag{11}$$

$$\mathsf{cov}(\xi_k, \xi_l) = \int (x_k - m_k)(x_l - m_l) f(x)\, dx = r_{kl}.$$

4. Let us discuss some properties of Gaussian vectors.

Theorem 1

(a) *The components of a Gaussian vector are uncorrelated if and only if they are independent.*

(b) *A vector $\xi = (\xi_1, \ldots, \xi_n)$ is Gaussian if and only if, for every vector $\lambda = (\lambda_1, \ldots, \lambda_n)$, $\lambda_k \in R$, the random variable $(\xi, \lambda) = \lambda_1\xi_1 + \cdots + \lambda_n\xi_n$ has a Gaussian distribution.*

PROOF. (a) If the components of $\xi = (\xi_1, \ldots, \xi_n)$ are uncorrelated, it follows from the form of the characteristic function $\varphi_\xi(t)$ that it is a product of characteristic functions. Therefore, by Theorem 4 of §12, the components are independent.

The converse is evident, since independence always implies lack of correlation.

(b) If ξ is a Gaussian vector, it follows from (5) that

$$\mathsf{E}\exp\{it(\xi_1\lambda_1 + \cdots + \xi_n\lambda_n)\} = \exp\left\{it(\textstyle\sum \lambda_k m_k) - \frac{t^2}{2}\left(\textstyle\sum r_{kl}\lambda_k\lambda_l\right)\right\}, \quad t \in R,$$

and consequently

$$(\xi, \lambda) \sim \mathcal{N}(\textstyle\sum \lambda_k m_k, \sum r_{kl}\lambda_k\lambda_l).$$

Conversely, to say that the random variable $(\xi, \lambda) = \xi_1 \lambda_1 + \cdots + \xi_n \lambda_n$ is Gaussian means, in particular, that

$$\mathsf{E} e^{i(\xi, \lambda)} = \exp\left\{ i\mathsf{E}(\xi, \lambda) - \frac{V(\xi, \lambda)}{2} \right\} = \exp\{ i \sum \lambda_k \mathsf{E}\xi_k - \tfrac{1}{2} \sum \lambda_k \lambda_l \mathrm{cov}(\xi_k, \xi_l) \}.$$

Since $\lambda_1, \ldots, \lambda_n$ are arbitrary it follows from Definition 1 that the vector $\xi = (\xi_1, \ldots, \xi_n)$ is Gaussian.

This completes the proof of the theorem.

Remark. Let (θ, ξ) be a Gaussian vector with $\theta = (\theta_1, \ldots, \theta_k)$ and $\xi = (\xi_1, \ldots, \xi_k)$. If θ and ξ are uncorrelated, i.e. $\mathrm{cov}(\theta_i, \xi_j) = 0$, $i = 1, \ldots, k$; $j = 1, \ldots, l$, they are independent.

The proof is the same as for conclusion (a) of the theorem.

Let $\xi = (\xi_1, \ldots, \xi_n)$ be a Gaussian vector; let us suppose, for simplicity, that its mean-value vector is zero. If rank $\mathbb{R} = r < n$, then (as was shown in §11), there are $n - r$ linear relations connecting $\xi_1, \ldots, \xi_n$. We may then suppose that, say, $\xi_1, \ldots, \xi_r$ are linearly independent, and the others can be expressed linearly in terms of them. Hence all the basic properties of the vector $\xi = \xi_1, \ldots, \xi_n$ are determined by the first r components $(\xi_1, \ldots, \xi_r)$ for which the corresponding covariance matrix is already known to be nonsingular.

Thus we may suppose that the original vector $\xi = (\xi_1, \ldots, \xi_n)$ had linearly independent components and therefore that $|\mathbb{R}| > 0$.

Let $\mathcal{O}$ be an orthogonal matrix that diagonalizes $\mathbb{R}$,

$$\mathcal{O}^T \mathbb{R} \mathcal{O} = D.$$

The diagonal elements of D are positive and therefore determine the inverse matrix. Put $B^2 = D$ and

$$\beta = B^{-1} \mathcal{O}^T \xi.$$

Then it is easily verified that

$$\mathsf{E} e^{i(t, \beta)} = \mathsf{E} e^{i \beta^T t} = e^{-(1/2)(Et, t)},$$

i.e. the vector $\beta = (\beta_1, \ldots, \beta_n)$ is a Gaussian vector with components that are uncorrelated and therefore (Theorem 1) independent. Then if we write $A = \mathcal{O}B$ we find that the original Gaussian vector $\xi = (\xi_1, \ldots, \xi_n)$ can be represented as

$$\xi = A\beta, \tag{12}$$

where $\beta = (\beta_1, \ldots, \beta_n)$ is a Gaussian vector with independent components, $\beta_k \sim \mathcal{N}(0, 1)$. Hence we have the following result. Let $\xi = (\xi_1, \ldots, \xi_n)$ be a vector with linearly independent components such that $E\xi_k = 0$, $k = 1$, ..., n. This vector is Gaussian if and only if there are independent Gaussian variables $\beta_1, \ldots, \beta_n$, $\beta_k \sim \mathcal{N}(0, 1)$, and a nonsingular matrix A of order n such that $\xi = A\beta$. Here $\mathbb{R} = AA^T$ is the covariance matrix of ξ.

If $|\mathbb{R}| \neq 0$, then by the Gram–Schmidt method (see §11)

$$\xi_k = \hat{\xi}_k + b_k \varepsilon_k, \qquad k = 1, \ldots, n, \tag{13}$$

where since $\varepsilon = (\varepsilon_1, \ldots, \varepsilon_k) \sim \mathcal{N}(0, E)$ is a Gaussian vector,

$$\hat{\xi}_k = \sum_{l-1}^{k-1} (\xi_k, \varepsilon_l)\varepsilon_l, \tag{14}$$

$$b_k = \|\xi_k - \hat{\xi}_k\| \tag{15}$$

and

$$\mathcal{L}\{\xi_1, \ldots, \xi_k\} = \mathcal{L}\{\varepsilon_1, \ldots, \varepsilon_k\}. \tag{16}$$

We see immediately from the orthogonal decomposition (13) that

$$\hat{\xi}_k = E(\xi_k | \xi_{k-1}, \ldots, \xi_1). \tag{17}$$

From this, with (16) and (14), it follows that in the Gaussian case the conditional expectation $E(\xi_k | \xi_{k-1}, \ldots, \xi_1)$ is a linear function of $(\xi_1, \ldots, \xi_{k-1})$:

$$E(\xi_k | \xi_{k-1}, \ldots, \xi_1) = \sum_{i=1}^{k=1} a_i \xi_i. \tag{18}$$

(This was proved in §8 for the case $k = 2$.)

Since, according to a remark made in Theorem 1 of §8, $E(\xi_k | \xi_{k-1}, \ldots, \xi_1)$ is an optimal estimator (in the mean-square sense) for ξ_k in terms of $\xi_1, \ldots, \xi_{k-1}$, it follows from (18) that in the Gaussian case the optimal estimator is *linear*.

We shall use these results in looking for optimal estimators of $\theta = (\theta_1, \ldots, \theta_k)$ in terms of $\xi = (\xi_1, \ldots, \xi_l)$ under the hypothesis that (θ, ξ) is Gaussian. Let

$$m_\theta = E\theta, \qquad m_\xi = E\xi$$

be the column-vector mean values and

$$V_{\theta\theta} \equiv \text{cov}(\theta, \theta) \equiv \|\text{cov}(\theta_i, \theta_j)\|, \qquad 1 \leq i, j \leq k,$$

$$V_{\theta\xi} \equiv \text{cov}(\theta, \xi) \equiv \|\text{cov}(\theta_i, \xi_j)\|, \qquad 1 \leq i \leq k, 1 \leq j \leq l,$$

$$V_{\xi\xi} \equiv \text{cov}(\xi, \xi) \equiv \|\text{cov}(\xi_i, \xi_j)\|, \qquad 1 \leq i, j \leq l$$

the covariance matrices. Let us suppose that $V_{\xi\xi}$ has an inverse. Then we have the following theorem.

Theorem 2 (Theorem on Normal Correlation). *For a Gaussian vector* (θ, ξ), *the optimal estimator* $E(\theta | \xi)$ *of* θ *in terms of* ξ, *and its error matrix*

$$\Delta = E[\theta - E(\theta | \xi)][\theta - E(\theta(\xi)]^T$$

are given by the formulas

$$E(\theta|\xi) = m_\theta + V_{\theta\xi} V_{\xi\xi}^{-1}(\xi - m_\xi), \tag{19}$$

$$\Delta = V_{\theta\theta} - V_{\theta\xi} V_{\xi\xi}^{-1}(V_{\theta\xi})^T. \tag{20}$$

PROOF. Form the vector

$$\eta = (\theta - m_\theta) - V_{\theta\xi} V_{\xi\xi}^{-1}(\xi - m_\xi). \tag{21}$$

We can verify at once that $E\eta(\xi - m_\xi)^T = 0$, i.e. η is not correlated with $(\xi - m_\xi)$. But since (θ, ξ) is Gaussian, the vector (η, ξ) is also Gaussian. Hence by the remark on Theorem 1, η and $\xi - m_\xi$ are independent. Therefore η and ξ are independent, and consequently $E(\eta|\xi) = E\eta = 0$. Therefore

$$E[\theta - m_\theta|\xi] - V_{\theta\xi} V_{\xi\xi}^{-1}(\xi - m_\xi) = 0.$$

which establishes (19).

To establish (20) we consider the conditional covariance

$$\text{cov}(\theta, \theta|\xi) \equiv E[(\theta - E(\theta|\xi))(\theta - E(\theta|\xi))^T|\xi]. \tag{22}$$

Since $\theta - E(\theta|\xi) = \eta$, and η and ξ are independent, we find that

$$\begin{aligned}
\text{cov}(\theta, \theta|\xi) &= E(\eta\eta^T|\xi) = E\eta\eta^T \\
&= V_{\theta\theta} + V_{\theta\xi}^{-1} V_{\xi\xi} V_{\xi\xi}^{-1} V_{\theta\xi}^T - 2V_{\theta\xi} V_{\xi\xi}^{-1} V_{\xi\xi} V_{\xi\xi}^{-1} V_{\theta\xi}^T \\
&= V_{\theta\theta} - V_{\theta\xi} V_{\xi\xi}^{-1} V_{\theta\xi}^T.
\end{aligned}$$

Since $\text{cov}(\theta, \theta|\xi)$ does not depend on "chance," we have

$$\Delta = E\,\text{cov}(\theta, \theta|\xi) = \text{cov}(\theta, \theta|\xi),$$

and this establishes (20).

Corollary. *Let $(\theta, \xi_1, \ldots, \xi_n)$ be an $(n + 1)$-dimensional Gaussian vector, with $\xi_1, \ldots, \xi_n$ independent. Then*

$$E(\theta|\xi_1, \ldots, \xi_n) = E\theta + \sum_{i=1}^{n} \frac{\text{cov}(\theta, \xi_i)}{V\xi_i} (\xi_i - E\xi_i),$$

$$\Delta = V\theta - \sum_{i=1}^{n} \frac{\text{cov}^2(\theta, \xi_i)}{V\xi_i}$$

(cf. (8.12) and (8.13)).

5. Let $\xi_1, \xi_2, \ldots$ be a sequence of Gaussian random vectors that converge in probability to ξ. Let us show that ξ is also Gaussian.

In accordance with (a) of Theorem 1, it is enough to establish this only for random variables.

Let $m_n = \mathsf{E}\xi_n$, $\sigma_n^2 = \mathsf{V}\xi_n$. Then by Lebesgue's dominated convergence theorem

$$\lim_{n\to\infty} e^{itm_n - (1/2)\sigma_n^2 t^2} = \lim_{n\to\infty} \mathsf{E}e^{it\xi_n} = \mathsf{E}e^{it\xi}.$$

It follows from the existence of the limit on the left-hand side that there are numbers m and σ^2 such that

$$m = \lim_{n\to\infty} m_n, \qquad \sigma^2 = \lim_{n\to\infty} \sigma_n^2.$$

Consequently

$$\mathsf{E}e^{it\xi} = e^{itm - (1/2)\sigma^2 t^2},$$

i.e. $\xi \sim \mathcal{N}(m, \sigma^2)$.

It follows, in particular, that the closed linear manifold $\mathscr{L}(\xi_1, \xi_2, \ldots)$ generated by the Gaussian variables $\xi_1, \xi_2, \ldots$ (see §11, Subsection 5) consists of Gaussian variables.

6. We now turn to the concept of Gaussian systems in general.

Definition 2. A collection of random variables $\xi = (\xi_\alpha)$, where α belongs to some index set $\mathfrak{A}$, is a *Gaussian system* if the random vector $(\xi_{\alpha_1}, \ldots, \xi_{\alpha_n})$ is Gaussian for every $n \geq 1$ and all indices $\alpha_1, \ldots, \alpha_n$ chosen from $\mathfrak{A}$.

Let us notice some properties of Gaussian systems.

(a) If $\xi = (\xi_\alpha)$, $\alpha \in \mathfrak{A}$, is a Gaussian system, then every subsystem $\xi' = (\xi'_\alpha)$, $\alpha' \in \mathfrak{A}' \subseteq \mathfrak{A}$, is also Gaussian.
(b) If ξ_α, $\alpha \in \mathfrak{A}$, are independent Gaussian variables, then the system $\xi = (\xi_\alpha)$, $\alpha \in \mathfrak{A}$, is Gaussian.
(c) If $\xi = (\xi_\alpha)$, $\alpha \in \mathfrak{A}$, is a Gaussian system, the closed linear manifold $\mathscr{L}(\xi)$, consisting of all variables of the form $\sum_{i=1}^n c_{\alpha_i}\xi_{\alpha_i}$, together with their mean-square limits, forms a Gaussian system.

Let us observe that the converse of (a) is false in general. For example, let ξ_1 and η_1 be independent and $\xi_1 \sim \mathcal{N}(0, 1)$, $\eta_1 \sim \mathcal{N}(0, 1)$. Define the system

$$(\xi, \eta) = \begin{cases} (\xi_1, |\eta_1|) & \text{if } \xi_1 \geq 0, \\ (\xi_1, -|\eta_1|) & \text{if } \xi_1 < 0. \end{cases} \tag{23}$$

Then it is easily verified that ξ and η are both Gaussian, but (ξ, η) is not.

Let $\xi = (\xi_\alpha)_{\alpha \in \mathfrak{A}}$ be a Gaussian system with mean-value vector $m = (m_\alpha)$, $\alpha \in \mathfrak{A}$, and covariance matrix $\mathbb{R} = (r_{\alpha\beta})_{\alpha, \beta \in \mathfrak{A}}$, where $m_\alpha = \mathsf{E}\xi_\alpha$. Then $\mathbb{R}$ is evidently symmetric ($r_{\alpha\beta} = r_{\beta\alpha}$) and nonnegative definite in the sense that for every vector $c = (c_\alpha)_{\alpha \in \mathfrak{A}}$ with values in $R^{\mathfrak{A}}$, and only a finite number of nonzero coordinates c_α,

$$(\mathbb{R}c, c) \equiv \sum_{\alpha, \beta} r_{\alpha\beta} c_\alpha c_\beta \geq 0. \tag{24}$$

We now ask the converse question. Suppose that we are given a parameter set $\mathfrak{A} = \{\alpha\}$, a vector $m = (m_\alpha)_{\alpha \in \mathfrak{A}}$ and a symmetric nonnegative definite matrix $\mathbb{R} = (r_{\alpha\beta})_{\alpha, \beta \in \mathfrak{A}}$. Do there exist a probability space $(\Omega, \mathscr{F}, \mathsf{P})$ and a Gaussian system of random variables $\xi = (\xi_\alpha)_{\alpha \in \mathfrak{A}}$ on it, such that

$$\mathsf{E}\xi_\alpha = m_\alpha,$$

$$\operatorname{cov}(\xi_\alpha, \xi_\beta) = r_{\alpha, \beta}, \qquad \alpha, \beta \in \mathfrak{A}?$$

If we take a finite set $\alpha_1, \ldots, \alpha_n$, then for the vector $\bar{m} = (m_{\alpha_1}, \ldots, m_{\alpha_n})$ and the matrix $\bar{\mathbb{R}} = (r_{\alpha\beta})$, $\alpha, \beta = \alpha_1, \ldots, \alpha_n$, we can construct in R^n the Gaussian distribution $F_{\alpha_1, \ldots, \alpha_n}(x_1, \ldots, x_n)$ with characteristic function

$$\varphi(t) = \exp\{i(t, \bar{m}) - \tfrac{1}{2}(\mathbb{R}t, t)\}, \qquad t = (t_{\alpha_1}, \ldots, t_{\alpha_n}).$$

It is easily verified that the family

$$\{F_{\alpha_1, \ldots, \alpha_n}(x_1, \ldots, x_n); \alpha_i \in \mathfrak{A}\}$$

is consistent. Consequently by Kolmogorov's theorem (Theorem 1, §9, and Remark 2 on this) the answer to our question is positive.

7. If $\mathfrak{A} = \{1, 2, \ldots\}$, then in accordance with the terminology of §5 the system of random variables $\xi = (\xi_\alpha)_{\alpha \in \mathfrak{A}}$ is a *random sequence* and is denoted by $\xi = (\xi_1, \xi_2, \ldots)$. A Gaussian sequence is completely described by its mean-value vector $m = (m_1, m_2, \ldots)$ and covariance matrix $\mathbb{R} = \|r_{ij}\|$, $r_{ij} = \operatorname{cov}(\xi_i, \xi_j)$. In particular, if $r_{ij} = \sigma_i^2 \delta_{ij}$, then $\xi = (\xi_1, \xi_2, \ldots)$ is a Gaussian sequence of independent random variables with $\xi_i \sim \mathcal{N}(m_i, \sigma_i^2)$, $i \geq 1$.

When $\mathfrak{A} = [0, 1], [0, \infty), (-\infty, \infty), \ldots$, the system $\xi = (\xi_t)$, $t \in \mathfrak{A}$, is a *random process with continuous time*.

Let us mention some examples of Gaussian random processes. If we take their mean values to be zero, their probabilistic properties are completely described by the covariance matrices $\|r_{st}\|$. We write $r(s, t)$ instead of r_{st} and call it the *covariance function*.

EXAMPLE 1. If $T = [0, \infty)$ and

$$r(s, t) = \min(s, t), \qquad (25)$$

the Gaussian process $\xi = (\xi_t)_{t \geq 0}$ with this covariance function (see Problem 2) and $\xi_0 \equiv 0$ is a *Brownian motion* or *Wiener process*.

Observe that this process has *independent increments*; that is, for arbitrary $t_1 < t_2 < \cdots < t_n$ the random variables

$$\xi_{t_2} - \xi_{t_1}, \ldots, \xi_{t_n} - \xi_{t_{n-1}}$$

are independent. In fact, because the process is Gaussian it is enough to verify only that the increments are uncorrelated. But if $s < t < u < v$ then

$$\mathsf{E}[\xi_t - \xi_s][\xi_v - \xi_u] = [r(t, v) - r(t, u)] - [r(s, v) - r(s, u)]$$
$$= (t - t) - (s - s) = 0.$$

EXAMPLE 2. The process $\xi = (\xi_t)$, $0 \leq t \leq 1$, with $\xi_0 \equiv 0$ and

$$r(s, t) = \min(s, t) - st \tag{26}$$

is a *conditional Wiener process* (observe that since $r(1, 1) = 0$ we have $\mathsf{P}(\xi_1 = 0) = 1$).

EXAMPLE 3. The process $\xi = (\xi_t)$, $-\infty < t < \infty$, with

$$r(s, t) = e^{-|t-s|} \tag{27}$$

is a *Gauss–Markov process.*

8. PROBLEMS

1. Let ξ_1, ξ_2, ξ_3 be independent Gaussian random variables, $\xi_i \sim \mathcal{N}(0, 1)$. Show that

$$\frac{\xi_1 + \xi_2\xi_3}{\sqrt{1 + \xi_3^2}} \sim \mathcal{N}(0, 1).$$

(In this case we encounter the interesting problem of describing the nonlinear transformations of independent Gaussian variables $\xi_1, \ldots, \xi_n$ whose distributions are still Gaussian.)

2. Show that (25), (26) and (27) are nonnegative definite (and consequently are actually covariance functions).

3. Let A be an $m \times n$ matrix. An $n \times m$ matrix $A^{\oplus}$ is a *pseudoinverse* of A if there are matrices U and V such that

$$AA^{\oplus}A = A, \qquad A^{\oplus} = UA^{\mathsf{T}} = A^{\mathsf{T}}V.$$

Show that $A^{\oplus}$ exists and is unique.

4. Show that (19) and (20) in the theorem on normal correlation remains valid when $\mathsf{V}_{\xi\xi}$ is singular provided that $\mathsf{V}_{\xi\xi}^{-1}$ is replaced by $\mathsf{V}_{\xi\xi}^{\oplus}$.

5. Let $(\theta, \xi) = (\theta_1, \ldots, \theta_k; \xi_1, \ldots, \xi_l)$ be a Gaussian vector with nonsingular matrix $\Delta \equiv \mathsf{V}_{\theta\theta} - \mathsf{V}_{\xi\xi}^{\oplus}\mathsf{V}_{\theta\xi}^*$. Show that the distribution function

$$\mathsf{P}(\theta \leq a|\xi) = \mathsf{P}(\theta_1 \leq a_1, \ldots, \theta_k \leq a_k|\xi)$$

has (P-a.s.) the density $p(a_1, \ldots, a_k|\xi)$ defined by

$$\frac{|\Delta^{-1/2}|}{(2\pi)^{k/2}} \exp\{-\tfrac{1}{2}(a - \mathsf{E}(\theta|\xi))^{\mathsf{T}}\Delta^{-1}(a - \mathsf{E}(\theta|\xi))\}.$$

6. (S. N. Bernstein). Let ξ and η be independent identically distributed random variables with finite variances. Show that if $\xi + \eta$ and $\xi - \eta$ are independent, then ξ and η are Gaussian.

Convergence of Probability Measures. Central Limit Theorem

§1. Weak Convergence of Probability Measures and Distributions

1. Many important results of probability theory are formulated as limit theorems. So, indeed, were James Bernoulli's law of large numbers, as well as the De Moivre–Laplace limit theorem, the theorems with which the true theory of probability began.

In the present chapter we discuss two central aspects of limit theorems: one is the concept of weak convergence; the other is the method of characteristic functions, one of the most powerful methods for proving and refining limit theorems.

We begin by recalling the statement of the law of large numbers (Chapter I, §5) for the Bernoulli scheme.

Let $\xi_1, \xi_2, \ldots$ be a sequence of independent identically distributed random variables with $\mathsf{P}(\xi_i = 1) = p$, $\mathsf{P}(\xi_i = 0) = q$, $p + q = 1$. In terms of the concept of convergence in probability (Chapter II, §10), Bernoulli's law of large numbers can be stated as follows:

$$\frac{S_n}{n} \xrightarrow{\mathsf{P}} p, \qquad n \to \infty, \tag{1}$$

where $S_n = \xi_1 + \cdots + \xi_n$. (It will be shown in Chapter IV that in fact we have convergence with probability 1.)

We put

$$F_n(x) = \mathsf{P}\left\{\frac{S_n}{n} \leq x\right\},$$

$$F(x) = \begin{cases} 1, & x \geq p, \\ 0, & x < p, \end{cases} \tag{2}$$

where $F(x)$ is the distribution function of the degenerate random variable $\xi \equiv p$. Also let P_n and P be the probability measures on $(R, \mathscr{B}(R))$ corresponding to the distributions F_n and F.

In accordance with Theorem 2 of §10, Chapter II, convergence in probability, $S_n/n \xrightarrow{\mathsf{P}} p$, implies convergence in distribution, $S_n/n \xrightarrow{d} p$, which means that

$$\mathsf{E}f\left(\frac{S_n}{n}\right) \to \mathsf{E}f(p), \qquad n \to \infty, \tag{3}$$

for every function $f = f(x)$ belonging to the class $\mathbb{C}(R)$ of bounded continuous functions on R.

Since

$$\mathsf{E}f\left(\frac{S_n}{n}\right) = \int_R f(x)\mathsf{P}_n(dx), \qquad \mathsf{E}f(p) = \int_R f(x)\mathsf{P}(dx),$$

(3) can be written in the form

$$\int_R f(x)\mathsf{P}_n(dx) \to \int_R f(x)\mathsf{P}(dx), \qquad f \in \mathbb{C}(R), \tag{4}$$

or (in accordance with §6 of Chapter II) in the form

$$\int_R f(x)\,dF_n(x) \to \int_R f(x)\,dF(x), \qquad f \in \mathbb{C}(R). \tag{5}$$

In analysis, (4) is called <u>weak convergence</u> (of P_n to P, $n \to \infty$) and written $\mathsf{P}_n \xrightarrow{w} \mathsf{P}$. It is also natural to call (5) weak convergence of F_n to F and denote it by $F_n \xrightarrow{w} F$.

Thus we may say that in a Bernoulli scheme

$$\frac{S_n}{n} \xrightarrow{\mathsf{P}} p \Rightarrow F_n \xrightarrow{w} F. \tag{6}$$

It is also easy to see from (1) that, for the distribution functions defined in (2),

$$F_n(x) \to F(x), \qquad n \to \infty,$$

for all points $x \in R$ *except for the single point* $x = p$, where $F(x)$ has a discontinuity.

This shows that weak convergence $F_n \to F$ *does not imply* pointwise convergence of $F_n(x)$ to $F(x)$, $n \to \infty$, for *all* points $x \in R$. However, it turns out that, both for Bernoulli schemes and for arbitrary distribution functions, weak convergence is equivalent (see Theorem 2 below) to "convergence in general" in the sense of the following definition.

Definition 1. A sequence of distribution functions $\{F_n\}$, defined on the real line, converges *in general* to the distribution function F (notation: $F_n \Rightarrow F$) if as $n \to \infty$

$$F_n(x) \to F(x), \qquad x \in P_C(F),$$

where $P_C(F)$ is the set of points of continuity of $F = F(x)$.

For Bernoulli schemes, $F = F(x)$ is degenerate, and it is easy to see (see Problem 7 of §10, Chapter II) that

$$(F_n \Rightarrow F) \Rightarrow \left(\frac{S_n}{n} \xrightarrow{P} p\right).$$

Therefore, taking account of Theorem 2 below,

$$\left(\frac{S_n}{n} \xrightarrow{P} p\right) \Rightarrow (F_n \xrightarrow{w} F) \Leftrightarrow (F_n \Rightarrow F) \Rightarrow \left(\frac{S_n}{n} \xrightarrow{P} p\right) \tag{7}$$

and consequently the law of large numbers can be considered as a theorem on the weak convergence of the distribution functions defined in (2).

Let us write

$$F_n(x) = \mathsf{P}\left\{\frac{S_n - np}{\sqrt{npq}} \le x\right\},$$

$$F(x) = \frac{1}{\sqrt{2\pi}} \int_{-\infty}^{x} e^{-u^2/2} \, du. \tag{8}$$

The De Moivre–Laplace theorem (§6, Chapter I) states that $F_n(x) \to F(x)$ for all $x \in R$, and consequently $F_n \Rightarrow F$. Since, as we have observed, weak convergence $F_n \xrightarrow{w} F$ and convergence in general, $F_n \Rightarrow F$, are equivalent, we may therefore say that the De Moivre–Laplace theorem is also a theorem on the weak convergence of the distribution functions defined by (8).

These examples justify the concept of weak convergence of probability measures that will be introduced below in Definition 2. Although, on the real line, weak convergence is equivalent to convergence in general of the corresponding distribution functions, it is preferable to use weak convergence from the beginning. This is because in the first place it is easier to work with, and in the second place it remains useful in more general spaces than the real line, and in particular for metric spaces, including the especially important spaces R^n, R^∞, C and D (see §3 of Chapter II).

2. Let $(E, \mathscr{E}, \rho)$ be a metric space with metric $\rho = \rho(x, y)$ and σ-algebra $\mathscr{E}$ of Borel subsets generated by the open sets, and let $\mathsf{P}, \mathsf{P}_1, \mathsf{P}_2, \ldots$ be probability measures on $(E, \mathscr{E}, \rho)$.

Definition 2. A sequence of probability measures $\{\mathsf{P}_n\}$ *converges weakly* to the probability measure P (notation: $\mathsf{P}_n \xrightarrow{w} \mathsf{P}$) if

$$\int_E f(x)\mathsf{P}_n(dx) \to \int_E f(x)\mathsf{P}(dx) \tag{9}$$

for every function $f = f(x)$ in the class $\mathbb{C}(E)$ of continuous bounded functions on E.

Definition 3. A sequence of probability measures $\{P_n\}$ *converges in general* to the probability measure P (notation: $P_n \Rightarrow P$) if

$$P_n(A) \rightarrow P(A) \tag{10}$$

for every set A of $\mathscr{E}$ for which

$$P(\partial A) = 0. \tag{11}$$

(Here ∂A denotes the boundary of A:

$$\partial A = [A] \cap [\bar{A}],$$

where $[A]$ is the closure of A.)

The following fundamental theorem shows the equivalence of the concepts of weak convergence and convergence in general for probability measures, and contains still another equivalent statement.

Theorem 1. *The following statements are equivalent.*

(I) $P_n \overset{w}{\rightarrow} P$.
(II) $\varlimsup P_n(A) \leq P(A)$, A *closed*.
(III) $\varliminf P_n(A) \geq P(A)$, A *open*.
(IV) $P_n \Rightarrow P$.

PROOF. (I) $\Rightarrow$ (II). Let A be closed, $f(x) = I_A(x)$ and

$$f_\varepsilon(x) = g\left(\frac{1}{\varepsilon}\rho(x, A)\right), \qquad \varepsilon > 0,$$

where

$$\rho(x, A) = \inf\{\rho(x, y): y \in A\},$$

$$g(t) = \begin{cases} 1, & t \leq 0, \\ 1 - t, & 0 \leq t \leq 1, \\ 0, & t \geq 1. \end{cases}$$

Let us also put

$$A_\varepsilon = \{x: \rho(x, A) < \varepsilon\}$$

and observe that $A_\varepsilon \downarrow A$ as $\varepsilon \downarrow 0$.

Since $f_\varepsilon(x)$ is bounded, continuous, and satisfies

$$P_n(A) = \int_E I_A(x)P_n(dx) \leq \int_E f_\varepsilon(x)P_n(dx),$$

we have

$$\varlimsup_n P_n(A) \leq \varlimsup_n \int_E f_\varepsilon(x)P_n(dx) = \int_E f_\varepsilon(x)P(dx) \leq P(A_\varepsilon) \downarrow P(A), \ \varepsilon \downarrow 0,$$

which establishes the required implication.

The implications (II) $\Rightarrow$ (III) and (III) $\Rightarrow$ (II) become obvious if we take the complements of the sets concerned.

(III) $\Rightarrow$ (IV). Let $A^0 = A \backslash \partial A$ be the interior, and $[A]$ the closure, of A. Then from (II), (III), and the hypothesis $\mathsf{P}(\partial A) = 0$, we have

$$\overline{\lim_n} \, \mathsf{P}_n(A) \leq \overline{\lim_n} \, \mathsf{P}_n([A]) \leq \mathsf{P}([A]) = \mathsf{P}(A),$$

$$\underline{\lim_n} \, \mathsf{P}_n(A) \geq \underline{\lim_n} \, \mathsf{P}_n(A^0) \geq \mathsf{P}(A^0) = \mathsf{P}(A),$$

and therefore $\mathsf{P}_n(A) \to \mathsf{P}(A)$ for every A such that $\mathsf{P}(\partial A) = 0$.

(IV) $\to$ (I). Let $f = f(x)$ be a bounded continuous function with $|f(x)| \leq M$. We put

$$D = \{t \in R : \mathsf{P}\{x : f(x) = t\} \neq 0\}$$

and consider a decomposition $T_k = (t_0, t_1, \ldots, t_k)$ of $[-M, M]$:

$$-M = t_0 < t_1 < \cdots < t_k = M, \quad k \geq 1,$$

with $t_i \notin D$, $i = 0, 1, \ldots, k$. (Observe that D is at most countable since the sets $f^{-1}\{t\}$ are disjoint and P is finite.)

Let $B_i = \{x : t_i \leq f(x) < t_{i+1}\}$. Since $f(x)$ is continuous and therefore the set $f^{-1}(t_i, t_{i+1})$ is open, we have $\partial B_i \subseteq f^{-1}\{t_i\} \cup f^{-1}\{t_{i+1}\}$. The points $t_i, t_{i+1} \notin D$; therefore $\mathsf{P}(\partial B_i) = 0$ and, by (IV),

$$\sum_{i=0}^{k-1} t_i \mathsf{P}_n(B_i) \to \sum_{i=0}^{k-1} t_i \mathsf{P}(B_i). \tag{12}$$

But

$$\left| \int_E f(x) \mathsf{P}_n(dx) - \int_E f(x) \mathsf{P}(dx) \right| \leq \left| \int_E f(x) \mathsf{P}_n(dx) - \sum_{i=0}^{k-1} t_i \mathsf{P}_n(B_i) \right|$$

$$+ \left| \sum_{i=0}^{k-1} t_i \mathsf{P}_n(B_i) - \sum_{i=0}^{k-1} t_i \mathsf{P}(B_i) \right|$$

$$+ \left| \sum_{i=0}^{k-1} t_i \mathsf{P}(B_i) - \int_E f(x) \mathsf{P}(dx) \right|$$

$$\leq 2 \max_{0 \leq i \leq k-1} (t_{i+1} - t_i)$$

$$+ \left| \sum_{i=0}^{k-1} t_i \mathsf{P}_n(B_i) - \sum_{i=0}^{k-1} t_i \mathsf{P}(B_i) \right|,$$

whence, by (12), since the T_k ($k \geq 1$) are arbitrary,

$$\lim_n \int_E f(x) \mathsf{P}_n(dx) = \int_E f(x) \mathsf{P}(dx).$$

This completes the proof of the theorem.

Remark 1. The functions $f(x) = I_A(x)$ and $f_\varepsilon(x)$ that appear in the proof that (I) ⇒ (II) are respectively *upper semicontinuous* and *uniformly continuous*. Hence it is easy to show that each of the conditions of the theorem is equivalent to one of the following:

(V) $\int_E f(x)P_n(x)\,dx \to \int_E f(x)P(dx)$ *for all bounded uniformly continuous* $f(x)$;

(VI) $\overline{\lim}\int_E f(x)P_n(dx) \le \int_E f(x)P(dx)$ *for all bounded* $f(x)$ *that are upper semicontinuous* ($\overline{\lim} f(x_n) \le f(x)$, $x_n \to x$);

(VII) $\underline{\lim}_n \int_E f(x)P_n(dx) \ge \int_E f(x)P(dx)$ *for all bounded* $f(x)$ *that are lower semicontinuous* ($\underline{\lim} f(x_n) \ge f(x)$, $x_n \to x$).

Remark 2. Theorem 1 admits a natural generalization to the case when the probability measures P and P_n defined on $(E, \mathscr{E}, \rho)$ are replaced by *arbitrary* (not necessarily probability) *finite measures* μ and μ_n. For such measures we can introduce weak convergence $\mu_n \overset{w}{\to} \mu$ and convergence in general $\mu_n \Rightarrow \mu$ and, just as in Theorem 1, we can establish the equivalence of the following conditions:

(I*) $\mu_n \overset{w}{\to} \mu$;

(II*) $\overline{\lim}\,\mu_n(A) \le \mu(A)$, *where A is closed and* $\mu_n(E) \to \mu(E)$;

(III*) $\underline{\lim}\,\mu_n(A) \ge \mu(A)$, *where A is open and* $\mu_n(E) \to \mu(E)$;

(IV*) $\mu_n \Rightarrow \mu$.

Each of these is equivalent to any of (V*), (VI*), and (VII*), which are (V), (VI), and (VII) with P_n and P replaced by μ_n and μ.

3. Let $(R, \mathscr{B}(R))$ be the real line with the system $\mathscr{B}(R)$ of sets generated by the Euclidean metric $\rho(x, y) = |x - y|$ (compare Remark 2 of subsection 2 of §2 of Chapter II). Let P and $P_n, n \ge 1$, be probability measures on $(R, \mathscr{B}(R))$ and let F and $F_n, n \ge 1$, be the corresponding distribution functions.

Theorem 2. *The following conditions are equivalent:*

(1) $P_n \overset{w}{\to} P$,

(2) $P_n \Rightarrow P$,

(3) $F_n \overset{w}{\to} F$,

(4) $F_n \Rightarrow F$.

PROOF. Since $(2) \Leftrightarrow (1) \Leftrightarrow (3)$, it is enough to show that $(2) \Leftrightarrow (4)$.

If $P_n \Rightarrow P$, then in particular

$$P_n(-\infty, x] \to P(-\infty, x]$$

for all $x \in R$ such that $P\{x\} = 0$. But this means that $F_n \Rightarrow F$.

Now let $F_n \Rightarrow F$. To prove that $P_n \Rightarrow P$ it is enough (by Theorem 1) to show that $\underline{\lim}_n P_n(A) \ge P(A)$ for every open set A.

If A is open, there is a countable collection of disjoint open intervals $I_1, I_2, \ldots$ (of the form (a, b)) such that $A = \sum_{k=1}^\infty I_k$. Choose $\varepsilon > 0$ and in each interval $I_k = (a_k, b_k)$ select a subinterval $I'_k = (a'_k, b'_k]$ such that a'_k, $b'_k \in P_C(F)$ and $P(I_k) \leq P(I'_k) + \varepsilon \cdot 2^{-k}$. (Since $F(x)$ has at most countably many discontinuities, such intervals I'_k, $k \geq 1$, certainly exist.) By Fatou's lemma,

$$\varlimsup_n \mathsf{P}_n(A) = \varlimsup_n \sum_{k=1}^{\infty} \mathsf{P}_n(I_k) \geq \sum_{k=1}^{\infty} \varliminf_n \mathsf{P}_n(I_k)$$

$$\geq \sum_{k=1}^{\infty} \varliminf_n \mathsf{P}_n(I'_k).$$

But

$$\mathsf{P}_n(I'_k) = F_n(b'_k) - F_n(a'_k) \to F(b'_k) - F(a'_k) = \mathsf{P}(I'_k).$$

Therefore

$$\varliminf_n \mathsf{P}_n(A) \geq \sum_{k=1}^{\infty} \mathsf{P}(I'_k) \geq \sum_{k=1}^{\infty} (\mathsf{P}(I_k) - \varepsilon \cdot 2^{-k}) = \mathsf{P}(A) - \varepsilon.$$

Since $\varepsilon > 0$ is arbitrary, this shows that $\varliminf_n \mathsf{P}_n(A) \geq \mathsf{P}(A)$ if A is open. This completes the proof of the theorem.

4. Let $(E, \mathscr{E})$ be a measurable space. A collection $\mathscr{K}_0(E) \subseteq \mathscr{E}$ of subsets is a *determining class* if whenever two probability measures P and Q on $(E, \mathscr{E})$ satisfy

$$\mathsf{P}(A) = \mathsf{Q}(A) \qquad \text{for all} \quad A \in \mathscr{K}_0(E)$$

it follows that the measures are identical, i.e.

$$\mathsf{P}(A) = \mathsf{Q}(A) \qquad \text{for all} \quad A \in \mathscr{E}.$$

If $(E, \mathscr{E}, \rho)$ is a metric space, a collection $\mathscr{K}_1(E) \subseteq \mathscr{E}$ is a *convergence-determining class* if whenever probability measures $\mathsf{P}, \mathsf{P}_1, \mathsf{P}_2, \ldots$ satisfy

$$\mathsf{P}_n(A) \to \mathsf{P}(A) \qquad \text{for all} \quad A \in \mathscr{K}_1(E) \quad \text{with} \quad \mathsf{P}(\partial A) = 0$$

it follows that

$$\mathsf{P}_n(A) \to \mathsf{P}(A) \qquad \text{for all} \quad A \in E \quad \text{with} \quad \mathsf{P}(\partial A) = 0.$$

When $(E, \mathscr{E}) = (R, \mathscr{B}(R))$, we can take a determining class $\mathscr{K}_0(R)$ to be the class of "elementary" sets $\mathscr{K} = \{(-\infty, x], x \in R\}$ (Theorem 1, §3, Chapter II). It follows from the equivalence of (2) and (4) of Theorem 2 that this class $\mathscr{K}$ is also a convergence-determining class.

It is natural to ask about such determining classes in more general spaces. For R^n, $n \geq 2$, the class $\mathscr{K}$ of "elementary" sets of the form $(-\infty, x] = (-\infty, x_1] \times \cdots \times (-\infty, x_n]$, where $x = (x_1, \ldots, x_n) \in R^n$, is both a determining class (Theorem 2, §3, Chapter II) and a convergence-determining class (Problem 2).

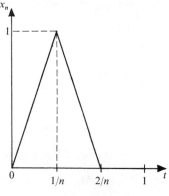

Figure 35

For R^{∞} the cylindrical sets $\mathscr{K}_0(R^{\infty})$ are the "elementary" sets whose probabilities uniquely determine the probabilities of the Borel sets (Theorem 3, §3, Chapter II). It turns out that in this case the class of cylindrical sets is also the class of convergence-determining sets (Problem 3). Therefore $\mathscr{K}_1(R^{\infty}) = \mathscr{K}_0(R^{\infty})$.

We might expect that the cylindrical sets would still constitute determining classes in more general spaces. However, this is, in general, not the case.

For example, consider the space $(C, \mathscr{B}_0(C), \rho)$ with the uniform metric ρ (see subsection 6, §2, Chapter II). Let P be the probability measure concentrated on the element $x = x(t) \equiv 0$, $0 \le t \le 1$, and let P_n, $n \ge 1$, be the probability measures each of which is concentrated on the element $x = x_n(t)$ shown in Figure 35. It is easy to see that $\mathsf{P}_n(A) \to \mathsf{P}(A)$ for all cylindrical sets A with $\mathsf{P}(\partial A) = 0$. But if we consider, for example, the set

$$A = \{\alpha \in C : |\alpha(t)| \le \tfrac{1}{2}, 0 \le t \le 1\} \in \mathscr{B}_0(C),$$

then $\mathsf{P}(\partial A) = 0$, $\mathsf{P}_n(A) = 0$, $\mathsf{P}(A) = 1$ and consequently $\mathsf{P}_n \not\Rightarrow \mathsf{P}$.

Therefore $\mathscr{K}_0(C) = \mathscr{B}_0(C)$ but $\mathscr{K}_0(C) \subset \mathscr{K}_1(C)$ (with strict inclusion).

5. PROBLEMS

1. Let us say that a function $F = F(x)$, defined on R^n, is *continuous at* $x \in R^n$ provided that, for every $\varepsilon > 0$, there is a $\delta > 0$ such that $|F(x) - F(y)| < \varepsilon$ for all $y \in R^n$ that satisfy

$$x - \delta e < y < x + \delta e,$$

where $e = (1, \ldots, 1) \in R^n$. Let us say that a sequence of distribution functions $\{F_n\}$ *converges in general* to the distribution function F ($F_n \Rightarrow F$) if $F_n(x) \to F(x)$, for all points $x \in R^n$ where $F = F(x)$ is continuous.

   Show that the conclusion of Theorem 2 remains valid for R^n, $n > 1$. (See the remark on Theorem 2.)

2. Show that the class $\mathcal{K}$ of "elementary" sets in R^n is a convergence-determining class.

3. Let E be one of the spaces R^∞, C or D. Let us say that a sequence $\{\mathsf{P}_n\}$ of probability measures (defined on the σ-algebra $\mathcal{E}$ of Borel sets generated by the open sets) *converges in general in the sense of finite-dimensional distributions* to the probability measure P (notation: $\mathsf{P}_n \overset{f}{\Rightarrow} \mathsf{P}$) if $\mathsf{P}_n(A) \to \mathsf{P}(A)$, $n \to \infty$, for all *cylindrical* sets A with $\mathsf{P}(\partial A) = 0$.

   For R^∞, show that

   $$(\mathsf{P}_n \overset{f}{\Rightarrow} \mathsf{P}) \Leftrightarrow (\mathsf{P}_n \Rightarrow \mathsf{P}).$$

4. Let F and G be distribution functions on the real line and let

   $$L(F, G) = \inf\{h > 0 : F(x - h) - h \le G(x) \le F(x + h) + h\}$$

   be the *Lévy distance* (between F and G). Show that convergence in general is equivalent to convergence in the Lévy metric:

   $$(F_n \Rightarrow F) \Leftrightarrow L(F_n, F) \to 0.$$

5. Let $F_n \Rightarrow F$ and let F be continuous. Show that in this case $F_n(x)$ converges uniformly to $F(x)$:

   $$\sup_x |F_n(x) - F(x)| \to 0, \qquad n \to \infty.$$

6. Prove the statement in Remark 1 on Theorem 1.

7. Establish the equivalence of (I*)–(IV*) as stated in Remark 2 on Theorem 1.

8. Show that $\mathsf{P}_n \overset{w}{\to} \mathsf{P}$ if and only if every subsequence $\{\mathsf{P}_{n'}\}$ of $\{\mathsf{P}_n\}$ contains a subsequence $\{\mathsf{P}_{n''}\}$ such that $\mathsf{P}_{n''} \overset{w}{\to} \mathsf{P}$.

§2. Relative Compactness and Tightness of Families of Probability Distributions

1. If we are given a sequence of probability measures, then before we can consider the question of its (weak) convergence to some probability measure, we have of course to establish whether the sequence converges in general to some measure, or has at least one convergent subsequence.

   For example, the sequence $\{\mathsf{P}_n\}$, where $\mathsf{P}_{2n} = \mathsf{P}$, $\mathsf{P}_{2n+1} = \mathsf{Q}$, and P and Q are different probability measures, is evidently not convergent, but has the two convergent subsequences $\{\mathsf{P}_{2n}\}$ and $\{\mathsf{P}_{2n+1}\}$

   It is easy to construct a sequence $\{\mathsf{P}_n\}$ of probability measures P_n, $n \ge 1$, that not only fails to converge, but contains no convergent subsequences at all. All that we have to do is to take P_n, $n \ge 1$, to be concentrated at $\{n\}$ (that is, $\mathsf{P}_n\{n\} = 1$). In fact, since $\lim_n \mathsf{P}_n(a, b] = 0$ whenever $a < b$, a limit measure would have to be identically zero, contradicting the fact that $1 = \mathsf{P}_n(R) \not\to 0$,

$n \to \infty$. It is interesting to observe that in this example the corresponding sequence $\{F_n\}$ of distribution functions,

$$F_n(x) = \begin{cases} 1, & x \geq n, \\ 0, & x < n, \end{cases}$$

is evidently convergent: for every $x \in R$,

$$F_n(x) \to G(x) \equiv 0.$$

However, the limit function $G = G(x)$ is not a distribution function (in the sense of Definition 1 of §3, Chapter II).

This instructive example shows that the space of distribution functions is not compact. It also shows that if a sequence of distribution functions is to converge to a limit that is also a distribution function, we must have some hypothesis that will prevent mass from "escaping to infinity."

After these introductory remarks, which illustrate the kinds of difficulty that can arise, we turn to the basic definitions.

2. Let us suppose that all measures are defined on the metric space $(E, \mathscr{E}, \rho)$.

Definition 1. A family of probability measures $\mathscr{P} = \{\mathsf{P}_a; a \in \mathfrak{A}\}$ is *relatively compact* if every sequence of measures from $\mathscr{P}$ contains a subsequence which converges weakly to a probability measure.

We emphasize that in this definition the limit measure is to be a *probability measure*, although it need not belong to the original class $\mathscr{P}$. (This is why the word "relatively" appears in the definition.)

It is often far from simple to verify that a given family of probability measures is relatively compact. Consequently it is desirable to have simple and useable tests for this property. We need the following definitions.

Definition 2. A family of probability measures $\mathscr{P} = \{\mathsf{P}_a; \alpha \in \mathfrak{A}\}$ is *tight* if, for every $\varepsilon > 0$, there is a compact set $K \subseteq E$ such that

$$\sup_{\alpha \in \mathfrak{A}} \mathsf{P}_a(E \setminus K) \leq \varepsilon. \tag{1}$$

Definition 3. A family of distribution functions $F = \{F_\alpha; \alpha \in \mathfrak{A}\}$ defined on $R^n, n \geq 1$, is *relatively compact* (or *tight*) if the same property is possessed by the family $\mathscr{P} = \{\mathsf{P}_\alpha; \alpha \in \mathfrak{A}\}$ of probability measures, where P_α is the measure constructed from F_α.

3. The following result is fundamental for the study of weak convergence of probability measures.

Theorem 1 (Prohorov's Theorem). *Let* $\mathscr{P} = \{\mathsf{P}_\alpha; \alpha \in \mathfrak{A}\}$ *be a family of probability measures defined on a complete separable metric space* $(E, \mathscr{E}, \rho)$. *Then* $\mathscr{P}$ *is relatively compact if and only if it is tight.*

We shall give the proof only when the space is the real line. (The proof can be carried over, almost unchanged, to arbitrary Euclidean spaces R^n, $n \geq 2$. Then the theorem can be extended successively to R^∞, to σ-compact spaces; and finally to general complete separable metric spaces, by reducing each case to the preceding one.)

Necessity. Let the family $\mathscr{P} = \{\mathsf{P}_\alpha : \alpha \in \mathfrak{A}\}$ of probability measures defined on $(R, \mathscr{B}(R))$ be relatively compact but not tight. Then there is an $\varepsilon > 0$ such that for every compact $K \subseteq R$

$$\sup_\alpha \mathsf{P}_\alpha(R \backslash K) > \varepsilon,$$

and therefore, for each interval $I = (a, b)$,

$$\sup_\alpha \mathsf{P}_\alpha(R \backslash I) > \varepsilon.$$

It follows that for every interval $I_n = (-n, n)$, $n \geq 1$, there is a measure P_{α_n} such that

$$\mathsf{P}_{\alpha_n}(R \backslash I_n) > \varepsilon.$$

Since the original family $\mathscr{P}$ is relatively compact, we can select from $\{\mathsf{P}_{\alpha_n}\}_{n \geq 1}$ a subsequence $\{\mathsf{P}_{\alpha_{n_k}}\}$ such that $\mathsf{P}_{\alpha_{n_k}} \xrightarrow{w} \mathsf{Q}$, where Q is a probability measure. Then, by the equivalence of conditions (I) and (II) in Theorem 1 of §1, we have

$$\varlimsup_{k \to \infty} \mathsf{P}_{\alpha_{n_k}}(R \backslash I_n) \leq \mathsf{Q}(R \backslash I_n) \tag{2}$$

for every $n \geq 1$. But $\mathsf{Q}(R \backslash I_n) \downarrow 0$, $n \to \infty$, and the left side of (2) exceeds $\varepsilon > 0$. This contradiction shows that relatively compact sets are tight.

To prove the sufficiency we need a general result (Helly's theorem) on the *sequential compactness* of families of generalized distribution functions (Subsection 2 of §3 of Chapter II).

Let $\mathscr{I} = \{G\}$ be the collection of generalized distribution functions $G = G(x)$ that satisfy:

(1) $G(x)$ is nondecreasing;
(2) $0 \leq G(-\infty), G(+\infty) \leq 1$;
(3) $G(x)$ is continuous on the right.

Then $\mathscr{I}$ clearly contains the class of distribution functions $\mathscr{F} = \{F\}$ for which $F(-\infty) = 0$ and $F(+\infty) = 1$.

Theorem 2 (Helly's Theorem). *The class $\mathscr{I} = \{G\}$ of generalized distribution functions is sequentially compact, i.e. for every sequence $\{G_n\}$ of functions from $\mathscr{I}$ we can find a function $G \in \mathscr{I}$ and a sequence $\{n_k\} \subseteq \{n\}$ such that*

$$G_{n_k}(x) \to G(x), \qquad k \to \infty,$$

for every point x of the set $P_C(G)$ of points of continuity of $G = G(x)$.

PROOF. Let $T = \{x_1, x_2, \ldots\}$ be a countable dense subset of R. Since the sequence of numbers $\{G_n(x_1)\}$ is *bounded*, there is a subsequence $N_1 = \{n_1^{(1)}, n_2^{(1)}, \ldots\}$ such that $G_{n_i^{(1)}}(x_1)$ approaches a limit g_1 as $i \to \infty$. Then we extract from N_1 a subsequence $N_2 = \{n_1^{(2)}, n_2^{(2)}, \ldots\}$ such that $G_{n_i^{(2)}}(x_2)$ approaches a limit g_2 as $i \to \infty$; and so on.

On the set $T \subseteq R$ we can define a function $G_T(x)$ by

$$G_T(x_i) = g_i, \qquad x_i \in T,$$

and consider the "Cantor" diagonal sequence $N = \{n_1^{(1)}, n_2^{(2)}, \ldots\}$. Then, for each $x_i \in T$, as $m \to \infty$, we have

$$G_{n_m^{(m)}}(x_i) \to G_T(x_i).$$

Finally, let us define $G = G(x)$ for all $x \in R$ by putting

$$G(x) = \inf\{G_T(y): y \in T, y > x\}. \tag{3}$$

We claim that $G = G(x)$ is the required function and $G_{n_m^{(m)}}(x) \to G(x)$ at all points x of continuity of G.

Since all the functions G_n under consideration are nondecreasing, we have $G_{n_m^{(m)}}(x) \le G_{n_m^{(m)}}(y)$ for all x and y that belong to T and satisfy the inequality $x \le y$. Hence for such x and y,

$$G_T(x) \le G_T(y).$$

It follows from this and (3) that $G = G(x)$ is nondecreasing.

Now let us show that it is continuous on the right. Let $x_k \downarrow x$ and $d = \lim_k G(x_k)$. Clearly $G(x) \le d$, and we have to show that actually $G(x) = d$. Suppose the contrary, that is, let $G(x) < d$. It follows from (3) that there is a $y \in T$, $x < y$, such that $G_T(y) < d$. But $x < x_k < y$ for sufficiently large k, and therefore $G(x_k) \le G_T(y) < d$ and $\lim G(x_k) < d$, which contradicts $d = \lim_k G(x_k)$. Thus we have constructed a function G that belongs to $\mathscr{I}$.

We now establish that $G_{n_m^{(m)}}(x^0) \to G(x^0)$ for every $x^0 \in P_C(G)$.

If $x^0 < y \in T$, then

$$\overline{\lim_m} \, G_{n_m^{(m)}}(x^0) \le \overline{\lim_m} \, G_{n_m^{(m)}}(y) = G_T(y),$$

whence

$$\overline{\lim_m} \, G_{n_m^{(m)}}(x^0) \le \inf\{G_T(y): y > x^0, y \in T\} = G(x^0). \tag{4}$$

On the other hand, let $x^1 < y < x^0$, $y \in T$. Then

$$G(x^1) \le G_T(y) = \lim_m G_{n_m^{(m)}}(y) = \underline{\lim_m} \, G_{n_m^{(m)}}(y) \le \underline{\lim_m} \, G_{n_m^{(m)}}(x^0).$$

Hence if we let $x^1 \uparrow x^0$ we find that

$$G(x^0 -) \le \underline{\lim_m} \, G_{n_m^{(m)}}(x^0). \tag{5}$$

But if $G(x^0 -) = G(x^0)$ we can infer from (4) and (5) that $G_{n_k^{(m)}}(x^0) \to G(x^0)$, $m \to \infty$.

This completes the proof of the theorem.

We can now complete the proof of Theorem 1.

Sufficiency. Let the family $\mathscr{P}$ be tight and let $\{\mathsf{P}_n\}$ be a sequence of probability measures from $\mathscr{P}$. Let $\{F_n\}$ be the corresponding sequence of distribution functions.

By Helly's theorem, there are a subsequence $\{F_{n_k}\} \subseteq \{F_n\}$ and a generalized distribution function $G \in \mathscr{I}$ such that $F_{n_k}(x) \to G(x)$ for $x \in P_C(G)$. Let us show that because $\mathscr{P}$ was assumed tight, the function $G = G(x)$ is in fact a genuine distribution function $(G(-\infty) = 0, G(+\infty) = 1)$.

Take $\varepsilon > 0$, and let $I = (a, b]$ be the interval for which

$$\sup_n \mathsf{P}_n(R \setminus I) < \varepsilon,$$

or, equivalently,

$$1 - \varepsilon \le \mathsf{P}_n(a, b], \qquad n \ge 1.$$

Choose points $a', b' \in P_C(G)$ such that $a' < a, b' > b$. Then $1 - \varepsilon \le \mathsf{P}_{n_k}(a, b] \le \mathsf{P}_{n_k}(a', b'] = F_{n_k}(b') - F_{n_k}(a') \to G(b') - G(a')$. It follows that $G(+\infty) - G(-\infty) = 1$, and since $0 \le G(-\infty) \le G(+\infty) \le 1$, we have $G(-\infty) = 0$ and $G(+\infty) = 1$.

Therefore the limit function $G = G(x)$ is a distribution function and $F_{n_k} \Rightarrow G$. Together with Theorem 2 of §1 this shows that $\mathsf{P}_{n_k} \xrightarrow{w} \mathsf{Q}$, where Q is the probability measure corresponding to the distribution function G. This completes the proof of Theorem 1.

4. PROBLEMS

1. Carry out the proofs of Theorems 1 and 2 for $R^n, n \ge 2$.

2. Let P_α be a Gaussian measure on the real line, with parameters m_α and $\sigma_\alpha^2, \alpha \in \mathfrak{A}$. Show that the family $\mathscr{P} = \{\mathsf{P}_\alpha; \alpha \in \mathfrak{A}\}$ is tight if and only if

$$|m_\alpha| \le a, \qquad \sigma_\alpha^2 \le b, \qquad \alpha \in \mathfrak{A}.$$

3. Construct examples of tight and nontight families $\mathscr{P} = \{\mathsf{P}_\alpha; \alpha \in \mathfrak{A}\}$ of probability measures defined on $(R^\infty, \mathscr{B}(R^\infty))$.

§3. Proofs of Limit Theorems by the Method of Characteristic Functions

1. The proofs of the first limit theorems of probability theory—the law of large numbers, and the De Moivre–Laplace and Poisson theorems for Bernoulli schemes—were based on direct analysis of the limit functions of the distributions F_n, which are expressed rather simply in terms of binomial probabilities. (In the Bernoulli scheme, we are adding random variables that take only two values, so that in principle we can find F_n explicitly.) However, it is practically impossible to apply a similar direct method to the study of more complicated random variables.

The first step in proving limit theorems for sums of arbitrarily distributed random variables was taken by Chebyshev. The inequality that he discovered, and which is now known as Chebyshev's inequality, not only makes it possible to give an elementary proof of James Bernoulli's law of large numbers, but also lets us establish very general conditions for this law to hold, when stated in the form

$$\mathsf{P}\left\{ \left| \frac{S_n}{n} - \frac{\mathsf{E}S_n}{n} \right| \geq \varepsilon \right\} \to 0, \qquad n \to \infty, \quad \text{every } \varepsilon > 0, \tag{1}$$

for sums $S_n = \xi_1 + \cdots + \xi_n$, $n \geq 1$, of independent random variables. (See Problem 2.)

Furthermore, Chebyshev created (and Markov perfected) the "moment method" which made it possible to show that the conclusion of the De Moivre–Laplace theorem, written in the form

$$\mathsf{P}\left\{ \frac{S_n - \mathsf{E}S_n}{\sqrt{\mathsf{V}S_n}} \leq x \right\} \to \frac{1}{\sqrt{2\pi}} \int_{-\infty}^{x} e^{-u^2/2}\, du, \tag{2}$$

is "universal," in the sense that it is valid under very general hypotheses concerning the nature of the random variables. For this reason it is known as the *central limit theorem* of probability theory.

Somewhat later Lyapunov proposed a different method for proving the central limit theorem, based on the idea (which goes back to Laplace) of the characteristic function of a probability distribution. Subsequent developments have shown that Lyapunov's method of characteristic functions is extremely effective for proving the most diverse limit theorems. Consequently it has been extensively developed and widely applied.

In essence, the method is as follows.

2. We already know (Chapter II, §12) that there is a one-to-one correspondence between distribution functions and characteristic functions. Hence we can study the properties of distribution functions by using the corresponding characteristic functions. It is a fortunate circumstance that weak convergence $F_n \overset{w}{\to} F$ of distributions is equivalent to pointwise convergence $\varphi_n \to \varphi$ of the corresponding characteristic functions. Moreover, we have the following result, which provides the basic method of proving theorems on weak convergence for distributions on the real line.

Theorem 1 (Continuity Theorem). *Let* $\{F_n\}$ *be a sequence of distribution functions* $F_n = F_n(x)$, $x \in R$, *and let* $\{\varphi_n\}$ *be the corresponding sequence of characteristic functions,*

$$\varphi_n(t) = \int_{-\infty}^{\infty} e^{itx} \, dF_n(x), \qquad t \in R.$$

(1) *If* $F_n \overset{w}{\to} F$, *where* $F = F(x)$ *is a distribution function, then* $\varphi_n(t) \to \varphi(t)$, $t \in R$, *where* $\varphi(t)$ *is the characteristic function of* $F = F(x)$.

(2) *If* $\lim_n \varphi_n(t)$ *exists for each* $t \in R$ *and* $\varphi(t) = \lim_n \varphi_n(t)$ *is continuous at* $t = 0$, *then* $\varphi(t)$ *is the characteristic function of a probability distribution* $F = F(x)$, *and*

$$F_n \overset{w}{\to} F.$$

The proof of conclusion (1) is an immediate consequence of the definition of weak convergence, applied to the functions $\operatorname{Re} e^{itx}$ and $\operatorname{Im} e^{itx}$.

The proof of (2) requires some preliminary propositions.

Lemma 1. *Let* $\{\mathsf{P}_n\}$ *be a tight family of probability measures. Suppose that every weakly convergent subsequence* $\{\mathsf{P}_{n'}\}$ *of* $\{\mathsf{P}_n\}$ *converges to the same probability measure* P. *Then the whole sequence* $\{\mathsf{P}_n\}$ *converges to* P.

PROOF. Suppose that $\mathsf{P}_n \nrightarrow \mathsf{P}$. Then there is a bounded continuous function $f = f(x)$ such that

$$\int_R f(x)\mathsf{P}_n(dx) \nrightarrow \int_R f(x)\mathsf{P}(dx).$$

It follows that there exist $\varepsilon > 0$ and an infinite sequence $\{n'\} \subseteq \{n\}$ such that

$$\left| \int_R f(x)\mathsf{P}_{n'}(dx) - \int_R f(x)\mathsf{P}(dx) \right| \geq \varepsilon > 0. \tag{3}$$

By Prohorov's theorem (§2) we can select a subsequence $\{\mathsf{P}_{n''}\}$ of $\{\mathsf{P}_{n'}\}$ such that $\mathsf{P}_{n''} \overset{w}{\to} \mathsf{Q}$, where Q is a probability measure.

By the hypotheses of the lemma, $\mathsf{Q} = \mathsf{P}$, and therefore

$$\int_R f(x)\mathsf{P}_{n''}(dx) \to \int_R f(x)\mathsf{P}(dx),$$

which leads to a contradiction with (3). This completes the proof of the lemma.

Lemma 2. *Let* $\{\mathsf{P}_n\}$ *be a tight family of probability measures on* $(R, \mathscr{B}(R))$. *A necessary and sufficient condition for the sequence* $\{\mathsf{P}_n\}$ *to converge weakly to a probability measure is that for each* $t \in R$ *the limit* $\lim_n \varphi_n(t)$ *exists, where* $\varphi_n(t)$ *is the characteristic function of* P_n:

$$\varphi_n(t) = \int_R e^{itx}\mathsf{P}_n(dx).$$

PROOF. If $\{P_n\}$ is tight, by Prohorov's theorem there are a subsequence $\{P_{n'}\}$ and a probability measure P such that $P_{n'} \xrightarrow{w} P$. Suppose that the whole sequence $\{P_n\}$ does not converge to P ($P_n \xrightarrow{w}\!\!\!\!/\ P$). Then, by Lemma 1, there are a subsequence $\{P_{n''}\}$ and a probability measure Q such that $P_{n''} \xrightarrow{w} Q$, and $P \neq Q$.

Now we use the existence of $\lim_n \varphi_n(t)$ for each $t \in R$. Then

$$\lim_{n'} \int_R e^{itx} P_{n'}(dx) = \lim_{n''} \int_R e^{itx} P_{n''}(dx)$$

and therefore

$$\int_R e^{itx} P(dx) = \int_R e^{itx} Q(dx), \qquad t \in R.$$

But the characteristic function determines the distribution uniquely (Theorem 2, §12, Chapter II). Hence P = Q, which contradicts the assumption that $P_n \xrightarrow{w}\!\!\!\!/\ P$.

The converse part of the lemma follows immediately from the definition of weak convergence.

The following lemma estimates the "tails" of a distribution function in terms of the behavior of its characteristic function in a neighborhood of zero.

Lemma 3. Let $F = F(x)$ be a distribution function on the real line and let $\varphi = \varphi(t)$ be its characteristic function. Then there is a constant $K > 0$ such that for every $a > 0$

$$\int_{|x| \geq 1/a} dF(x) \leq \frac{K}{a} \int_0^a [1 - \operatorname{Re} \varphi(t)]\, dt. \tag{4}$$

PROOF. Since $\operatorname{Re} \varphi(t) = \int_{-\infty}^{\infty} \cos tx\, dF(x)$, we find by Fubini's theorem that

$$\frac{1}{a} \int_0^a [1 - \operatorname{Re} \varphi(t)]\, dt = \frac{1}{a} \int_0^a \left[\int_{-\infty}^{\infty} (1 - \cos tx)\, dF(x)\right] dt$$

$$= \int_{-\infty}^{\infty} \left[\frac{1}{a} \int_0^a (1 - \cos tx)\, dt\right] dF(x)$$

$$= \int_{-\infty}^{\infty} \left(1 - \frac{\sin ax}{ax}\right) dF(x)$$

$$\geq \inf_{|y| \geq 1} \left(1 - \frac{\sin y}{y}\right) \cdot \int_{|ax| \geq 1} dF(x)$$

$$= \frac{1}{K} \int_{|x| \geq 1/a} dF(x),$$

where

$$\frac{1}{K} = \inf_{|y| \geq 1} \left(1 - \frac{\sin y}{y} \right) = 1 - \sin 1 \geq \tfrac{1}{7},$$

so that (4) holds with $K = 7$. This establishes the lemma.

Proof of conclusion (2) of Theorem 1. Let $\varphi_n(t) \to \varphi(t)$, $n \to \infty$, where $\varphi(t)$ is continuous at 0. Let us show that it follows that the family of probability measures $\{P_n\}$ is tight, where P_n is the measure corresponding to F_n.

By (4) and the dominated convergence theorem,

$$P_n \left\{ R \backslash \left(-\frac{1}{a}, \frac{1}{a} \right) \right\} = \int_{|x| \geq 1/a} dF_n(x) \leq \frac{K}{a} \int_0^a [1 - \mathrm{Re}\, \varphi_n(t)]\, dt$$

$$\to \frac{K}{a} \int_0^a [1 - \mathrm{Re}\, \varphi(t)]\, dt$$

as $n \to \infty$.

Since, by hypothesis, $\varphi(t)$ is continuous at 0 and $\varphi(0) = 1$, for every $\varepsilon > 0$ there is an $a > 0$ such that

$$P_n \left\{ R \backslash \left(-\frac{1}{a}, \frac{1}{a} \right) \right\} \leq \varepsilon$$

for all $n \geq 1$. Consequently $\{P_n\}$ is tight, and by Lemma 2 there is a probability measure P such that

$$P_n \overset{w}{\to} P.$$

Hence

$$\varphi_n(t) = \int_{-\infty}^\infty e^{itx} P_n(dx) \to \int_{-\infty}^\infty e^{itx} P(dx),$$

but also $\varphi_n(t) \to \varphi(t)$. Therefore $\varphi(t)$ is the characteristic function of P. This completes the proof of the theorem.

Corollary. *Let $\{F_n\}$ be a sequence of distribution functions and $\{\varphi_n\}$ the corresponding sequence of characteristic functions. Also let F be a distribution function and φ its characteristic function. Then $F_n \overset{w}{\to} F$ if and only if $\varphi_n(t) \to \varphi(t)$ for all $t \in R$.*

Remark. Let $\eta, \eta_1, \eta_2, \ldots$ be random variables and $F_{\eta_n} \overset{w}{\to} F_\eta$. In accordance with the definition of §10 of Chapter II, we then say that *the random variables $\eta_1, \eta_2, \ldots$ converge to η in distribution, and write $\eta_n \overset{d}{\to} \eta$.*

Since this notation is self-explanatory, we shall frequently use it instead of $F_{\eta_n} \overset{w}{\to} F_\eta$ when stating limit theorems.

3. In the next section, Theorem 1 will be applied to prove the central limit theorem for independent but not identically distributed random variables. In the present section we shall merely apply the method of characteristic functions to prove some simple limit theorems.

Theorem 2 (Law of Large Numbers). *Let $\xi_1, \xi_2, \ldots$ be a sequence of independent identically distributed random variables with $\mathsf{E}|\xi_1| < \infty$, $S_n = \xi_1 + \cdots + \xi_n$ and $\mathsf{E}\xi_1 = m$. Then $S_n/n \xrightarrow{P} m$, that is, for every $\varepsilon > 0$*

$$\mathsf{P}\left\{ \left| \frac{S_n}{n} - m \right| \geq \varepsilon \right\} \to 0, \qquad n \to \infty.$$

PROOF. Let $\varphi(t) = \mathsf{E}e^{it\xi_1}$ and $\varphi_{S_n/n}(t) = \mathsf{E}e^{itS_n/n}$. Since the random variables are independent, we have

$$\varphi_{S_n/n}(t) = \left[\varphi\left(\frac{t}{n} \right) \right]^n$$

by (II.12.6). But according to (II.12.14)

$$\varphi(t) = 1 + itm + o(t), \qquad t \to 0.$$

Therefore for each given $t \in R$

$$\varphi\left(\frac{t}{n} \right) = 1 + i\frac{t}{n}m + o\left(\frac{1}{n} \right), \qquad n \to \infty,$$

and therefore

$$\varphi_{S_n/n}(t) = \left[1 + i\frac{t}{n}m + o\left(\frac{1}{n} \right) \right]^n \to e^{itm}.$$

The function $\varphi(t) = e^{itm}$ is continuous at 0 and is the characteristic function of the degenerate probability distribution that is concentrated at m. Therefore

$$\frac{S_n}{n} \xrightarrow{d} m,$$

and consequently (see Problem 7, §10, Chapter II)

$$\frac{S_n}{n} \xrightarrow{P} m.$$

This completes the proof of the theorem.

Theorem 3 (Central Limit Theorem for *Independent Identically Distributed Random Variables*). *Let $\xi_1, \xi_2, \ldots$ be a sequence of independent identically distributed (nondegenerate) random variables with $E\xi_1^2 < \infty$ and $S_n = \xi_1 + \cdots + \xi_n$. Then as $n \to \infty$*

$$P\left\{\frac{S_n - ES_n}{\sqrt{VS_n}} \le x\right\} \to \Phi(x), \qquad x \in R, \tag{5}$$

where

$$\Phi(x) = \frac{1}{\sqrt{2\pi}} \int_{-\infty}^{x} e^{-u^2/2} \, du.$$

PROOF. Let $E\xi_1 = m$, $V\xi_1 = \sigma^2$ and

$$\varphi(t) = E e^{it(\xi_1 - m)}.$$

Then if we put

$$\varphi_n(t) = E \exp\left\{it \frac{S_n - ES_n}{\sqrt{VS_n}}\right\},$$

we find that

$$\varphi_n(t) = \left[\varphi\left(\frac{t}{\sigma\sqrt{n}}\right)\right]^n.$$

But by (II.12.14)

$$\varphi(t) = 1 - \frac{\sigma^2 t^2}{2} + o(t^2), \qquad t \to 0.$$

Therefore

$$\varphi_n(t) = \left[1 - \frac{\sigma^2 t^2}{2\sigma^2 n} + o\left(\frac{1}{n}\right)\right]^n \to e^{-t^2/2}.$$

as $n \to \infty$ for fixed t.

The function $e^{-t^2/2}$ is the characteristic function of a random variable (denoted by $\mathcal{N}(0, 1)$) with mean zero and unit variance. This, by Theorem 1, also establishes (5). In accordance with the remark in Theorem 1, this can also be written in the form

$$\frac{S_n - ES_n}{\sqrt{VS_n}} \xrightarrow{d} \mathcal{N}(0, 1). \tag{6}$$

This completes the proof of the theorem.

The preceding two theorems have dealt with the behavior of the probabilities of (normalized and symmetrized) sums of independent and identically distributed random variables. However, in order to state Poisson's theorem (§6, Chapter I) we have to use a more general model.

Let us suppose that for each $n \geq 1$ we are given a sequence of independent random variables $\xi_{n1}, \ldots, \xi_{nn}$. In other words, let there be given a triangular array

$$\begin{pmatrix} \xi_{11} \\ \xi_{21}, \xi_{22} \\ \xi_{31}, \xi_{32}, \xi_{33} \end{pmatrix}$$

of random variables, those in each row being independent. Put $S_n = \xi_{n1} + \cdots + \xi_{nn}$.

Theorem 4 (Poisson's Theorem). *For each $n \geq 1$ let the independent random variables $\xi_{n1}, \ldots, \xi_{nn}$ be such that*

$$\mathsf{P}(\xi_{nk} = 1) = p_{nk}, \qquad \mathsf{P}(\xi_{nk} = 0) = q_{nk},$$

$p_{nk} + q_{nk} = 1.$ *Suppose that*

$$\max_{1 \leq k \leq n} p_{nk} \to 0, \qquad n \to \infty,$$

and $\sum_{k=1}^n p_{nk} \to \lambda > 0, n \to \infty$. Then, for each $m = 0, 1, \ldots$,

$$\mathsf{P}(S_n = m) \to \frac{e^{-\lambda} \lambda^m}{m!}, \qquad n \to \infty. \tag{7}$$

PROOF. Since

$$\mathsf{E} e^{it\xi_{nk}} = p_{nk} e^{it} + q_{nk}$$

for $1 \leq k \leq n$, by our assumptions we have

$$\varphi_{S_n}(t) = \mathsf{E} e^{itS_n} = \prod_{k=1}^n (p_{nk} e^{it} + q_{nk})$$

$$= \prod_{k=1}^n (1 + p_{nk}(e^{it} - 1)) \to \exp\{\lambda(e^{it} - 1)\}, \qquad n \to \infty.$$

The function $\varphi(t) = \exp\{\lambda(e^{it} - 1)\}$ is the characteristic function of the Poisson distribution (II.12.11), so that (7) is established.

If $\pi(\lambda)$ denotes a Poisson random variable with parameter λ, then (7) can be written like (6), in the form

$$S_n \xrightarrow{d} \pi(\lambda).$$

This completes the proof of the theorem.

4. PROBLEMS

1. Prove Theorem 1 for $R^n, n \geq 2$.

2. Let $\xi_1, \xi_2, \ldots$ be a sequence of independent random variables with finite means $\mathsf{E}|\xi_n|$ and variances $\mathsf{V}\xi_n$ such that $\mathsf{V}\xi_n \leq K < \infty$, where K is a constant. Use Chebyshev's inequality to prove the law of large numbers (1).

3. Show, as a corollary to Theorem 1, that the family $\{\varphi_n\}$ is *uniformly continuous* and that $\varphi_n \to \varphi$ uniformly on every finite interval.

4. Let ξ_n, $n \geq 1$, be random variables with characteristic functions $\varphi_{\xi_n}(t)$, $n \geq 1$. Show that $\xi_n \xrightarrow{d} 0$ if and only if $\varphi_{\xi_n}(t) \to 1$, $n \to \infty$, in some neighborhood of $t = 0$.

5. Let $X_1, X_2, \ldots$ be a sequence of independent random vectors (with values in R^k) with mean zero and (finite) covariance matrix Γ. Show that

$$\frac{X_1 + \cdots + X_n}{\sqrt{n}} \xrightarrow{d} \mathscr{N}(0, \Gamma).$$

(Compare Theorem 3.)

§4. Central Limit Theorem for Sums of Independent Random Variables

1. Let us suppose that for every $n \geq 1$ we have a sequence

$$\xi_{n1}, \xi_{n2}, \ldots, \xi_{nn}$$

of independent random variables with

$$\mathsf{E}\xi_{nk} = 0, \qquad \mathsf{V}\xi_{nk} = \sigma_{nk}^2 > 0, \qquad \sum_{k=1}^{n} \sigma_{nk}^2 = 1.$$

Let $S_n = \xi_{n1} + \cdots + \xi_{nn}$, $F_{nk}(x) = \mathsf{P}(\xi_{nk} \leq x)$,

$$\Phi(x) = (2\pi)^{-1/2} \int_{-\infty}^{x} e^{-y^2/2}\, dy, \qquad \Phi_{nk}(x) = \Phi(x/\sigma_{nk}).$$

Theorem 1. *A sufficient (and necessary) condition that*

$$S_n \xrightarrow{d} \mathscr{N}(0, 1)$$

is that

(Λ) $$\sum_{k=1}^{n} \int_{|x| > \varepsilon} |x| \, |F_{nk}(x) - \Phi_{nk}(x)| \, dx \to 0, \qquad n \to \infty,$$

for every $\varepsilon > 0$.

This theorem implies, in particular, the traditional statement of the central limit theorem under the *Lindeberg condition.*

Theorem 2. *Suppose that the Lindeberg condition is satisfied, that is, that for every $\varepsilon > 0$*

(L) $$\sum_{k=1}^{n} \int_{|x| > \varepsilon} x^2 \, dF_{nk}(x) \to 0, \qquad n \to \infty;$$

then $S_n \xrightarrow{d} \mathscr{N}(0, 1)$.

Before proving these theorems (notice that Theorem 2 is an easy corollary of Theorem 1) we discuss the significance of conditions (Λ) and (L).
Since

$$\max_{1 \le k \le n} \mathsf{E}\xi_{nk}^2 \le \varepsilon^2 + \sum_{k=1}^{n} \mathsf{E}(\xi_{nk}^2 I(|\xi_{nk}| > \varepsilon)),$$

it follows from the Lindeberg condition (L) that

$$\max_{1 \le k \le n} \mathsf{E}\xi_{nk}^2 \to 0, \qquad n \to \infty. \tag{1}$$

From this it follows (by Chebyshev's inequality) that the random variables are *asymptotically infinitesimal* (negligible in the limit), that is, that, for every $\varepsilon > 0$,

$$\max_{1 \le k \le n} \mathsf{P}\{|\xi_{nk}| > \varepsilon\} \to 0, \qquad n \to \infty. \tag{2}$$

Consequently we may say that Theorem 2 provides a condition for the validity of the central limit theorem when the random variables that are summed are asymptotically infinitesimal.

Limit theorems which depend on a condition of this type are known as theorems with a classical formulation.

It is easy to give examples which satisfy neither the Lindeberg condition nor the condition of being asymptotically infinitesimal, but where the central limit theorem nevertheless holds. Here is a particularly simple example.

Let $\xi_1, \xi_2, \dots$ be a sequence of independent normally distributed random variables with $\mathsf{E}\xi_n = 0, \mathsf{V}\xi_1 = 1, \mathsf{V}\xi_k = 2^{k-2}, k \ge 2$. Put $S_n = \xi_{n1} + \cdots + \xi_{nn}$ with

$$\xi_{nk} = \xi_k \bigg/ \sqrt{\sum_{i=1}^{n} \mathsf{V}\xi_i}.$$

It is easily verified (Problem 1) that neither the Lindeberg condition nor the condition of being asymptotically infinitesimal is satisfied, although the central limit theorem is evident since S_n is normally distributed with $\mathsf{E}S_n = 0$, $\mathsf{V}S_n = 1$.

Later (Theorem 3) we shall show that the Lindeberg condition (L) implies condition (Λ). Nevertheless we may say that Theorem 1 also covers "non-classical" situations (in which no condition of being asymptotically infinitesimal is used). In this sense we say that (Λ) is an example of a *non-classical* condition for the validity of the central limit theorem.

2. PROOF OF THEOREM 1. We shall not take the time to verify the necessity of (Λ), but we prove its sufficiency.
Let

$$f_{nk}(t) = \mathsf{E}e^{it\xi_{nk}}, \qquad f_n(t) = \mathsf{E}e^{itS_n},$$

$$\varphi_{nk}(t) = \int_{-\infty}^{\infty} e^{itx} \, d\Phi_{nk}(x), \qquad \varphi(t) = \int_{-\infty}^{\infty} e^{itx} \, d\Phi(x).$$

It follows from §12, Chapter II, that

$$\varphi_{nk}(t) = e^{-(1/2)t^2\sigma_{nk}^2}, \qquad \varphi(t) = e^{-(1/2)t^2}.$$

By the corollary to Theorem 1 of §3, we have $S_n \xrightarrow{d} \mathcal{N}(0, 1)$ if and only if $f_n(t) \to \varphi(t)$, $n \to \infty$, for all real t.

We have

$$f_n(t) - \varphi(t) = \prod_{k=1}^{n} f_{nk}(t) - \prod_{k=1}^{n} \varphi_{nk}(t).$$

Since $|f_{nk}(t)| \le 1$ and $|\varphi_{nk}(t)| \le 1$, we obtain

$$|f_n(t) - \varphi(t)| = \left| \prod_{k=1}^{n} f_{nk}(t) - \prod_{k=1}^{n} \varphi_{nk}(t) \right|$$

$$\le \sum_{k=1}^{n} |f_{nk}(t) - \varphi_{nk}(t)| = \sum_{k=1}^{n} \left| \int_{-\infty}^{\infty} e^{itx} \, d(F_{nk} - \Phi_{nk}) \right|$$

$$= \sum_{k=1}^{n} \left| \int_{-\infty}^{\infty} (e^{itx} - itx + \tfrac{1}{2}t^2x^2) \, d(F_{nk} - \Phi_{nk}) \right|, \qquad (3)$$

where we have used the equations

$$\int_{-\infty}^{\infty} x^i \, dF_{nk} = \int_{-\infty}^{\infty} x^i \, d\Phi_{nk}, \qquad i = 1, 2.$$

Let us integrate by parts (Theorem 11 of Chapter II, §6, and Remark 2 following it) in the integral

$$\int_{a}^{b} (e^{itx} - itx + \tfrac{1}{2}t^2x^2) \, d(F_{nk} - \Phi_{nk}),$$

and then let $a \to -\infty$ and $b \to \infty$. Since we have

$$x^2(1 - F_{nk}(x) + F_{nk}(-x)) \to 0$$

and

$$x^2(1 - \Phi_{nk}(x) + \Phi_{nk}(-x)) \to 0, \qquad x \to \infty,$$

we obtain

$$\int_{-\infty}^{\infty} (e^{itx} - itx + \tfrac{1}{2}t^2x^2) \, d(F_{nk} - \Phi_{nk})$$

$$= it \int_{-\infty}^{\infty} (e^{itx} - 1 - itx)(F_{nk}(x) - \Phi_{nk}(x)) \, dx. \qquad (4)$$

From (3) and (4),

$$|f_n(t) - \varphi(t)| \le \sum_{k=1}^{n} \left| t \int_{-\infty}^{\infty} (e^{itx} - 1 - itx)(F_{nk}(x) - \Phi_{nk}(x))\, dx \right|$$

$$\le \tfrac{1}{2}|t|^3\varepsilon \sum_{k=1}^{n} \int_{|x|\le\varepsilon} |x||F_{nk}(x) - \Phi_{nk}(x)|\, dx$$

$$+ 2t^2 \sum_{k=1}^{n} \int_{|x|>\varepsilon} |x||F_{nk}(x) - \Phi_{nk}(x)|\, dx$$

$$\le \varepsilon|t|^3 \sum_{k=1}^{n} \sigma_{nk}^2 + 2t^2 \sum_{k=1}^{n} \int_{|x|>\varepsilon} |x||F_{nk}(x) - \Phi_{nk}(x)|\, dx, \quad (5)$$

where we have used the inequality

$$\int_{|x|\le\varepsilon} |x||F_{nk}(x) - \Phi_{nk}(x)|\, dx \le 2\sigma_{nk}^2, \tag{6}$$

which is easily deduced from (71), §6, Chapter II.

Since $\varepsilon > 0$ is arbitrary, it follows from (5) and (Λ) that $f_n(t) \to \varphi(t)$ as $n \to \infty$, for all $t \in R$.

This completes the proof of the theorem.

3. The following theorem gives the connections between (Λ) and (L).

Theorem 3.

(1) (L) $\Rightarrow$ (Λ).
(2) If $\max_{1 \le k \le n} \mathsf{E}\xi_{nk}^2 \to 0$, $n \to \infty$, then (Λ) $\Rightarrow$ (L).

PROOF. (1) We noticed above that (L) implies that $\max_{1 \le k \le n} \sigma_{nk}^2 \to 0$. Consequently, since $\sum_{k=1}^{n} \sigma_{nk}^2 = 1$, we obtain

$$\sum_{k=1}^{n} \int_{|x|>\varepsilon} x^2\, d\Phi_{nk}(x) \le \int x^2\, d\Phi(x) \to 0, \qquad n \to \infty, \tag{7}$$

where the integration on the right is over $|x| > \varepsilon/\sqrt{\max_{1 \le k \le n} \sigma_{nk}^2}$. This, together with (L), shows that

$$\sum_{k=1}^{n} \int_{|x|>\varepsilon} x^2\, d[F_{nk}(x) + \Phi_{nk}(x)] \to 0, \qquad n \to \infty, \tag{8}$$

for every $\varepsilon > 0$. Now fix $\varepsilon > 0$ and let $h = h(x)$ be a continuously differentiable even function such that $|h(x)| \le x^2$, $h'(x)\,\mathrm{sgn}\,x \ge 0$, $h(x) = x^2$ for $|x| > 2\varepsilon$, $h(x) = 0$ for $|x| \le \varepsilon$, and $|h'(x)| \le 4x$ for $\varepsilon < |x| \le 2\varepsilon$. Then, by (8),

$$\sum_{k=1}^{n} \int_{|x|>\varepsilon} h(x)\, d[F_{nk}(x) + \Phi_{nk}(x)] \to 0, \qquad n \to \infty.$$

By integration by parts we then find that, as $n \to \infty$,

$$\sum_{k=1}^{n} \int_{x \geq \varepsilon} h'(x)[(1 - F_{nk}(x)) + (1 - \Phi_{nk}(x))] \, dx$$

$$= \sum_{k=1}^{n} \int_{x \geq \varepsilon} h(x) \, d[F_{nk} + \Phi_{nk}] \to 0,$$

$$\sum_{k=1}^{n} \int_{x \leq -\varepsilon} h'(x)[F_{nk}(x) + \Phi_{nk}(x)] \, dx = \sum_{k=1}^{n} \int_{x \leq -\varepsilon} h(x) \, d[F_{nk} + \Phi_{nk}] \to 0.$$

Since $h'(x) = 2x$ for $|x| \geq 2\varepsilon$, we therefore have

$$\sum_{k=1}^{n} \int_{|x| \geq 2\varepsilon} |x| \, |F_{nk}(x) - \Phi_{nk}(x)| \, dx \to 0, \qquad n \to \infty.$$

Consequently, since $\varepsilon > 0$ is arbitrary, we obtain (L) $\Rightarrow$ (Λ).

(2) For the function $h = h(x)$ introduced above, we obtain by (7) and the condition $\max_{1 \leq k \leq n} \sigma_{nk}^2 \to 0$ that

$$\sum_{k=1}^{n} \int_{|x| > \varepsilon} h(x) \, d\Phi_{nk} \leq \sum_{k=1}^{n} \int_{|x| > \varepsilon} x^2 \, d\Phi_{nk} \to 0, \qquad n \to \infty. \qquad (9)$$

Again integrating by parts, we find that when (Λ) is satisfied,

$$\left| \sum_{k=1}^{n} \int_{|x| \geq \varepsilon} h(x) \, d[F_{nk} - \Phi_{nk}] \right| \leq \left| \sum_{k=1}^{n} \int_{x \geq \varepsilon} h(x) \, d[(1 - F_{nk}) - (1 - \Phi_{nk})] \right|$$

$$+ \left| \sum_{k=1}^{n} \int_{x \leq -\varepsilon} h(x) \, d[F_{nk} - \Phi_{nk}] \right|$$

$$\leq \sum_{k=1}^{n} \int_{x \geq \varepsilon} h'(x)[(1 - F_{nk}) - (1 - \Phi_{nk})] \, dx$$

$$+ \sum_{k=1}^{n} \int_{x \leq -\varepsilon} |h'(x)| \, |F_{nk} - \Phi_{nk}| \, dx \qquad (10)$$

$$\leq \sum_{k=1}^{n} \int_{|x| \geq \varepsilon} |h'(x)| \, |F_{nk} - \Phi_{nk}| \, dx$$

$$\leq 4 \sum_{k=1}^{n} \int_{|x| \geq \varepsilon} |x| \, |F_{nk}(x) - \Phi_{nk}(x)| \, dx \to 0.$$

It follows from (9) and (10) that

$$\sum_{k=1}^{n} \int_{|x| \geq 2\varepsilon} x^2 \, dF_{nk}(x) \leq \sum_{k=1}^{n} \int_{|x| \geq \varepsilon} h(x) \, dF_{nk}(x) \to 0, \qquad n \to \infty;$$

that is, (L) is satisfied.

4. PROOF OF THEOREM 2. According to Theorem 3, Condition (L) implies (Λ); hence Theorem 2 follows at once from Theorem 1.

5. We mention some corollaries in which $\xi_1, \xi_2, \ldots$ is a sequence of independent random variables with finite second moments. Let $m_k = \mathsf{E}\xi_k$, $\sigma_k^2 = \mathsf{V}\xi_k > 0$, $S_n = \xi_1 + \cdots + \xi_n$, $V_n^2 = \sum_{k=1}^{n} \sigma_k^2$, and let $F_k = F_k(x)$ be the distribution function of ξ_k.

Corollary 1. *Let the Lindeberg condition be satisfied: for every $\varepsilon > 0$,*

$$\frac{1}{V_n^2} \sum_{k=1}^{n} \int_{\{x:|x-m_k| \geq \varepsilon V_n\}} |x - m_k|^2 \, dF_k(x) \to 0, \qquad n \to \infty. \tag{11}$$

Then

$$\frac{S_n - \mathsf{E}S_n}{\sqrt{\mathsf{V}S_n}} \xrightarrow{d} \mathcal{N}(0, 1). \tag{12}$$

Corollary 2. *Let the Lyapunov condition be satisfied:*

$$\frac{1}{V_n^{2+\delta}} \sum_{k=1}^{n} \mathsf{E}|\xi_k - m_k|^{2+\delta} \to 0, \qquad n \to \infty. \tag{13}$$

Then the central limit theorem (12) holds.

It is enough to prove that the Lyapunov condition implies the Lindeberg condition.

Let $\varepsilon > 0$; then

$$\mathsf{E}|\xi_k - m_k|^{2+\delta} = \int_{-\infty}^{\infty} |x - m_k|^{2+\delta} \, dF_k(x)$$

$$\geq \int_{\{x:|x-m_k| \geq \varepsilon V_n\}} |x - m_k|^{2+\delta} \, dF_k(x)$$

$$\geq \varepsilon^{\delta} V_n^{\delta} \int_{\{x:|x-m_k| \geq \varepsilon V_n\}} (x - m_k)^2 \, dF_k(x)$$

and therefore

$$\frac{1}{V_n^2} \sum_{k=1}^{n} \int_{\{x:|x-m_k| \geq \varepsilon V_n\}} (x - m_k)^2 \, dF_k(x) \leq \varepsilon^{-\delta} V_n^{-2-\delta} \sum_{k=1}^{n} \mathsf{E}|\xi_k - m_k|^{2+\delta} \to 0.$$

Corollary 3. *Let $\xi_1, \xi_2, \ldots$ be independent identically distributed random variables with $m = \mathsf{E}\xi_1$ and $0 < \sigma^2 = \mathsf{V}\xi_1 < \infty$. Then*

$$\frac{1}{V_n^2} \sum_{k=1}^{n} \int_{\{x:|x-m| \geq \varepsilon V_n\}} (x - m)^2 \, dF_k(x)$$

$$= \frac{n}{n\sigma^2} \int_{\{x:|x-m| \geq \varepsilon \sigma^2 \sqrt{n}\}} (x - m)^2 \, dF_1(x) \to 0$$

since $\{x:|x - m| \geq \varepsilon \sigma^2 \sqrt{n}\} \downarrow \varnothing$, $n \to \infty$, and $\sigma^2 = \mathsf{E}|\xi_1 - m|^2 < \infty$.

Therefore the Lindeberg condition is satisfied and consequently Theorem 3 of §3 follows from Theorem 2.

Corollary 4. *Let* $\xi_1, \xi_2, \ldots$ *be independent random variables such that, for all* $n \geq 1$,

$$|\xi_n| \leq K,$$

where K *is a constant and* $V_n \to \infty$ *as* $n \to \infty$. *Then by Chebyshev's inequality*

$$\int_{\{x:|x-m_k|\geq \varepsilon V_n\}} |x - m_k|^2 \, dF_k(x) = \mathsf{E}[(\xi_k - m_k)^2 I\{|\xi_k - m_k| \geq \varepsilon V_n)]$$

$$\leq (2K)^2 \mathsf{P}\{|\xi_k - m_k| \geq \varepsilon V_n\} \leq (2k)^2 \frac{\sigma_k^2}{\varepsilon^2 V_n^2} \to 0, \qquad n \to \infty.$$

Consequently the Lindeberg condition is again applicable, and the central limit theorem holds.

6. We remarked (without proof) in Theorem 1 that condition (Λ) is also necessary. The following (Lindeberg–Feller) theorem shows that, with the supplementary condition $\max_{1 \leq k \leq n} \mathsf{E}\xi_{nk}^2 \to 0$, the Lindeberg condition (L) is also necessary.

Theorem 4. *Let* $\max_{1 \leq k \leq n} \mathsf{E}\xi_{nk}^2 \to 0$, $n \to \infty$. *Then* (L) *is necessary and sufficient for the validity of the central limit theorem:* $S_n \xrightarrow{d} \mathcal{N}(0, 1)$.

The proof is based on the following proposition, which estimates the "tails" of the variance in terms of the behavior of the characteristic function at the origin (compare Lemma 3, §3, Chapter III).

Lemma. *Let* ξ *be a random variable with distribution function* $F = F(x)$, $\mathsf{E}\xi = 0$, $\mathsf{V}\xi = \sigma^2 < \infty$. *Then for each* $a > 0$

$$\int_{|x|\geq 1/a} x^2 \, dF(x) \leq \frac{1}{a^2} [\operatorname{Re} f(\sqrt{\sigma}a) - 1 + 3\sigma^2 a^2]. \tag{14}$$

PROOF. We have

$$\operatorname{Re} f(t) - 1 + \tfrac{1}{2}\sigma^2 t^2 = \tfrac{1}{2}\sigma^2 t^2 - \int_{-\infty}^{\infty} [1 - \cos tx] \, dF(x)$$

$$= \tfrac{1}{2}\sigma^2 t^2 - \int_{|x|\leq 1/a} [1 - \cos tx] \, dF(x)$$

$$- \int_{|x|>1/a} [1 - \cos tx] \, dF(x)$$

$$\geq \tfrac{1}{2}\sigma^2 t^2 - \tfrac{1}{2}t^2 \int_{|x|\leq 1/a} x^2 \, dF(x) - 2a^2 \int_{|x|>1/a} x^2 \, dF(x)$$

$$= (\tfrac{1}{2}t^2 - 2a^2) \int_{|x|>1/a} x^2 \, dF(x).$$

Taking $t = a\sqrt{\sigma}$, we obtain (14), as required.

PROOF OF THEOREM 4. The sufficiency was established in Theorem 2. We now prove the necessity.

Let

$$f_{nk}(t) = \mathsf{E}e^{it\xi_{nk}}, \qquad \mathsf{E}\xi_{nk} = 0, \qquad \mathsf{V}\xi_{nk} = \sigma_{nk}^2 > 0,$$

$$\sum_{1}^{n} \sigma_{nk}^2 = 1; \qquad \max_{1 \le k \le n} \sigma_{nk}^2 \to 0, \qquad n \to \infty. \tag{15}$$

Since

$$\prod_{k=1}^{n} f_{nk}(t) \to e^{-(1/2)t^2}, \tag{16}$$

we can find, for a given t, a number $n_0 = n_0(t)$ such that $\prod_{k=1}^{n} f_{nk}(t) > 0$ for $n \ge n_0(t)$ and consequently

$$\ln \prod_{k=1}^{n} f_{nk}(t) = \sum_{k=1}^{n} \ln f_{nk}(t),$$

where the logarithms are well defined. Then since

$$|f_{nk}(t) - 1| \le \sigma_{nk}^2 t^2,$$

we have, by (15),

$$\left| \sum_{k=1}^{n} \{ \ln\, [1 + (f_{nk}(t) - 1)] - [f_{nk}(t) - 1] \} \right|$$

$$\le \sum_{k=1}^{n} |f_{nk}(t) - 1|^2$$

$$\le \frac{t^4}{4} \cdot \max_{1 \le k \le n} \sigma_{nk}^2 \cdot \sum_{k=1}^{n} \sigma_{nk}^2$$

$$= \frac{t^4}{4} \max_{1 \le k \le n} \sigma_{nk}^2 \to 0, \qquad n \to \infty.$$

Consequently, by using (16), we have

$$\mathrm{Re} \sum_{k=1}^{n} [f_{nk}(t) - 1] + \tfrac{1}{2}t^2 = \sum_{k=1}^{n} [\mathrm{Re}\, f_{nk}(t) - 1 + \tfrac{1}{2}t^2\sigma_{nk}^2] \to 0.$$

In particular, if we take $t = a\sqrt{\sigma}$ we find that

$$\sum_{k=1}^{n} [\mathrm{Re}\, f_{nk}(a\sqrt{\sigma}) - 1 + 3a^2\sigma_{nk}^2] \to 0, \qquad n \to \infty,$$

and therefore, by (14), and for every $\varepsilon = 1/a > 0$,

$$\sum_{k=1}^{n} \int_{|x| \ge \varepsilon} x^2 \, dF_{nk}(x) \le \varepsilon^2 \sum_{k=1}^{n} [\mathrm{Re}\, f_{nk}(a\sqrt{\sigma}) - 1 + 3a^2\sigma^2] \to \infty, \qquad n \to \infty,$$

which shows that the Lindeberg condition is satisfied.

7. The method that we used for Theorem 1 can be used to obtain a corresponding condition for the central limit theorem without assuming that the second moments are finite.

For each $n \geq 1$ let

$$\xi_{n1}, \xi_{n1}, \ldots, \xi_{nn}$$

be independent random variables with $\mathsf{E}\xi_{nk} = 0$,

$$S_n = \xi_{n1} + \cdots + \xi_{nn}, \qquad F_{nk}(x) = \mathsf{P}(\xi_{nk} \leq x).$$

Let $g = g(x)$ be a bounded nonnegative even function with the following properties: $g(x) = x^2$ for $|x| \leq 1$, $\min_{|x| \geq 1} g(x) > 0$, $|g'(x)| \leq$ const.

Define $\Delta_{nk}(g)$ by the equation

$$\int_{-\infty}^{\infty} g(x)\, dF_{nk}(x) = \int_{-\infty}^{\infty} g(x)\, d\Phi\left(\frac{x}{\sqrt{\Delta_{nk}(g)}}\right).$$

Theorem 5. *Let*

$$\sum_{k=1}^{n} \Delta_{nk}(g) \to \sigma^2$$

and for each $\varepsilon > 0$ let

$$\sum_{k=1}^{n} \int_{|x| > \varepsilon} \left| F_{nk}(x) - \Phi\left(\frac{x}{\sqrt{\Delta_{nk}(g)}}\right) \right| dx \to 0.$$

Then

$$S_n \xrightarrow{d} \mathcal{N}(0, \sigma^2).$$

The proof is left to the reader (Problem 4); it can be carried out along the same lines as the proof of Theorem 1.

8. PROBLEMS

1. Let $\xi_1, \xi_2, \ldots$ be a sequence of independent normally distributed random variables with $\mathsf{E}\xi_k = 0, k \geq 1$, and $\mathsf{V}\xi_1 = 1, \mathsf{V}\xi_k = 2^{k-2}, k \geq 2$. Show that $\{\xi_k\}$ does not satisfy the Lindeberg condition and also is not asymptotically infinitesimal.

2. Prove (4).

3. Let $\xi_1, \xi_2, \ldots$ be a sequence of independent identically distributed random variables with $\mathsf{E}\xi_1 = 0, \mathsf{E}\xi_1^2 = 1$. Show that

$$\max\left(\frac{|\xi_1|}{\sqrt{n}}, \ldots, \frac{|\xi_n|}{\sqrt{n}}\right) \xrightarrow{d} 0.$$

4. Prove Theorem 5. (Hint: use the method of the proof of Theorem 1, applying integration by parts twice in the integral $\int_a^b (e^{itn} - itx + \frac{1}{2}t^2x^2)\, d(F_{nk} - \Phi_{nk}).)$

§5. Infinitely Divisible and Stable Distributions

1. In stating Poisson's theorem in §3 we found it necessary to use a triangular array, supposing that for each $n \geq 1$ there was a sequence of independent random variables $\{\xi_{n,k}\}$, $1 \leq k \leq n$.

Put

$$T_n = \xi_{n,1} + \cdots + \xi_{n,n}, \qquad n \geq 1. \tag{1}$$

The idea of an infinitely divisible distribution arises in the following problem: how can we determine all the distributions that can be expressed as limits of sequences of distributions of random variables T_n, $n \geq 1$?

Generally speaking, the problem of limit distributions is indeterminate in such great generality. Indeed, if ξ is a random variable and $\xi_{n,1} = \xi$, $\xi_{n,k} = 0$, $1 < k \leq n$, then $T_n \equiv \xi$ and consequently the limit distribution is the distribution of ξ, which can be arbitrary.

In order to have a more meaningful problem, we shall suppose in the present section that the variables $\xi_{n,1}, \ldots, \xi_{n,n}$ are, for each $n \geq 1$, not only independent, but also identically distributed.

Recall that this was the situation in Poisson's theorem (Theorem 4 of §3). The same framework also includes the central limit theorem (Theorem 3 of §3) for sums $S_k = \xi_1 + \cdots + \xi_n$, $n \geq 1$, of independent identically distributed random variables $\xi_1, \xi_2, \ldots$. In fact, if we put

$$\xi_{n,k} = \frac{\xi_k - \mathsf{E}\xi_k}{V_n}, \qquad V_n^2 = \mathsf{V} S_n,$$

then

$$T_n = \sum_{k=1}^{n} \xi_{n,k} = \frac{S_n - \mathsf{E} S_n}{V_n}.$$

Consequently both the normal and the Poisson distributions can be presented as limits in a triangular array. If $T_n \to T$, it is intuitively clear that since T_n is a sum of independent identically distributed random variables, the limit variable T must also be a sum of independent identically distributed random variables. With this in mind, we introduce the following definition.

Definition 1. A random variable T, its distribution F_T, and its characteristic function φ_T are said to be infinitely divisible if, for each $n \geq 1$, there are independent identically distributed random variables $\eta_1, \ldots, \eta_n$ such that† $T \overset{d}{=} \eta_1 + \cdots + \eta_n$ (or, equivalently, $F_T = F_{\eta_1} * \cdots * F_{\eta_n}$, or $\varphi_T = (\varphi_{\eta_1})^n$).

Theorem 1. *A random variable T can be a limit of sums $T_n = \sum_{k=1}^{n} \xi_{n,k}$ if and only if T is infinitely divisible.*

---

† The notation $\xi \overset{d}{=} \eta$ means that the random variables ξ and η agree in distribution, i.e. $F_\xi(x) = F_\eta(x)$, $x \in R$.

PROOF. If T is infinitely divisible, for each $n \geq 1$ there are independent identically distributed random variables $\xi_{n,1}, \ldots, \xi_{n,k}$ such that $T \stackrel{d}{=} \xi_{n,1} + \cdots + \xi_{n,k}$, and this means that $T \stackrel{d}{=} T_n, n \geq 1$.

Conversely, let $T_n \stackrel{d}{\to} T$. Let us show that T is infinitely divisible, i.e. for each k there are independent identically distributed random variables $\eta_1, \ldots, \eta_k$ such that $T \stackrel{d}{=} \eta_1 + \cdots + \eta_k$.

Choose a $k \geq 1$ and represent T_{nk} in the form $\zeta_n^{(1)} + \cdots + \zeta_n^{(k)}$, where

$$\zeta_n^{(1)} = \xi_{nk,1} + \cdots + \xi_{nk,n}, \ldots, \zeta_n^{(k)} = \xi_{nk,n(k-1)+1} + \cdots + \xi_{nk,nk}.$$

Since $T_{nk} \stackrel{d}{\to} T, n \to \infty$, the sequence of distribution functions corresponding to the random variables $T_{nk}, n \geq 1$, is relatively compact and therefore, by Prohorov's theorem, is tight. Moreover,

$$[P(\zeta_n^{(1)} > z)]^k = P(\zeta_n^{(1)} > z, \ldots, \zeta_n^{(k)} > z) \leq P(T_{nk} > kz)$$

and

$$[P(\zeta_n^{(1)} < -z)]^k = P(\zeta_n^{(1)} < -z, \ldots, \zeta_n^{(k)} < -z) \leq P(T_{nk} < -kz).$$

The family of distributions for $\zeta_n^{(1)}, n \geq 1$, is tight because of the preceding two inequalities and because the family of distributions for $T_{nk}, n \geq 1$, is tight. Therefore there are a subsequence $\{n_i\} \subseteq \{n\}$ and a random variable η_1 such that $\zeta_{n_i}^{(1)} \stackrel{d}{\to} \eta_1$ as $n_i \to \infty$. Since the variables $\zeta_n^{(1)}, \ldots, \zeta_n^{(k)}$ are identically distributed, we have $\zeta_{n_i}^{(2)} \stackrel{d}{\to} \eta_2, \ldots, \zeta_{n_i}^{(k)} \stackrel{d}{\to} \eta_k$, where $\eta_1 \stackrel{d}{=} \eta_2 \stackrel{d}{=} \cdots = \eta_k$. Since $\zeta_n^{(1)}, \ldots, \zeta_n^{(k)}$ are independent, it follows from the corollary to Theorem 1 of §3 that $\eta_1, \ldots, \eta_k$ are independent and

$$T_{n_i k} = \zeta_{n_i}^{(1)} + \cdots + \zeta_{n_i}^{(k)} \stackrel{d}{\to} \eta_1 + \cdots + \eta_k.$$

But $T_{n_i k} \stackrel{d}{\to} T$; therefore (Problem 1)

$$T \stackrel{d}{=} \eta_1 + \cdots + \eta_k.$$

This completes the proof of the theorem.

Remark. The conclusion of the theorem remains valid if we replace the hypothesis that $\xi_{n,1}, \ldots, \xi_{n,n}$ are identically distributed for each $n \geq 1$ by the hypothesis that they are uniformly asymptotically infinitesimal (4.2).

2. To test whether a given random variable T is infinitely divisible, it is simplest to begin with its characteristic function $\varphi(t)$. If we can find characteristic functions $\varphi_n(t)$ such that $\varphi(t) = [\varphi_n(t)]^n$ for every $n \geq 1$, then T is infinitely divisible.

In the Gaussian case,

$$\varphi(t) = e^{itm} e^{-(1/2)t^2\sigma^2},$$

and if we put

$$\varphi_n(t) = e^{itm/n} e^{-(1/2)t^2\sigma^2/n},$$

we see at once that $\varphi(t) = [\varphi_n(t)]^n$.

In the Poisson case,

$$\varphi(t) = \exp\{\lambda(e^{it} - 1)\},$$

and if we put $\varphi_n(t) = \exp\{(\lambda/n)(e^{it} - 1)\}$ then $\varphi(t) = [\varphi_n(t)]^n$.

If a random variable T has a Γ-distribution with density

$$f(x) = \begin{cases} \dfrac{x^{\alpha-1}e^{-x/\beta}}{\Gamma(\alpha)\beta^\alpha}, & x \geq 0, \\ 0, & x < 0, \end{cases}$$

it is easy to show that its characteristic function is

$$\varphi(t) = \frac{1}{(1 - i\beta t)^\alpha}.$$

Consequently $\varphi(t) = [\varphi_n(t)]^n$ where

$$\varphi_n(t) = \frac{1}{(1 - i\beta t)^{\alpha/n}},$$

and therefore T is infinitely divisible.

We quote without proof the following result on the general form of the characteristic functions of infinitely divisible distributions.

Theorem 2 (Lévy–Khinchin Theorem). *A random variable T is infinitely divisible if and only if $\varphi(t) = \exp \psi(t)$ and*

$$\psi(t) = it\beta - \frac{t^2\sigma^2}{2} + \int_{-\infty}^{\infty} \left(e^{itx} - 1 - \frac{itx}{1+x^2}\right) \frac{1+x^2}{x^2} \, d\lambda(x), \qquad (2)$$

where $\beta \in R$, $\sigma^2 \geq 0$ and λ is a finite measure on $(R, \mathscr{B}(R))$ with $\lambda\{0\} = 0$.

3. Let $\xi_1, \xi_2, \ldots$ be a sequence of independent identically distributed random variables and $S_n = \xi_1 + \cdots + \xi_n$. Suppose that there are constants b_n and $a_n > 0$, and a random variable T, such that

$$\frac{S_n - b_n}{a_n} \xrightarrow{d} T. \qquad (3)$$

We ask for a description of the distributions (random variables T) that can be obtained as limit distributions in (3).

If the independent identically distributed random variables $\xi_1, \xi_2, \ldots$ satisfy $0 < \sigma^2 \equiv \mathsf{V}\xi_1 < \infty$, then if we put $b_n = n\mathsf{E}\xi_1$ and $a_n = \sigma\sqrt{n}$, we find by §4 that T is the normal distribution $\mathcal{N}(0, 1)$.

If $f(x) = \theta/\pi(x^2 + \theta^2)$ is the Cauchy density (with parameter $\theta > 0$) and $\xi_1, \xi_2, \ldots$ are independent random variables with density $f(x)$, the characteristic functions $\varphi_{\xi_1}(t)$ are equal to $e^{-\theta|t|}$ and therefore $\varphi_{S_n/n}(t) = (e^{-\theta|t|/n})^n = e^{-\theta|t|}$, i.e. S_n/n also has a Cauchy distribution (with the same parameter θ).

Consequently there are other limit distributions besides the normal: the Cauchy distribution, for example.

If we put $\xi_{nk} = (\xi_k/a_n) - (b_n/na_n)$, $1 \le k \le n$, we find that

$$\frac{S_n - b_n}{a_n} = \sum_{k=1}^{n} \xi_{n,k} \quad (= T_n).$$

Therefore all conceivable distributions for T that can conceivably appear as limits in (3) are necessarily (in agreement with Theorem 1) infinitely divisible. However, the specific characteristics of the variable $T_n = (S_n - b_n)/a_n$ may make it possible to obtain further information on the structure of the limit distributions that arise.

For this reason we introduce the following definition.

Definition 2. A random variable T, its distribution function $F(x)$, and its characteristic function $\varphi(t)$ are *stable* if, for every $n \ge 1$, there are constants $a_n > 0$, b_n, and independent random variables $\xi_1, \ldots, \xi_n$, distributed like T, such that

$$a_n T + b_n \overset{d}{=} \xi_1 + \cdots + \xi_n \qquad (4)$$

or, equivalently, $F[(x - b_n)/a_n] = \underbrace{F * \cdots * F(x)}_{n \text{ times}}$, or

$$[\varphi(t)]^n = [\varphi(a_n t)]e^{ib_n t}. \qquad (5)$$

Theorem 3. *A necessary and sufficient condition for the random variable T to be a limit in distribution of random variables $(S_n - b_n)/a_n$, $a_n > 0$, is that T is stable.*

PROOF. If T is stable, then by (4)

$$T \overset{d}{=} \frac{S_n - b_n}{a_n},$$

where $S_n = \xi_1 + \cdots + \xi_n$, and consequently $(S_n - b_n)/a_n \overset{d}{\to} T$.

Conversely, let $\xi_1, \xi_2, \ldots$ be a sequence of independent identically distributed random variables, $S_n = \xi_1 + \cdots + \xi_n$ and $(S_n - b_n)/a_n \to T$, $a_n > 0$. Let us show that T is a stable random variable.

If T is degenerate, it is evidently stable. Let us suppose that T is nondegenerate.

Choose $k \ge 1$ and write

$$S_n^{(1)} = \xi_1 + \cdots + \xi_n, \ldots, \quad S_n^{(k)} = \xi_{(k-1)n+1} + \cdots + \xi_{kn},$$

$$T_n^{(1)} = \frac{S_n^{(1)} - b_n}{a_n}, \ldots, T_n^{(k)} = \frac{S_n^{(k)} - b_n}{a_n}.$$

It is clear that all the variables $T_n^{(1)}, \ldots, T_n^{(k)}$ have the same distribution and

$$T_n^{(i)} \overset{d}{\to} T, \qquad n \to \infty, \quad i = 1, \ldots, k.$$

Write

$$U_n^{(k)} = T_n^{(1)} + \cdots + T_n^{(k)}.$$

Then

$$U_n^{(k)} \overset{d}{\to} T^{(1)} + \cdots + T^{(k)},$$

where $T^{(1)} \overset{d}{=} \cdots \overset{d}{=} T^{(k)} \overset{d}{=} T$.

On the other hand,

$$U_n^{(k)} = \frac{\xi_1 + \cdots + \xi_{kn} - kb_n}{a_n}$$

$$= \frac{a_{kn}}{a_n}\left(\frac{\xi_1 + \cdots + \xi_{kn} - b_{kn}}{a_{kn}}\right) + \frac{b_{kn} - kb_n}{a_n}$$

$$= \alpha_n^{(k)} V_{kn} + \beta_n^{(k)}, \tag{6}$$

where

$$\alpha_n^{(k)} = \frac{a_{kn}}{a_n}, \qquad \beta_n^{(k)} = \frac{b_{kn} - kb_n}{a_n},$$

and

$$V_{kn} = \frac{\xi_1 + \cdots + \xi_{kn} - b_{kn}}{a_{kn}}.$$

It is clear from (6) that

$$V_{kn} = \frac{U_n^{(k)} - \beta_n^{(k)}}{\alpha_n^{(k)}},$$

where $V_{kn} \overset{d}{\to} T$, $U_n^{(k)} \overset{d}{\to} T^{(1)} + \cdots + T^{(k)}$, $n \to \infty$.

It follows from the lemma established below that there are constants $\alpha^{(k)} > 0$ and $\beta^{(k)}$ such that $\alpha_n^{(k)} \to \alpha^{(k)}$ and $\beta_n^{(k)} \to \beta^{(k)}$ as $n \to \infty$. Therefore

$$T \overset{d}{=} \frac{T^{(1)} + \cdots + T^{(k)} - \beta^{(k)}}{\alpha^{(k)}},$$

which shows that T is a stable random variable.

This completes the proof of the theorem.

We now state and prove the lemma that we used above.

Lemma. *Let* $\xi_n \overset{d}{\to} \xi$ *and let there be constants* $a_n > 0$ *and* b_n *such that*

$$a_n \xi_n + b_n \overset{d}{\to} \tilde{\xi},$$

where the random variables ξ *and* $\tilde{\xi}$ *are not degenerate. Then there are constants* $a > 0$ *and* b *such that* $\lim a_n = a$, $\lim b_n = b$, *and*

$$\tilde{\xi} = a\xi + b.$$

PROOF. Let φ_n, φ and $\tilde{\varphi}$ be the characteristic functions of ξ_n, ξ and $\tilde{\xi}$, respectively. Then $\varphi_{a_n\xi_n + b_n}(t)$, the characteristic function of $a_n\xi_n + b_n$, is equal to $e^{itb_n}\varphi_n(a_nt)$ and, by Theorem 1 and Problem 3 of §3,

$$e^{itb_n}\varphi_n(a_nt) \to \tilde{\varphi}(t), \tag{7}$$

$$\varphi_n(t) \to \varphi(t) \tag{8}$$

uniformly on every finite interval of length t.

Let $\{n_i\}$ be a subsequence of $\{n\}$ such that $a_{n_i} \to a$. Let us first show that $a < \infty$. Suppose that $a = \infty$. By (7),

$$\sup_{|t|\leq c} ||\,\varphi_n(a_nt)| - |\tilde{\varphi}(t)|\,| \to 0, \qquad n \to \infty$$

for every $c > 0$. We replace t by t_0/a_{n_i}. Then, since $a_{n_i} \to \infty$, we have

$$\left|\left|\varphi_{n_i}\left(a_{n_i}\frac{t_0}{a_{n_i}}\right)\right| - \left|\tilde{\varphi}\left(\frac{t_0}{a_{n_i}}\right)\right|\right| \to 0$$

and therefore

$$|\varphi_{n_i}(t_0)| \to |\tilde{\varphi}(0)| = 1.$$

But $|\varphi_{n_i}(t_0)| \to |\varphi(t_0)|$. Therefore $|\varphi(t_0)| = 1$ for every $t_0 \in R$, and consequently, by Theorem 5, §12, Chapter II, the random variable ξ must be degenerate, which contradicts the hypotheses of the lemma.

Thus $a < \infty$. Now suppose that there are two subsequences $\{n_i\}$ and $\{n_i'\}$ such that $a_{n_i} \to a$, $a_{n_i'} \to a'$, where $a \neq a'$; suppose for definiteness that $0 \leq a' < a$. Then by (7) and (8),

$$|\varphi_{n_i}(a_{n_i}t)| \to |\varphi(at)|, \qquad |\varphi_{n_i}(a_{n_i}t)| \to |\tilde{\varphi}(t)|$$

and

$$|\varphi_{n_i'}(a_{n_i'}t)| \to |\varphi(a't)|, \qquad |\varphi_{n_i'}(a_{n_i'}t)| \to |\tilde{\varphi}(t)|.$$

Consequently

$$|\varphi(at)| = |\varphi(a't)|,$$

and therefore, for all $t \in R$,

$$|\varphi(t)| = \left|\varphi\left(\frac{a'}{a}t\right)\right| = \cdots = \left|\varphi\left(\left(\frac{a'}{a}\right)^n t\right)\right| \to 1, \qquad n \to \infty.$$

Therefore $|\varphi(t)| \equiv 1$ and, by Theorem 5 of §12, Chapter II, it follows that ξ is a degenerate random variable. This contradiction shows that $a = a'$ and therefore that there is a finite limit $\lim a_n = a$, with $a \geq 0$.

Let us now show that there is a limit $\lim b_n = b$, and that $a > 0$. Since (8) is satisfied uniformly on each finite interval, we have

$$\varphi_n(a_nt) \to \varphi(at),$$

and therefore, by (7), the limit $\lim_{n \to \infty} e^{itb_n}$ exists for all t such that $\varphi(at) \neq 0$. Let $\delta > 0$ be such that $\varphi(at) \neq 0$ for all $|t| < \delta$. For such t, $\lim e^{itb_n}$ exists. Hence we can deduce (Problem 9) that $\overline{\lim} |b_n| < \infty$.

Let there be two sequences $\{n_i\}$ and $\{n_i'\}$ such that $\lim b_{n_i} = b$ and $\lim b_{n_i'} = b'$. Then

$$e^{itb} = e^{itb'},$$

for $|t| < \delta$, and consequently $b = b'$. Thus there is a finite limit $b = \lim b_n$ and, by (7),

$$\tilde{\varphi}(t) = e^{itb} \varphi(at),$$

which means that $\tilde{\xi} \overset{d}{=} a\xi + b$. Since $\tilde{\xi}$ is not degenerate, we have $a > 0$.

This completes the proof of the lemma.

4. We quote without proof a theorem on the general form of the characteristic functions of stable distributions.

Theorem 4 (Lévy–Khinchin Representation). *A random variable T is stable if and only if its characteristic function $\varphi(t)$ has the form $\varphi(t) = \exp \psi(t)$,*

$$\psi(t) = it\beta - d|t|^\alpha \left(1 + i\theta \frac{t}{|t|} G(t, a) \right), \qquad (9)$$

where $0 < \alpha < 2, \beta \in R, d \geq 0, |\theta| \leq 1, t/|t| = 0$ for $t = 0$, and

$$G(t, \alpha) = \begin{cases} \tan \frac{1}{2}\pi\alpha & \text{if } \alpha \neq 1, \\ (2/\pi) \log |t| & \text{if } \alpha = 1. \end{cases} \qquad (10)$$

Observe that it is easy to exhibit characteristic functions of symmetric stable distributions:

$$\varphi(t) = e^{-d|t|^\alpha}, \qquad (11)$$

where $0 < \alpha \leq 2, d \geq 0$.

5. Problems

1. Show that $\xi \overset{d}{=} \eta$ if $\xi_n \overset{d}{\to} \xi$ and $\xi_n \overset{d}{\to} \eta$.

2. Show that if φ_1 and φ_2 are infinitely divisible characteristic functions, so is $\varphi_1 \cdot \varphi_2$.

3. Let φ_n be infinitely divisible characteristic functions and let $\varphi_n(t) \to \varphi(t)$ for every $t \in R$, where $\varphi(t)$ is a characteristic function. Show that $\varphi(t)$ is infinitely divisible.

4. Show that the characteristic function of an infinitely divisible distribution cannot take the value 0.

5. Give an example of a random variable that is infinitely divisible but not stable.

6. Show that a stable random variable ξ always satisfies the inequality $E|\xi|^r < \infty$ for all $r \in (0, \alpha)$.

7. Show that if ξ is a stable random variable with parameter $0 < \alpha \le 1$, then $\varphi(t)$ is not differentiable at $t = 0$.

8. Prove that $e^{-d|t|^\alpha}$ is a characteristic function provided that $d \ge 0$, $0 < \alpha \le 2$.

9. Let $(b_n)_{n \ge 1}$ be a sequence of numbers such that $\lim_n e^{itb_n}$ exists for all $|t| < \delta$, $\delta > 0$. Show that $\overline{\lim} |b_n| < \infty$.

§6. Rapidity of Convergence in the Central Limit Theorem

1. Let $\xi_{n1}, \ldots, \xi_{nn}$ be a sequence of independent random variables, $S_n = \xi_{n1} + \cdots + \xi_{nn}$, $F_n(x) = P(S_n \le x)$. If $S_n \to \mathcal{N}(0, 1)$, then $F_n(x) \to \Phi(x)$ for every $x \in R$. Since $\Phi(x)$ is continuous, the convergence here is actually uniform (Problem 5 in §1):

$$\sup_x |F_n(x) - \Phi(x)| \to 0, \qquad n \to \infty. \tag{1}$$

In particular, it follows that

$$P(S_n \le x) - \Phi\left(\frac{x - \mathsf{E}S_n}{\sqrt{\mathsf{V}S_n}}\right) \to 0, \qquad n \to \infty$$

(under the assumption that $\mathsf{E}S_n$ and $\mathsf{V}S_n$ exist and are finite).

It is natural to ask how rapid the convergence in (1) is. We shall establish a result for the case when

$$S_n = \frac{\xi_1 + \cdots + \xi_n}{\sigma \sqrt{n}}, \qquad n \ge 1,$$

where $\xi_1, \xi_2, \ldots$ is a sequence of independent identically distributed random variables with $\mathsf{E}\xi_k = 0$, $\mathsf{V}\xi_k = \sigma^2$ and $\mathsf{E}|\xi_1|^3 < \infty$.

Theorem (Berry and Esseen). *We have the bound*

$$\sup_x |F_n(x) - \Phi(x)| \le \frac{C\mathsf{E}|\xi_1|^3}{\sigma^3 \sqrt{n}}, \tag{2}$$

where C is an absolute constant $((2\pi)^{-1/2} \le C < 0.8)$.

PROOF. For simplicity, let $\sigma^2 = 1$ and $\beta_3 = \mathsf{E}|\xi_1|^3$. By Esseen's inequality (Subsection 10, §12, Chapter II)

$$\sup_x |F_n(x) - \Phi(x)| \le \frac{2}{\pi} \int_0^T \left| \frac{f_n(t) - \varphi(t)}{t} \right| dt + \frac{24}{\pi T} \frac{1}{\sqrt{2\pi}} \tag{3}$$

where $\varphi(t) = e^{-t^2/2}$ and

$$f_n(t) = [f(t/\sqrt{n})]^n,$$

with $f(t) = \mathsf{E}e^{it\xi_1}$.

In (3) we may take T *arbitrarily*. Let us choose

$$T = \sqrt{n}/(5\beta_3).$$

We are going to show that for this T,

$$|f_n(t) - \varphi(t)| \le \frac{7}{6}\frac{\beta_3}{\sqrt{n}}|t|^3 e^{-t^2/4}, \qquad |t| \le T. \tag{4}$$

The required estimate (2), with C an absolute constant, will follow immediately from (3) by means of (4). (A more detailed analysis shows that $C < 0.8$.)

We now turn to the proof of (4).

By Taylor's formula with integral remainder,

$$f(t) = 1 + \frac{t}{1!}f'(0) + \frac{t^2}{2!}f''(0) + \frac{t^3}{2}\int_0^1 (1 - v)^2 f'''(vt)\,dv. \tag{5}$$

Hence

$$f\left(\frac{t}{\sqrt{n}}\right) = 1 - \frac{t^2}{2n} + \frac{\theta\beta_3 t^3}{6n^{3/2}},$$

where $|\theta| \le 1$.

If $|t| \le \sqrt{n}/(5\beta_3)$, we have, since $\beta_3 \ge \sigma^3 = 1$.

$$\frac{t^2}{2n} + \frac{|t^3|\beta_3}{6n^{3/2}} \le \frac{1}{25}.$$

Consequently

$$f(t/\sqrt{n}) \ge \tfrac{24}{25}$$

for $|t| \le T = \sqrt{n}/(5\beta_3)$, and hence we may write

$$[f(t/\sqrt{n})]^n = e^{n\ln nf(t/\sqrt{n})}. \tag{6}$$

By (5) (with $f(t)$ replaced by $\ln f(t/\sqrt{n})$) we find that

$$\ln f(t/\sqrt{n}) = -\frac{t^2}{2n} + \frac{\theta t^3}{6n^{3/2}}(\ln f)'''(\theta_1 t/\sqrt{n}); \tag{7}$$

here $|\theta_1| \le 1$ and

$$|(\ln f)'''| = |[f'''\cdot f^2 - 3f''\cdot f'\cdot f + 2(f')^5]\cdot f^{-3}|$$
$$\le (\beta_3 + 3\beta_2\beta_1 + 2\beta_1^3)(\tfrac{24}{25})^{-3} \le 7\beta_3, \tag{8}$$

where $\beta_k = \mathsf{E}|\xi_1|^k, k = 1, 2, 3$.

Using the inequality $|e^z - 1| \leq |z|e^{|z|}$, we can now show, for $|t| \leq T = \sqrt{n}/(5\beta^3)$, that

$$|[f(t/\sqrt{n})]^n - e^{-t^2/2}| = |e^{n \ln f(t/\sqrt{n})} - e^{-t^2/2}|$$

$$\leq \frac{7}{6} \frac{\beta_3 |t|^3}{\sqrt{n}} \exp\left\{ -\frac{t^2}{2} + \frac{7}{6} |t|^3 \frac{\beta_3}{\sqrt{n}} \right\}$$

$$\leq \frac{7}{6} \frac{\beta_3 |t|^3}{\sqrt{n}} e^{-t^2/4}.$$

This completes the proof of the theorem.

Remark. We observe that unless we make some supplementary hypothesis about the behavior of the random variables that are added, (2) cannot be improved. In fact, let $\xi_1, \xi_2, \ldots$ be independent identically distributed random variables with

$$P(\xi_k = 1) = P(\xi_k = -1) = \tfrac{1}{2}.$$

It is evident by symmetry that

$$2P\left(\sum_{k=1}^{2n} \xi_k < 0 \right) + P\left(\sum_{k=1}^{2n} \xi_k = 0 \right) = 1,$$

and hence by Stirling's formula

$$\left| P\left(\sum_{k=1}^{2n} \xi_k < 0 \right) - \tfrac{1}{2} \right| = \tfrac{1}{2}P\left(\sum_{k=1}^{2n} \xi_k = 0 \right)$$

$$= \tfrac{1}{2}C_{2n}^n \cdot 2^{-2n} \sim \frac{1}{2\sqrt{\pi n}} = \frac{1}{\sqrt{(2\pi) \cdot (2n)}}.$$

It follows, in particular, that the constant C in (2) cannot be less than $(2\pi)^{-1/2}$.

2. PROBLEMS

1. Prove (8).

2. Let $\xi_1, \xi_2, \ldots$ be independent identically distributed random variables with $E\xi_k = 0$, $V\xi_k = \sigma^2$ and $E|\xi_1|^3 < \infty$.

   It is known [53] that the following *nonuniform inequality* holds: for all $x \in R$,

   $$|F_n(x) - \Phi(x)| \leq \frac{CE|\xi_1|^3}{\sigma^3\sqrt{n}} \cdot \frac{1}{(1 + |x|)^3}.$$

   Prove this, at least for Bernoulli random variables.

§7. Rapidity of Convergence in Poisson's Theorem

1. Let $\eta_1, \eta_2, \ldots, \eta_n$ be independent Bernoulli random variables, taking the values 1 and 0 with probabilities

$$\mathsf{P}(\eta_k = 1) = p_k, \qquad \mathsf{P}(\eta_k = 0) = 1 - p_k, \qquad 1 \le k \le n.$$

Write

$$S_n = \eta_1 + \cdots + \eta_n,$$

$$P_k = \mathsf{P}(S = k), \qquad \pi_k = \frac{\lambda^k e^{-\lambda}}{k!}, \qquad k = 0, 1, \ldots; \quad \lambda > 0.$$

In §6 of Chapter I we observe that when $p_1 = \cdots = p_n = p$ and $\lambda = np$ we have Prohorov's inequality,

$$\sum_{k=0}^{\infty} |P_k - \pi_k| \le C_1(\lambda)p,$$

where

$$C_1(\lambda) = 2 \min(2, \lambda).$$

When the p_k are not necessarily equal, but $\sum_{k=1}^{n} p_k = \lambda$, LeCam showed that

$$\sum_{k=0}^{\infty} |P_k - \pi_k| \le C_2(\lambda) \max_{1 \le k \le n} p_k,$$

where $C_2(\lambda) = 2 \min(9, \lambda)$.

The object of the present section is to prove the following theorem, which provides an estimate of the approximation of the P_k by the π_k, specifically not including the assumption that $\sum_{k=1}^{n} p_k = \lambda$. Although the proof does not produce very good constants (see $C(\lambda)$ below), it may be of interest because of its simplicity.

Theorem.

(1) *We have the following inequality:*

$$\sum_{k=0}^{\infty} |P_k - \pi_k| \le \left(2 + 4\sum_{k=1}^{n} p_k\right) e^{2\lambda} \min_{i} \sup_{0 \le s \le 1} \left| \sum_{k=0}^{[ns]} p_{i_k} - \lambda s \right|, \qquad (1)$$

where min *is taken over all permutations* $i = (i_1, i_2, \ldots, i_n)$ *of* $(1, 2, \ldots, n)$, $p_{i_0} = 0$, *and* $[ns]$ *is the integral part of* ns.

(2) *If* $\sum_{k=1}^{n} p_k = \lambda$, *then*

$$\sum_{k=0}^{\infty} |P_k - \pi_k| \le C(\lambda) \min_{i} \sup_{0 \le s \le 1} \left| \sum_{k=0}^{ns} p_{i_k} - \lambda s \right|$$

$$\le C(\lambda) \max_{1 \le k \le n} p_k, \qquad (2)$$

where

$$C(\lambda) = (2 + 4\lambda)e^{2\lambda}.$$

2. The key to the proof is the following lemma.

Lemma 1. *Let* $S(t) = \sum_{k=0}^{[nt]} \eta_k,$ *where* $\eta_0 = 0, 0 \leq t \leq 1,$

$$P_k(t) = \mathsf{P}(S(t) = k), \qquad \pi_k(t) = \frac{(\lambda t)^k e^{-\lambda t}}{k!}, \qquad k = 0, 1, \ldots .$$

Then for every t *in* $0 \leq t \leq 1,$

$$\sum_{k=0}^{\infty} |P_k(t) - \pi_k(t)| \leq e^{2\lambda t}\left(2 + 4\sum_{k=0}^{[nt]} p_k\right) \sup_{0 \leq s \leq t} \left| \sum_{k=0}^{[ns]} p_k - \lambda s \right|. \tag{3}$$

PROOF. Let us introduce the variables

$$X_k(t) = I(S(t) = k),$$

where $I(A)$ is the indicator of A. For each sample point, the function $S(t),$ $0 \leq t \leq 1,$ is a generalized distribution function, for which, consequently, the Lebesgue–Stieltjes integral

$$\int_0^t X_k(s-)\, dS(s)$$

is defined; it is in fact just the sum

$$\sum_{j=1}^{[nt]} X_k\left(\frac{j-1}{n}\right)\eta_j.$$

A simple argument shows that $X_k(t), k \geq 0,$ satisfy

$$X_0(t) = 1 - \int_0^t X_0(s-)\, dS(s),$$

$$X_k(t) = - \int_0^t [X_k(s-) - X_{k-1}(s-)]\, dS(s), \qquad k \geq 1, \tag{4}$$

where $X_0(0) = 1$ and $X_k(0) = 0$ for $k \geq 1.$

Now $\mathsf{E} X_k(t) = P_k(t)$ and

$$\mathsf{E} \int_0^t X_k(s-)\, dS(s) = \mathsf{E} \sum_{j=1}^{[nt]} X_k\left(\frac{j-1}{n}\right)\eta;$$

$$= \sum_{j=1}^{[nt]} \mathsf{E} X_k\left(\frac{j-1}{n}\right)\mathsf{E}\eta_j = \sum_{j=1}^{[nt]} P_k\left(\frac{j-1}{n}\right)p_j$$

$$= \int_0^t P_k(s-)\, dA(s),$$

where

$$A(t) = \sum_{k=0}^{[nt]} p_k \quad (=\mathsf{E} S(t)).$$

Hence if we average the left-hand and right-hand sides of (4) we find that

$$P_0(t) = 1 - \int_0^t P_0(s-)\, dA(s),$$

$$P_k(t) = - \int_0^t [P_k(s-) - P_{k-1}(s-)]\, dA(s), \qquad k \geq 1. \tag{5}$$

In turn, it is easily verified that $\pi_k(t)$, $k \geq 0$, $0 \leq t \leq 1$, satisfy the similar system

$$\pi_0(t) = 1 - \int_0^t \pi_0(s-)\, d(\lambda s),$$

$$\pi_k(t) = - \int_0^t [\pi_k(s-) - \pi_{k-1}(s-)]\, d(\lambda s), \qquad k \geq 1.$$

Therefore

$$\pi_0(t) - P_0(t) = - \int_0^t [\pi_0(s-) - P_0(s-)]\, d(\lambda s)$$

$$+ \int_0^t P_0(s-)\, d(A(s) - \lambda s) \tag{6}$$

and

$$\pi_k(t) - P_k(t) = - \int_0^t [\pi_k(s-) - P_k(s-)]\, d(\lambda s)$$

$$+ \int_0^t [\pi_{k-1}(s-) - P_{k-1}(s-)]\, d(\lambda s)$$

$$+ \int_0^t [P_k(s-) - P_{k-1}(s-)]\, d[A(s) - \lambda s]. \tag{7}$$

By the formula for integration by parts (namely "$dUV = U\, dV + V\, dU$"; see Theorem 11, §6, Chapter II) and by (5),

$$\int_0^t P_0(s-)\, d(A(s) - \lambda s) = (A(t) - \lambda t)P_0(t) + \int_0^t (A(s) - \lambda s)P_0(s-)\, dA(s), \tag{8}$$

$$\int_0^t [P_k(s-) - P_{k-1}(s-)]\, d(A(s) - \lambda s)$$

$$= (A(t) - \lambda t)(P_k(t) - P_{k-1}(t))$$

$$+ \int_0^t [P_k(s-) - 2P_{k-1}(s-) + P_{k-2}(s-)](A(s) - \lambda s)\, dA(s), \tag{9}$$

where it is convenient to suppose that $P_{-1}(s) \equiv 0$.

From (6)–(9) we obtain

$$\sum_{k=0}^{\infty} |\pi_k(t) - P_k(t)| \le 2 \int_0^t \sum_{k=0}^{\infty} |\pi_k(s-) - P_k(s-)| \, d(\lambda s)$$

$$+ 2|A(t) - \lambda t| + 4A(t) \max_{0 \le s \le t} |A(s) - \lambda s|$$

$$\le 2 \int_0^t \sum_{k=0}^{\infty} |\pi_k(s-) - P_k(s-)| \, d(\lambda s)$$

$$+ (2 + 4A(t)) \max_{0 \le s \le t} |A(s) - \lambda s|.$$

Hence, by Lemma 2, which will be proved in Subsection 3,

$$\sum_{k=0}^{\infty} |P_k(t) - \pi_k(t)| \le e^{2\lambda t}(2 + 4A(t)) \max_{0 \le s \le t} |A(s) - \lambda s|, \qquad (10)$$

where we recall that $A(t) = \sum_{k=0}^{[nt]} p_k$.

This completes the proof of Lemma 1.

3. Proof of the Theorem. Inequality (1) follows immediately from Lemma 1 if we observe that $P_k = P_k(1)$, $\pi_k = \pi_k(1)$, and that the probability $P_k = \mathsf{P}\{\eta_1 + \cdots + \eta_n = k\}$ is the same as $\mathsf{P}\{\eta_{i_1} + \cdots + \eta_{i_n} = k\}$, where $(i_1, i_2, \ldots, i_n)$ is an arbitrary permutation of $(1, 2, \ldots, n)$.

Moreover, the first inequality in (2) and the estimate (3) follow from (1). We have only to show that

$$\min_i \sup_{0 \le s \le 1} \left| \sum_{k=0}^{[ns]} p_{ik} - \lambda s \right| \le \max_{1 \le k \le n} p_k, \qquad (11)$$

where we may evidently suppose that $\lambda = 1$.

We write $F_i(s) = \sum_{k=0}^{ns} p_{i_k}$, $G(s) = s$, $0 \le s \le 1$. These are distribution functions: $F_i(s)$ is a discrete distribution function with masses $p_{i_1}, p_{i_2}, \ldots, p_{i_n}$ at the points $1/n, 2/n, \ldots, 1$; and $G(s)$ is a uniform distribution on $[0, 1]$. Our object is to find a permutation $i^* = (i_1^*, \ldots, i_n^*)$ such that

$$\sup_{0 \le s \le 1} |F_i^*(s) - G(s)| \le \max_{1 \le k \le n} p_k.$$

Since

$$\sup_{0 \le s \le 1} |F_i^*(s) - G(s)| = \max_{1 \le k \le n} \left| F_i\left(\frac{k}{n} -\right) - \frac{k}{n} \right|,$$

it is sufficient to study the deviations $F_{i^*}(s-) - G(s)$ only at the points $s = k/n, \; k = 1, \ldots, n$.

We observe that if all the p_k are equal $(p_1 = \cdots = p_n = 1/n)$, then

$$\sup_{0 \le s \le 1} |F_i(s) - G(s)| = \frac{1}{n} = \max_{1 \le k \le n} p_k.$$

We shall accordingly suppose that at least one of $p_1, \ldots, p_n$ is not equal to $1/n$. With this assumption, we separate the set of numbers $p_1, \ldots, p_n$ into the union of two (nonempty) sets

$$A = \{p_i : p_i > 1/n\} \quad \text{and} \quad B = \{p_i : p_i \leq 1/n\}.$$

To simplify the notation, we write $F^*(s) = F_{i_*}(s)$, $p_{i_k} = p_k^*$. It is clear that $F^*(1) = 1$, $F^*(1 - (1/n)) = 1 - p_n^*$,

$$F^*\left(1 - \frac{2}{n}\right) = 1 - (p_n^* + p_{n-1}^*), \ldots, F^*\left(\frac{1}{n}\right) = 1 - (p_n^* + \cdots + p_2^*).$$

Hence we see that the distribution $F^*(s)$, $0 \leq s \leq 1$, can be generated by successively choosing p_n^*, then p_{n-1}^*, etc.

The following picture indicates the inductive construction of p_n^*, $p_{n-1}^*, \ldots, p_1^*$:

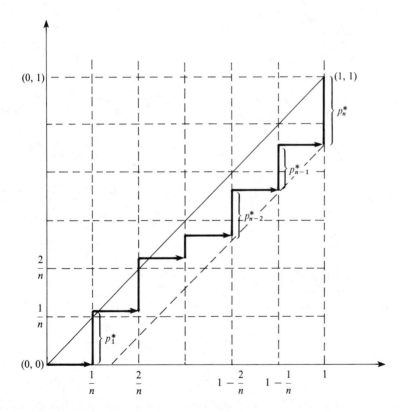

On the right-hand side of the square $[0, 1] \times [0, 1]$ we start from $(1, 1)$ and descend an amount p_n^*, where p_n^* is the largest number (or one of the largest numbers) in A, and from the point $(1, 1 - p_n^*)$ we draw a (dotted) line parallel to the diagonal of the square that extends from $(0, 0)$ to $(1, 1)$.

Now we draw a horizontal line segment of length $1/n$ from the point $(1, 1 - p_n^*)$. Its left-hand end will be at the point $(1 - (1/n), 1 - p_n^*)$, from which we descend an amount p_{n-1}^*, where p_{n-1}^* is the largest number (or one of the largest numbers) in B. Since $p_{n-1}^* \leq 1/n$, it is easily seen that this line segment does not intersect the dotted line and therefore $G(1 - (1/n)) - F^*((1 - (1/n))-) \leq p_n^*$.

From the point $(1 - (1/n), 1 - p_n^* - p_{n-1}^*)$, we again draw a horizontal line segment of length $1/n$. There are two possibilities: either the left-hand end of this interval $(1 - (2/n), 1 - p_n^* - p_{n-1}^*)$ falls below the diagonal or on it; or the point $(1 - (2/n), 1 - p_n^* - p_{n-1}^*)$ is above the diagonal. In the first case, we descend from this point by a line segment of length p_{n-2}^*, where p_{n-2}^* is the largest number (or one of the largest numbers) in the set $B \backslash \{p_{n-1}^*\}$. (This set is not empty, since $p_1^* + \cdots + p_{n-2}^* > (n-2)/n$.) Again, it is clear that $G(1 - (2/n)) - F^*((1 - (2/n))-) \leq p_n^*$. In the second case we descend by a line segment of length p_{n-2}^*, where p_{n-2}^* is the largest number (or one of the largest numbers) in the set $A \backslash \{p_n^*\}$. (This set is not empty since $p_1^* + \cdots + p_{n-2}^* > (n-2)/2$.) Since $p_{n-2}^* \leq p_n^*$, it is clear that in this case

$$\left| G\left(1 - \frac{2}{n}\right) - F^*\left(\left(1 - \frac{2}{n}\right)-\right) \right| \leq p_n^*.$$

Continuing in this way, we construct the sequence $p_{n-3}^*, \ldots, p_1^*$. It is clear from the construction that

$$\left| G\left(1 - \frac{k}{n}\right) - F^*\left(\left(1 - \frac{k}{n}\right)-\right) \right| \leq p_n^*$$

for $1 \leq k \leq n$.

Since

$$\min_i \ \sup_{0 \leq s \leq 1} \left| \sum_{k=0}^{ns} p_{i_k} - s \right| \leq \sup_{0 \leq s \leq 1} |F^*(s) - G(s)| \leq p_n^*,$$

we have also established the second inequality in (2).

Remark. Let us observe that the lower bound

$$\min_i \ \sup_{0 \leq s \leq 1} \left| \sum_{k=0}^{[ns]} p_{i_k} - s \right| \geq \tfrac{1}{2} p_n^*$$

is evident.

4. Let $A = A(t), t \geq 0$, be a nondecreasing function, continuous on the right, with limits on the left, and with $A(0) = 0$. In accordance with Theorem 12 of §6, Chapter II, the equation

$$Z_t = K + \int_0^t Z_{s-} \, dA(s) \tag{12}$$

has (in the class of locally bounded functions that are continuous on the right and have limits on the left) a unique solution, given by the formula

$$Z_t = K\mathscr{E}_t(A), \tag{13}$$

where

$$\mathscr{E}_t(A) = e^{A(t)} \prod_{0 \leq s \leq t} (1 + \Delta A(s))e^{-\Delta A(s)}. \tag{14}$$

Let us now suppose that the function $V(t)$, $t \geq 0$, which is locally bounded, continuous on the right, and with limits on the left, satisfies

$$V_t \leq K + \int_0^t V_{s-} \, dA(s), \tag{15}$$

where K is a constant, for every $t \geq 0$.

Lemma 2. *For every $t \geq 0$,*

$$V_t \leq K\mathscr{E}_t(A). \tag{16}$$

PROOF. Let $T = \inf\{t \geq 0: V_t > K\mathscr{E}_t(A)\}$, where $\inf\{\varnothing\} = \infty$. If $T = \infty$, then (16) holds. Suppose $T < \infty$; we show that this leads to a contradiction.

By the definition of T,

$$V_T \geq K\mathscr{E}_T(A).$$

From this and (12),

$$V_T \geq K\mathscr{E}_T(A) = K + K \int_0^T \mathscr{E}_{s-}(A) \, dA_s$$

$$\geq K + \int_0^T V_{s-} \, dA(s) \geq V_T. \tag{17}$$

If $V_T > K\mathscr{E}_T(A)$, inequality (17) yields $V_T > V_T$, which is impossible, since $|V_T| < \infty$.

Now let $V_T = K\mathscr{E}_T(A)$. Then, by (17),

$$V_T = K + \int_0^T V_{s-} \, dA(s).$$

From the definition of T, and the continuity on the right of V_t, $K\mathscr{E}_t(A)$ and $A(t)$, it follows that there is an $h > 0$ such that when $T < t \leq T + h$ we have

$$V_t > K\mathscr{E}_t(A) \quad \text{and} \quad A_{T+h} - A_T \leq \tfrac{1}{2}.$$

Let us write $\psi_t = V_t - K\mathscr{E}_t(A)$. Then

$$0 < \psi_t \leq \int_T^t \psi_{s-} \, dA_s, \qquad T < t \leq T + h,$$

and therefore

$$0 \leq \sup \psi_t \leq \tfrac{1}{2} \sup_{T \leq t \leq T+\delta} \psi_t.$$

Hence it follows that $\psi_t = 0$ for $T \le t \le T + h$, which contradicts the assumption that $T < \infty$.

Corollary (Gronwall–Bellman Lemma). *In* (15) *let* $A(t) = \int_0^t a(s)\,ds$ *and* $K \ge 0$. *Then*

$$V_t \le k \exp\left\{\int_0^t a(s)\,ds\right\}. \tag{18}$$

5. PROBLEMS

1. Prove formula (4).

2. Let $A = A(t)$, $B = B(t)$, $t \ge 0$, be functions of locally bounded variation, continuous on the right and with limits on the left. Let $A(0) = B(0) = 0$ and $\Delta A(t) > -1$, $t \ge 0$. Show that the equation

$$Z_t = \int_0^t Z_{s-}\,dA(s) + B(t)$$

has a unique solution $\mathscr{E}_t(A, B)$ of locally bounded variation, given by

$$\mathscr{E}_t(A, B) = \mathscr{E}_t(A)\int_0^t \mathscr{E}_s^{-1}(A)\,dB(s).$$

3. Let ξ and η be random variables taking the values $0, 1, \dots$.

Let

$$\rho(\xi, \eta) = \sup|P(\xi \in A) - P(\eta \in A)|,$$

where sup is taken over all subsets of $\{0, 1, \dots\}$.
   Prove that

(1) $\rho(\xi, \eta) = \frac{1}{2}\sum_{k=0}^{\infty}|P(\xi = k) - P(\eta = k)|$;
(2) $\rho(\xi, \eta) \le \rho(\xi, \zeta) + \rho(\zeta, \eta)$;
(3) if ζ is independent of (ξ, η), then

$$\rho(\xi + \zeta, \eta + \zeta) \le \rho(\xi, \eta);$$

(4) If the vectors $(\xi_1, \dots, \xi_n)$ and $(\eta_1, \dots, \eta_n)$ are independent, then

$$\rho\left(\sum_{i=1}^n \xi_i, \sum_{i=1}^n \eta_i\right) \le \sum_{i=1}^n \rho(\xi_i, \eta_i).$$

4. Let $\xi = \xi(p)$ be a Bernoulli random variable with $P(\xi = 1) = p$, $P(\xi = 0) = 1 - p$, $0 < p < 1$; and $\pi = \pi(p)$ a Poisson random variable with $E\pi = p$. Show that

$$\rho(\xi(p), \pi(p)) = p(1 - e^{-p}) \le p^2.$$

5. Let $\xi = \xi(p)$ be a Bernoulli random variable with $P(\xi = 1) = p$, $P(\xi = 0) = 1 - p$, $0 < p < 1$, and let $\pi = \pi(\lambda)$ be a Poisson random variable such that $P(\xi = 0) = P(\pi = 0)$. Show that $\lambda = -\ln(1 - p)$ and

$$\rho(\xi(p), \pi(\lambda)) = 1 - e^{-\lambda} - \lambda e^{-\lambda} \le \tfrac{1}{2}\lambda^2.$$

6. Show, using Property (4) of Problem 3, and the conclusions of Problems 4 and 5, that if $\xi_1 = \xi_1(p_1), \ldots, \xi_n = \xi_n(p_n)$ are independent Bernoulli random variables, $0 < p_i < 1$, and $\lambda_i = -\ln(1 - p_i)$, $1 \le i \le n$, then

$$\rho\left(\sum_{i=1}^n \xi_i(p_i), \pi\left(\sum_{i=1}^n p_i\right)\right) \le \sum_{i=1}^n p_i^2$$

and

$$\rho\left(\sum_{i=1}^n \xi_i(p_i), \pi\left(\sum_{i=1}^n \lambda_i\right)\right) \le \tfrac{1}{2}\sum_{i=1}^n \lambda_i^2.$$

CHAPTER IV
Sequences and Sums of Independent Random Variables

§1. Zero-or-One Laws

1. The series $\sum_{n=1}^{\infty} (1/n)$ diverges and the series $\sum_{n=1}^{\infty} (-1)^n(1/n)$ converges. We ask the following question. What can we say about the convergence or divergence of a series $\sum_{n=1}^{\infty} (\xi_n/n)$, where $\xi_1, \xi_2, \ldots$ is a sequence of independent identically distributed Bernoulli random variables with $P(\xi_1 = +1) = P(\xi_1 = -1) = \frac{1}{2}$? In other words, what can be said about the convergence of a series whose general term is $\pm 1/n$, where the signs are chosen in a random manner, according to the sequence $\xi_1, \xi_2, \ldots$?

Let

$$A_1 = \left\{ \omega : \sum_{n=1}^{\infty} \frac{\xi_n}{n} \text{ converges} \right\}$$

be the set of sample points for which $\sum_{n=1}^{\infty} (\xi_n/n)$ converges (to a finite number) and consider the probability $P(A_1)$ of this set. It is far from clear, to begin with, what values this probability might have. However, it is a remarkable fact that we are able to say that the probability can have only two values, 0 or 1. This is a corollary of Kolmogorov's "zero-one law," whose statement and proof form the main content of the present section.

2. Let $(\Omega, \mathscr{F}, P)$ be a probability space, and let $\xi_1, \xi_2, \ldots$ be a sequence of random variables. Let $\mathscr{F}_n^{\infty} = \sigma(\xi_n, \xi_{n+1}, \ldots)$ be the σ-algebra generated by $\xi_n, \xi_{n+1}, \ldots$, and write

$$\mathscr{X} = \bigcap_{n=1}^{\infty} \mathscr{F}_n^{\infty}.$$

Since an intersection of σ-algebras is again a σ-algebra, $\mathscr{X}$ is a σ-algebra. It is called a *tail algebra* (or terminal or asymptotic algebra), because every event $A \in \mathscr{X}$ is independent of the values of $\xi_1, \ldots, \xi_n$ for every finite number n, and is determined, so to speak, only by the behavior of the infinitely remote values of $\xi_1, \xi_2, \ldots$.

Since, for every $k \geq 1$,

$$A_1 \equiv \left\{ \sum_{n=1}^{\infty} \frac{\xi_n}{n} \text{ converges} \right\} = \left\{ \sum_{n=k}^{\infty} \frac{\xi_n}{n} \text{ converges} \right\} \in \mathscr{F}_k^{\infty},$$

we have $A_1 \in \bigcap_k \mathscr{F}_k^{\infty} \equiv \mathscr{X}$. In the same way, if $\xi_1, \xi_2, \ldots$ is any sequence,

$$A_2 = \left\{ \sum_n \xi_n \text{ converges} \right\} \in \mathscr{X}.$$

The following events are also tail events:

$$A_3 = \{\xi_n \in I_n \text{ for infinitely many } n\},$$

where $I_n \in \mathscr{B}(R)$, $n \geq 1$;

$$A_4 = \left\{ \overline{\lim_n} \, \xi_n < \infty \right\};$$

$$A_5 = \left\{ \overline{\lim_n} \, \frac{\xi_1 + \cdots + \xi_n}{n} < \infty \right\};$$

$$A_6 = \left\{ \overline{\lim_n} \, \frac{\xi_1 + \cdots + \xi_n}{n} < c \right\};$$

$$A_7 = \left\{ \frac{S_n}{n} \text{ converges} \right\};$$

$$A_8 = \left\{ \overline{\lim_n} \, \frac{S_n}{\sqrt{2n \log n}} = 1 \right\}.$$

On the other hand,

$$B_1 = \{\xi_n = 0 \text{ for all } n \geq 1\},$$

$$B_2 = \left\{ \lim_n(\xi_1 + \cdots + \xi_n) \text{ exists and is less than } c \right\}$$

are examples of events that do not belong to $\mathscr{X}$.

Let us now suppose that our random variables are *independent*. Then by the Borel–Cantelli lemma it follows that

$$P(A_3) = 0 \Leftrightarrow \sum P(\xi_n \in I_n) < \infty,$$

$$P(A_3) = 1 \Leftrightarrow \sum P(\xi_n \in I_n) = \infty.$$

Therefore the probability of A_3 can take only the values 0 or 1 according to the convergence or divergence of $\sum P(\xi_n \in I_n)$. This is Borel's zero-one law.

Theorem 1 (Kolmogorov's Zero-One Law). *Let* $\xi_1, \xi_2, \ldots$ *be a sequence of independent random variables and let* $A \in \mathscr{X}$. *The* $\mathsf{P}(A)$ *can only have one of the values zero or one.*

PROOF. The idea of the proof is to show that every tail event A is independent of itself and therefore $\mathsf{P}(A \cap A) = \mathsf{P}(A) \cdot \mathsf{P}(A)$, i.e. $\mathsf{P}(A) = \mathsf{P}^2(A)$, so that $\mathsf{P}(A) = 0$ or 1.

If $A \in \mathscr{X}$ then $A \in \mathscr{F}_1^\infty = \sigma\{\xi_1, \xi_2, \ldots\} = \sigma(\bigcup_n \mathscr{F}_1^n)$, where $\mathscr{F}_1^n = \sigma\{\xi_1, \ldots, \xi_n\}$, and we can find (Problem 8, §3, Chapter II) sets $A_n \in \mathscr{F}_1^n$, $m \geq 1$, such that $\mathsf{P}(A \triangle A_n) \to 0$, $n \to \infty$. Hence

$$\mathsf{P}(A_n) \to \mathsf{P}(A), \quad \mathsf{P}(A_n \cap A) \to \mathsf{P}(A). \tag{1}$$

But if $A \in \mathscr{X}$, the events A_n and A are independent for every $n \geq 1$. Hence it follows from (1) that $\mathsf{P}(A) = \mathsf{P}^2(A)$ and therefore $\mathsf{P}(A) = 0$ or 1.

This completes the proof of the theorem.

Corollary. *Let* η *be a random variable that is measurable with respect to the tail* σ-*algebra* $\mathscr{X}$, *i.e.* $\{\eta \in B\} \in \mathscr{X}$, $B \in \mathscr{B}(R)$. *Then* η *is degenerate, i.e. there is a constant* c *such that* $\mathsf{P}(\eta = c) = 1$.

3. Theorem 2 below provides an example of a nontrivial application of Kolmogorov's zero-one law.

Let $\xi_1, \xi_2, \ldots$ be a sequence of independent Bernoulli random variables with $\mathsf{P}(\xi_n = 1) = p$, $\mathsf{P}(\xi_n = -1) = q$, $p + q = 1$, $n \geq 1$, and let $S_n = \xi_1 + \cdots + \xi_n$. It seems intuitively clear that in the symmetric case ($p = \frac{1}{2}$) a "typical" path of the random walk $S_n, n \geq 1$, will cross zero infinitely often, whereas when $p \neq \frac{1}{2}$ it will go off to infinity. Let us give a precise formulation.

Theorem 2. (a) *If* $p = \frac{1}{2}$ *then* $\mathsf{P}(S_n = 0 \text{ i.o.}) = 1$.
(b) *If* $p \neq \frac{1}{2}$, *then* $\mathsf{P}(S_n = 0 \text{ i.o.}) = 0$.

PROOF. We first observe that the event $B = (S_n = 0 \text{ i.o.})$ is not a tail event, i.e. $B \notin \mathscr{X} = \bigcap \mathscr{F}_n^\infty$, $\mathscr{F}_n^\infty = \sigma\{\xi_n, \xi_{n+1}, \ldots\}$. Consequently it is, in principle, not clear that B should have only the values 0 or 1.

Statement (b) is easily proved by applying (the first part of) the Borel–Cantelli lemma. In fact, if $B_{2n} = \{S_{2n} = 0\}$, then by Stirling's formula

$$\mathsf{P}(B_{2n}) = C_{2n}^n p^n q^n \sim \frac{(4pq)^n}{\sqrt{\pi n}}$$

and therefore $\sum \mathsf{P}(B_{2n}) < \infty$. Consequently $\mathsf{P}(S_n = 0 \text{ i.o.}) = 0$.

To prove (a), it is enough to prove that the event

$$A = \left\{ \overline{\lim} \, \frac{S_n}{\sqrt{n}} = \infty, \, \underline{\lim} \, \frac{S_n}{\sqrt{n}} = -\infty \right\}$$

has probability 1 (since $A \subseteq B$).

Let

$$A_c = \left\{ \overline{\lim} \frac{S_n}{\sqrt{n}} > c \right\} \cap \left\{ \underline{\lim} \frac{S_n}{\sqrt{n}} < -c \right\} (= A_c' \cap A_c'').$$

Then $A_c \downarrow A, c \to \infty$, and all the events A, A_c, A_c', A_c'' are tail events. Let us show that $P(A_c') = P(A_c'') = 1$ for each $c > 0$. Since $A_c' \in \mathscr{X}$ and $A_c'' \in \mathscr{X}$, it is sufficient to show only that $P(A_c') > 0$, $P(A_c'') > 0$. But by Problem 5

$$P\left(\underline{\lim} \frac{S_n}{\sqrt{n}} < -c \right) = P\left(\overline{\lim} \frac{S_n}{\sqrt{n}} > c \right) \geq \overline{\lim} P\left(\frac{S_n}{\sqrt{n}} > c \right) > 0,$$

where the last inequality follows from the De Moivre–Laplace theorem.

Thus $P(A_c) = 1$ for all $c > 0$ and therefore $P(A) = \lim_{c \to \infty} P(A_c) = 1$.

This completes the proof of the theorem.

4. Let us observe again that $B = \{S_n = 0 \text{ i.o.}\}$ is not a tail event. Nevertheless, it follows from Theorem 2 that, for a Bernoulli scheme, the probability of this event, just as for tail events, takes only the values 0 and 1. This phenomenon is not accidental: it is a corollary of the Hewitt–Savage zero-one law, which for independent identically distributed random variables extends the result of Theorem 1 to the class of "symmetric" events (which includes the class of tail events).

Let us give the essential definitions. A one-to-one mapping $\pi = (\pi_1, \pi_2, \dots)$ of the set $(1, 2, \dots)$ on itself is said to be a finite permutation if $\pi_n = n$ for every n with a finite number of exceptions.

If $\xi = \xi_1, \xi_2, \dots$ is a sequence of random variables, $\pi(\xi)$ denotes the sequence $(\xi_{\pi_1}, \xi_{\pi_2}, \dots)$. If A is the event $\{\xi \in B\}$, $B \in \mathscr{B}(R^\infty)$, then $\pi(A)$ denotes the event $\{\pi(\xi) \in B\}$, $B \in \mathscr{B}(R^\infty)$.

We call an event $A = \{\xi \in B\}$, $B \in \mathscr{B}(R^\infty)$, *symmetric* if $\pi(A)$ coincides with A for every finite permutation π.

An example of a symmetric event is $A = \{S_n = 0 \text{ i.o.}\}$, where $S_n = \xi_1 + \dots + \xi_n$. Moreover, we may suppose (Problem 4) that every event in the tail σ-algebra $\mathscr{X}(S) = \bigcap \mathscr{F}_n^\infty(S) = \sigma\{\omega : S_n, S_{n+1}, \dots\}$ generated by $S_1 = \xi_1, S_2 = \xi_1 + \xi_2, \dots$ is symmetric.

Theorem 3 (Hewitt–Savage Zero-One Law). *Let $\xi_1, \xi_2, \dots$ be a sequence of independent identically distributed random variables, and*

$$A = \{\omega : (\xi_1, \xi_2, \dots) \in B\}$$

a symmetric event. Then $P(A) = 0$ or 1.

PROOF. Let $A = \{\xi \in B\}$ be a symmetric event. Choose sets $B_n \in \mathscr{B}(R^n)$ such that, for $A_n = \{\omega : (\xi_1, \dots, \xi_n) \in B_n\}$,

$$P(A \bigtriangleup A_n) \to 0, \qquad n \to \infty. \tag{2}$$

Since the random variables $\xi_1, \xi_2, \ldots$ are independent and identically distributed, the probability distributions $P_\xi(B) = P(\xi \in B)$ and $P_{\pi_n(\xi)}(B) = P(\pi_n(\zeta) \in B)$ coincide. Therefore

$$P(A \triangle A_n) = P_\xi(B \triangle B_n) = P_{\pi_n(\xi)}(B \triangle B_n). \tag{3}$$

Since A is symmetric, we have

$$A \equiv \{\xi \in B\} = \pi_n(A) \equiv \{\pi_n(\xi) \in B\}.$$

Therefore

$$P_{\pi_n(\xi)}(B \triangle B_n) = P\{\pi_n(\xi) \in B) \triangle (\pi_n(\xi) \in B_n)\}$$
$$= P\{(\xi \in B) \triangle (\pi_n(\xi) \in B_n)\} = P\{A \triangle \pi_n(A_n)\}. \tag{4}$$

Hence, by (3) and (4),

$$P(A \triangle A_n) = P(A \triangle \pi_n(A_n)). \tag{5}$$

It then follows from (2) that

$$P(A \triangle (A_n \cap \pi_n(A_n))) \to 0, \qquad n \to \infty. \tag{6}$$

Hence, by (2), (5) and (6), we obtain

$$P(A_n) \to P(A), \qquad P(\pi_n(A)) \to P(A),$$
$$P(A_n \cap \pi_n(A_n)) \to P(A). \tag{7}$$

Moreover, since ξ_1 and ξ_2 are independent,

$$P(A_n \cap \pi_n(A_n)) = P\{(\xi_1, \ldots, \xi_n) \in B_n, (\xi_{n+1}, \ldots, \xi_{2n}) \in B_n\}$$
$$= P\{(\xi_1, \ldots, \xi_n) \in B_n\} \cdot P\{(\xi_{n+1}, \ldots, \xi_{2n}) \in B_n\}$$
$$= P(A_n)P(\pi_n(A_n)),$$

whence by (7)

$$P(A) = P^2(A)$$

and therefore $P(A) = 0$ or 1.

This completes the proof of the theorem.

5. PROBLEMS

1. Prove the corollary to Theorem 1.

2. Show that if (ξ_n) is a sequence of independent random variables, the random variables $\overline{\lim}\, \xi_n$ and $\underline{\lim}\, \xi_n$ are degenerate.

3. Let (ξ_n) be a sequence of independent random variables, $S_n = \xi_1 + \cdots + \xi_n$, and let the constants b_n satisfy $0 < b_n \uparrow \infty$. Show that the random variables $\overline{\lim}(S_n/b_n)$ and $\underline{\lim}(S_n/b_n)$ are degenerate.

4. Let $S_n = \xi_1 + \cdots + \xi_n$, $n \geq 1$, and $\mathcal{X}(S) = \bigcap \mathcal{F}_n^\infty(S)$, $\mathcal{F}_n^\infty(S) = \sigma\{\omega: S_n, S_{n+1}, \ldots\}$. Show that every event in $\mathcal{X}(S)$ is symmetric.

5. Let (ξ_n) be a sequence of random variables. Show that $\{\overline{\lim}\, \xi_n > c\} \supseteq \overline{\lim}\{\xi_n > c\}$ for each $c > 0$.

§2. Convergence of Series

1. Let us suppose that $\xi_1, \xi_2, \ldots$ is a sequence of independent random variables, $S_n = \xi_1 + \cdots + \xi_n$, and let A be the set of sample points ω for which $\sum \xi_n(\omega)$ converges to a finite limit. It follows from Kolmogorov's zero-one law that $P(A) = 0$ or 1, i.e. the series $\sum \xi_n$ converges or diverges with probability 1. The object of the present section is to give criteria that will determine whether a sum of independent random variables converges or diverges.

Theorem 1 (Kolmogorov and Khinchin).
(a) *Let* $E\xi_n = 0, n \geq 1$. *Then if*

$$\sum E\xi_n^2 < \infty, \tag{1}$$

the series $\sum \xi_n$ *converges with probability* 1.
(b) *If the random variables* $\xi_n, n \geq 1$, *are uniformly bounded* (i.e., $P(|\xi_n| \leq c)$ $= 1, c < \infty$), *the converse is true: the convergence of* $\sum \xi_n$ *with probability* 1 *implies* (1).

The proof depends on

Kolmogorov's Inequality

(a) *Let* $\xi_1, \xi_2, \ldots, \xi_n$ *be independent random variables with* $E\xi_i = 0, E\xi_i^2 < \infty$, $i \leq n$. *Then for every* $\varepsilon > 0$

$$P\left\{ \max_{1 \leq k \leq n} |S_k| \geq \varepsilon \right\} \leq \frac{ES_n^2}{\varepsilon^2}. \tag{2}$$

(b) *If also* $P(|\xi_i| \leq c) = 1, i \leq n$, *then*

$$P\left\{ \max_{1 \leq k \leq n} |S_k| \geq \varepsilon \right\} \geq 1 - \frac{(c + \varepsilon)^2}{ES_n^2}. \tag{3}$$

PROOF. (a) Put

$$A = \{\max |S_k| \geq \varepsilon\},$$

$$A_k = \{|S_i| < \varepsilon, i = 1, \ldots, k - 1, |S_k| \geq \varepsilon\}, \qquad 1 \leq k \leq n.$$

Then $A = \sum A_k$ and

$$ES_n^2 \geq ES_n^2 I_A = \sum ES_n^2 I_{A_k}.$$

But

$$ES_n^2 I_{A_k} = E(S_k + (\xi_{k+1} + \cdots + \xi_n))^2 I_{A_k}$$
$$= ES_k^2 I_{A_k} + 2 E S_k(\xi_{k+1} + \cdots + \xi_n) I_{A_k} + E(\xi_{k+1} + \cdots + \xi_n)^2 I_{A_k}$$
$$\geq ES_k^2 I_{A_k},$$

since

$$ES_k(\xi_{k+1} + \cdots + \xi_n) I_{A_k} = ES_k I_{A_k} \cdot E(\xi_{k+1} + \cdots + \xi_n) = 0$$

because of independence and the conditions $E\xi_i = 0, i \leq n$. Hence

$$ES_n^2 \geq \sum ES_k^2 I_{A_k} \geq \varepsilon^2 \sum P(A_k) = \varepsilon^2 P(A),$$

which proves the first inequality.

(b) To prove (3), we observe that

$$ES_n^2 I_A = ES_n^2 - ES_n^2 I_{\bar{A}} \geq ES_n^2 - \varepsilon^2 P(\bar{A}) = ES_n^2 - \varepsilon^2 + \varepsilon^2 P(A). \qquad (4)$$

On the other hand, on the set A_k

$$|S_{k-1}| \leq \varepsilon, \qquad |S_k| \leq |S_{k-1}| + |\xi_k| \leq \varepsilon + c$$

and therefore

$$ES_n^2 I_A = \sum_k ES_k^2 I_{A_k} + \sum_k E(I_{A_k}(S_n - S_k)^2)$$

$$\leq (\varepsilon + c)^2 \sum_k P(A_k) + \sum_{k=1}^n P(A_k) \sum_{j=k+1}^n E\xi_j^2$$

$$\leq P(A)\left[(\varepsilon + c)^2 + \sum_{j=1}^n E\xi_j^2\right] = P(A)[(\varepsilon + c)^2 + ES_n^2]. \qquad (5)$$

From (4) and (5) we obtain

$$P(A) \geq \frac{ES_n^2 - \varepsilon^2}{(\varepsilon + c)^2 + ES_n^2 - \varepsilon^2} = 1 - \frac{(\varepsilon + c)^2}{(\varepsilon + c)^2 + ES_n^2 - \varepsilon^2} \geq 1 - \frac{(\varepsilon + c)^2}{ES_n^2}.$$

This completes the proof of (3).

PROOF OF THEOREM 1. (a) By Theorem 4 of §10, Chapter II, the sequence $(S_n), n \geq 1$, converges with probability 1, if and only if it is fundamental with probability 1. By Theorem 1 of §10, Chapter II, the sequence $(S_n), n \geq 1$, is fundamental (P-a.s.) if and only if

$$P\left\{\sup_{k \geq 1} |S_{n+k} - S_n| \geq \varepsilon\right\} \to 0, \qquad n \to \infty. \qquad (6)$$

By (2),

$$P\left\{\sup_{k \geq 1} |S_{n+k} - S_n| \geq \varepsilon\right\} = \lim_{N \to \infty} P\left\{\max_{1 \leq k \leq N} |S_{n+k} - S_n| \geq \varepsilon\right\}$$

$$\leq \lim_{N \to \infty} \frac{\sum_{k=n}^{n+N} E\xi_k^2}{\varepsilon^2} = \frac{\sum_{k=n}^{\infty} E\xi_k^2}{\varepsilon^2}.$$

Therefore (6) is satisfied if $\sum_{k=1}^{\infty} E\xi_k^2 < \infty$, and consequently $\sum \xi_k$ converges with probability 1.

(b) Let $\sum \xi_k$ converge. Then, by (6), for sufficiently large n,

$$P\left\{\sup_{k \geq 1} |S_{n+k} - S_n| \geq \varepsilon\right\} < \tfrac{1}{2}. \tag{7}$$

By (3),

$$P\left\{\sup_{k \geq 1} |S_{n+k} - S_n| \geq \varepsilon\right\} \geq 1 - \frac{(c + \varepsilon)^2}{\sum_{k=n}^{\infty} \mathsf{E}\xi_k^2}.$$

Therefore if we suppose that $\sum_{k=1}^{\infty} \mathsf{E}\xi_k^2 = \infty$, we obtain

$$P\left\{\sup_{k \geq 1} |S_{n+k} - S_n| \geq \varepsilon\right\} = 1,$$

which contradicts (7).

This completes the proof of the theorem.

EXAMPLE. If $\xi_1, \xi_2, \ldots$ is a sequence of independent Bernoulli random variables with $P(\xi_n = +1) = P(\xi_n = -1) = \tfrac{1}{2}$, then the series $\sum \xi_n a_n$, with $|a_n| \leq c$, converges with probability 1, if and only if $\sum a_n^2 < \infty$.

2. Theorem 2 (Two-Series Theorem). *A sufficient condition for the convergence of the series $\sum \xi_n$ of independent random variables, with probability 1, is that both series $\sum \mathsf{E}\xi_n$ and $\sum \mathsf{V}\xi_n$ converge. If $P(|\xi_n| \leq c) = 1$, the condition is also necessary.*

PROOF. If $\sum \mathsf{V}\xi_n < \infty$, then by Theorem 1 the series $\sum (\xi_n - \mathsf{E}\xi_n)$ converges (P-a.s.). But by hypothesis the series $\sum \mathsf{E}\xi_n$ converges; hence $\sum \xi_n$ converges (P-a.s.)

To prove the necessity we use the following symmetrization method. In addition to the sequence $\xi_1, \xi_2, \ldots$ we consider a different sequence $\tilde{\xi}_1, \tilde{\xi}_2, \ldots$ of independent random variables such that $\tilde{\xi}_n$ has the same distribution as ξ_n, $n \geq 1$. (When the original sample space is sufficiently rich, the existence of such a sequence follows from Theorem 1 of §9, Chapter II. We can also show that this assumption involves no loss of generality.)

Then if $\sum \xi_n$ converges (P-a.s.), the series $\sum \tilde{\xi}_n$ also converges, and hence so does $\sum (\xi_n - \tilde{\xi}_n)$. But $\mathsf{E}(\xi_n - \tilde{\xi}_n) = 0$ and $P(|\xi_n - \tilde{\xi}_n| \leq 2c) = 1$. Therefore $\sum \mathsf{V}(\xi_n - \tilde{\xi}_n) < \infty$ by Theorem 1. In addition,

$$\sum \mathsf{V}\xi_n = \tfrac{1}{2} \sum \mathsf{V}(\xi_n - \tilde{\xi}_n) < \infty.$$

Consequently, by Theorem 1, $\sum (\xi_n - \mathsf{E}\xi_n)$ converges with probability 1, and therefore $\sum \mathsf{E}\xi_n$ converges.

Thus if $\sum \xi_n$ converges (P-a.s.) (and $P(|\xi_n| \leq c) = 1, n \geq 1$) it follows that both $\sum \mathsf{E}\xi_n$ and $\sum \mathsf{V}\xi_n$ converge.

This completes the proof of the theorem.

3. The following theorem provides a necessary and sufficient condition for the convergence of $\sum \xi_n$ without any boundedness condition on the random variables.

Let c be a constant and

$$\xi^c = \begin{cases} \xi, & |\xi| \le c, \\ 0, & |\xi| > c. \end{cases}$$

Theorem 3 (Kolmogorov's Three-Series Theorem). *Let $\xi_1, \xi_2, \ldots$ be a sequence of independent random variables. A necessary condition for the convergence of $\sum \xi_n$ with probability 1 is that the series*

$$\sum \mathsf{E}\xi_n^c, \qquad \sum \mathsf{V}\xi_n^c, \qquad \sum \mathsf{P}(|\xi_n| \ge c)$$

converge for every $c > 0$; a sufficient condition is that these series converge for some $c > 0$.

PROOF. *Sufficiency.* By the two-series theorem, $\sum \xi_n^c$ converges with probability 1. But if $\sum \mathsf{P}(|\xi_n| \ge c) < \infty$, then by the Borel–Cantelli lemma we have $\sum I(|\xi_n| \ge c) < \infty$ with probability 1. Therefore $\xi_n = \xi_n^c$ for all n with at most finitely many exceptions. Therefore $\sum \xi_n$ also converges (P-a.s.).

Necessity. If $\sum \xi_n$ converges (P-a.s.) then $\xi_n \to 0$ (P-a.s.), and therefore, for every $c > 0$, at most a finite number of the events $\{|\xi_n| \ge c\}$ can occur (P-a.s.). Therefore $\sum I(|\xi_n| \ge c) < \infty$ (P-a.s.), and, by the second part of the Borel–Cantelli lemma, $\sum \mathsf{P}(|\xi_n| > c) < \infty$. Moreover, the convergence of $\sum \xi_n$ implies the convergence of $\sum \xi_n^c$. Therefore, by the two-series theorem, both of the series $\sum \mathsf{E}\xi_n^c$ and $\sum \mathsf{V}\xi_n^c$ converge.

This completes the proof of the theorem.

Corollary. *Let $\xi_1, \xi_2, \ldots$ be independent variables with $\mathsf{E}\xi_n = 0$. Then if*

$$\sum \mathsf{E} \frac{\xi_n^2}{1 + |\xi_n|} < \infty,$$

the series $\sum \xi_n$ converges with probability 1.

For the proof we observe that

$$\sum \mathsf{E} \frac{\xi_n^2}{1 + |\xi_n|} < \infty \Leftrightarrow \sum \mathsf{E}[\xi_n^2 I(|\xi_n| \le 1) + |\xi_n| I(|\xi_n| > 1)] < \infty.$$

Therefore if $\xi_n^1 = \xi_n I(|\xi_n| \le 1)$, we have

$$\sum \mathsf{E}(\xi_n^1)^2 < \infty.$$

Since $\mathsf{E}\xi_n = 0$, we have

$$\sum |\mathsf{E}\xi_n^1| = \sum |\mathsf{E}\xi_n I(|\xi_n| \le 1)| = \sum |\mathsf{E}\xi_n I(|\xi_n| > 1)|$$
$$\le \sum \mathsf{E}|\xi_n| I(|\xi_n| > 1) < \infty.$$

Therefore both $\sum \mathsf{E}\xi_n^1$ and $\sum \mathsf{V}\xi_n^1$ converge. Moreover, by Chebyshev's inequality,

$$\mathsf{P}\{|\xi_n| > 1\} = \mathsf{P}\{|\xi_n| I(|\xi_n| > 1) > 1\} \le \mathsf{E}(|\xi_n| I(|\xi_n| > 1)).$$

Therefore $\sum \mathsf{P}(|\xi_n| > 1) < \infty$. Hence the convergence of $\sum \xi_n$ follows from the three-series theorem.

4. Problems

1. Let $\xi_1, \xi_2, \ldots$ be a sequence of independent random variables, $S_n = \xi_1, \ldots, \xi_n$. Show, using the three-series theorem, that
   (a) if $\sum \xi_n^2 < \infty$ (P-a.s.) then $\sum \xi_n$ converges with probability 1, if and only if $\sum E \, \xi_i I(|\xi_i| \leq 1)$ converges;
   (b) if $\sum \xi_n$ converges (P-a.s.) then $\sum \xi_n^2 < \infty$ (P-a.s.) if and only if
   $$\sum (E|\xi_n| I(|\xi_n| \leq 1))^2 < \infty.$$

2. Let $\xi_1, \xi_2, \ldots$ be a sequence of independent random variables. Show that $\sum \xi_n^2 < \infty$ (P-a.s.) if and only if
   $$\sum E \frac{\xi_n^2}{1 + \xi_n^2} < \infty.$$

3. Let $\xi_1, \xi_2, \ldots$ be a sequence of independent random variables. Show that $\sum \xi_n$ converges (P-a.s.) if and only if it converges in probability.

§3. Strong Law of Large Numbers

1. Let $\xi_1, \xi_2, \ldots$ be a sequence of independent random variables with finite second moments; $S_n = \xi_1 + \cdots + \xi_n$. By Problem 2, §3, Chapter III, if the numbers $V\xi_i$ are uniformly bounded, we have the law of large numbers:

$$\frac{S_n - ES_n}{n} \xrightarrow{P} 0, \qquad n \to \infty. \tag{1}$$

A *strong law of large numbers* is a proposition in which convergence in probability is replaced by *convergence with probability 1*.

One of the earliest results in this direction is the following theorem.

Theorem 1 (Cantelli). *Let $\xi_1, \xi_2, \ldots$ be independent random variables with finite fourth moments and let*

$$E|\xi_n - E\xi_n|^4 \leq C, \qquad n \geq 1,$$

for some constant C. Then as $n \to \infty$

$$\frac{S_n - ES_n}{n} \to 0 \quad (P\text{-}a.s.). \tag{2}$$

PROOF. Without loss of generality, we may assume that $E\xi_n = 0$ for $n \geq 1$. By the corollary to Theorem 1, §10, Chapter II, we will have $S_n/n \to 0$ (P-a.s.) provided that

$$\sum P\left\{\left|\frac{S_n}{n}\right| \geq \varepsilon\right\} < \infty$$

for every $\varepsilon > 0$. In turn, by Chebyshev's inequality, this will follow from

$$\sum E\left|\frac{S_n}{n}\right|^4 < \infty.$$

Let us show that this condition is actually satisfied under our hypotheses. We have

$$S_n^4 = (\xi_1 + \cdots + \xi_n)^4 = \sum_{i=1}^{n} \xi_i^4 - \sum_{\substack{i,j \\ i<j}} \frac{4!}{2!2!} \xi_i^2 \xi_j^2$$

$$+ \sum_{\substack{i \neq j \\ i \neq k \\ j < k}} \frac{4!}{2!1!1!} \xi_i^2 \xi_j \xi_k + \sum_{i<j<k<l} 4! \xi_i \xi_j \xi_k \xi_l$$

$$+ \sum_{i \neq j} \frac{4!}{3!1!} \xi_i^3 \xi_j.$$

Remembering that $\mathsf{E}\xi_k = 0$, $k \leq n$, we then obtain

$$\mathsf{E}S_n^4 = \sum_{i=1}^{n} \mathsf{E}\xi_i^4 + 6 \sum_{\substack{i,j=1 \\ i<j}}^{n} \mathsf{E}\xi_i^2 \mathsf{E}\xi_j^2 \leq nC + 6 \sum_{\substack{i,j=1 \\ i<j}}^{n} \sqrt{\mathsf{E}\xi_i^4 \cdot \mathsf{E}\xi_j^4}$$

$$\leq nC + \frac{6n(n-1)}{2} C = (3n^2 - 2n)C < 3n^2 C.$$

Consequently

$$\sum \mathsf{E}\left(\frac{S_n}{n}\right)^4 \leq 3C \sum \frac{1}{n^2} < \infty.$$

This completes the proof of the theorem.

2. The hypotheses of Theorem 1 can be considerably weakened by the use of more precise methods. In this way we obtain a stronger law of large numbers.

Theorem 2 (Kolmogorov). *Let $\xi_1, \xi_2, \ldots$ be a sequence of independent random variables with finite second moments, and let there be positive numbers b_n such that $b_n \uparrow \infty$ and*

$$\sum \frac{\mathsf{V}\xi_n}{b_n^2} < \infty. \tag{3}$$

Then

$$\frac{S_n - \mathsf{E}S_n}{b_n} \to 0 \quad (\text{P-a.s.}). \tag{4}$$

In particular, if

$$\sum \frac{\mathsf{V}\xi_n}{n^2} < \infty \tag{5}$$

then

$$\frac{S_n - \mathsf{E}S_n}{n} \to 0 \quad (\text{P-a.s.}) \tag{6}$$

For the proof of this, and of Theorem 2 below, we need two lemmas.

Lemma 1 (Toeplitz). *Let $\{a_n\}$ be a sequence of nonnegative numbers, $b_n = \sum_{i=1}^{n} a_i$, $b_n > 0$ for $n \geq 1$, and $b_n \uparrow \infty$, $n \to \infty$. Let $\{x_n\}$ be a sequence of numbers converging to x. Then*

$$\frac{1}{b_n} \sum_{j=1}^{n} a_j x_j \to x. \qquad (7)$$

In particular, if $a_n = 1$ then

$$\frac{x_1 + \cdots + x_n}{n} \to x. \qquad (8)$$

PROOF. Let $\varepsilon > 0$ and let $n_0 = n_0(\varepsilon)$ be such that $|x_n - x| \leq \varepsilon/2$ for all $n \geq n_0$. Choose $n_1 > n_0$ so that

$$\frac{1}{b_{n_1}} \sum_{j=1}^{n_0} |x_j - x| < \varepsilon/2.$$

Then, for $n > n_1$,

$$\left| \frac{1}{b_n} \sum_{j=1}^{n} a_j x_j - x \right| \leq \frac{1}{b_n} \sum_{j=1}^{n} a_j |x_j - x|$$

$$= \frac{1}{b_n} \sum_{j=1}^{n_0} a_j |x_j - x| + \frac{1}{b_n} \sum_{j=n_0+1}^{n} a_j |x_j - x|$$

$$\leq \frac{1}{b_{n_1}} \sum_{j=1}^{n_0} a_j |x_j - x| + \frac{1}{b_n} \sum_{j=n_0+1}^{n} a_j |x_j - x|$$

$$\leq \frac{\varepsilon}{2} + \frac{b_n - b_{n_0}}{b_n} \frac{\varepsilon}{2} \leq \varepsilon.$$

This completes the proof of the lemma.

Lemma 2 (Kronecker). *Let $\{b_n\}$ be a sequence of positive increasing numbers, $b_n \uparrow \infty$, $n \to \infty$, and let $\{x_n\}$ be a sequence of numbers such that $\sum x_n$ converges. Then*

$$\frac{1}{b_n} \sum_{j=1}^{n} b_j x_j \to 0, \qquad n \to \infty. \qquad (9)$$

In particular, if $b_n = n$, $x_n = y_n/n$ and $\sum (y_n/n)$ converges, then

$$\frac{y_1 + \cdots + y_n}{n} \to 0, \qquad n \to \infty. \qquad (10)$$

PROOF. Let $b_0 = 0$, $S_0 = 0$, $S_n = \sum_{j=1}^{n} x_j$. Then (by summation by parts)

$$\sum_{j=1}^{n} b_j x_j = \sum_{j=1}^{n} b_j (S_j - S_{j-1}) = b_n S_n - b_0 S_0 - \sum_{j=1}^{n} S_{j-1}(b_j - b_{i-1})$$

and therefore

$$\frac{1}{b_n} \sum_{j=1}^{n} b_j x_j = S_n - \frac{1}{b_n} \sum_{j=1}^{n} S_{j-1} a_j \to 0,$$

since, if $S_n \to x$, then by Toeplitz' lemma,

$$\frac{1}{b_n} \sum_{j=1}^{n} S_{j-1} a_j \to x.$$

This establishes the lemma.

PROOF OF THEOREM 1. Since

$$\frac{S_n - \mathsf{E}S_n}{b_n} = \frac{1}{b_n} \sum_{k=1}^{n} b_k \left(\frac{\xi_k - \mathsf{E}\xi_k}{b_k} \right),$$

a sufficient condition for (4) is, by Kronecker's lemma, that the series $\sum [(\xi_k - \mathsf{E}\xi_k)/b_k]$ converges (P-a.s.). But this series does converge by (3) of Theorem 1, §2.

This completes the proof of the theorem.

EXAMPLE 1. Let $\xi_1, \xi_2, \ldots$ be a sequence of independent Bernoulli random variables with $P(\xi_n = 1) = P(\xi_n = -1) = \frac{1}{2}$. Then, since $\sum [1/(n \log^2 n)] < \infty$, we have

$$\frac{S_n}{\sqrt{n} \log n} \to 0 \quad (\text{P-a.s.}). \tag{11}$$

3. In the case when the variables $\xi_1, \xi_2, \ldots$ are not only independent but also identically distributed, we can obtain a strong law of large numbers without requiring (as in Theorem 2) the existence of the second moment, provided that the first absolute moment exists.

Theorem 3 (Kolmogorov). *Let* $\xi_1, \xi_2, \ldots$ *be a sequence of independent identically distributed random variables with* $\mathsf{E}|\xi_1| < \infty$. *Then*

$$\frac{S_n}{n} \to m \quad (\text{P-a.s.}) \tag{12}$$

where $m = \mathsf{E}\xi_1$.

We need the following lemma.

Lemma 3. *Let* ξ *be a nonnegative random variable. Then*

$$\sum_{n=1}^{\infty} P(\xi \geq n) \leq \mathsf{E}\xi \leq 1 + \sum_{n=1}^{\infty} P(\xi \geq n). \tag{13}$$

The proof consists of the following chain of inequalities:

$$\sum_{n=1}^{\infty} P(\xi \geq n) = \sum_{n=1}^{\infty} \sum_{k \geq n} P(k \leq \xi < k + 1)$$

$$= \sum_{k=1}^{\infty} k P(k \leq \xi < k + 1) = \sum_{k=0}^{\infty} E[kI(k \leq \xi < k + 1)]$$

$$\leq \sum_{k=0}^{\infty} E[\xi I(k \leq \xi < k + 1)]$$

$$= E\xi \leq \sum_{k=0}^{\infty} E[(k + 1)I(k \leq \xi < k + 1)]$$

$$= \sum_{k=0}^{\infty} (k + 1)P(k \leq \xi < k + 1)$$

$$= \sum_{n=1}^{\infty} P(\xi \geq n) + \sum_{k=0}^{\infty} P(k \leq \xi < k + 1) = \sum_{n=1}^{\infty} P(\xi \geq n) + 1.$$

PROOF OF THEOREM 3. By Lemma 3 and the Borel–Cantelli lemma,

$$E|\xi_1| < \infty \Leftrightarrow \sum P\{|\xi_1| \geq n\} < \infty$$
$$\Leftrightarrow \sum P\{|\xi_n| \geq n\} < \infty \Leftrightarrow P\{|\xi_n| \geq n \text{ i.o.}\} = 0.$$

Hence $|\xi_n| < n$, except for a finite number of n, with probability 1.

Let us put

$$\tilde{\xi}_n = \begin{cases} \xi_n, & |\xi_n| < n, \\ 0, & |\xi_n| \geq n, \end{cases}$$

and suppose that $E\xi_n = 0$, $n \geq 1$. Then $(\xi_1 + \cdots + \xi_n)/n \to 0$ (P-a.s.), if and only if $(\tilde{\xi}_1 + \cdots + \tilde{\xi}_n)/n \to 0$ (P-a.s.). Note that in general $E\tilde{\xi}_n \neq 0$ but

$$E\tilde{\xi}_n = E\xi_n I(|\xi_n| < n) = E\xi_1 I(|\xi_1| < n) \to E\xi_1 = 0.$$

Hence by Toeplitz' lemma

$$\frac{1}{n} \sum_{k=1}^{n} E\tilde{\xi}_k \to 0, \qquad n \to \infty,$$

and consequently $(\xi_1 + \cdots + \xi_n)/n \to 0$ (P-a.s.), if and only if

$$\frac{(\tilde{\xi}_1 - E\tilde{\xi}_1) + \cdots + (\tilde{\xi}_n - E\tilde{\xi}_n)}{n} \to 0, \qquad n \to \infty \text{ (P-a.s.)}, \quad n \to \infty. \quad (14)$$

Write $\bar{\xi}_n = \tilde{\xi}_n - E\tilde{\xi}_n$. By Kronecker's lemma, (14) will be established if $\sum (\bar{\xi}_n/n)$ converges (P-a.s.). In turn, by Theorem 1 of §2, this will follow if we show that, when $E|\xi_1| < \infty$, the series $\sum (V\tilde{\xi}_n/n^2)$ converges.

We have

$$\sum \frac{V\xi_n}{n^2} \le \sum_{n=1}^{\infty} \frac{E\bar{\xi}_n^2}{n^2} = \sum_{n=1}^{\infty} \frac{1}{n^2} E[\xi_n I(|\xi_n| < n)]^2$$

$$= \sum_{n=1}^{\infty} \frac{1}{n^2} E[\xi_1^2 I(|\xi_1| < n)] = \sum_{n=1}^{\infty} \frac{1}{n^2} \sum_{k=1}^{n} E[\xi_1^2 I(k-1) \le |\xi_1| < k)]$$

$$= \sum_{k=1}^{\infty} E[\xi_1^2 I(k-1 \le |\xi_1| < k)] \cdot \sum_{n=k}^{\infty} \frac{1}{n^2}$$

$$\le 2 \sum_{k=1}^{\infty} \frac{1}{k} E[\xi_1^2 I(k-1 \le |\xi_1| < k)]$$

$$\le 2 \sum_{k=1}^{\infty} E[|\xi_1| I(k-1 \le |\xi_1| < k)] = 2E|\xi_1| < \infty.$$

This completes the proof of the theorem.

Remark 1. The theorem admits a converse in the following sense. Let $\xi_1, \xi_2, \ldots$ be a sequence of independent identically distributed random variables such that

$$\frac{\xi_1 + \cdots + \xi_n}{n} \to C,$$

with probability 1, where C is a (finite) constant. Then $E|\xi_1| < \infty$ and $C = E\xi_1$. In fact, if $S_n/n \to C$ (P-a.s.) then

$$\frac{\xi_n}{n} = \frac{S_n}{n} - \left(\frac{n-1}{n}\right) \frac{S_{n-1}}{n-1} \to 0 \quad \text{(P-a.s.)}$$

and therefore $P(|\xi_n| > n \text{ i.o.}) = 0$. By the Borel–Cantelli lemma,

$$\sum P(|\xi_1| > n) < \infty,$$

and by Lemma 3 we have $E|\xi_1| < \infty$. Then it follows from the theorem that $C = E\xi_1$.

Consequently for independent identically distributed random variables the condition $E|\xi_1| < \infty$ is necessary and sufficient for the convergence (with probability 1) of the ratio S_n/n to a finite limit.

Remark 2. If the expectation $m = E\xi_1$ exists but is not necessarily finite, the conclusion (10) of the theorem remains valid.
  In fact, let, for example, $E\xi_1^- < \infty$ and $E\xi_1^+ = \infty$. With $C > 0$, put

$$S_n^C = \sum_{i=1}^{n} \xi_i I(\xi_i \le C).$$

Then (P-a.s.).

$$\varliminf_n \frac{S_n}{n} \geq \varliminf_n \frac{S_n^C}{n} = \mathsf{E}\xi_1 I(\xi_1 \leq C).$$

But as $C \to \infty$,

$$\mathsf{E}\xi_1 I(\xi_1 \leq C) \to \mathsf{E}\xi_1 = \infty;$$

therefore $S_n/n \to +\infty$ (P-a.s.)

4. Let us give some applications of the strong law of large numbers.

EXAMPLE 1 (Application to number theory). Let $\Omega = [0, 1)$, let $\mathscr{B}$ be the algebra of Borel subsets of Ω and let P be Lebesgue measure on $[0, 1)$. Consider the binary expansions $\omega = 0 . \omega_1\omega_2 \ldots$ of numbers $\omega \in \Omega$ (with infinitely many 0's) and define random variables $\xi_1(\omega), \xi_2(\omega), \ldots$ by putting $\xi_n(\omega) = \omega_n$. Since, for all $n \geq 1$ and all $x_1, \ldots, x_n$ taking the values 0 or 1,

$$\{\omega: \xi_1(\omega) = x_1, \ldots, \xi_n(\omega) = x_n\}$$
$$= \left\{\omega: \frac{x_1}{2} + \frac{x_2}{2^2} + \cdots + \frac{x_n}{2^n} \leq \omega < \frac{x_1}{2} + \cdots + \frac{x_n}{2^n} + \frac{1}{2^n}\right\},$$

the P-measure of this set is $1/2^n$. It follows that $\xi_1, \xi_n, \ldots$ is a sequence of independent identically distributed random variables with

$$\mathsf{P}(\xi_1 = 0) = \mathsf{P}(\xi_1 = 1) = \tfrac{1}{2}.$$

Hence, by the strong law of large numbers, we have the following result of Borel: *almost every number in* $[0, 1)$ *is normal, in the sense that with probability* 1 *the proportion of zeros and ones in its binary expansion tends to* $\frac{1}{2}$, *i.e.*

$$\frac{1}{n}\sum_{k=1}^n I(\xi_k = 1) \to \tfrac{1}{2} \quad \text{(P-a.s.)}.$$

EXAMPLE 2 (The Monte Carlo method). Let $f(x)$ be a continuous function defined on $[0, 1]$, with values on $[0, 1]$. The following idea is the foundation of the statistical method of calculating $\int_0^1 f(x)\, dx$ (the "Monte Carlo method").

Let $\xi_1, \eta_1, \xi_2, \eta_2, \ldots$ be a sequence of independent random variables, uniformly distributed on $[0, 1]$. Put

$$\rho_i = \begin{cases} 1 & \text{if } f(\xi_i) > \eta_i, \\ 0 & \text{if } f(\xi_i) < \eta_i. \end{cases}$$

It is clear that

$$\mathsf{E}\rho_1 = \mathsf{P}\{f(\xi_1) > \eta_1\} = \int_0^1 f(x)\, dx.$$

By the strong law of large numbers (Theorem 3)

$$\frac{1}{n} \sum_{i=1}^{n} \rho_i \to \int_{0}^{1} f(x)\, dx \quad \text{(P-a.s.)}.$$

Consequently we can approximate an integral $\int_0^1 f(x)\, dx$ by taking a simulation consisting of a pair of random variables (ξ_i, η_i), $i \geq 1$, and then calculating ρ_i and $(1/n) \sum_{i=1}^{n} \rho_i$.

5. PROBLEMS

1. Show that $E\xi^2 < \infty$ if and only if $\sum_{n=1}^{\infty} nP(|\xi| > n) < \infty$.

2. Supposing that $\xi_1, \xi_2, \ldots$ are independent and identically distributed, show that if $E|\xi_1|^\alpha < \infty$ for some α, $0 < \alpha < 1$, then $S_n/n^{1/\alpha} \to 0$ (P-a.s.), and if $E|\xi_1|^\beta < \infty$ for some β, $1 \leq \beta < 2$, then $(S_n - nE\xi_1)/n^{1/\beta} \to 0$ (P-a.s.).

3. Let $\xi_1, \xi_2, \ldots$ be a sequence of independent identically distributed random variables and let $E|\xi_1| = \infty$. Show that

$$\overline{\lim_{n}} \left| \frac{S_n}{n} - a_n \right| = \infty \quad \text{(P-a.s.)}$$

for every sequence of constants $\{a_n\}$.

4. Show that a rational number on $[0, 1)$ is never normal (in the sense of Example 1, Subsection 4).

§4. Law of the Iterated Logarithm

1. Let $\xi_1, \xi_2, \ldots$ be a sequence of independent Bernoulli random variables with $P(\xi_n = 1) = P(\xi_n = -1) = \frac{1}{2}$; let $S_n = \xi_1 + \cdots + \xi_n$. It follows from the proof of Theorem 2, §1, that

$$\overline{\lim} \frac{S_n}{\sqrt{n}} = +\infty, \qquad \underline{\lim} \frac{S_n}{\sqrt{n}} = -\infty. \tag{1}$$

with probability 1. On the other hand, by (3.11),

$$\frac{S_n}{\sqrt{n \log n}} \to 0 \quad \text{(P-a.s.)}. \tag{2}$$

Let us compare these results.

It follows from (1) that with probability 1 the paths of $(S_n)_{n \geq 1}$ intersect the "curves" $\pm \varepsilon \sqrt{n}$ infinitely often for any given ε; but at the same time (2) shows that they only finitely often leave the region bounded by the curves $\pm \varepsilon \sqrt{n} \log n$. These two results yield useful information on the amplitude of the oscillations of the symmetric random walk $(S_n)_{n \geq 1}$. The law of the iterated logarithm, which we present below, improves this picture of the amplitude of the oscillations of $(S_n)_{n \geq 1}$.

Let us introduce the following definition. We call a function $\varphi^* = \varphi^*(n)$, $n \geq 1$, *upper* (for $(S_n)_{n \geq 1}$) if, with probability 1, $S_n \leq \varphi^*(n)$ for all n from $n = n_0(\omega)$ on.

We call a function $\varphi_* = \varphi_*(n), n \geq 1$, *lower* (for $(S_n)_{n \geq 1}$) if, with probability 1, $S_n > \varphi_*(n)$ for infinitely many n.

Using these definitions, and appealing to (1) and (2), we can say that every function $\varphi^* = \varepsilon \sqrt{n} \log n, \varepsilon > 0$, is upper, whereas $\varphi_* = \varepsilon \sqrt{n}$ is lower, $\varepsilon > 0$.

Let $\varphi = \varphi(n)$ be a function and $\varphi_\varepsilon^* = (1 + \varepsilon)\varphi, \varphi_{*\varepsilon} = (1 - \varepsilon)\varphi$, where $\varepsilon > 0$. Then it is easily seen that

$$\left\{ \overline{\lim} \, \frac{S_n}{\varphi(n)} \leq 1 \right\} = \left\{ \lim_n \left[\sup_{m \geq n} \frac{S_m}{\varphi(m)} \right] \leq 1 \right\}$$

$$\Leftrightarrow \left\{ \sup_{m \geq n_1(\varepsilon)} \frac{S_m}{\varphi(m)} \leq 1 + \varepsilon \text{ for every } \varepsilon > 0, \text{ from some } n_1(\varepsilon) \text{ on} \right\}$$

$$\Leftrightarrow \{ S_m \leq (1 + \varepsilon)\varphi(m) \text{ for every } \varepsilon > 0, \text{ from some } n_1(\varepsilon) \text{ on} \}.$$

$$(3)$$

In the same way,

$$\left\{ \overline{\lim} \, \frac{S_n}{\varphi(n)} \geq 1 \right\} = \left\{ \lim_n \left[\sup_{m \geq n} \frac{S_m}{\varphi(m)} \right] \geq 1 \right\}$$

$$\Leftrightarrow \left\{ \sup_{m \geq n_2(\varepsilon)} \frac{S_m}{\varphi(m)} \leq 1 + \varepsilon \text{ for every } \varepsilon > 0, \text{ from some } n_1(\varepsilon) \text{ on} \right\}$$

$$\Leftrightarrow \begin{array}{l} \{ S_m \geq (1 - \varepsilon)\varphi(m) \text{ for every } \varepsilon > 0 \text{ and for infinitely} \\ \text{many } m \text{ larger than some } n_3(\varepsilon) \geq n_2(\varepsilon) \}. \end{array} \quad (4)$$

It follows from (3) and (4) that in order to verify that each function $\varphi_\varepsilon^* = (1 + \varepsilon)\varphi, \varepsilon > 0$, is upper, we have to show that

$$\mathsf{P}\left\{ \overline{\lim} \, \frac{S_n}{\varphi(n)} \leq 1 \right\} = 1. \quad (5)$$

But to show that $\varphi_{*\varepsilon} = (1 - \varepsilon)\varphi, \varepsilon > 0$, is lower, we have to show that

$$\mathsf{P}\left\{ \overline{\lim} \, \frac{S_n}{\varphi(n)} \geq 1 \right\} = 1. \quad (6)$$

2. Theorem 1 (Law of the Iterated Logarithm). *Let $\xi_1, \xi_2, \ldots$ be a sequence of independent identically distributed random variables with $\mathsf{E}\xi_i = 0$ and $\mathsf{E}\xi_i^2 = \sigma^2 > 0$. Then*

$$\mathsf{P}\left\{\overline{\lim}\ \frac{S_n}{\psi(n)} = 1\right\} = 1, \tag{7}$$

where

$$\psi(n) = \sqrt{2\sigma^2 n \log \log n}. \tag{8}$$

For uniformly bounded random variables, the law of the iterated logarithm was established by Khinchin (1924). In 1929 Kolmogorov generalized this result to a wide class of independent variables. Under the conditions of Theorem 1, the law of the iterated logarithm was established by Hartman and Wintner (1941).

Since the proof of Theorem 1 is rather complicated, we shall confine ourselves to the special case when the random variables ξ_n are normal, $\xi_n \sim \mathcal{N}(0, 1), n \geq 1$.

We begin by proving two auxiliary results.

Lemma 1. *Let $\xi_1, \ldots, \xi_n$ be independent random variables that are symmetrically distributed ($\mathsf{P}(\xi_k \in B) = \mathsf{P}(-\xi_k \in B)$ for every $B \in \mathcal{B}(R), k \leq n$). Then for every real number a*

$$\mathsf{P}\left(\max_{1 \leq k \leq n} S_k > a\right) \leq 2\mathsf{P}(S_n > a). \tag{9}$$

PROOF. Let $A = \{\max_{1 \leq k \leq n} S_k > a\}$, $A_k = \{S_i \leq a, i \leq k - 1; S_k > a\}$ and $B = \{S_n > a\}$. Since $S_n > a$ on A_k (because $S_k \leq S_n$), we have

$$\mathsf{P}(B \cap A_k) \geq \mathsf{P}(A_k \cap \{S_n \geq S_k\}) = \mathsf{P}(A_k)\mathsf{P}(S_n \geq S_k)$$
$$= \mathsf{P}(A_k)\mathsf{P}(\xi_{k+1} + \cdots + \xi_n \geq 0).$$

By the symmetry of the distributions of the random variables $\xi_1, \ldots, \xi_n$, we have

$$\mathsf{P}(\xi_{k+1} + \cdots + \xi_n > 0) = \mathsf{P}(\xi_{k+1} + \cdots + \xi_n < 0).$$

Hence $\mathsf{P}(\xi_{k+1} + \cdots + \xi_n > 0) \geq \frac{1}{2}$, and therefore

$$\mathsf{P}(B) \geq \sum_{k=1}^{n} \mathsf{P}(A_k \cap B) \geq \frac{1}{2} \sum_{k=1}^{n} \mathsf{P}(A_k) = \frac{1}{2} \mathsf{P}(A),$$

which establishes (9).

Lemma 2. *Let $S_n \sim \mathcal{N}(0, \sigma^2(n))$, $\sigma^2(n) \uparrow \infty$, and let $a(n), n \geq 1$, satisfy $a(n)/\sigma(n) \to \infty, n \to \infty$. Then*

$$\mathsf{P}(S_n > a(n)) \sim \frac{\sigma(n)}{\sqrt{2\pi a(n)}} \exp\{-\tfrac{1}{2}a^2(n)/\sigma^2(n)\}. \tag{10}$$

The proof follows from the asymptotic formula

$$\frac{1}{\sqrt{2\pi}} \int_x^\infty e^{-y^2/2} \, dy \sim \frac{1}{\sqrt{2\pi}x} e^{-x^2/2}, \qquad x \to \infty,$$

since $S_n/\sigma(n) \sim \mathcal{N}(0, 1)$.

PROOF OF THEOREM 1 (for $\xi_i \sim \mathcal{N}(0, 1)$).

Let us first establish (5). Let $\varepsilon > 0$, $\lambda = 1 + \varepsilon$, $n_k = \lambda^k$, where $k \geq k_0$, and k_0 is chosen so that $\ln \ln k_0$ is defined. We also define

$$A_k = \{S_n > \lambda\psi(n) \text{ for some } n \in (n_k, n_{k+1}]\}, \tag{11}$$

and put

$$A = \{A_k \text{ i.o.}\} = \{S_n > \lambda\psi(n) \text{ for infinitely many } n\}.$$

In accordance with (3), we can establish (5) by showing that $\mathsf{P}(A) = 0$.

Let us show that $\sum \mathsf{P}(A_k) < \infty$. Then $\mathsf{P}(A) = 0$ by the Borel–Cantelli lemma.

From (11), (9) and (10) we find that

$$\mathsf{P}(A_k) \leq \mathsf{P}\{S_n > \lambda\psi(n_k) \text{ for some } n \in (n_k, n_{k+1})\}$$

$$\leq \mathsf{P}\{S_n > \lambda\psi(n_k) \text{ for some } n \leq n_{k+1}\}$$

$$\leq 2P\{S_{n_{k+1}} > \lambda\psi(n_k)\} \sim \frac{2\sqrt{n_k}}{\sqrt{2\pi}\,\lambda\psi(n_k)} \exp\{-\tfrac{1}{2}\lambda^2[\psi(n_k)/\sqrt{n_k}]^2\}$$

$$\leq C_1 \exp(-\lambda \ln \ln \lambda^k) \leq Ce^{-\lambda \ln k} = C_2 k^{-\lambda},$$

where C_1 and C_2 are constants. But $\sum_{k=1}^\infty k^{-\lambda} < \infty$, and therefore

$$\sum \mathsf{P}(A_k) < \infty.$$

Consequently (5) is established.

We turn now to the proof of (6). In accordance with (4) we must show that, with $\lambda = 1 - \varepsilon$, $\varepsilon > 0$, we have with probability 1 that $S_n \geq \lambda\psi(n)$ for infinitely many n.

Let us apply (5), which we just proved, to the sequence $(-S_n)_{n \geq 1}$. Then we find that for all n, with finitely many exceptions, $-S_n \leq 2\psi(n)$ (P-a.s.). Consequently if $n_k = N^k$, $N > 1$, then for sufficiently large k, either

$$S_{n_{k-1}} \geq -2\psi(n_{k-1})$$

or

$$S_{n_k} \geq Y_k - 2\psi(n_{k-1}), \tag{12}$$

where $Y_k = S_{n_k} - S_{n_{k-1}}$.

Hence if we show that for infinitely many k

$$Y_k > \lambda\psi(n_k) + 2\psi(n_{k-1}), \tag{13}$$

this and (12) show that (P-a.s.) $S_{n_k} > \lambda \psi(n_k)$ for infinitely many k. Take some $\lambda' \in (\lambda, 1)$. Then there is an $N > 1$ such that for all k

$$\lambda'[2(N^k - N^{k-1}) \ln \ln N^k]^{1/2} > \lambda(2N^k \ln \ln N^k)^{1/2}$$
$$+ 2(2N^{k-1} \ln \ln N^{k-1})^{1/2} \equiv \lambda\psi(N^k) + 2\psi(N^{k-1}).$$

It is now enough to show that

$$Y_k > \lambda'[2(N^k - N^{k-1}) \ln \ln N^k]^{1/2} \tag{14}$$

for infinitely many k. Evidently $Y_k \sim \mathcal{N}(0, N^k - N^{k-1})$. Therefore, by Lemma 2,

$$\mathsf{P}\{Y_k > \lambda'[2(N^k - N^{k-1}) \ln \ln N^k]^{1/2}\} \sim \frac{1}{\sqrt{2\pi}\lambda'(2 \ln \ln N^k)^{1/2}} e^{-(\lambda')^2 \ln \ln N^k}$$

$$\geq \frac{C_1}{(\ln k)^{1/2}} k^{-(\lambda')^2} \geq \frac{C_2}{k \ln k}.$$

Since $\sum (1/k \ln k) = \infty$, it follows from the second part of the Borel–Cantelli lemma that, with probability 1, inequality (14) is satisfied for infinitely many k, so that (6) is established.

This completes the proof of the theorem.

Remark 1. Applying (7) to the random variables $(-S_n)_{n \geq 1}$, we find that

$$\varliminf \frac{S_n}{\varphi(n)} = -1. \tag{15}$$

It follows from (7) and (15) that the law of the iterated logarithm can be put in the form

$$\mathsf{P}\left\{\varlimsup \frac{|S_n|}{\varphi(n)} = 1\right\} = 1. \tag{16}$$

Remark 2. The law of the iterated logarithm says that for every $\varepsilon > 0$ each function $\psi_\varepsilon^* = (1 + \varepsilon)\psi$ is upper, and $\psi_{*\varepsilon} = (1 - \varepsilon)\psi$ is lower.

The conclusion (7) is also equivalent to the statement that, for each $\varepsilon > 0$,

$$\mathsf{P}\{|S_n| \geq (1 - \varepsilon)\psi(n) \text{ i.o.}\} = 1,$$
$$\mathsf{P}\{|S_n| \geq (1 + \varepsilon)\psi(n) \text{ i.o.}\} = 0.$$

3. PROBLEMS

1. Let $\xi_1, \xi_2, \ldots$ be a sequence of independent random variables with $\xi_n \sim \mathcal{N}(0, 1)$. Show that

$$\mathsf{P}\left\{\varlimsup \frac{\xi_n}{\sqrt{2 \ln n}} = 1\right\} = 1.$$

2. Let $\xi_1, \xi_2, \ldots$ be a sequence of independent random variables, distributed according to Poisson's law with parameter $\lambda > 0$. Show that (independently of λ)

$$P\left\{\overline{\lim} \, \frac{\xi_n \ln \ln n}{\ln n} = 1\right\} = 1.$$

3. Let $\xi_1, \xi_2, \ldots$ be a sequence of independent identically distributed random variables with

$$Ee^{it\xi_1} = e^{-|t|^\alpha}, \qquad 0 < \alpha < 2.$$

Show that

$$P\left\{\overline{\lim} \left|\frac{S_n}{n^{1/\alpha}}\right|^{1/(\ln \ln n)} = e^{1/\alpha}\right\} = 1.$$

4. Establish the following generalization of (9). Let $\xi_1, \ldots, \xi_n$ be independent random variables. *Lévy's inequality*

$$P\left\{\max_{0 \le k \le n} [S_k + \mu(S_n - S_k)] > a\right\} \le 2P(S_n > a), \qquad S_0 = 0,$$

holds for every real a, where $\mu(\xi)$ is the median of ξ, i.e. a constant such that

$$P(\xi \ge \mu(\xi)) \ge \tfrac{1}{2}, \qquad P(\xi \le \mu(\xi)) \ge \tfrac{1}{2}.$$

CHAPTER V
Stationary (Strict Sense) Random Sequences and Ergodic Theory

§1. Stationary (Strict Sense) Random Sequences. Measure-Preserving Transformations

1. Let $(\Omega, \mathscr{F}, \mathsf{P})$ be a probability space and $\xi = (\xi_1, \xi_2, \ldots)$ a sequence of random variables or, as we say, a *random sequence*. Let $\theta_k \xi$ denote the sequence $(\xi_{k+1}, \xi_{k+2}, \ldots)$.

Definition 1. A random sequence ξ is *stationary* (*in the strict sense*) if the probability distributions of $\theta_k \xi$ and ξ are the same for every $k \geq 1$:

$$\mathsf{P}((\xi_1, \xi_2, \ldots) \in B) = \mathsf{P}((\xi_{k+1}, \xi_{k+2}, \ldots) \in B), \qquad B \in \mathscr{B}(R^\infty).$$

The simplest example is a sequence $\xi = (\xi_1, \xi_2, \ldots)$ of independent identically distributed random variables. Starting from such a sequence, we can construct a broad class of stationary sequences $\eta = (\eta_1, \eta_2, \ldots)$ by choosing any Borel function $g(x_1, \ldots, x_n)$ and setting $\eta_k = g(\xi_k, \xi_{k+1}, \ldots, \xi_{k+1})$.

If $\xi = (\xi_1, \xi_2, \ldots)$ is a sequence of independent identically distributed random variables with $\mathsf{E}|\xi_1| < \infty$ and $\mathsf{E}\xi_1 = m$, the law of large numbers tells us that, with probability 1,

$$\frac{\xi_1 + \cdots + \xi_n}{n} \to m, \qquad n \to \infty.$$

In 1931 Birkhoff obtained a remarkable generalization of this fact for the case of stationary sequences. The present chapter consists mainly of a proof of Birkhoff's theorem.

The following presentation is based on the idea of measure-preserving transformations, something that brings us in contact with an interesting branch of analysis (ergodic theory), and at the same time shows the connection between this theory and stationary random proceesses.

Let $(\Omega, \mathcal{F}, \mathsf{P})$ be a probability space.

Definition 2. A transformation T of Ω into Ω is *measurable* if, for every $A \in \mathcal{F}$,

$$T^{-1}A = \{\omega: T\omega \in A\} \in \mathcal{F}.$$

Definition 3. A measurable transformation T is a *measure-preserving transformation* (or morphism) if, for every $A \in F$,

$$\mathsf{P}(T^{-1}A) = \mathsf{P}(A).$$

Let T be a measure-preserving transformation, T^n its nth iterate, and $\xi_1 = \xi_1(\omega)$ a random variable. Put $\xi_k(\omega) = \xi_1(T^{n-1}\omega)$, $n \geq 2$, and consider the sequence $\xi = (\xi_1, \xi_2, \ldots)$. We claim that this sequence is stationary.

In fact, let $A = \{\omega: \xi \in B\}$ and $A_1 = \{\omega: \theta_1\xi \in B\}$, where $B \in \mathcal{B}(R^\infty)$. Since $A = \{\omega: (\xi_1(\omega), \xi_1(T\omega), \ldots) \in B\}$, and $A_1 = \{\omega: (\xi_1(T\omega), \xi_1(T^2\omega), \ldots) \in B\}$, we have $\omega \in A_1$ if and only if either $T\omega \in A$ or $A_1 = T^{-1}A$. But $\mathsf{P}(T^{-1}A) = \mathsf{P}(A)$, and therefore $\mathsf{P}(A_1) = \mathsf{P}(A)$. Similarly $\mathsf{P}(A_k) = \mathsf{P}(A)$ for every $A_k = \{\omega: \theta_k\xi \in B\}$, $k \geq 2$.

Thus we can use measure-preserving transformations to construct stationary (strict sense) random variables.

In a certain sense, there is a converse result: for every stationary sequence ξ considered on $(\Omega, \mathcal{F}, \mathsf{P})$ we can construct a new probability space $(\tilde{\Omega}, \tilde{\mathcal{F}}, \tilde{\mathsf{P}})$, a random variable $\tilde{\xi}_1(\tilde{\omega})$ and a measure-preserving transformation $\tilde{T}$, such that the distribution of $\tilde{\xi} = \{\tilde{\xi}_1(\tilde{\omega}), \tilde{\xi}_1(\tilde{T}\tilde{\omega}), \ldots\}$ coincides with the distribution of ξ.

In fact, take $\tilde{\Omega}$ to be the coordinate space R^∞ and put $\tilde{\mathcal{F}} = \mathcal{B}(R^\infty)$, $\tilde{\mathsf{P}} = P_\xi$, where $P_\xi(B) = \mathsf{P}\{\omega: \xi \in B\}$, $B \in \mathcal{B}(R^\infty)$. The action of $\tilde{T}$ on $\tilde{\Omega}$ is given by

$$\tilde{T}(x_1, x_2, \ldots) = (x_2, x_3, \ldots).$$

If $\tilde{\omega} = (x_1, x_2, \ldots)$, put

$$\tilde{\xi}_1(\tilde{\omega}) = x_1, \quad \tilde{\xi}_n(\tilde{\omega}) = \tilde{\xi}_1(\tilde{T}^{n-1}\tilde{\omega}), \qquad n \geq 2.$$

Now let $A = \{\tilde{\omega}: (x_1, \ldots, x_k) \in B\}$, $B \in \mathcal{B}(R^k)$, and

$$\tilde{T}^{-1}A = \{\tilde{\omega}: (x_2, \ldots, x_{k+1}) \in B\}.$$

Then the property of being stationary means that

$$\tilde{\mathsf{P}}(A) = \mathsf{P}\{\omega: (\xi_1, \ldots, \xi_k) \in B\} = \mathsf{P}\{\omega: (\xi_2, \ldots, \xi_{k+1}) \in B\} = \tilde{\mathsf{P}}(\tilde{T}^{-1}A),$$

i.e. T is a measure-preserving transformation. Since $\tilde{\mathsf{P}}\{\tilde{\omega}: (\tilde{\xi}_1, \ldots, \tilde{\xi}_k) \in B\} = \tilde{\mathsf{P}}\{\omega: (\xi_1, \ldots, \xi_k) \in B\}$ for every k, it follows that ξ and $\tilde{\xi}$ have the same distribution.

Here are some examples of measure-preserving transformations.

EXAMPLE 1. Let $\Omega = \{\omega_1, \ldots, \omega_n\}$ consist of n points (a finite number), $n \geq 2$, let $\mathscr{F}$ be the collection of its subsets, and let $T\omega_i = \omega_{i+1}$, $1 \leq i \leq n - 1$, and $T_{\omega_n} = \omega_1$. If $\mathsf{P}(\omega_i) = 1/n$, the transformation T is measure-preserving.

EXAMPLE 2. If $\Omega = [0, 1)$, $\mathscr{F} = \mathscr{B}([0, 1))$, P is Lebesgue measure, $\lambda \in [0, 1)$, then $Tx = (x + \lambda) \bmod 1$ and $T = 2x \bmod 1$ are both measure-preserving transformations.

2. Let us pause to consider the physical hypotheses that led to the consideration of measure-preserving transformations.

Let us suppose that Ω is the phase space of a system that evolves (in discrete time) according to a given law of motion. If ω is the state at instant $n = 1$, then $T^n\omega$, where T is the translation operator induced by the given law of motion, is the state attained by the system after n steps. Moreover, if A is some set of states ω then $T^{-1}A = \{\omega : T\omega \in A\}$ is, by definition, the set of states ω that lead to A in one step. Therefore if we interpret Ω as an incompressible fluid, the condition $P(T^{-1}A) = P(A)$ can be thought of as the rather natural condition of conservation of volume. (For the classical conservative Hamiltonian systems, Liouville's theorem asserts that the corresponding transformation T preserves Lebesgue measure.)

3. One of the earliest results on measure-preserving transformations was Poincaré's recurrence theorem (1912).

Theorem 1. *Let* $(\Omega, \mathscr{F}, \mathsf{P})$ *be a probability space, let* T *be a measure-preserving transformation, and let* $A \in F$. *Then, for almost every point* $\omega \in A$, *we have* $T^n\omega \in A$ *for infinitely many* $n \geq 1$.

PROOF. Let $C = \{\omega \in A : T^n\omega \notin A, \text{ for all } n \geq 1\}$. Since $C \cap T^{-n}C = \varnothing$ for all $n \geq 1$, we have $T^{-m}C \cap T^{-(m+n)}C = T^{-m}(C \cap T^{-n}C) = \varnothing$. Therefore the sequence $\{T^{-n}C\}$ consists of disjoint sets of equal measure. Therefore $\sum_{n=0}^{\infty} \mathsf{P}(C) = \sum_{n=0}^{\infty} \mathsf{P}(T^{-n}C) \leq \mathsf{P}(\Omega) = 1$ and consequently $\mathsf{P}(C) = 0$. Therefore, for almost every point $\omega \in A$, for at least one $n \geq 1$, we have $T^n\omega \in A$. It follows that $T^n\omega \in A$ for infinitely many n.

Let us apply the preceding result to T^k, $k \geq 1$. Then for every $\omega \in A \setminus N$, where N is a set of probability zero, the union of the corresponding sets corresponding to the various values of k, there is an n_k such that $(T^k)^{n_k}\omega \in A$. It is then clear that $T^n\omega \in A$ for infinitely many n. This completes the proof of the theorem.

Corollary. *Let* $\xi(\omega) \geq 0$. *Then*

$$\sum_{k=0}^{\infty} \xi(T^k\omega) = \infty \quad (\text{P-}a.s.)$$

on the set $\{\omega : \xi(\omega) > 0\}$.

In fact, let $A_n = \{\omega: \xi(\omega) \geq 1/n\}$. Then, according to the theorem, $\sum_{k=0}^{\infty} \xi(T^k\omega) = \infty$ (P-a.s.) on A_n, and the required result follows by letting $n \to \infty$.

Remark. The theorem remains valid if we replace the probability measure P by any finite measure μ with $\mu(\Omega) < \infty$.

4. PROBLEMS

1. Let T be a measure-preserving transformation and $\xi = \xi(\omega)$ a random variable whose expectation $E\xi(\omega)$ exists. Show that $E\xi(\omega) = E\xi(T\omega)$.

2. Show that the transformations in Examples 1 and 2 are measure-preserving.

3. Let $\Omega = [0, 1)$, $F = \mathscr{B}([0, 1))$ and let P be a measure whose distribution function is continuous. Show that the transformations $Tx = \lambda x, 0 < \lambda < 1$, and $Tx = x^2$ are not measure-preserving.

§2. Ergodicity and Mixing

1. In the present section T denotes a measure-preserving transformation on the probability space $(\Omega, \mathscr{F}, P)$.

Definition 1. A set $A \in \mathscr{F}$ is *invariant* if $T^{-1}A = A$. A set $A \in \mathscr{F}$ is *almost invariant* if A and $T^{-1}A$ differ only by a set of measure zero, i.e. $P(A \triangle T^{-1}A) = 0$.

It is easily verified that the classes $\mathscr{I}$ and $\mathscr{I}^*$ of invariant or almost invariant sets, respectively, are σ-algebras.

Definition 2. A measure-preserving transformation T is *ergodic* (or *metrically transitive*) if every invariant set A has measure either zero or one.

Definition 3. A random variable $\xi = \xi(\omega)$ is *invariant* (or *almost invariant*) if $\xi(\omega) = \xi(T\omega)$ for all $\omega \in \Omega$ (or for almost all $\omega \in \Omega$).

The following lemma establishes a connection between invariant and almost invariant sets.

Lemma 1. *If A is almost invariant, there is an invariant set B such that* $P(A \triangle B) = 0$.

PROOF. Let $B = \overline{\lim} \, T^{-n}A$. Then $T^{-1}B = \overline{\lim} \, T^{-(n+1)}A = B$, i.e. $B \in \mathscr{I}$. It is easily seen that $A \triangle B \subseteq \bigcup_{k=0}^{\infty} (T^{-k}A \triangle T^{-(k+1)}A)$. But

$$P(T^{-k}A \triangle T^{-(k+1)}A) = P(A \triangle T^{-1}A) = 0.$$

Hence $P(A \triangle B) = 0$.

Lemma 2. *A transformation T is ergodic if and only if every almost invariant set has measure zero or one.*

PROOF. Let $A \in \mathscr{I}^*$; then according to Lemma 1 there is an invariant set B such that $P(A \triangle B) = 0$. But T is ergodic and therefore $P(B) = 0$ or 1. Therefore $P(A) = 0$ or 1. The converse is evident, since $\mathscr{I} \subseteq \mathscr{I}^*$. This completes the proof of the lemma.

Theorem 1. *Let T be a measure-preserving transformation. Then the following conditions are equivalent:*

(1) *T is ergodic;*
(2) *every almost invariant random variable is (P-a.s.) constant;*
(3) *every invariant random variable is (P-a.s.) constant.*

PROOF. (1) $\Leftrightarrow$ (2). Let T be ergodic and ξ almost invariant, i.e. (P-a.s.) $\xi(\omega) = \xi(T\omega)$. Then for every $c \in R$ we have $A_c = \{\omega : \xi(\omega) \leq c\} \in \mathscr{I}^*$, and then $P(A_c) = 0$ or 1 by Lemma 2. Let $C = \sup\{c : P(A_c) = 0\}$. Since $A_c \uparrow \Omega$ as $c \uparrow \infty$ and $A_c \downarrow \varnothing$ as $c \downarrow -\infty$, we have $|C| < \infty$. Then

$$P\{\omega : \xi(\omega) < C\} = P\left\{\bigcup_{n=1}^{\infty} \left\{\xi(\omega) \leq C - \frac{1}{n}\right\}\right\} = 0$$

and similarly $P\{\omega : \xi(\omega) > C\} = 0$. Consequently $P\{\omega : \xi(\omega) = C\} = 1$.
  (2) $\Rightarrow$ (3). Evident.
  (3) $\Rightarrow$ (1). Let $A \in \mathscr{I}$; then I_A is an invariant random variable and therefore, (P-a.s.), $I_A = 0$ or $I_A = 1$, whence $P(A) = 0$ or 1,

Remark. The conclusion of the theorem remains valid in the case when "random variable" is replaced by "bounded random variable".

We illustrate the theorem with the following example.

EXAMPLE. Let $\Omega = [0, 1)$, $\mathscr{F} = \mathscr{B}([0, 1))$, let P be Lebesgue measure and let $T\omega = (\omega + \lambda) \bmod 1$. Let us show that T is ergodic if and only if λ is irrational.
  Let $\xi = \xi(\omega)$ be a random variable with $\mathsf{E}\xi^2(\omega) < \infty$. Then we know that the Fourier series $\sum_{n=-\infty}^{\infty} c_n e^{2\pi i n \omega}$ of $\xi(\omega)$ converges in the mean square sense, $\sum |c_n|^2 < \infty$, and, because T is a measure-preserving transformation (Example 2, §1), we have (Problem 1, §1) that for the random variable ξ

$$c_n \mathsf{E}\xi(\omega)e^{2\pi i n \xi(\omega)} = \mathsf{E}\xi(T\omega)e^{2\pi i n T\omega} = e^{2\pi i n \lambda}\mathsf{E}\xi(T\omega)e^{2\pi i n \omega}$$
$$= e^{2\pi i n \lambda}\mathsf{E}\xi(\omega)e^{2\pi i n \omega} = c_n e^{2\pi i n \lambda}.$$

So $c_n(1 - e^{2\pi i n \lambda}) = 0$. By hypothesis, λ is irrational and therefore $e^{2\pi i n \lambda} \neq 1$ for all $n \neq 0$. Therefore $c_n = 0$, $n \neq 0$, $\xi(\omega) = c_0$ (P-a.s.), and T is ergodic by Theorem 1.

On the other hand, let λ be rational, i.e. $\lambda = k/m$, where k and m are integers. Consider the set

$$A = \bigcup_{k=0}^{2m-2} \left\{ \omega: \frac{k}{2m} \leq \omega < \frac{k+1}{2m} \right\}.$$

It is clear that this set is invariant; but $P(A) = \frac{1}{2}$. Consequently T is not ergodic.

2. Definition 4. A measure-preserving transformation is *mixing* (or has the mixing property) if, for all A and $B \in F$,

$$\lim_{n \to \infty} P(A \cap T^{-n}B) = P(A)P(B). \tag{1}$$

The following theorem establishes a connection between ergodicity and mixing.

Theorem 2. *Every mixing transformation T is ergodic.*

PROOF. Let $A \in \mathcal{F}$, $B \in \mathcal{I}$. Then $B = T^{-n}B$, $n \geq 1$, and therefore

$$P(A \cap T^{-n}B) = P(A \cap B)$$

for all $n \geq 1$. Because of (1), $P(A \cap B) = P(A)P(B)$. Hence we find, when $A = B$, that $P(B) = P^2(B)$, and consequently $P(B) = 0$ or 1. This completes the proof.

3. PROBLEMS

1. Show that a random variable ξ is invariant if and only if it is $\mathcal{I}$-measurable.

2. Show that a set A is almost invariant if and only if either

$$P(T^{-1}A \setminus A) = 0 \quad \text{or} \quad P(A \setminus T^{-1}A) = 0.$$

3. Show that the transformation considered in the example of Subsection 1 of the present section is not mixing.

4. Show that a transformation is mixing if and only if, for all random variables ξ and η with $E\xi^2 < \infty$ and $E\eta^2 < \infty$,

$$E\xi(T^n\omega)\eta(\omega) \to E\xi(\omega)E\eta(\omega), \qquad n \to \infty.$$

§3. Ergodic Theorems

1. Theorem 1 (Birkhoff and Khinchin). *Let T be a measure-preserving transformation and $\xi = \xi(\omega)$ a random variable with $E|\xi| < \infty$. Then (P-a.s.)*

$$\lim_{n} \frac{1}{n} \sum_{k=0}^{n-1} \xi(T^k\omega) = E(\xi | \mathcal{I}). \tag{1}$$

If also T is ergodic then (P-a.s.)

$$\lim_n \frac{1}{n} \sum_{k=0}^{n-1} \xi(T^k \omega) = \mathsf{E}\xi. \tag{2}$$

The proof given below is based on the following proposition, whose simple proof was given by A. Garsia (1965).

Lemma (Maximal Ergodic Theorem). *Let T be a measure-preserving transformation, let ξ be a random variable with $\mathsf{E}|\xi| < \infty$, and let*

$$S_k(\omega) = \xi(\omega) + \xi(T\omega) + \cdots + \xi(T^{k-1}\omega),$$

$$M_k(\omega) = \max\{0, S_1(\omega), \ldots, S_k(\omega)\}.$$

Then

$$\mathsf{E}[\xi(\omega)I_{\{M_n > 0\}}(\omega)] \geq 0$$

for every $n \geq 1$.

PROOF. If $n \geq k$, we have $M_n(T\omega) \geq S_k(T\omega)$ and therefore $\xi(\omega) + M_n(T\omega) \geq \xi(\omega) + S_k(T\omega) = S_{k+1}(\omega)$. Since it is evident that $\xi(\omega) \geq S_1(\omega) - M_n(T\omega)$, we have

$$\xi(\omega) \geq \max\{S_1(\omega), \ldots, S_n(\omega)\} - M_n(T\omega).$$

Therefore

$$\mathsf{E}[\xi(\omega)I_{\{M_n > 0\}}(\omega)] \geq \mathsf{E}(\max(S_1(\omega), \ldots, S_n(\omega)) - M_n(T\omega)),$$

But $\max(S_1, \ldots, S_n) = M_n$ on the set $\{M_n > 0\}$. Consequently,

$$\mathsf{E}[\xi(\omega)I_{\{M_n > 0\}}(\omega)] \geq \mathsf{E}\{(M_n(\omega) - M_n(T\omega))I_{\{M_n(\omega) > 0\}}\}$$
$$\geq \mathsf{E}\{M_n(\omega) - M_n(T\omega)\} = 0,$$

since if T is a measure-preserving transformation we have $\mathsf{E}M_n(\omega) = \mathsf{E}M_n(T\omega)$ (Problem 1, §1).

This completes the proof of the lemma.

PROOF OF THE THEOREM. Let us suppose that $\mathsf{E}(\xi|\mathcal{I}) = 0$ (otherwise replace ξ by $\xi - \mathsf{E}(\xi|\mathcal{I})$).

Let $\bar{\eta} = \overline{\lim}(S_n/n)$ and $\underline{\eta} = \underline{\lim}(S_n/n)$. It will be enough to establish that (P-a.s.)

$$0 \leq \underline{\eta} \leq \bar{\eta} \leq 0.$$

Consider the random variable $\bar{\eta} = \bar{\eta}(\omega)$. Since $\bar{\eta}(\omega) = \bar{\eta}(T\omega)$, the variable $\bar{\eta}$ is invariant and consequently, for every $\varepsilon > 0$, the set $A_\varepsilon = \{\bar{\eta}(\omega) > \varepsilon\}$ is also invariant. Let us introduce the new random variable

$$\xi^*(\omega) = (\xi(\omega) - \varepsilon)I_A(\omega),$$

and put

$$S_k^*(\omega) = \xi^*(\omega) + \cdots + \xi^*(T^{k-1}\omega), \qquad M_k^*(\omega) = \max(0, S_1^*, \ldots, S_k^*).$$

Then, by the lemma,

$$E[\xi^* I_{\{M_n^* > 0\}}] \geq 0$$

for every $n \geq 1$. But as $n \to \infty$,

$$\{M_n^* > 0\} = \left\{ \max_{1 \leq k \leq n} S_k^* > 0 \right\} \uparrow \left\{ \sup_{k \geq 1} S_k^* > 0 \right\} = \left\{ \sup_{k \geq 1} \frac{S_k^*}{k} > 0 \right\}$$

$$= \left\{ \sup_{k \geq 1} \frac{S_k}{k} > \varepsilon \right\} \cap A_\varepsilon = A_\varepsilon,$$

where the last equation follows because $\sup_{k \geq 1}(S_k^*/k) \geq \bar{\eta}$, and $A_\varepsilon = \{\omega : \bar{\eta} > \varepsilon\}$.

Moreover, $E|\xi^*| \leq E|\xi| + \varepsilon$. Hence, by the dominated convergence theorem,

$$0 \leq E[\xi^* I_{\{M_n^* > 0\}}] \to E[\xi^* I_A].$$

Thus

$$0 \leq E[\xi^* I_{A_\varepsilon}] = E[(\xi - \varepsilon) I_{A_\varepsilon}] = E[\xi I_{A_\varepsilon}] - \varepsilon P(A_\varepsilon)$$
$$= E[E(\xi | \mathscr{I}) I_{A_\varepsilon}] - \varepsilon P(A_\varepsilon) = -\varepsilon P(A_\varepsilon),$$

so that $P(A_\varepsilon) = 0$ and therefore $P(\bar{\eta} \leq 0) = 1$.

Similarly, if we consider $-\xi(\omega)$ instead of $\xi(\omega)$, we find that

$$\overline{\lim}\left(-\frac{S_n}{n} \right) = -\underline{\lim} \frac{S_n}{n} = -\underline{\eta}$$

and $P(-\underline{\eta} \leq 0) = 1$, i.e. $P(\underline{\eta} \geq 0) = 1$. Therefore $0 \leq \underline{\eta} \leq \bar{\eta} \leq 0$ (P-a.s.) and the first part of the theorem is established.

To prove the second part, we observe that since $E(\xi | \mathscr{I})$ is an invariant random variable, we have $E(\xi | \mathscr{I}) = E\xi$ (P-a.s.) in the ergodic case.

This completes the proof of the theorem.

Corollary. *A measure-preserving transformation T is ergodic if and only if, for all A and $B \in \mathscr{F}$,*

$$\lim_n \frac{1}{n} \sum_{k=0}^{n-1} P(A \cap T^{-k}B) = P(A)P(B). \tag{3}$$

To prove the ergodicity of T we use $A = B \in \mathscr{I}$ in (3). Then $A \cap T^{-k}B = B$ and therefore $P(B) = P^2(B)$, i.e. $P(B) = 0$ or 1. Conversely, let T be ergodic. Then if we apply (2) to the random variable $\xi = I_B(\omega)$, where $B \in \mathscr{F}$, we find that (P-a.s.)

$$\lim_n \frac{1}{n} \sum_{k=0}^{n-1} I_{T^{-k}B}(\omega) = P(B).$$

If we now integrate both sides over $A \in \mathscr{F}$ and use the dominated convergence theorem, we obtain (3) as required.

2. We now show that, under the hypotheses of Theorem 1, there is not only almost sure convergence in (1) and (2), but also convergence in mean. (This result will be used below in the proof of Theorem 3.)

Theorem 2. *Let T be a measure-preserving transformation and let $\xi = \xi(\omega)$ be a random variable with $\mathsf{E}\,|\xi| < \infty$. Then*

$$\mathsf{E} \left| \frac{1}{n} \sum_{k=0}^{n-1} \xi(T^k \omega) - \mathsf{E}(\xi \mid \mathscr{I}) \right| \to 0, \qquad n \to \infty. \tag{4}$$

If also T is ergodic, then

$$\mathsf{E} \left| \frac{1}{n} \sum_{k=0}^{n-1} \xi(T^k \omega) - \mathsf{E}\xi \right| \to 0, \qquad n \to \infty. \tag{5}$$

PROOF. For every $\varepsilon > 0$ there is a bounded random variable $\eta(|\eta(\omega)| \le M)$ such that $\mathsf{E}\,|\xi - \eta| \le \varepsilon$. Then

$$\mathsf{E} \left| \frac{1}{n} \sum_{k=0}^{n-1} \xi(T^k \omega) - \mathsf{E}(\xi \mid \mathscr{I}) \right| \le \mathsf{E} \left| \frac{1}{n} \sum_{k=0}^{n-1} (\xi(T^k \omega) - \eta(T^k \omega)) \right|$$

$$+ \mathsf{E} \left| \frac{1}{n} \sum_{k=0}^{n-1} \eta(T^k \omega) - \mathsf{E}(\eta \mid \mathscr{I}) \right| + \mathsf{E}\,|\mathsf{E}(\xi \mid \mathscr{I}) - \mathsf{E}(\eta \mid \mathscr{I})|. \tag{6}$$

Since $|\eta| \le M$, then by the dominated convergence theorem and by using (1) we find that the second term on the right of (6) tends to zero as $n \to \infty$. The first and third terms are each at most ε. Hence for sufficiently large n the left-hand side of (6) is less than 2ε, so that (4) is proved. Finally, if T is ergodic, then (5) follows from (4) and the remark that $\mathsf{E}(\xi \mid I) = \mathsf{E}\xi$ (P-a.s.).

This completes the proof of the theorem.

3. We now turn to the question of the validity of the ergodic theorem for stationary (strict sense) random sequences $\xi = (\xi_1, \xi_2, \ldots)$ defined on a probability space $(\Omega, \mathscr{F}, \mathsf{P})$. In general, $(\Omega, \mathscr{F}, \mathsf{P})$ need not carry any measure-preserving transformations, so that it is not possible to apply Theorem 1 directly. However, as we observed in §1, we can construct a coordinate probability space $(\tilde{\Omega}, \tilde{\mathscr{F}}, \tilde{\mathsf{P}})$, random variables $\tilde{\xi} = (\tilde{\xi}_1, \tilde{\xi}_2, \ldots)$, and a measure-preserving transformation $\tilde{T}$ such that $\tilde{\xi}_n(\tilde{\omega}) = \tilde{\xi}_1(\tilde{T}^{n-1}\tilde{\omega})$ and the distributions of ξ and $\tilde{\xi}$ are the same. Since such properties as almost sure convergence and convergence in the mean are defined only for probability distributions, from the convergence of $(1/n)\sum_{k=1}^{n} \tilde{\xi}_1(\tilde{T}^{k-1}\tilde{\omega})$ (P-a.s. and in mean) to a random variable $\tilde{\eta}$ it follows that $(1/n)\sum_{k=1}^{n} \xi_k(\omega)$ also converges (P-a.s. and in mean) to a random variable η such that $\eta \stackrel{d}{=} \tilde{\eta}$. It

follows from Theorem 1 that if $\tilde{\mathsf{E}}|\tilde{\xi}_1| < \infty$ then $\quad = \tilde{E}(\tilde{\xi}_1|\tilde{\mathscr{I}})$, where $\tilde{\mathscr{I}}$ is a collection of invariant sets ($\tilde{\mathsf{E}}$ is the average with respect to the measure $\tilde{\mathsf{P}}$). We now describe the structure of η.

Definition 1. A set $A \in \mathscr{F}$ is *invariant* with respect to the sequence ξ if there is a set $B \in \mathscr{B}(R\infty)$ such that for $n \geq 1$

$$A = \{\omega : (\xi_n, \xi_{n+1}, \ldots) \in B\}.$$

The collection of all such invariant sets is a σ-algebra, denoted by $\mathscr{I}_\xi$.

Definition 2. A stationary sequence ξ is *ergodic* if the measure of every invariant set is either 0 or 1.

Let us now show that the random variable η can be taken equal to $\mathsf{E}(\xi_1|\mathscr{I}_\xi)$. In fact, let $A \in \mathscr{I}_\xi$. Then since

$$\mathsf{E}\left|\frac{1}{n}\sum_{k=1}^{n-1}\xi_k - \eta\right| \to 0,$$

we have

$$\frac{1}{n}\sum_{k=1}^{n}\int_A \xi_k\, dP \to \int_A \eta\, dP. \tag{7}$$

Let $B \in \mathscr{B}(R^\infty)$ be such that $A = \{\omega : (\xi_k, \xi_{k+1}, \ldots) \in B\}$ for all $k \geq 1$. Then since ξ is stationary,

$$\int_A \xi_k\, dP = \int_{\{\omega : (\xi_k, \xi_{k+1}, \cdots) \in B\}} \xi_k\, dP = \int_{\{\omega : (\xi_1, \xi_2, \cdots) \in B\}} \xi_1\, dP = \int_A \xi_1\, dP.$$

Hence it follows from (7) that for all $A \in \mathscr{I}_\xi$, which implies (see §7, Chapter II) that $\eta = \mathsf{E}(\xi_1|\mathscr{I}_\xi)$. Here $\mathsf{E}(\xi_1|\mathscr{I}_\xi) = \mathsf{E}\xi_1$ if ξ is ergodic.

Therefore we have proved the following theorem.

Theorem 3 (Ergodic Theorem). *Let* $\xi = (\xi_1, \xi_2, \ldots)$ *be a stationary (strict sense) random sequence with* $\mathsf{E}|\xi_1| < \infty$. *Then* (P-*a.s., and in the mean*)

$$\lim \frac{1}{n}\sum_{k=1}^{n}\xi_k(\omega) = \mathsf{E}(\xi_1|\mathscr{I}_\xi).$$

If ξ *is also an ergodic sequence, then* (P-*a.s., and in the mean*)

$$\lim \frac{1}{n}\sum_{k=1}^{n}\xi_k(\omega) = \mathsf{E}\xi_1.$$

---

4. PROBLEMS

1. Let $\xi = (\xi_1, \xi_2, \ldots)$ be a Gaussian stationary sequence with $\mathsf{E}\xi_n = 0$ and covariance function $R(n) = \mathsf{E}\xi_{k+n}\xi_k$. Show that $R(n) \to 0$ is a sufficient condition for ξ to be ergodic.

2. Show that every sequence $\xi = (\xi_1, \xi_2, \ldots)$ of independent identically distributed random variables is ergodic.

3. Show that a stationary sequence ξ is ergodic if and only if

$$\frac{1}{n} \sum_{i-1}^{n} I_B(\xi_i, \ldots, \xi_{i+k}) \to P((\xi_1, \ldots, \xi_{1+k}) \in B) \quad \text{(P-a.s.)}$$

for every $B \in \mathcal{B}(R)$, $k = 1, 2, \ldots$.

CHAPTER VI
Stationary (Wide Sense) Random Sequences. L^2-Theory

§1. Spectral Representation of the Covariance Function

1. According to the definition given in the preceding chapter, a random sequence $\xi = (\xi_1, \xi_2, \ldots)$ is stationary in the strict sense if, for every set $B \in \mathcal{B}(R^\infty)$ and every $n \geq 1$,

$$P\{(\xi_1, \xi_2, \ldots) \in B\} = P\{(\xi_{n+1}, \xi_{n+2}, \ldots) \in B\}. \tag{1}$$

It follows, in particular, that if $E\xi_1^2 < \infty$ then $E\xi_n$ is independent of n:

$$E\xi_n = E\xi_1, \tag{2}$$

and the covariance $\text{cov}(\xi_{n+m}\xi_n) = E(\xi_{n+m} - E\xi_{n+m})(\xi_n - E\xi_n)$ depends only on m:

$$\text{cov}(\xi_{n+m}, \xi_n) = \text{cov}(\xi_{1+m}, \xi_1). \tag{3}$$

In the present chapter we study sequences that are stationary in the wide sense (and have finite second moments), namely those for which (1) is replaced by the (weaker) conditions (2) and (3).

The random variables ξ_n are understood to be defined for $n \in \mathbb{Z} = \{0, \pm 1, \ldots\}$ and to be complex-valued. The latter assumption not only does not complicate the theory, but makes it more elegant. It is also clear that results for real random variables can easily be obtained as special cases of the corresponding results for complex random variables.

Let $H^2 = H^2(\Omega, \mathcal{F}, P)$ be the space of (complex) random variables $\xi = \alpha + i\beta$, α, $\beta \in R$, with $E|\xi|^2 < \infty$, where $|\xi|^2 = \alpha^2 + \beta^2$. If ξ and $\eta \in H^2$, we put

$$(\xi, \eta) = E\xi\bar{\eta}, \tag{4}$$

where $\bar\eta = \alpha - i\beta$ is the complex conjugate of $\eta = \alpha + i\beta$ and

$$\|\xi\| = (\xi, \xi)^{1/2}. \tag{5}$$

As for real random variables, the space H^2 (more precisely, the space of equivalence classes of random variables; compare §§10 and 11 of Chapter II) is complete under the scalar product (ξ, η) and norm $\|\xi\|$. In accordance with the terminology of functional analysis, H^2 is called the complex (or unitary) Hilbert space (of random variables considered on the probability space $(\Omega, \mathscr{F}, P)$).

If $\xi, \eta \in H^2$ their *covariance* is

$$\operatorname{cov}(\xi, \eta) = E(\xi - E\xi)(\overline{\eta - E\eta}). \tag{6}$$

It follows from (4) and (6) that if $E\xi = E\eta = 0$ then

$$\operatorname{cov}(\xi, \eta) = (\xi, \eta). \tag{7}$$

Definition. A sequence of complex random variables $\xi = (\xi_n)_{n \in \mathbb{Z}}$ with $E|\xi_n|^2 < \infty$, $n \in \mathbb{Z}$, is *stationary (in the wide sense)* if, for all $n \in \mathbb{Z}$,

$$E\xi_n = E\xi_0,$$

$$\operatorname{cov}(\xi_{k+n}, \xi_k) = \operatorname{cov}(\xi_n, \xi_0), \qquad k \in \mathbb{Z}. \tag{8}$$

As a matter of convenience, we shall always suppose that $E\xi_0 = 0$. This involves no loss of generality, but does make it possible (by (7)) to identify the covariance with the scalar product and hence to apply the methods and results of the theory of Hilbert spaces.

Let us write

$$R(n) = \operatorname{cov}(\xi_n, \xi_0), \qquad n \in \mathbb{Z}, \tag{9}$$

and (assuming $R(0) = E|\xi_0|^2 \neq 0$)

$$\rho(n) = \frac{R(n)}{R(0)}, \qquad n \in \mathbb{Z}. \tag{10}$$

We call $R(n)$ the *covariance function*, and $\rho(n)$, the *correlation function*, of the sequence ξ (assumed stationary in the wide sense).

It follows immediately from (9) that $R(n)$ is nonnegative-definite, i.e. for all complex numbers $a_1, \ldots, a_m$ and $t_1, \ldots, t_m \in \mathbb{Z}$, $m \geq 1$, we have

$$\sum_{i, j = 1}^m a_i \bar{a}_j R(t_i - t_j) \geq 0. \tag{11}$$

It is then easy to deduce (either from (11) or directly from (9)) the following properties of the covariance function (see Problem 1):

$$R(0) \geq 0, \qquad R(-n) = \overline{R(n)}, \qquad |R(n)| \leq R(0),$$

$$|R(n) - R(m)|^2 \leq 2R(0)[R(0) - \operatorname{Re} R(n - m)]. \tag{12}$$

2. Let us give some examples of stationary sequences $\xi = (\xi_n)_{n\in\mathbb{Z}}$. (From now on, the words "in the wide sense" and the statement $n \in \mathbb{Z}$ will both be omitted.)

EXAMPLE 1. Let $\xi_n = \xi_0 \cdot g(n)$, where $\mathsf{E}\xi_0 = 0$, $\mathsf{E}\xi_0^2 = 1$ and $g = g(n)$ is a function. The sequence $\xi = (\xi_n)$ will be stationary if and only if $g(k+n)\overline{g(k)}$ depends only on n. Hence it is easy to see that there is a λ such that

$$g(n) = g(0)e^{i\lambda n}.$$

Consequently the sequence of random variables

$$\xi_n = \xi_0 \cdot g(0)e^{i\lambda n}$$

is stationary with

$$R(n) = |g(0)|^2 e^{i\lambda n}.$$

In particular, the random "constant" $\xi \equiv \xi_0$ is a stationary sequence.

EXAMPLE 2. *An almost periodic sequence.* Let

$$\xi_n = \sum_{k=1}^{N} z_k e^{i\lambda_k n}, \tag{13}$$

where $z_1, \ldots, z_N$ are orthogonal $(\mathsf{E}z_i\bar{z}_j = 0, i \neq j)$ random variables with zero means and $\mathsf{E}|z_k|^2 = \sigma_k^2 > 0$; $-\pi \leq \lambda_k < \pi$, $k = 1, \ldots, N$; $\lambda_i \neq \lambda_j$, $i \neq j$. The sequence $\xi = (\xi_n)$ is stationary with

$$R(n) = \sum_{k=1}^{N} \sigma_k^2 e^{i\lambda_k n}. \tag{14}$$

As a generalization of (13) we now suppose that

$$\xi_n = \sum_{k=-\infty}^{\infty} z_k e^{i\lambda_k n}, \tag{15}$$

where z_k, $k \in \mathbb{Z}$, have the same properties as in (13). If we suppose that $\sum_{k=-\infty}^{\infty} \sigma_k^2 < \infty$, the series on the right of (15) converges in mean-square and

$$R(n) = \sum_{k=-\infty}^{\infty} \sigma_k^2 e^{i\lambda_k n}. \tag{16}$$

Let us introduce the function

$$F(\lambda) = \sum_{\{k:\, \lambda_k \leq \lambda\}} \sigma_k^2. \tag{17}$$

Then the covariance function (16) can be written as a Lebesgue–Stieltjes integral,

$$R(n) = \int_{-\pi}^{\pi} e^{i\lambda n}\, dF(\lambda). \tag{18}$$

The stationary sequence (15) is represented as a sum of "harmonics" $e^{i\lambda_k n}$ with "frequencies" λ_k and random "amplitudes" z_k of "intensities" $\sigma_k^2 = \mathsf{E}|z_k|^2$. Consequently the values of $F(\lambda)$ provide complete information on the "spectrum" of the sequence ξ, i.e. on the intensity with which each frequency appears in (15). By (18), the values of $F(\lambda)$ also completely determine the structure of the covariance function $R(n)$.

Up to a constant multiple, a (nondegenerate) $F(\lambda)$ is evidently a distribution function, which in the examples considered so far has been piecewise constant. It is quite remarkable that the covariance function of every stationary (wide sense) random sequence can be represented (see the theorem in Subsection 3) in the form (18), where $F(\lambda)$ is a distribution function (up to normalization), whose support is concentrated on $[-\pi, \pi)$, i.e. $F(\lambda) = 0$ for $\lambda < -\pi$ and $F(\lambda) = F(\pi)$ for $\lambda > \pi$.

The result on the integral representation of the covariance function, if compared with (15) and (16), suggests that every stationary sequence also admits an "integral" representation. This is in fact the case, as will be shown in §3 by using what we shall learn to call stochastic integrals with respect to orthogonal stochastic measures (§2).

EXAMPLE 3 (White noise). Let $\varepsilon = (\varepsilon_n)$ be an orthonormal sequence of random variables, $\mathsf{E}\varepsilon_n = 0$, $\mathsf{E}\varepsilon_i\bar{\varepsilon}_j = \delta_{ij}$, where δ_{ij} is the Kronecker delta. Such a sequence is evidently stationary, and

$$R(n) = \begin{cases} 1 & n = 0, \\ 0, & n \neq 0. \end{cases}$$

Observe that $R(n)$ can be represented in the form

$$R(n) = \int_{-\pi}^{\pi} e^{i\lambda n}\, dF(\lambda), \tag{19}$$

where

$$F(\lambda) = \int_{-\pi}^{\lambda} f(v)\, dv; \quad f(\lambda) = \frac{1}{2\pi}, \quad -\pi \leq \lambda < \pi. \tag{20}$$

Comparison of the spectral functions (17) and (20) shows that whereas the spectrum in Example 2 is discrete, in the present example it is absolutely continuous with constant "spectral density" $f(\lambda) \equiv \frac{1}{2}\pi$. In this sense we can say that the sequence $\varepsilon = (\varepsilon_n)$ "consists of harmonics of equal intensities." It is just this property that has led to calling such a sequence $\varepsilon = (\varepsilon_n)$ "white noise" by analogy with white light, which consists of different frequencies with the same intensities.

EXAMPLE 4 (Moving averages) Starting from the white noise $\varepsilon = (\varepsilon_n)$ introduced in Example 3, let us form the new sequence

$$\xi_n = \sum_{k=-\infty}^{\infty} a_k \varepsilon_{n-k}, \tag{21}$$

where a_k are complex numbers such that $\sum_{k=-\infty}^{\infty} |a_k|^2 < \infty$. By Parseval's equation,

$$\text{cov}(\xi_{n+m}, \xi_m) = \text{cov}(\xi_n, \xi_0) = \sum_{k=-\infty}^{\infty} a_{n+k}\bar{a}_k,$$

so that $\xi = (\xi_k)$ is a stationary sequence, which we call the sequence obtained from $\varepsilon = (\varepsilon_k)$ by a (*two-sided*) *moving average*.

In the special case when the a_k of negative index are zero, i.e.

$$\xi_n = \sum_{k=0}^{\infty} a_k \varepsilon_{n-k},$$

the sequence $\xi = (\xi_n)$ is a *one-sided moving average*. If, in addition, $a_k = 0$ for $k > p$, i.e. if

$$\xi_n = a_0 \varepsilon_n + a_1 \varepsilon_{n-1} + \cdots + a_p \varepsilon_{n-p}, \tag{22}$$

then $\xi = (\xi_n)$ is a *moving average of order p*.

We can show (Problem 5) that (22) has a covariance function of the form $R(n) = \int_{-\pi}^{\pi} e^{i\lambda n} f(\lambda)\, d\lambda$, where the spectral density is

$$f(\lambda) = \frac{1}{2\pi} |P(e^{-i\lambda})|^2 \tag{23}$$

with

$$P(z) = a_0 + a_1 z + \cdots + a_p z^p.$$

EXAMPLE 5 (Autoregression). Again let $\varepsilon = (\varepsilon_n)$ be white noise. We say that a random sequence $\xi = (\xi_n)$ is described by an *autoregressive model* of order q if

$$\xi_n + b_1 \xi_{n-1} + \cdots + b_q \xi_{n-q} = \varepsilon_n. \tag{24}$$

Under what conditions on $b_1, \ldots, b_n$ can we say that (24) has a stationary solution? To find an answer, let us begin with the case $q = 1$:

$$\xi_n = \alpha \xi_{n-1} + \varepsilon_n, \tag{25}$$

where $\alpha = -b_1$. If $|\alpha| < 1$, it is easy to verify that the stationary sequence $\tilde{\xi} = (\tilde{\xi}_n)$ with

$$\tilde{\xi}_n = \sum_{j=0}^{\infty} \alpha^j \varepsilon_{n-j} \tag{26}$$

is a solution of (25). (The series on the right of (26) converges in mean-square.) Let us now show that, in the class of stationary sequences $\xi = (\xi_n)$ (with finite second moments) this is the only solution. In fact, we find from (25), by successive iteration, that

$$\xi_n = \alpha \xi_{n-1} + \varepsilon_n = \alpha[\alpha \xi_{n-2} + \varepsilon_{n-1}] + \varepsilon_n = \cdots = \alpha^k \xi_{n-k} + \sum_{j=0}^{k-1} \alpha^j \varepsilon_{n-j}.$$

Hence it follows that

$$\mathsf{E}\left[\xi_n - \sum_{j=0}^{k-1} \alpha^j \varepsilon_{n-j}\right]^2 = \mathsf{E}[\alpha^k \xi_{n-k}]^2 = \alpha^{2k} \mathsf{E}\xi_{n-k}^2 = \alpha^{2k} \mathsf{E}\xi_0^2 \to 0, \qquad k \to \infty.$$

Therefore when $|\alpha| < 1$ a stationary solution of (25) exists and is representable as the one-sided moving average (26).

There is a similar result for every $q > 1$: if all the zeros of the polynomial

$$Q(z) = 1 + b_1 z + \cdots + b_q z^q \tag{27}$$

lie outside the unit disk, then the autoregression equation (24) has a unique stationary solution, which is representable as a one-sided moving average (Problem 2). Here the covariance function $R(n)$ can be represented (Problem 5) in the form

$$R(n) = \int_{-\pi}^{\pi} e^{i\lambda n} \, dF(\lambda), \qquad F(\lambda) = \int_{-\pi}^{\lambda} f(v) \, dv, \tag{28}$$

where

$$f(\lambda) = \frac{1}{2\pi} \cdot \frac{1}{|Q(e^{-i\lambda})|^2}. \tag{29}$$

In the special case $q = 1$, we find easily from (25) that $\mathsf{E}\xi_0 = 0$,

$$\mathsf{E}\xi_0^2 = \frac{1}{1 - |\alpha|^2},$$

and

$$R(n) = \frac{\alpha^n}{1 - |\alpha|^2}, \qquad n \geq 0$$

(when $n < 0$ we have $R(n) = \overline{R(-n)}$), Here

$$f(\lambda) = \frac{1}{2\pi} \cdot \frac{1}{|1 - \alpha e^{-i\lambda}|^2}.$$

EXAMPLE 6. This example illustrates how autoregression arises in the construction of probabilistic models in hydrology. Consider a body of water; we try to construct a probabilistic model of the deviations of the level of the water from its average value because of variations in the inflow and evaporation from the surface.

If we take a year as the unit of time and let H_n denote the water level in year n, we obtain the following *balance equation*:

$$H_{n+1} = H_n - KS(H_n) + \Sigma_{n+1}, \tag{30}$$

where Σ_{n+1} is the inflow in year $(n + 1)$, $S(H)$ is the area of the surface of the water at level H, and K is the coefficient of evaporation.

Let $\xi_n = H_n - \bar{H}$ be the deviation from the mean level (which is obtained from observations over many years) and suppose that $S(H) = S(\bar{H}) + c(H - \bar{H})$. Then it follows from the balance equation that ξ_n satisfies

$$\xi_{n+1} = \alpha\xi_n + \varepsilon_{n+1} \tag{31}$$

with $\alpha = 1 - cK$, $\varepsilon_n = \Sigma_n - KS(\bar{H})$. It is natural to assume that the random variables ε_n have zero means and are identically distributed. Then, as we showed in Example 5, equation (31) has (for $|\alpha| < 1$) a unique stationary solution, which we think of as the steady-state solution (with respect to time in years) of the oscillations of the level in the body of water.

As an example of practical conclusions that can be drawn from a (theoretical) model (31), we call attention to the possibility of predicting the level for the following year from the results of the observations of the present and preceding years. It turns out (see also Example 2 in §6) that (in the mean-square sense) the optimal linear estimator of ξ_{n+1} in terms of the values of $\ldots, \xi_{n-1}, \xi_n$ is simply $\alpha\xi_n$.

EXAMPLE 7 (Autoregression and moving average (mixed model)). If we suppose that the right-hand side of (24) contains $\alpha_0\varepsilon_n + \alpha_1\varepsilon_{n-1} + \cdots + \alpha_p\varepsilon_{n-p}$ instead of ε_n, we obtain a mixed model with autoregression and moving average of order (p, q):

$$\xi_n + b_1\xi_{n-1} + \cdots + b_q\xi_{n-q} = a_0\varepsilon_n + a_1\varepsilon_{n-1} + \cdots + a_p\varepsilon_{n-p}. \tag{32}$$

Under the same hypotheses as in Example 5 on the zeros it will be shown later (Corollary 2 to Theorem 3 of §3) that (32) has the stationary solution $\xi = (\xi_n)$ for which the covariance function is $R(n) = \int_{-\pi}^{\pi} e^{i\lambda n} dF(\lambda)$ with $F(\lambda) = \int_{-\pi}^{\lambda} f(v)\, dv$, where

$$f(\lambda) = \frac{1}{2\pi} \cdot \left| \frac{P(e^{-i\lambda})}{Q(e^{-i\lambda})} \right|^2.$$

3. Theorem (Herglotz). *Let $R(n)$ be the covariance function of a stationary (wide sense) random sequence with zero mean. Then there is, on*

$$([-\pi, \pi), \mathscr{B}([-\pi, \pi))),$$

a finite measure $F = F(B)$, $B \in \mathscr{B}([-\pi, \pi))$, such that for every $n \in \mathbb{Z}$

$$R(n) = \int_{-\pi}^{\pi} e^{i\lambda n} F(d\lambda). \tag{33}$$

PROOF. For $N \geq 1$ and $\lambda \in [-\pi, \pi]$, put

$$f_N(\lambda) = \frac{1}{2\pi N} \sum_{k=1}^{N} \sum_{l=1}^{N} R(k - l)e^{-ik\lambda}e^{il\lambda}. \tag{34}$$

Since $R(n)$ is nonnegative definite, $f_N(\lambda)$ is nonnegative. Since there are $N - |m|$ pairs (k, l) for which $k - l = m$, we have

$$f_N(\lambda) = \frac{1}{2\pi} \sum_{|m| < N} \left(1 - \frac{|m|}{N}\right) R(m) e^{-im\lambda}. \qquad (35)$$

Let

$$F_N(B) = \int_B f_N(\lambda) \, d\lambda, \qquad B \in \mathcal{B}([-\pi, \pi)).$$

Then

$$\int_{-\pi}^{\pi} e^{i\lambda n} F_N(d\lambda) = \int_{-\pi}^{\pi} e^{i\lambda n} f_N(\lambda) \, d\lambda = \begin{cases} \left(1 - \dfrac{|n|}{N}\right) R(n), & |n| < N, \\ 0, & |n| \geq N. \end{cases} \qquad (36)$$

The measures F_N, $N \geq 1$, are supported on the interval $[-\pi, \pi]$ and $F_N([-\pi, \pi]) = R(0) < \infty$ for all $N \geq 1$. Consequently the family of measures $\{F_N\}$, $N \geq 1$, is tight, and by Prohorov's theorem (Theorem 1 of §2 of Chapter III) there are a sequence $\{N_k\} \subseteq \{N\}$ and a measure F such that $F_{N_k} \xrightarrow{w} F$. (The concepts of tightness, relative compactness, and weak convergence, together with Prohorov's theorem, can be extended in an obvious way from probability measures to any finite measures.)

It then follows from (36) that

$$\int_{-\pi}^{\pi} e^{i\lambda n} F(d\lambda) = \lim_{N_k \to \infty} \int_{-\pi}^{\pi} e^{i\lambda n} F_{N_k}(d\lambda) = R(n).$$

The measure F so constructed is supported on $[-\pi, \pi]$. Without changing the integral $\int_{-\infty}^{\infty} e^{i\lambda n} F(d\lambda)$, we can redefine F by transferring the "mass" $F(\{\pi\})$, which is concentrated at π, to $-\pi$. The resulting new measure (which we again denote by F) will be supported on $[-\pi, \pi)$.

This completes the proof of the theorem.

Remark 1. The measure $F = F(B)$ involved in (33) is known as the *spectral measure*, and $F(\lambda) = F([-\pi, \lambda])$ as the *spectral function*, of the stationary sequence with covariance function $R(n)$.

In Example 2 above the spectral measure was discrete (concentrated at λ_k, $k = 0, \pm 1, \ldots$). In Examples 3–6 the spectral measures were absolutely continuous.

Remark 2. The spectral measure F is uniquely defined by the covariance function. In fact, let F_1 and F_2 be two spectral measures and let

$$\int_{-\pi}^{\pi} e^{i\lambda n} F_1(d\lambda) = \int_{-\pi}^{\pi} e^{i\lambda n} F_2(d\lambda), \qquad n \in \mathbb{Z}.$$

Since every bounded continuous function $g(\lambda)$ can be uniformly approximated on $[-\pi, \pi)$ by trigonometric polynomials, we have

$$\int_{-\pi}^{\pi} g(\lambda) F_1(d\lambda) = \int_{-\pi}^{\pi} g(\lambda) F_2(d\lambda).$$

It follows (compare the proof in Theorem 2, §12, Chapter II) that $F_1(B) = F_2(B)$ for all $B \in \mathcal{B}([-\pi, \pi))$.

Remark 3. If $\xi = (\xi_n)$ is a stationary sequence of real random variables ξ_n, then

$$R(n) = \int_{-\pi}^{\pi} \cos \lambda n \, F(d\lambda).$$

4. PROBLEMS

1. Derive (12) from (11).

2. Show that the autoregression equation (24) has a stationary solution if all the zeros of the polynomial $Q(z)$ defined by (27) lie outside the unit disk.

3. Prove that the covariance function (28) admits the representation (29) with spectral density given by (30).

4. Show that the sequence $\xi = (\xi_n)$ of random variables, where

$$\xi_n = \sum_{k=1}^{\infty} (\alpha_k \sin \lambda_k n + \beta_k \cos \lambda_k n)$$

and α_k and β_k are real random variables, can be represented in the form

$$\xi_n = \sum_{k=-\infty}^{\infty} z_k e^{i\lambda_k n}$$

with $z_k = \frac{1}{2}(\beta_k - i\alpha_k)$ for $k \geq 0$ and $z_k = \bar{z}_{-k}$, $\lambda_k = -\lambda_{-k}$ for $k < 0$.

5. Show that the spectral functions of the sequences (22) and (24) have densities given respectively by (23) and (29).

6. Show that if $\sum |R(n)| < \infty$, the spectral function $F(\lambda)$ has density $f(\lambda)$ given by

$$f(\lambda) = \frac{1}{2\pi} \sum_{n=-\infty}^{\infty} e^{-i\lambda n} R(n).$$

§2. Orthogonal Stochastic Measures and Stochastic Integrals

1. As we observed in §1, the integral representation of the covariance function and the example of a stationary sequence

$$\xi_n = \sum_{k=-\infty}^{\infty} z_k e^{i\lambda_k n} \tag{1}$$

with pairwise orthogonal random variables z_k, $k \in \mathbb{Z}$, suggest the possibility of representing an arbitrary stationary sequence as a corresponding integral generalization of (1).

If we put

$$Z(\lambda) = \sum_{\{k:\, \lambda_k \leq \lambda\}} z_k, \tag{2}$$

we can rewrite (1) in the form

$$\xi_n = \sum_{k=-\infty}^{\infty} e^{i\lambda_k n}\, \Delta Z(\lambda_k), \tag{3}$$

where $\Delta Z(\lambda_k) \equiv Z(\lambda_k) - Z(\lambda_k -) = z_k$.

The right-hand side of (3) reminds us of an approximating sum for an integral $\int_{-\pi}^{\pi} e^{i\lambda n}\, dZ(\lambda)$ of Riemann–Stieltjes type. However, in the present case $Z(\lambda)$ is a random function (it also depends on ω). Hence it is clear that for an integral representation of a general stationary sequence we need to use functions $Z(\lambda)$ that do not have bounded variation for each ω. Consequently the simple interpretation of $\int_{-\pi}^{\pi} e^{i\lambda n}\, dZ(\lambda)$ as a Riemann–Stieltjes integral for each ω is inapplicable.

2. By analogy with the general ideas of the Lebesgue, Lebesgue–Stieltjes and Riemann–Stieltjes integrals (§6, Chapter II), we begin by defining stochastic measure.

Let $(\Omega, \mathscr{F}, \mathsf{P})$ be a probability space, and let E be a subset, with an algebra $\mathscr{E}_0$ of subsets and the σ-algebra $\mathscr{E}$ generated by $\mathscr{E}_0$.

Definition 1. A complex-valued function $Z(\Delta) = Z(\omega; \Delta)$, defined for $\omega \in \Omega$ and $\Delta \in \mathscr{E}_0$, is a *finitely additive stochastic measure* if

(1) $\mathsf{E}|Z(\Delta)|^2 < \infty$ for every $\Delta \in \mathscr{E}_0$;
(2) for every pair Δ_1 and Δ_2 of disjoint sets in $\mathscr{E}_0$,

$$Z(\Delta_1 + \Delta_2) = Z(\Delta_1) + Z(\Delta_2) \quad \text{(P-a.s.)} \tag{4}$$

Definition 2. A finitely additive stochastic measure $Z(\Delta)$ is an *elementary stochastic measure* if, for all disjoint sets $\Delta_1, \Delta_2, \ldots$ of $\mathscr{E}_0$ such that $\Delta = \sum_{k=1}^{\infty} \Delta_k \in \mathscr{E}_0$,

$$\mathsf{E}\left| Z(\Delta) - \sum_{k=1}^{n} Z(\Delta_k) \right|^2 \to 0, \qquad n \to \infty. \tag{5}$$

Remark 1. In this definition of an elementary stochastic measure on subsets of $\mathscr{E}_0$, it is assumed that its values are in the Hilbert space $H^2 = H^2(\Omega, \mathscr{F}, \mathsf{P})$, and that countable additivity is understood in the mean-square sense (5). There are other definitions of stochastic measures, without the requirement of the existence of second moments, where countable additivity is defined (for example) in terms of convergence in probability or with probability one.

Remark 2. In analogy with nonstochastic measures, one can show that for finitely additive stochastic measures the condition (5) of countable additivity (in the mean-square sense) is equivalent to continuity (in the mean-square sense) at "zero":

$$\mathsf{E}\,|Z(\Delta_n)|^2 \to 0, \qquad \Delta_n \downarrow \varnothing, \qquad \Delta_n \in \mathscr{E}_0. \tag{6}$$

A particularly important class of elementary stochastic measures consists of those that are orthogonal according to the following definition.

Definition 3. An elementary stochastic measure $Z(\Delta)$, $\Delta \in \mathscr{E}_0$, is *orthogonal* (or a *measure with orthogonal values*) if

$$\mathsf{E}Z(\Delta_1)\overline{Z(\Delta_2)} = 0 \tag{7}$$

for every pair of disjoint sets Δ_1 and Δ_2 in $\mathscr{E}_0$; or, equivalently, if

$$\mathsf{E}Z(\Delta_1)\overline{Z(\Delta_2)} = \mathsf{E}\,|Z(\Delta_1 \cap \Delta_2)|^2 \tag{8}$$

for all Δ_1 and Δ_2 in $\mathscr{E}_0$.

We write

$$m(\Delta) = \mathsf{E}\,|Z(\Delta)|^2, \qquad \Delta \in \mathscr{E}_0. \tag{9}$$

For elementary orthogonal stochastic measures, the set function $m = m(\Delta)$, $\Delta \in \mathscr{E}_0$, is, as is easily verified, a finite measure, and consequently by Carathéodory's theorem (§3, Chapter II) it can be extended to $(E, \mathscr{E})$. The resulting measure will again be denoted by $m = m(\Delta)$ and called the *structure function* (of the elementary orthogonal stochastic measure $Z = Z(\Delta)$, $\Delta \in \mathscr{E}_0$).

The following question now arises naturally: since the set function $m = m(\Delta)$ defined on $(E, \mathscr{E}_0)$ admits an extension to $(E, \mathscr{E})$, where $\mathscr{E} = \sigma(\mathscr{E}_0)$, cannot an elementary orthogonal stochastic measure $Z = Z(\Delta)$, $\Delta \in \mathscr{E}_0$, be extended to sets Δ in E in such a way that $\mathsf{E}\,|Z(\Delta)|^2 = m(\Delta)$, $\Delta \in \mathscr{E}$?

The answer is affirmative, as follows from the construction given below. This construction, at the same time, leads to the stochastic integral which we need for the integral representation of stationary sequences.

3. Let $Z = Z(\Delta)$ be an elementary orthogonal stochastic measure, $\Delta \in \mathscr{E}_0$, with structure function $m = m(\Delta)$, $\Delta \in \mathscr{E}$. For every function

$$f(\lambda) = \sum f_k I_{\Delta_k}, \qquad \Delta_k \in \mathscr{E}_0, \tag{10}$$

with only a finite number of different (complex) values, we define the random variable

$$\mathscr{I}(f) = \sum f_k Z(\Delta_k).$$

Let $L^2 = L^2(E, \mathscr{E}, m)$ be the Hilbert space of complex-valued functions with the scalar product

$$\langle f, g \rangle = \int_E f(\lambda)\bar{g}(\lambda)m(d\lambda)$$

and the norm $\|f\| = \langle f, f \rangle^{1/2}$, and let $H^2 = H^2(\Omega, \mathscr{F}, \mathsf{P})$ be the Hilbert space of complex-valued random variables with the scalar product

$$(\xi, \eta) = \mathsf{E}\xi\bar{\eta}$$

and the norm $\|\xi\| = (\xi, \xi)^{1/2}$.

Then it is clear that, for every pair of functions f and g of the form (10),

$$(\mathscr{I}(f), \mathscr{I}(g)) = \langle f, g \rangle$$

and

$$\|\mathscr{I}(f)\|^2 = \|f\|^2 = \int_E |f(\lambda)|^2 m(d\lambda).$$

Now let $f \in L^2$ and let $\{f_n\}$ be functions of type (10) such that $\|f - f_n\| \to 0$, $n \to \infty$ (the existence of such functions follows from Problem 2). Consequently

$$\|\mathscr{I}(f_n) - \mathscr{I}(f_m)\| = \|f_n - f_m\| \to 0, \qquad n, m \to \infty.$$

Therefore the sequence $\{\mathscr{I}(f_n)\}$ is fundamental in the mean-square sense and by Theorem 7, §10, Chapter II, there is a random variable (denoted by $\mathscr{I}(f)$) such that $\mathscr{I}(f) \in H^2$ and $\|\mathscr{I}(f_n) - \mathscr{I}(f)\| \to 0, n \to \infty$.

The random variable $\mathscr{I}(f)$ constructed in this way is uniquely defined (up to stochastic equivalence) and is independent of the choice of the approximating sequence $\{f_n\}$. We call it the *stochastic integral* of $f \in L^2$ with respect to the elementary orthogonal stochastic measure Z and denote it by

$$\mathscr{I}(f) = \int_E f(\lambda)Z(d\lambda).$$

We note the following basic properties of the stochastic integral $\mathscr{I}(f)$; these are direct consequences of its construction (Problem 1). Let g, f, and $f_n \in L^2$. Then

$$(\mathscr{I}(f), \mathscr{I}(g)) = \langle f, g \rangle; \tag{11}$$

$$\|\mathscr{I}(f)\| = \|f\|; \tag{12}$$

$$\mathscr{I}(af + bg) = a\mathscr{I}(f) + b\mathscr{I}(g) \quad \text{(P-a.s.)} \tag{13}$$

where a and b are constants;

$$\|\mathscr{I}(f_n) - \mathscr{I}(f)\| \to 0, \tag{14}$$

if $\|f_n - f\| \to 0, n \to \infty$.

4. Let us use the preceding definition of the stochastic integral to *extend* the elementary stochastic measure $Z(\Delta)$, $\Delta \in \mathscr{E}_0$, to sets in $\mathscr{E} = \sigma(\mathscr{E}_0)$.

Since m is assumed to be finite, we have $I_\Delta = I_\Delta(\lambda) \in L^2$ for all $\Delta \in \mathscr{E}$. Write $\tilde{Z}(\Delta) = \mathscr{I}(I_\Delta)$. It is clear that $\tilde{Z}(\Delta) = Z(\Delta)$ for $\Delta \in \mathscr{E}_0$. It follows from (13) that if $\Delta_1 \cap \Delta_2 = \varnothing$ for Δ_1 and $\Delta_2 \in \mathscr{E}$, then

$$\tilde{Z}(\Delta_1 + \Delta_2) = \tilde{Z}(\Delta_1) + \tilde{Z}(\Delta_2) \quad \text{(P-a.s.)}$$

and it follows from (12) that

$$\mathsf{E}\,|\tilde{Z}(\Delta)|^2 = m(\Delta), \qquad \Delta \in \mathscr{E}.$$

Let us show that the random set function $\tilde{Z}(\Delta)$, $\Delta \in \mathscr{E}$, is countably additive in the mean-square sense. In fact, let $\Delta_k \in \mathscr{E}$ and $\Delta = \sum_{k=1}^{\infty} \Delta_k$. Then

$$\tilde{Z}(\Delta) - \sum_{k=1}^{n} \tilde{Z}(\Delta_k) = \mathscr{I}(g_n),$$

where

$$g_n(\lambda) = I_\Delta(\lambda) - \sum_{k=1}^{n} I_{\Delta_k}(\lambda) = I_{\Sigma_n}(\lambda), \qquad \Sigma_n = \sum_{k=n+1}^{\infty} \Delta_k.$$

But

$$\mathsf{E}\,|\mathscr{I}(g_n)|^2 = \|g_n\|^2 = m(\Sigma_n) \downarrow 0, \qquad n \to \infty,$$

i.e.

$$\mathsf{E}\,|\tilde{Z}(\Delta) - \sum_{k=1}^{n} \tilde{Z}(\Delta_k)|^2 \to 0, \qquad n \to \infty.$$

It also follows from (11) that

$$\mathsf{E}\,\tilde{Z}(\Delta_1)\overline{\tilde{Z}}(\Delta_2) = 0$$

when $\Delta_1 \cap \Delta_2 = \varnothing$, $\Delta_1, \Delta_2 \in \mathscr{E}$.

Thus our function $\tilde{Z}(\Delta)$, defined on $\Delta \in \mathscr{E}$, is countably additive in the mean-square sense and coincides with $Z(\Delta)$ on the sets $\Delta \in \mathscr{E}_0$. We shall call $\tilde{Z}(\Delta)$, $\Delta \in \mathscr{E}$, an orthogonal stochastic measure (since it is an extension of the elementary orthogonal stochastic measure $Z(\Delta)$) with respect to the structure function $m(\Delta)$, $\Delta \in \mathscr{E}$; and we call the integral $\mathscr{I}(f) = \int_E f(\lambda)\tilde{Z}(d\lambda)$, defined above, a stochastic integral with respect to this measure.

5. We now consider the case $(E, \mathscr{E}) = (R, \mathscr{B}(R))$, which is the most important for our purposes. As we know (§3, Chapter II), there is a one-to-one correspondence between finite measures $m = m(\Delta)$ on $(R, \mathscr{B}(R))$ and certain (generalized) distribution functions $G = G(x)$, with $m(a, b] = G(b) - G(a)$.

It turns out that there is something similar for orthogonal stochastic measures. We introduce the following definition.

Definition 4. A set of (complex-valued) random variables $\{Z_\lambda\}$, $\lambda \in R$, defined on $(\Omega, \mathscr{F}, P)$, is a *random process with orthogonal increments* if

(1) $E|Z_\lambda|^2 < \infty$, $\lambda \in R$;
(2) for every $\lambda \in R$

$$E|Z_\lambda - Z_{\lambda_n}|^2 \to 0, \qquad \lambda_n \downarrow \lambda, \qquad \lambda_n \in R;$$

(3) whenever $\lambda_1 < \lambda_2 < \lambda_3 < \lambda_4$,

$$E(Z_{\lambda_4} - Z_{\lambda_3})(\overline{Z_{\lambda_2} - Z_{\lambda_1}}) = 0.$$

Condition (3) is the condition of orthogonal increments. Condition (1) means that $Z_\lambda \in H^2$. Finally, condition (2) is included for technical reasons; it is a requirement of continuity on the right (in the mean-square sense) at each $\lambda \in R$.

Let $Z = Z(\Delta)$ be an orthogonal stochastic measure with respect to the structure function $m = m(\Delta)$, of finite measure, with the (generalized) distribution function $G(\lambda)$. Let us put

$$Z_\lambda = Z(-\infty, \lambda].$$

Then

$$E|Z_\lambda|^2 = m(-\infty, \lambda] = G(\lambda) < \infty, \qquad E|Z_\lambda - Z_{\lambda_n}|^2 = m(\lambda_n, \lambda] \downarrow 0, \lambda_n \downarrow \lambda,$$

and (evidently) 3) is satisfied also. Then this process $\{Z_\lambda\}$ is called a process *with orthogonal increments*.

On the other hand, if $\{Z_\lambda\}$ is such a process with $E|Z_\lambda|^2 = G(\lambda)$, $G(-\infty) = 0$, $G(+\infty) < \infty$, we put

$$Z(\Delta) = Z_b - Z_a$$

when $\Delta = (a, b]$. Let $\mathscr{E}_0$ be the algebra of sets

$$\Delta = \sum_{k=1}^{n} (a_k, b_k] \quad \text{and} \quad Z(\Delta) = \sum_{k=1}^{n} Z(a_k, b_k].$$

It is clear that

$$E|Z(\Delta)|^2 = m(\Delta),$$

where $m(\Delta) = \sum_{k=1}^{n} [G(b_k) - G(a_k)]$ and

$$EZ(\Delta_1)\bar{Z}(\Delta_2) = 0$$

for disjoint intervals $\Delta_1 = (a_1, b_1]$ and $\Delta_2 = (a_2, b_2]$.

Therefore $Z = Z(\Delta)$, $\Delta \in \mathscr{E}_0$, is an elementary stochastic measure with orthogonal values. The set function $m = m(\Delta)$, $\Delta \in \mathscr{E}_0$, has a unique extension to a measure on $\mathscr{E} = \mathscr{B}(R)$, and it follows from the preceding constructions that $Z = Z(\Delta)$, $\Delta \in \mathscr{E}_0$, can also be extended to the set $\Delta \in \mathscr{E}$, where $\mathscr{E} = \mathscr{B}(R)$, and $E|Z(\Delta)|^2 = m(\Delta)$, $\Delta \in B(\mathscr{R})$.

Therefore there is a one-to-one correspondence between processes $\{Z_\lambda\}$, $\lambda \in R$, with orthogonal increments and $\mathsf{E}|Z_\lambda|^2 = G(\lambda)$, $G(-\infty) = 0$, $G(+\infty) < \infty$, and orthogonal stochastic measures $Z = Z(\Delta)$, $\Delta \in \mathscr{B}(R)$, with structure functions $m = m(\Delta)$. The correspondence is given by

$$Z_\lambda = Z(-\infty, \lambda], \qquad G(\lambda) = m(-\infty, \lambda]$$

and

$$Z(a, b] = Z_b - Z_a, \qquad m(a, b] = G(b) - G(a).$$

By analogy with the usual notation of the theory of Riemann–Stieltjes integration, the stochastic integral $\int_R f(\lambda)\, dZ_\lambda$, where $\{Z_\lambda\}$ is a process with orthogonal increments, means the stochastic integral $\int_R f(\lambda) Z(d\lambda)$ with respect to the corresponding process with an orthogonal stochastic measure.

6. PROBLEMS

1. Prove the equivalence of (5) and (6).

2. Let $f \in L^2$. Using the results of Chapter II (Theorem 1 of §4, the Corollary to Theorem 3 of §6, and Problem 9 of §3), prove that there is a sequence of functions f_n of the form (10) such that $\|f - f_n\| \to 0$, $n \to \infty$.

3. Establish the following properties of an orthogonal stochastic measure $Z(\Delta)$ with structure function $m(\Delta)$:

$$\mathsf{E}|Z(\Delta_1) - Z(\Delta_2)|^2 = m(\Delta_1 \triangle \Delta_2),$$

$$Z(\Delta_1 \setminus \Delta_2) = Z(\Delta_1) - Z(\Delta_1 \cap \Delta_2) \quad \text{(P-a.s.)},$$

$$Z(\Delta_1 \triangle \Delta_2) = Z(\Delta_1) + Z(\Delta_2) - 2Z(\Delta_1 \cap \Delta_2) \quad \text{(P-a.s.)}.$$

§3. Spectral Representation of Stationary (Wide Sense) Sequences

1. If $\xi = (\xi_n)$ is a stationary sequence with $\mathsf{E}\xi_n = 0$, $n \in \mathbb{Z}$, then by the theorem of §1, there is a finite measure $F = F(\Delta)$ on $([-\pi, \pi), \mathscr{B}([-\pi, \pi)))$ such that its covariance function $R(n) = \mathrm{cov}(\xi_{k+n}, \xi_k)$ admits the spectral representation

$$R(n) = \int_{-\pi}^{\pi} e^{i\lambda n} F(d\lambda). \tag{1}$$

The following result provides the corresponding spectral representation of the sequence $\xi = (\xi_n)$, $n \in \mathbb{Z}$, itself.

Theorem 1. *There is an orthogonal stochastic measure* $Z = Z(\Delta)$, $\Delta \in \mathcal{B}([-\pi, \pi))$, *such that for every* $n \in \mathbb{Z}$ (P-*a.s.*)

$$\xi_n = \int_{-\pi}^{\pi} e^{i\lambda n} Z(d\lambda). \tag{2}$$

Moreover, $\mathsf{E}|Z(\Delta)|^2 = F(\Delta)$.

The simplest proof is based on properties of Hilbert spaces.

Let $L^2(F) = L^2(E, \mathcal{E}, F)$ be a Hilbert space of complex functions, $E = [-\pi, \pi)$, $\mathcal{E} = \mathcal{B}([-\pi, \pi))$, with the scalar product

$$\langle f, g \rangle = \int_{-\pi}^{\pi} f(\lambda)\bar{g}(\lambda)F(d\lambda), \tag{3}$$

and let $L_0^2(F)$ be the linear manifold $(L_0^2(F) \subseteq L^2(F))$ spanned by $e_n = e_n(\lambda)$, $n \in \mathbb{Z}$, where $e_n(\lambda) = e^{i\lambda n}$.

Observe that since $E = [-\pi, \pi)$ and F is finite, the closure of $L_0^2(F)$ coincides (Problem 1) with $L^2(F)$:

$$\overline{L_0^2}(F) = L^2(F).$$

Also let $L_0^2(\xi)$ be the linear manifold spanned by the random variables ξ_n, $n \in \mathbb{Z}$, and let $L^2(\xi)$ be its closure in the mean-square sense (with respect to P).

We establish a one-to-one correspondence between the elements of $L_0^2(F)$ and $L_0^2(\xi)$, denoted by "$\leftrightarrow$", by setting

$$e_n \leftrightarrow \xi_n, \qquad n \in \mathbb{Z}, \tag{4}$$

and defining it for elements in general (more precisely, for equivalence classes of elements) by linearity:

$$\sum \alpha_n e_n \leftrightarrow \sum \alpha_n \xi_n \tag{5}$$

(here we suppose that only finitely many of the complex numbers α_n are different from zero).

Observe that (5) is a consistent definition, in the sense that $\sum \alpha_n e_n = 0$ almost everywhere with respect to F if and only if $\sum \alpha_n \xi_n = 0$ (P-a.s.).

The correspondence "$\leftrightarrow$" is an *isometry*, i.e. it preserves scalar products. In fact, by (3),

$$\langle e_n, e_m \rangle = \int_{-\pi}^{\pi} e_n(\lambda)\overline{e_m}(\lambda)F(d\lambda) = \int_{-\pi}^{\pi} e^{i\lambda(n-m)}F(d\lambda) = R(n - m)$$

$$= \mathsf{E}\xi_n\bar{\xi}_m = (\xi_n, \xi_m)$$

and similarly

$$\left\langle \sum \alpha_n e_n, \sum \beta_n e_n \right\rangle = \left(\sum \alpha_n \xi_n, \sum \beta_n \xi_n \right). \tag{6}$$

Now let $\eta \in L^2(\xi)$. Since $L^2(\xi) = \bar{L}_0^2(\xi)$, there is a sequence $\{\eta_n\}$ such that $\eta_n \in L_0^2(\xi)$ and $\|\eta_n - \eta\| \to 0$, $n \to \infty$. Consequently $\{\eta_n\}$ is a fundamental sequence and therefore so is the sequence $\{f_n\}$, where $f_n \in L_0^2(F)$ and $f_n \leftrightarrow \eta_n$. The space $L^2(F)$ is complete and consequently there is an $f \in L^2(F)$ such that $\|f_n - f\| \to 0$.

There is an evident converse: if $f \in L^2(F)$ and $\|f - f_n\| \to 0$, $f_n \in L_0^2(F)$, there is an element η of $L^2(\xi)$ such that $\|\eta - \eta_n\| \to 0$, $\eta_n \in L_0^2(\xi)$ and $\eta_n \leftrightarrow f_n$.

Up to now the isometry "$\leftrightarrow$" has been defined only as between elements of $L_0^2(\xi)$ and $L_0^2(F)$. We extend it by continuity, taking $f \leftrightarrow \eta$ when f and η are the elements considered above. It is easily verified that the correspondence obtained in this way is one-to-one (between classes of equivalent random variables and of functions), is linear, and preserves scalar products.

Consider the function $f(\lambda) = I_\Delta(\lambda)$, where $\Delta \in \mathcal{B}([-\pi, \pi))$, and let $Z(\Delta)$ be the element of $L^2(\xi)$ such that $I_\Delta(\lambda) \leftrightarrow Z(\Delta)$. It is clear that $\|I_\Delta(\lambda)\|^2 = F(\Delta)$ and therefore $\mathsf{E}|Z(\Delta)|^2 = F(\Delta)$. Moreover, if $\Delta_1 \cap \Delta_2 = \varnothing$, we have $\mathsf{E}Z(\Delta_1)Z(\Delta_2) = 0$ and $\mathsf{E}|Z(\Delta) - \sum_{k=1}^n Z(\Delta_k)|^2 \to 0$, $n \to \infty$, where $\Delta = \sum_{k=1}^\infty \Delta_k$.

Hence the family of elements $Z(\Delta)$, $\Delta \in \mathcal{B}([-\pi, \pi))$, form an orthogonal stochastic measure, with respect to which (according to §2) we can define the stochastic integral

$$\mathscr{I}(f) = \int_{-\pi}^{\pi} f(\lambda)Z(d\lambda), \qquad f \in L^2(F).$$

Let $f \in L^2(F)$ and $\eta \leftrightarrow f$. Denote the element η by $\Phi(f)$ (more precisely, select single representatives from the corresponding equivalence classes of random variables or functions). Let us show that (P-a.s.)

$$\mathscr{I}(f) = \Phi(f). \tag{7}$$

In fact, if

$$f(\lambda) = \sum \alpha_k I_{\Delta_k}(\lambda) \tag{8}$$

is a finite linear combination of functions $I_{\Delta_k}(\lambda)$, $\Delta_k = (a_k, b_k]$, then, by the very definition of the stochastic integral, $\mathscr{I}(f) = \sum \alpha_k Z(\Delta_k)$, which is evidently equal to $\Phi(f)$. Therefore (7) is valid for functions of the form (8). But if $f \in L^2(F)$ and $\|f_n - f\| \to 0$, where f_n are functions of the form (8), then $\|\Phi(f_n) - \Phi(f)\| \to 0$ and $\|\mathscr{I}(f_n) - \mathscr{I}(f)\| \to 0$ (by (2.14)). Therefore $\Phi(f) = \mathscr{I}(f)$ (P-a.s.).

Consider the function $f(\lambda) = e^{i\lambda n}$. Then $\Phi(e^{i\lambda n}) = \xi_n$ by (4), but on the other hand $\mathscr{I}(e^{i\lambda n}) = \int_{-\pi}^\pi e^{i\lambda n}Z(d\lambda)$. Therefore

$$\xi_n = \int_{-\pi}^{\pi} e^{i\lambda n}Z(d\lambda), \qquad n \in \mathbb{Z} \quad \text{(P-a.s.)}$$

by (7). This completes the proof of the theorem.

Corollary 1. *Let* $\xi = (\xi_n)$ *be a stationary sequence of real random variables* ξ_n, $n \in \mathbb{Z}$. *Then the stochastic measure* $Z = Z(\Delta)$ *involved in the spectral representation* (2) *has the property that*

$$Z(\Delta) = \overline{Z(-\Delta)} \tag{9}$$

for every $\Delta = \mathscr{B}([-\pi, \pi))$, *where* $-\Delta = \{\lambda: -\lambda \in \Delta\}$.

In fact, let $f(\lambda) = \sum \alpha_k e^{i\lambda k}$ and $\eta = \sum \alpha_k \xi_k$ (finite sums). Then $f \leftrightarrow \eta$ and therefore

$$\bar{\eta} = \sum \bar{\alpha}_k \xi_k \leftrightarrow \sum \bar{\alpha}_k e^{i\lambda k} = \overline{f(-\lambda)}. \tag{10}$$

Since $\mathscr{I}_\Delta(\lambda) \leftrightarrow Z(\Delta)$, it follows from (10) that either $\mathscr{I}_\Delta(-\lambda) \leftrightarrow \overline{Z(\Delta)}$ or $\mathscr{I}_{-\Delta}(\lambda) \leftrightarrow \overline{Z(\Delta)}$. On the other hand, $\mathscr{I}_{-\Delta}(\lambda) \leftrightarrow Z(-\Delta)$. Therefore $\overline{Z(\Delta)} = Z(-\Delta)$ (P-a.s.).

Corollary 2. *Again let* $\xi = (\xi_n)$ *be a stationary sequence of real random variables* ξ_n *and* $Z(\Delta) = Z_1(\Delta) + iZ_2(\Delta)$. *Then*

$$\mathsf{E}Z_1(\Delta_1)Z_2(\Delta_2) = 0 \tag{11}$$

for every Δ_1 *and* Δ_2; *and if* $\Delta_1 \cap \Delta_2 = \varnothing$ *then*

$$\mathsf{E}Z_1(\Delta_1)Z_1(\Delta_2) = 0, \qquad \mathsf{E}Z_2(\Delta_1)Z_2(\Delta_2) = 0. \tag{12}$$

In fact, since $Z(\Delta) = \overline{Z}(-\Delta)$, we have

$$Z_1(-\Delta) = Z_1(\Delta), \qquad Z_2(-\Delta) = -Z_2(\Delta). \tag{13}$$

Moreover, since $\mathsf{E}Z(\Delta_1)\overline{Z}(\Delta_2) = \mathsf{E}|Z(\Delta_1 \cap \Delta_2)|^2$, we have Im $\mathsf{E}Z(\Delta_1)\overline{Z}(\Delta_2) = 0$, i.e.

$$\mathsf{E}Z_1(\Delta_1)Z_2(\Delta_2) + \mathsf{E}Z_2(\Delta_1)Z_1(\Delta_2) = 0. \tag{14}$$

If we take the interval $-\Delta_1$ instead of Δ_1 we therefore obtain

$$\mathsf{E}Z_1(-\Delta_1)Z_2(\Delta_2) + \mathsf{E}Z_2(-\Delta_1)Z_1(\Delta_2) = 0,$$

which, by (13), can be transformed into

$$\mathsf{E}Z_1(\Delta_1)Z_2(\Delta_2) - \mathsf{E}Z_2(\Delta_1)Z_1(\Delta_2) = 0. \tag{15}$$

Then (11) follows from (14) and (15).

On the other hand, if $\Delta_1 \cap \Delta_2 = \varnothing$ then $\mathsf{E}Z(\Delta_1)\overline{Z}(\Delta_2) = 0$, whence Re $\mathsf{E}Z(\Delta_1)\overline{Z}(\Delta_2) = 0$ and Re $\mathsf{E}Z(-\Delta_1)\overline{Z}(\Delta_2) = 0$, which, with (13), provides an evident proof of (12).

Corollary 3. *Let* $\xi = (\xi_n)$ *be a Gaussian sequence. Then, for every family* $\Delta_1, \ldots, \Delta_k$, *the vector* $(Z_1(\Delta_1), \ldots, Z_1(\Delta_k), Z_2(\Delta_1), \ldots, Z_2(\Delta_k))$ *is normally distributed.*

In fact, the linear manifold $L_0^2(\xi)$ consists of (complex-valued) Gaussian random variables η, i.e. the vector (Re η, Im η) has a Gaussian distribution. Then, according to Subsection 5, §13, Chapter II, the closure of $L_0^2(\xi)$ also consists of Gaussian variables. It follows from Corollary 2 that, when $\xi = (\xi_n)$ is a Gaussian sequence, the real and imaginary parts of Z_1 and Z_2 are independent in the sense that the families of random variables $(Z_1(\Delta_1),$ $\ldots, Z_1(\Delta_k))$ and $(Z_2(\Delta_1), \ldots, Z_2(\Delta_k))$ are independent. It also follows from (12) that when the sets $\Delta_1, \ldots, \Delta_k$ are disjoint, the random variables $Z_i(\Delta_1), \ldots, Z_i(\Delta_k)$ are collectively independent, $i = 1, 2$.

Corollary 4. *If $\xi = (\xi_n)$ is a stationary sequence of real random variables, then* (P-a.s.)

$$\xi_n = \int_{-\pi}^{\pi} \cos \lambda n \, Z_1(d\lambda) + \int_{-\pi}^{\pi} \sin \lambda n \, Z_2(d\lambda). \tag{16}$$

Remark. If $\{Z_\lambda\}$, $\lambda \in [-\pi, \pi)$, is a process with orthogonal increments, corresponding to an orthogonal stochastic measure $Z = Z(\Delta)$, then in accordance with §2 the spectral representation (2) can also be written in the following form:

$$\xi_n = \int_{-\pi}^{\pi} e^{i\lambda n} \, dZ_\lambda, \qquad n \in \mathbb{Z}. \tag{17}$$

2. Let $\xi = (\xi_n)$ be a stationary sequence with the spectral representation (2) and let $\eta \in L^2(\xi)$. The following theorem describes the structure of such random variables.

Theorem 2. *If $\eta \in L^2(\xi)$, there is a function $\varphi \in L^2(F)$ such that* (P-a.s.)

$$\eta = \int_{-\pi}^{\pi} \varphi(\lambda) Z(d\lambda). \tag{18}$$

PROOF. If

$$\eta_n = \sum_{|k| \le n} \alpha_k \xi_k, \tag{19}$$

then by (2)

$$\eta_n = \int_{-\pi}^{\pi} \left(\sum_{|k| \le n} \alpha_k e^{i\lambda k} \right) Z(d\lambda), \tag{20}$$

i.e. (18) is satisfied with

$$\varphi_n(\lambda) = \sum_{|k| \le n} \alpha_n e^{i\lambda k}. \tag{21}$$

In the general case, when $\eta \in L^2(\xi)$, there are variables η_n of type (19) such that $\|\eta - \eta_n\| \to 0$, $n \to \infty$. But then $\|\varphi_n - \varphi_m\| = \|\eta_n - \eta_m\| \to 0$, $n, m \to \infty$.

Consequently $\{\varphi_n\}$ is fundamental in $L^2(F)$ and therefore there is a function $\varphi \in L^2(F)$ such that $\|\varphi - \varphi_n\| \to 0, n \to \infty$.

By property (2.14) we have $\|\mathscr{I}(\varphi_n) - \mathscr{I}(\varphi)\| \to 0$, and since $\eta_n = \mathscr{I}(\varphi_n)$ we also have $\eta = \mathscr{I}(\varphi)$ (P-a.s.).

This completes the proof of the theorem.

Remark. Let $H_0(\xi)$ and $H_0(F)$ be the respective closed linear manifolds spanned by the variables ξ_n and by the functions e_n when $n \leq 0$. Then if $\eta \in H_0(\xi)$ there is a function $\varphi \in H_0(F)$ such that (P-a.s.) $\eta = \int_{-\pi}^{\pi} \varphi(\lambda) Z(d\lambda)$.

3. Formula (18) describes the structure of the random variables that are obtained from ξ_n, $n \in \mathbb{Z}$, by linear transformations, i.e. in the form of finite sums (19) and their mean-square limits.

A special but important class of such linear transformations are defined by means of what are known as (linear) *filters*. Let us suppose that, at instant m, a system (filter) receives as input a signal x_m, and that the output of the system is, at instant n, the signal $h(n - m)x_m$, where $h = h(s)$, $s \in \mathbb{Z}$, is a complex valued function called the *impulse response* (of the filter).

Therefore the total signal obtained from the input can be represented in the form

$$y_n = \sum_{m=-\infty}^{\infty} h(n - m)x_m. \tag{22}$$

For physically realizable systems, the values of the input at instant n are determined only by the "past" values of the signal, i.e. the values x_m for $m \leq n$. It is therefore natural to call a filter with the impulse response $h(s)$ *physically realizable* if $h(s) = 0$ for all $s < 0$, in other words if

$$y_n = \sum_{m=-\infty}^{n} h(n - m)x_m = \sum_{m=0}^{\infty} h(m)x_{n-m}. \tag{23}$$

An important *spectral characteristic* of a filter with the impulse response h is its Fourier transform

$$\varphi(\lambda) = \sum_{m=-\infty}^{\infty} e^{-i\lambda m}h(m), \tag{24}$$

known as the *frequency characteristic* or *transfer function* of the filter.

Let us now take up conditions, about which nothing has been said so far, for the convergence of the series in (22) and (24). Let us suppose that the input is a stationary random sequence $\xi = (\xi_n)$, $n \in \mathbb{Z}$, with covariance function $R(n)$ and spectral decomposition (2). Then if

$$\sum_{k,l=-\infty}^{\infty} h(k)R(k - l)\bar{h}(l) < \infty, \tag{25}$$

the series $\sum_{m=-\infty}^{\infty} h(n-m)\xi_m$ converges in mean-square and therefore there is a stationary sequence $\eta = (\eta_n)$ with

$$\eta_n = \sum_{m=-\infty}^{\infty} h(n-m)\xi_m = \sum_{m=-\infty}^{\infty} h(m)\xi_{n-m}. \tag{26}$$

In terms of the spectral measure, (25) is evidently equivalent to saying that $\varphi(\lambda) \in L^2(F)$, i.e.

$$\int_{-\pi}^{\pi} |\varphi(\lambda)|^2 F(d\lambda) < \infty. \tag{27}$$

Under (25) or (27), we obtain the spectral representation

$$\eta_n = \int_{-\pi}^{\pi} e^{i\lambda n} \varphi(\lambda) Z(d\lambda). \tag{28}$$

of η from (26) and (2). Consequently the covariance function $R_\eta(n)$ of η is given by the formula

$$R_\eta(n) = \int_{-\pi}^{\pi} e^{i\lambda n} |\varphi(\lambda)|^2 F(d\lambda). \tag{29}$$

In particular, if the input to a filter with frequency characteristic $\varphi = \varphi(\lambda)$ is taken to be white noise $\varepsilon = (\varepsilon_n)$, the output will be a stationary sequence (moving average)

$$\eta_n = \sum_{m=-\infty}^{\infty} h(m)\varepsilon_{n-m} \tag{30}$$

with spectral density

$$f_\eta(\lambda) = \frac{1}{2\pi} |\varphi(\lambda)|^2.$$

The following theorem shows that there is a sense in which every stationary sequence with a spectral density is obtainable by means of a moving average.

Theorem 3. *Let $\eta = (\eta_n)$ be a stationary sequence with spectral density $f_\eta(\lambda)$. Then (possibly at the expense of enlarging the original probability space) we can find a sequence $\varepsilon = (\varepsilon_n)$ representing white noise, and a filter, such that the representation* (30) *holds.*

PROOF. For a given (nonnegative) function $f_\eta(\lambda)$ we can find a function $\varphi(\lambda)$ such that $f_\eta(\lambda) = (1/2\pi)|\varphi(\lambda)|^2$. Since $\int_{-\pi}^{\pi} f_\eta(\lambda)\, d\lambda < \infty$, we have $\varphi(\lambda) \in L^2(\mu)$, where μ is Lebesgue measure on $[-\pi, \pi)$. Hence φ can be represented as a Fourier series (24) with $h(m) = (1/2\pi)\int_{-\pi}^{\pi} e^{im\lambda}\varphi(\lambda)\, d\lambda$, where convergence is understood in the sense that

$$\int_{-\pi}^{\pi} \left| \varphi(\lambda) - \sum_{|m| \le n} e^{-i\lambda m} h(m) \right|^2 d\lambda \to 0, \qquad n \to \infty.$$

Let

$$\eta_n = \int_{-\pi}^{\pi} e^{i\lambda n} Z(d\lambda), \qquad n \in \mathbb{Z}.$$

Besides the measure $Z = Z(\Delta)$ we introduce another independent orthogonal stochastic measure $\tilde{Z} = \tilde{Z}(\Delta)$ with $\mathsf{E}\,|\tilde{Z}(a, b]|^2 = (b - a)/2\pi$. (The possibility of constructing such a measure depends, in general, on having a sufficiently "rich" original probability space.) Let us put

$$\bar{Z}(\Delta) = \int_{\Delta} \varphi^{\oplus}(\lambda) Z(d\lambda) + \int_{\Delta} [1 - \varphi^{\oplus}(\lambda)\varphi(\lambda)] \tilde{Z}(d\lambda),$$

where

$$a^{\oplus} = \begin{cases} a^{-1}, & \text{if } a \neq 0, \\ 0, & \text{if } a = 0. \end{cases}$$

The stochastic measure $\bar{Z} = \bar{Z}(\Delta)$ is a measure with orthogonal values, and for every $\Delta = (a, b]$ we have

$$\mathsf{E}\,|\bar{Z}(\Delta)|^2 = \frac{1}{2\pi} \int_{\Delta} |\varphi^{\oplus}(\lambda)|^2 |\varphi(\lambda)|^2 \, d\lambda + \frac{1}{2\pi} \int_{\Delta} |1 - \varphi^{\oplus}(\lambda)\varphi(\lambda)|^2 \, d\lambda = \frac{|\Delta|}{2\pi},$$

where $|\Delta| = b - a$. Therefore the stationary sequence $\varepsilon = (\varepsilon_n)$, $n \in \mathbb{Z}$, with

$$\varepsilon_n = \int_{-\pi}^{\pi} e^{i\lambda n} \bar{Z}(d\lambda),$$

is a white noise.

We now observe that

$$\int_{-\pi}^{\pi} e^{i\lambda n} \varphi(\lambda) \bar{Z}(d\lambda) = \int_{-\pi}^{\pi} e^{in\lambda} Z(d\lambda) = \eta_n \tag{31}$$

and, on the other hand, by property (2.14) (P-a.s.)

$$\int_{-\pi}^{\pi} e^{in\lambda} \varphi(\lambda) \bar{Z}(d\lambda) = \int_{-\pi}^{\pi} e^{i\lambda n} \left(\sum_{m=-\infty}^{\infty} e^{-i\lambda m} h(m) \right) \bar{Z}(d\lambda)$$

$$= \sum_{m=-\infty}^{\infty} h(m) \int_{-\pi}^{\pi} e^{i\lambda(n-m)} \bar{Z}(d\lambda) = \sum_{m=-\infty}^{\infty} h(m) \varepsilon_{n-m},$$

which, together with (31), establishes the representation (30).

This completes the proof of the theorem.

Remark. If $f_\eta(\lambda) > 0$ (almost everywhere with respect to Lebesgue measure), the introduction of the auxiliary measure $\tilde{Z} = \tilde{Z}(\Delta)$ becomes unnecessary (since then $1 - \varphi^{\oplus}(\lambda)\varphi(\lambda) = 0$ almost everywhere with respect to Lebesgue measure), and the reservation concerning the necessity of extending the original probability space can be omitted.

Corollary 1. *Let the spectral density $f_\eta(\lambda) > 0$ (almost everywhere with respect to Lebesgue measure) and*

$$f_\eta(\lambda) = \frac{1}{2\pi} |\varphi(\lambda)|^2,$$

where

$$\varphi(\lambda) = \sum_{k=0}^{\infty} e^{-i\lambda k} h(k), \qquad \sum_{k=0}^{\infty} |h(k)|^2 < \infty.$$

Then the sequence η admits a representation as a one-sided moving average,

$$\eta_n = \sum_{m=0}^{\infty} h(m)\varepsilon_{n-m}.$$

In particular, let $P(z) = a_0 + a_1 z + \cdots + a_p z^p$ be a polynomial that has no zeros on $\{z: |z| = 1\}$. Then the sequence $\eta = (\eta_n)$ with spectral density

$$f_\eta(\lambda) = \frac{1}{2\pi} |P(e^{-i\lambda})|^2$$

can be represented in the form

$$\eta_n = a_0 \varepsilon_n + a_1 \varepsilon_{n-1} + \cdots + a_p \varepsilon_{n-p}.$$

Corollary 2. *Let $\xi = (\xi_n)$ be a sequence with rational spectral density*

$$f_\xi(\lambda) = \frac{1}{2\pi} \left| \frac{P(e^{-i\lambda})}{Q(e^{-i\lambda})} \right|^2, \tag{32}$$

where $P(z) = a_0 + a_1 z + \cdots + a_p z^p$, $Q(z) = 1 + b_1 z + \cdots + b_q z^q$.

Let us show that if $P(z)$ and $Q(z)$ have no zeros on $\{z: |z| = 1\}$, there is a white noise $\varepsilon = \varepsilon(n)$ such that (P-a.s.)

$$\xi_n + b_1 \xi_{n-1} + \cdots + b_q \xi_{n-q} = a_0 \varepsilon_n + a_1 \varepsilon_{n-1} + \cdots + a_p \varepsilon_{n-p}. \tag{33}$$

Conversely, every stationary sequence $\xi = (\xi_n)$ that satisfies this equation with some white noise $\varepsilon = (\varepsilon_n)$ and some polynomial $Q(z)$ with no zeros on $\{z: |z| = 1\}$ has a spectral density (32).

In fact, let $\eta_n = \xi_n + b_1 \xi_{n-1} + \cdots + b_q \xi_{n-q}$. Then $f_\eta(\lambda) = (1/2\pi)|P(e^{-i\lambda})|^2$ and the required representation follows from Corollary 1.

On the other hand, if (33) holds and $F_\xi(\lambda)$ and $F_\eta(\lambda)$ are the spectral functions of ξ and η, then

$$F_\eta(\lambda) = \int_{-\pi}^{\lambda} |Q(e^{-iv})|^2 \, dF_\xi(v) = \frac{1}{2\pi} \int_{-\pi}^{\lambda} |P(e^{-iv})|^2 \, dv.$$

Since $|Q(e^{-iv})|^2 > 0$, it follows that $F_\xi(\lambda)$ has a density defined by (32).

4. The following mean-square ergodic theorem can be thought of as an analog of the law of large numbers for stationary (wide sense) random sequences.

Theorem 4. Let $\xi = (\xi_n)$, $n \in \mathbb{Z}$, be a stationary sequence with $\mathsf{E}\xi_n = 0$, covariance function (1), and spectral resolution (2). Then

$$\frac{1}{n}\sum_{k=0}^{n-1}\xi_k \overset{L^2}{\to} Z(\{0\}) \tag{34}$$

and

$$\frac{1}{n}\sum_{k=0}^{n-1}R(k) \to F(\{0\}). \tag{35}$$

PROOF. By (2),

$$\frac{1}{n}\sum_{k=0}^{n-1}\xi_k = \int_{-\pi}^{\pi}\frac{1}{n}\sum_{k=0}^{n-1}e^{ik\lambda}Z(d\lambda) = \int_{-\pi}^{\pi}\varphi_n(\lambda)Z(d\lambda),$$

where

$$\varphi_n(\lambda) = \frac{1}{n}\sum_{k=0}^{n-1}e^{ik\lambda} = \begin{cases} 1, & \lambda = 0, \\ \dfrac{1}{n}\cdot\dfrac{e^{in\lambda}-1}{e^{i\lambda}-1}, & \lambda \neq 0. \end{cases} \tag{36}$$

Since $|\sin\lambda| \geq (2/\pi)|\lambda|$ for $|\lambda| \leq \pi/2$, we have

$$|\varphi_n(\lambda)| = \left|\frac{\sin\dfrac{n\lambda}{2}}{n\sin\dfrac{\lambda}{2}}\right| \leq \frac{\pi}{2}\left|\frac{\sin\dfrac{n\lambda}{2}}{\dfrac{n\lambda}{2}}\right| \leq \frac{\pi}{2}.$$

Moreover, $\varphi_n(\lambda) \xrightarrow{L^2(F)} I_{\{0\}}(\lambda)$ and therefore by (2.14)

$$\int_{-\pi}^{\pi}\varphi_n(\lambda)Z(d\lambda) \overset{L^2}{\to} \int_{-\pi}^{\pi}I_{\{0\}}(\lambda)Z(d\lambda) = Z(\{0\}),$$

which establishes (34).

Relation (35) can be proved in a similar way.

This completes the proof of the theorem.

Corollary. If the spectral function is continuous at zero, i.e. $F(\{0\}) = 0$, then $Z(\{0\}) = 0$ (P-a.s.) and by (34) and (35),

$$\frac{1}{n}\sum_{k=0}^{n-1}R(k) \to 0 \Rightarrow \frac{1}{n}\sum_{k=0}^{n-1}\xi_k \overset{L^2}{\to} 0.$$

Since

$$\left|\frac{1}{n}\sum_{k=0}^{n-1}R(k)\right|^2 = \left|\mathsf{E}\left(\frac{1}{n}\sum_{k=0}^{n-1}\xi_k\right)\bar{\xi_0}\right|^2 \le \mathsf{E}|\xi_0|^2\mathsf{E}\left|\frac{1}{n}\sum_{k=0}^{n-1}\xi_k\right|^2,$$

the converse implication also holds:

$$\frac{1}{n}\sum_{k=0}^{n-1}\xi_k \xrightarrow{L^2} 0 \Rightarrow \frac{1}{n}\sum_{k=0}^{n-1}R(k) \to 0.$$

Therefore the condition $(1/n)\sum_{k=0}^{n-1}R(k) \to 0$ is necessary and sufficient for the convergence (in the mean-square sense) of the arithmetic means $(1/n)\sum_{k=0}^{n-1}\xi_k$ to zero. It follows that if the original sequences $\xi = (\xi_n)$ has expectation m (that is, $\mathsf{E}\xi_0 = m$), then

$$\frac{1}{n}\sum_{k=0}^{n-1}R(k) \to 0 \Leftrightarrow \frac{1}{n}\sum_{k=0}^{n-1}\xi_k \xrightarrow{L^2} m, \tag{37}$$

where $R(n) = \mathsf{E}(\xi_n - \mathsf{E}\xi_n)(\bar{\xi_0} - \overline{\mathsf{E}\xi_0})$.

Let us also observe that if $Z(\{0\}) \ne 0$ (P-a.s.) and $m = 0$, then ξ_n "contains a random constant α":

$$\xi_n = \alpha + \eta_n,$$

where $\alpha = Z(\{0\})$; and in the spectral representation $\eta_n = \int_{-\pi}^{\pi} e^{i\lambda n} Z_\eta(d\lambda)$ the measure $Z_\eta = Z_\eta(\Delta)$ is such that $Z_\eta(\{0\}) = 0$ (P-a.s.). Conclusion (34) means that the arithmetic mean converges in mean-square to precisely this random constant α.

5. PROBLEMS

1. Show that $\overline{L_0^2}(F) = L^2(F)$ (for the notation see the proof of Theorem 1).

2. Let $\xi = (\xi_n)$ be a stationary sequence with the property that $\xi_{n+N} = \xi_n$ for some N and all n. Show that the spectral representation of such a sequence reduces to (1.13).

3. Let $\xi = (\xi_n)$ be a stationary sequence such that $\mathsf{E}\xi_n = 0$ and

$$\frac{1}{N^2}\sum_{k=0}^{N}\sum_{l=0}^{N}R(k-l) = \frac{1}{N}\sum_{|k|\le N-1}R(k)\left[1 - \frac{|k|}{N}\right] \le CN^{-\alpha}$$

for some $C > 0$, $\alpha > 0$. Use the Borel–Cantelli lemma to show that then

$$\frac{1}{N}\sum_{k=0}^{N}\xi_k \to 0 \quad \text{(P-a.s.)}$$

4. Let the spectral density $f_\xi(\lambda)$ of the sequence $\xi = (\xi_n)$ be rational,

$$f_\xi(\lambda) = \frac{1}{2\pi}\frac{|P_{n-1}(e^{-i\lambda})|}{|Q_n(e^{-i\lambda})|}, \tag{38}$$

where $P_{n-1}(z) = a_0 + a_1 z + \cdots + a_{n-1}z^{n-1}$ and $Q_n(z) = 1 + b_1 z + \cdots + b_n z^n$, and all the zeros of these polynomials lie outside the unit disk.

Show that there is a white noise $\varepsilon = (\varepsilon_m)$, $m \in \mathbb{Z}$, such that the sequence (ξ_m) is a component of an n-dimensional sequence $(\xi_m^1, \xi_m^2, \ldots, \xi_m^n)$, $\xi_m^1 = \xi_m$, that satisfies the system of equations

$$\xi_{m+1}^i = \xi_m^{i+1} + \beta_i \varepsilon_{m+1}, \qquad i = 1, \ldots, n-1,$$

$$\xi_{m+1}^n = -\sum_{j=0}^{n-1} b_{n-j} \xi_m^{j+1} + \beta_n \varepsilon_{m+1}, \tag{39}$$

where $\beta_1 = a_0$, $\beta_i = a_{i-1} - \sum_{k=1}^{i-1} \beta_k b_{i-k}$.

§4. Statistical Estimation of the Covariance Function and the Spectral Density

1. Problems of the statistical estimation of various characteristics of the probability distributions of random sequences arise in the most diverse branches of science (geophysics, medicine, economics, etc.) The material presented in this section will give the reader an idea of the concepts and methods of estimation, and of the difficulties that are encountered.

To begin with, let $\xi = (\xi_n)$, $n \in \mathbb{Z}$, be a sequence, stationary in the wide sense (for simplicity, real) with expectation $E\xi_n = m$ and covariance $R(n) = \int_{-\pi}^{\pi} e^{i\lambda n} F(d\lambda)$.

Let $x_0, x_1, \ldots, x_{N-1}$ be the results of observing the random variables $\xi_0, \xi_1, \ldots, \xi_{N-1}$. How are we then to construct a "good" estimator of the (unknown) mean value m?

Let us put

$$m_N(x) = \frac{1}{N} \sum_{k=0}^{N-1} x_k. \tag{1}$$

Then it follows from the elementary properties of the expectation that this is a "good" estimator of m in the sense that it is *unbiased* "in the mean over all kinds of data $x_0, \ldots, x_{N-1}$", i.e.

$$E m_N(\xi) = E\left(\frac{1}{N} \sum_{k=0}^{N-1} \xi_k\right) = m. \tag{2}$$

In addition, it follows from Theorem 4 of §3 that when $(1/N) \sum_{k=0}^{N} R(k) \to 0$, $N \to \infty$, our estimator is *consistent* (in mean-square), i.e.

$$E|m_N(\xi) - m|^2 \to 0, \qquad N \to \infty. \tag{3}$$

Next we take up the problem of estimating the covariance function $R(n)$, the spectral function $F(\lambda) = F([-\pi, \lambda])$, and the spectral density $f(\lambda)$, all under the assumption that $m = 0$.

Since $R(n) = \mathsf{E}\xi_{n+k}\xi_k$, it is natural to estimate this function on the basis of N observations $x_0, x_1, \ldots, x_{N-1}$ (when $0 \le n < N$) by

$$\hat{R}_N(n; x) = \frac{1}{N-n} \sum_{k=0}^{N-n-1} x_{n+k}x_k.$$

It is clear that this estimator is unbiased in the sense that

$$\mathsf{E}\hat{R}_N(n; \xi) = R(n), \qquad 0 \le n < N.$$

Let us now consider the question of its consistency. If we replace ξ_k in (3.37) by $\xi_{n+k}\xi_k$ and suppose that the sequence $\xi = (\xi_n)$ under consideration has a fourth moment ($\mathsf{E}\xi_0^4 < \infty$), we find that the condition

$$\frac{1}{N} \sum_{k=0}^{N-1} \mathsf{E}[\xi_{n+k}\xi_k - R(n)][\xi_n\xi_0 - R(n)] \to 0, \qquad N \to \infty, \qquad (4)$$

is necessary and sufficient for

$$\mathsf{E}|\hat{R}_N(n; \xi) - R(n)|^2 \to 0, \qquad N \to \infty. \qquad (5)$$

Let us suppose that the original sequence $\xi = (\xi_n)$ is Gaussian (with zero mean and covariance $R(n)$). Then by (II.12.51)

$$\begin{aligned}
\mathsf{E}[\xi_{n+k}\xi_k - R(n)][\xi_n\xi_0 - R(n)] &= \mathsf{E}\xi_{n+k}\xi_k\xi_n\xi_0 - R^2(n) \\
&= \mathsf{E}\xi_{n+k}\xi_k \cdot \mathsf{E}\xi_n\xi_0 + \mathsf{E}\xi_{n+k}\xi_n \cdot \mathsf{E}\xi_k\xi_0 \\
&\quad + \mathsf{E}\xi_{n+k}\xi_0 \cdot \mathsf{E}\xi_k\xi_n - R^2(n) \\
&= R^2(k) + R(n+k)R(n-k).
\end{aligned}$$

Therefore in the Gaussian case condition (4) is equivalent to

$$\frac{1}{N} \sum_{k=0}^{N-1} [R^2(k) + R(n+k)R(n-k)] \to 0, \qquad N \to \infty. \qquad (6)$$

Since $|R(n+k)R(n-k)| \le |R(n+k)|^2 + |R(n-k)|^2$, the condition

$$\frac{1}{N} \sum_{k=0}^{N-1} R^2(k) \to 0, \qquad N \to \infty, \qquad (7)$$

implies (6). Conversely, if (6) holds for $n = 0$, then (7) is satisfied.

We have now established the following theorem.

Theorem. *Let $\xi = (\xi_n)$ be a Gaussian stationary sequence with $\mathsf{E}\xi_n = 0$ and covariance function $R(n)$. Then (7) is a necessary and sufficient condition that, for every $n \ge 0$, the estimator $\hat{R}_N(n; x)$ is mean-square consistent, (i.e. that (5) is satisfied).*

Remark. If we use the spectral representation of the covariance function, we obtain

$$\frac{1}{N} \sum_{k=0}^{N-1} R^2(k) = \int_{-\pi}^{\pi} \int_{-\pi}^{\pi} \frac{1}{N} \sum_{k=0}^{N-1} e^{i(\lambda - v)k} F(d\lambda) F(dv)$$

$$= \int_{-\pi}^{\pi} \int_{-\pi}^{\pi} f_N(\lambda, v) F(d\lambda) F(dv),$$

where (compare (3.35))

$$f_N(\lambda, v) = \begin{cases} 1, & \lambda = v, \\ \dfrac{1 - e^{i(\lambda - v)N}}{N[1 - e^{i(\lambda - v)}]}, & \lambda \neq v. \end{cases}$$

But as $N \to \infty$

$$f_N(\lambda, v) \to f(\lambda, v) = \begin{cases} 1, & \lambda = v, \\ 0, & \lambda \neq v. \end{cases}$$

Therefore

$$\frac{1}{N} \sum_{k=0}^{N-1} R^2(k) \to \int_{-\pi}^{\pi} \int_{-\pi}^{\pi} f(\lambda, v) F(d\lambda) F(dv)$$

$$= \int_{-\pi}^{\pi} F(\{\lambda\}) F(d\lambda) = \sum_{\lambda} F^2(\{\lambda\}),$$

where the sum over λ contains at most a countable number of terms since the measure F is finite.

Hence (7) is equivalent to

$$\sum_{\lambda} F^2(\{\lambda\}) = 0, \tag{8}$$

which means that the spectral function $F(\lambda) = F([-\pi, \lambda])$ is *continuous*.

2. We now turn to the problem of finding estimators for the spectral function $F(\lambda)$ and the spectral density $f(\lambda)$ (under the assumption that they exist).

A method that naturally suggests itself for estimating the spectral density follows from the proof of Herglotz' theorem that we gave earlier. Recall that the function

$$f_N(\lambda) = \frac{1}{2\pi} \sum_{|n| < N} \left(1 - \frac{|n|}{N}\right) R(n) e^{-i\lambda n} \tag{9}$$

introduced in §1 has the property that the function

$$F_N(\lambda) = \int_{-\pi}^{\lambda} f_N(v)\, dv$$

converges on the whole (Chapter III, §1) to the spectral function $F(\lambda)$. Therefore if $F(\lambda)$ has a density $f(\lambda)$, we have

$$\int_{-\pi}^{\lambda} f_N(v) \, dv \to \int_{-\pi}^{\lambda} f(v) \, dv \qquad (10)$$

for each $\lambda \in [-\pi, \pi)$.

Starting from these facts and recalling that an estimator for $R(n)$ (on the basis of the observations $x_0, x_1, \ldots, x_{N-1}$) is $\hat{R}_N(n; x)$, we take as an estimator for $f(\lambda)$ the function

$$\hat{f}_N(\lambda; x) = \frac{1}{2\pi} \sum_{|n| < N} \left(1 - \frac{|n|}{N} \right) \hat{R}_N(n; x) e^{-i\lambda n}, \qquad (11)$$

putting $\hat{R}_N(n; x) = \hat{R}_N(|n|; x)$ for $|n| < N$.

The function $\hat{f}_N(\lambda; x)$ is known as a *periodogram*. It is easily verified that it can also be represented in the following more convenient form:

$$\hat{f}_N(\lambda; x) = \frac{1}{2\pi N} \left| \sum_{n=0}^{N-1} x_n e^{-i\lambda n} \right|^2. \qquad (12)$$

Since $E\hat{R}_N(n; \xi) = R(n)$, $|n| < N$, we have

$$E\hat{f}_N(\lambda; \xi) = f_N(\lambda).$$

If the spectral function $F(\lambda)$ has density $f(\lambda)$, then, since $f_N(\lambda)$ can also be written in the form (1.34), we find that

$$f_N(\lambda) = \frac{1}{2\pi N} \sum_{k=0}^{N-1} \sum_{l=0}^{N-1} \int_{-\pi}^{\pi} e^{iv(k-l)} e^{i\lambda(l-k)} f(v) \, dv$$

$$= \int_{-\pi}^{\pi} \frac{1}{2\pi N} \left| \sum_{k=0}^{N-1} e^{i(v-\lambda)k} \right|^2 f(v) \, dv.$$

The function

$$\Phi_N(\lambda) = \frac{1}{2\pi N} \left| \sum_{k=0}^{N-1} e^{i\lambda k} \right|^2 = \frac{1}{2\pi N} \left| \frac{\sin \frac{\lambda}{2} N}{\sin \lambda/2} \right|^2$$

is the Fejér kernel. It is known, from the properties of this function, that for almost every λ (with respect to Lebesgue measure)

$$\int_{-\pi}^{\pi} \Phi_N(\lambda - v) f(v) \, dv \to f(\lambda). \qquad (13)$$

Therefore for almost every $\lambda \in [-\pi, \pi)$

$$E\hat{f}_N(\lambda; \xi) \to f(\lambda); \qquad (14)$$

in other words, the estimator $\hat{f}_N(\lambda; x)$ of $f(\lambda)$ on the basis of $x_0, x_1, \ldots, x_{N-1}$ is *asymptotically unbiased*.

In this sense the estimator $\hat{f}_N(\lambda; x)$ can be considered to be "good." However, at the individual observed values $x_0, \ldots, x_{N-1}$ the values of the periodogram $\hat{f}_N(\lambda; x)$ usually turn out to be far from the actual values $f(\lambda)$. In fact, let $\xi = (\xi_n)$ be a stationary sequence of independent Gaussian random variables, $\xi_n \sim \mathcal{N}(0, 1)$. Then $f(\lambda) \equiv 1/2\pi$ and

$$\hat{f}_N(\lambda; \xi) = \frac{1}{2\pi} \left| \frac{1}{\sqrt{N}} \sum_{k=0}^{N-1} \xi_k e^{-i\lambda k} \right|^2.$$

Then at the point $\lambda = 0$ we have $\hat{f}_N(0, \xi)$ coinciding in distribution with the square of the Gaussian random variable $\eta \sim \mathcal{N}(0, 1)$. Hence, for every N,

$$\mathsf{E} |\hat{f}_N(0; \xi) - f(0)|^2 = \frac{1}{4\pi^2} \mathsf{E} |\eta^2 - 1|^2 > 0.$$

Moreover, an easy calculation shows that if $f(\lambda)$ is the spectral density of a stationary sequence $\xi = (\xi_n)$ that is constructed as a moving average:

$$\xi_n = \sum_{k=0}^{\infty} a_k \varepsilon_{n-k} \tag{15}$$

with $\sum_{k=0}^{\infty} |a_k| < \infty$, $\sum_{k=0}^{\infty} |a_k|^2 < \infty$, where $\varepsilon = (\varepsilon_n)$ is white noise with $\mathsf{E}\varepsilon_0^4 < \infty$, then

$$\lim_{N \to \infty} \mathsf{E} |\hat{f}_N(\lambda; \xi) - f(\lambda)|^2 = \begin{cases} 2f^2(0), & \lambda = 0, \pm\pi, \\ f^2(\lambda), & \lambda \neq 0, \pm\pi. \end{cases} \tag{16}$$

Hence it is clear that the periodogram cannot be a satisfactory estimator of the spectral density. To improve the situation, one often uses an estimator for $f(\lambda)$ of the form

$$f_N^W(\lambda; x) = \int_{-\pi}^{\pi} W_N(\lambda - v) \hat{f}_N(v; x) \, dv, \tag{17}$$

which is obtained from the periodogram $f_N(\lambda; x)$ and a smoothing function $W_N(\lambda)$, and which we call a *spectral window*. Natural requirements on $W_N(\lambda)$ are:

(a) $W_N(\lambda)$ has a sharp maximum at $\lambda = 0$;
(b) $\int_{-\pi}^{\pi} W_N(\lambda) \, d\lambda = 1$;
(c) $\mathsf{P} |\hat{f}_N^W(\lambda; \xi) - f(\lambda)|^2 \to 0$, $N \to \infty$, $\lambda \in [-\pi, \pi)$.

By (14) and (b) the estimators $\hat{f}_N^W(\lambda; \xi)$ are asymptotically unbiased. Condition (c) is the condition of asymptotic consistency in mean-square, which, as we showed above, is violated for the periodogram. Finally, condition (a) ensures that the required frequency λ is "picked out" from the periodogram.

Let us give some examples of estimators of the form (17).

Bartlett's estimator is based on the spectral window

$$W_N(\lambda) = a_N B(a_N \lambda),$$

where $a_N \uparrow \infty$, $a_N/N \to 0$, $N \to \infty$, and

$$B(\lambda) = \frac{1}{2\pi} \left| \frac{\sin(\lambda/2)}{\lambda/2} \right|^2.$$

Parzen's estimator takes the spectral window to be

$$W_N(\lambda) = a_N P(a_N \lambda),$$

where a_N are the same as before and

$$P(\lambda) = \frac{3}{8\pi} \left| \frac{\sin(\lambda/4)}{\lambda/4} \right|^4.$$

Zhurbenko's estimator is constructed from a spectral window of the form

$$W_N(\lambda) = a_N Z(a_N \lambda)$$

with

$$Z(\lambda) = \begin{cases} -\dfrac{\alpha+1}{2\alpha} |\lambda|^\alpha + \dfrac{\alpha+1}{2\alpha}, & |\lambda| \leq 1, \\ 0, & |\lambda| > 1, \end{cases}$$

where $0 < \alpha \leq 2$ and the a_N are selected in a particular way.

We shall not spend any more time on problems of estimating spectral densities; we merely note that there is an extensive statistical literature dealing with the construction of spectral windows and the comparison of the corresponding estimators $\hat{f}_N^W(\lambda; x)$.

3. We now consider the problem of estimating the spectral function $F(\lambda) = F([-\pi, \lambda])$. We begin by defining

$$F_N(\lambda) = \int_{-\pi}^{\lambda} f_N(v)\, dv, \qquad \hat{F}_N(\lambda; x) = \int_{-\pi}^{\lambda} \hat{f}_N(v; x)\, dv,$$

where $\hat{f}_N(v; x)$ is the periodogram constructed with $(x_0, x_1, \ldots, x_{N-1})$.

It follows from the proof of Herglotz' theorem (§1) that

$$\int_{-\pi}^{\pi} e^{i\lambda n}\, dF_N(\lambda) \to \int_{-\pi}^{\pi} e^{i\lambda n}\, dF(\lambda)$$

for every $n \in \mathbb{Z}$. Hence it follows (compare the corollary to Theorem 1, §3, Chapter III) that $F_N \Rightarrow F$, i.e. $F_N(\lambda)$ converges to $F(\lambda)$ at each point of continuity of $F(\lambda)$.

Observe that

$$\int_{-\pi}^{\pi} e^{i\lambda n}\, d\hat{F}_N(\lambda; \xi) = \hat{R}_N(n; \xi)\left(1 - \frac{|n|}{N}\right)$$

for all $|n| < N$. Therefore if we suppose that $\hat{R}_N(n; \xi)$ converges to $R(n)$ with probability one as $N \to \infty$, we have

$$\int_{-\pi}^{\pi} e^{i\lambda n} \, d\hat{F}_N(\lambda; \xi) \to \int_{-\pi}^{\pi} e^{i\lambda n} \, dF(\lambda) \quad \text{(P-a.s.)}$$

and therefore $\hat{F}_N(\lambda; \xi) \Rightarrow F(\lambda)$ (P-a.s.).

It is then easy to deduce (if necessary, passing from a sequence to a subsequence) that if $\hat{R}_N(n; \xi) \to R(n)$ in probability, then $\hat{F}_N(\lambda; \xi) \Rightarrow F(\lambda)$ in probability.

4. PROBLEMS

1. In (15) let $\varepsilon_n \sim \mathcal{N}(0, 1)$. Show that

$$(N - n)\mathsf{V}\hat{R}_N(n, \xi) \to 2\pi \int_{-\pi}^{\pi} (1 + e^{2in\lambda})f^2(\lambda) \, d\lambda$$

for every n, as $N \to \infty$.

2. Establish (16) and the following generalization:

$$\lim_{N \to \infty} \mathrm{cov}(\hat{f}_N(\lambda; \xi), \hat{f}_N(v; \xi)) = \begin{cases} 2f^2(0), & \lambda = v = 0, \pm\pi, \\ f^2(\lambda), & \lambda = v \neq 0, \pm\pi, \\ 0, & \lambda \neq \pm v. \end{cases}$$

§5. Wold's Expansion

1. In contrast to the representation (3.2) which gives an expansion of a stationary sequence in the *frequency* domain, Wold's expansion operates in the *time* domain. The main point of this expansion is that a stationary sequence $\xi = (\xi_n)$, $n \in \mathbb{Z}$, can be represented as the sum of two stationary sequences, one of which is completely predictable (in the sense that its values are completely determined by its "past"), whereas the second does not have this property.

We begin with some definitions. Let $H_n(\xi) = \bar{L}^2(\xi^n)$ and $H(\xi) = \bar{L}^2(\xi)$ be closed linear manifolds, spanned respectively by $\xi^n = (\ldots, \xi_{n-1}, \xi_n)$ and $\xi = (\cdots \xi_{n-1}, \xi_n, \ldots)$. Let

$$S(\xi) = \bigcap_n H_n(\xi).$$

For every $\eta \in H(\xi)$, denote by

$$\hat{\pi}_n(\eta) = \hat{E}(\eta \,|\, H_n \,|\, \xi))$$

the projection of η on the subspace $H_n(\xi)$ (see §11, Chapter II). We also write

$$\hat{\pi}_{-\infty}(\eta) = \hat{E}(\eta \,|\, S(\xi)).$$

Every element $\eta \in H(\xi)$ can be represented as

$$\eta = \hat{\pi}_{-\infty}(\eta) + (\eta - \hat{\pi}_{-\infty}(\eta)),$$

where $\eta - \hat{\pi}_{-\infty}(\eta) \perp \hat{\pi}_{-\infty}(\eta)$. Therefore $H(\xi)$ is represented as the orthogonal sum

$$H(\xi) = S(\xi) \oplus R(\xi),$$

where $S(\xi)$ consists of the elements $\hat{\pi}_{-\infty}(\eta)$ with $\eta \in H(\xi)$, and $R(\xi)$ consists of the elements of the form $\eta - \hat{\pi}_{-\infty}(\eta)$.

We shall now assume that $E\xi_n = 0$ and $V\xi_n > 0$. Then $H(\xi)$ is automatically nontrivial (contains elements different from zero).

Definition 1. A stationary sequence $\xi = (\xi_n)$ is *regular* if

$$H(\xi) = R(\xi)$$

and *singular* if

$$H(\xi) = S(\xi).$$

Remark. Singular sequences are also called *deterministic* and regular sequences are called *purely* or *completely nondeterministic*. If $S(\xi)$ is a proper subspace of $H(\xi)$ we just say that ξ is *nondeterministic*.

Theorem 1. *Every stationary (wide sense) random sequence ξ has a unique decomposition*

$$\xi_n = \xi_n^r + \xi_n^s, \tag{1}$$

where $\xi^r = (\xi_n^r)$ is regular and $\xi^s = (\xi_n^s)$ is singular. Here ξ^r amd ξ^s are orthogonal ($\xi_n^r \perp \xi_m^s$ for all n and m).

PROOF. We define

$$\xi_n^s = \hat{E}(\xi_n/S(\xi)), \qquad \xi_n^r = \xi_n - \xi_n^s.$$

Since $\xi_n^r \perp S(\xi)$, for every n, we have $S(\xi^r) \perp S(\xi)$. On the other hand, $S(\xi^r) \subseteq S(\xi)$ and therefore $S(\xi^r)$ is trivial (contains only random sequences that coincide almost surely with zero). Consequently ξ^r is regular.

Moreover, $H_n(\xi) \subseteq H_n(\xi^s) \oplus H_n(\xi^r)$ and $H_n(\xi^s) \subseteq H_n(\xi)$, $H_n(\xi^r) \subseteq H_n(\xi)$. Therefore $H_n(\xi) = H_n(\xi^s) \oplus H_n(\xi^r)$ and hence

$$S(\xi) \subseteq H_n(\xi^s) \oplus H_n(\xi^r) \tag{2}$$

for every n. Since $\xi_n^r \perp S(\xi)$ it follows from (2) that

$$S(\xi) \subseteq H_n(\xi^s),$$

and therefore $S(\xi) \subseteq S(\xi^s) \subseteq H(\xi^s)$. But $\xi_n^s \subseteq S(\xi)$; hence $H(\xi^s) \subseteq S(\xi)$ and consequently

$$S(\xi) = S(\xi^s) = H(\xi^s),$$

which means that ξ^s is singular.

The orthogonality of ξ^s and ξ^r follows in an obvious way from $\xi_n^s \in S(\xi)$ and $\xi_n^r \perp S(\xi)$.

Let us now show that (1) is unique. Let $\xi_n = \eta_n^r + \eta_n^s$, where η^r and η^s are regular and singular orthogonal sequences. Then since $H_n(\eta^s) = H(\eta^s)$, we have

$$H_n(\xi) = H_n(\eta^r) \oplus H_n(\eta^s) = H_n(\eta^r) \oplus H(\eta^s),$$

and therefore $S(\xi) = S(\eta^r) \oplus H(\eta^s)$. But $S(\eta^r)$ is trivial, and therefore $S(\xi) = H(\eta^s)$.

Since $\eta_n^s \in H(\eta^s) = S(\xi)$ and $\eta_n^r \perp H(\eta^s) = S(\xi)$, we have $\hat{\mathsf{E}}(\xi_n \mid S(\xi)) = \hat{\mathsf{E}}(\eta_n^r + \eta_n^s \mid S(\xi)) = \eta_n^s$, i.e. η_n^s coincides with ξ_n^s; this establishes the uniqueness of (1).

This completes the proof of the theorem.

2. Definition 2. Let $\xi = (\xi_n)$ be a nondegenerate stationary sequence. A random sequence $\varepsilon = (\varepsilon_n)$ is an *innovation* sequence (for ξ) if

(a) $\varepsilon = (\varepsilon_n)$ consists of pairwise orthogonal random variables with $\mathsf{E}\varepsilon_n = 0$, $\mathsf{E}|\varepsilon_n|^2 = 1$;
(b) $H_n(\xi) = H_n(\varepsilon)$ for all $n \in \mathbb{Z}$.

Remark. The reason for the term "innovation" is that ε_{n+1} provides, so to speak, new "information" not contained in $H_n(\xi)$ (in other words, "innovates" in $H_n(\xi)$ the information that is needed for forming $H_{n+1}(\xi)$).

The following fundamental theorem establishes a connection between one-sided moving averages (Example 4, §1) and regular sequences.

Theorem 2. *A necessary and sufficient condition for a nondegenerate sequence ξ to be regular is that there are an innovation sequence $\varepsilon = (\varepsilon_n)$ and a sequence (a_n) of complex numbers, $n \geq 0$, with $\sum_{n=0}^{\infty} |a_n|^2 < \infty$, such that*

$$\xi_n = \sum_{k=0}^{\infty} a_k \varepsilon_{n-k} \quad \text{(P-a.s.)} \tag{3}$$

PROOF. *Necessity.* We represent $H_n(\xi)$ in the form

$$H_n(\xi) = H_{n-1}(\xi) \oplus B_n.$$

Since $H_n(\xi)$ is spanned by elements of $H_{n-1}(\xi)$ and elements of the form $\beta \cdot \xi_n$, where β is a complex number, the dimension (dim) of B_n is either zero or one. But the space $H_n(\xi)$ cannot coincide with $H_{n-1}(\xi)$ for any value of n.

In fact, if B_n is trivial for some n, then by stationarity B_k is trivial for all k, and therefore $H(\xi) = S(\xi)$, contradicting the assumption that ξ is regular. Thus B_n has the dimension dim $B_n = 1$. Let η_n be a nonzero element of B_n. Put

$$\varepsilon_n = \frac{\eta_n}{\|\eta_n\|},$$

where $\|\eta_n\|^2 = \mathsf{E}|\eta_n|^2 > 0$.

For given n and $k \geq 0$, consider the decomposition

$$H_n(\xi) = H_{n-k}(\xi) \oplus B_{n-k+1} \oplus \cdots \oplus B_n.$$

Then $\varepsilon_{n-k}, \ldots, \varepsilon_n$ is an orthogonal basis in $B_{n-k+1} \oplus \cdots \oplus B_n$ and

$$\xi_n = \sum_{j=0}^{k-1} a_j \varepsilon_{n-j} + \hat{\pi}_{n-k}(\xi_n), \tag{4}$$

where $a_j = \mathsf{E}\xi_n \bar{\varepsilon}_{n-j}$.

By Bessel's inequality (II.11.16)

$$\sum_{j=0}^{\infty} |a_j|^2 \leq \|\xi_n\|^2 < \infty.$$

It follows that $\sum_{j=0}^{\infty} a_i \varepsilon_{n-j}$ converges in mean square, and then, by (4), equation (3) will be established as soon as we show that $\hat{\pi}_{n-k}(\xi_n) \xrightarrow{L^2} 0$, $k \to \infty$.

It is enough to consider the case $n = 0$. Since

$$\hat{\pi}_{-k} = \hat{\pi}_0 + \sum_{i=0}^{k} [\hat{\pi}_{-i} - \hat{\pi}_{-i+1}],$$

and the terms that appear in this sum are orthogonal, we have for every $k \geq 0$

$$\sum_{i=0}^{k} \|\hat{\pi}_{-i} - \hat{\pi}_{-i+1}\|^2 = \left\| \sum_{i=0}^{k} (\hat{\pi}_{-i} - \hat{\pi}_{-i+1}) \right\|^2$$

$$= \|\hat{\pi}_{-k} - \hat{\pi}_0\|^2 \leq 4\|\xi_0\|^2 < \infty.$$

Therefore the limit $\lim_{k \to \infty} \hat{\pi}_{-k}$ exists (in mean square). Now $\hat{\pi}_{-k} \in H_{-k}(\xi)$ for each k, and therefore the limit in question must belong to $\bigcap_{k \geq 0} H_k(\xi) = S(\xi)$. But, by assumption, $S(\xi)$ is trivial, and therefore $\hat{\pi}_{-k} \xrightarrow{L^2} 0$, $k \to \infty$.

Sufficiency. Let the nondegenerate sequence ξ have a representation (3), where $\varepsilon = (\varepsilon_n)$ is an orthonormal system (not necessarily satisfying the condition $H_n(\xi) = H_n(\varepsilon)$, $n \in \mathbb{Z}$). Then $H_n(\xi) \subseteq H_n(\varepsilon)$ and therefore $S(\xi) = \bigcap_k H_k(\xi) \subseteq H_n(\varepsilon)$ for every n. But $\varepsilon_{n+1} \perp H_n(\varepsilon)$, and therefore $\varepsilon_{n+1} \perp S(\xi)$ and at the same time $\varepsilon = (\varepsilon_n)$ is a basis in $H(\xi)$. It follows that $S(\xi)$ is trivial, and consequently ξ is regular.

This completes the proof of the theorem.

Remark. It follows from the proof that a nondegenerate sequence ξ is regular if and only if it admits a representation as a one-sided moving average

$$\xi_n = \sum_{k=0}^{\infty} \tilde{a}_k \tilde{\varepsilon}_{n-k}, \tag{5}$$

where $\tilde{\varepsilon} = \tilde{\varepsilon}_n$ is an orthonormal system which (it is important to emphasize this!) does not necessarily satisfy the condition $H_n(\xi) = H_n(\tilde{\varepsilon})$, $n \in \mathbb{Z}$. In this sense the conclusion of Theorem 2 says more, and specifically that for a regular sequence ξ there exist $a = (a_n)$ and an orthonormal system $\varepsilon = (\varepsilon_n)$ such that not only (5), but also (3), is satisfied, with $H_n(\xi) = H_n(\varepsilon)$, $n \in \mathbb{Z}$.

The following theorem is an immediate corollary of Theorems 1 and 2.

Theorem 3 (Wold's Expansion). *If $\xi = (\xi_n)$ is a nondegenerate stationary sequence, then*

$$\xi_n = \xi_n^s + \sum_{k=0}^{\infty} a_k \varepsilon_{n-k}, \tag{6}$$

where $\sum_{k=0}^{\infty} |a_k|^2 < \infty$ and $\varepsilon = (\varepsilon_n)$ is an innovation sequence (for ξ^r).

3. The significance of the concepts introduced here (regular and singular sequences) becomes particularly clear if we consider the following (linear) extrapolation problem, for whose solution the Wold expansion (6) is especially useful.

Let $H_0(\xi) = \overline{L}^2(\xi^0)$ be the closed linear manifold spanned by the variables $\xi^0 = (\ldots, \xi_{-1}, \xi_0)$. Consider the problem of constructing an *optimal* (least-squares) *linear estimator* $\hat{\xi}_n$ of ξ_n in terms of the "past" $\xi^0 = (\ldots, \xi_{-1}, \xi_0)$. It follows from §11, Chapter II, that

$$\hat{\xi}_n = \hat{\mathsf{E}}(\xi_n | H_0(\xi)). \tag{7}$$

(In the notation of Subsection 1, $\hat{\xi}_n = \hat{\pi}_0(\xi_n)$.) Since ξ^r and ξ^s are orthogonal and $H_0(\xi) = H_0(\xi^r) \oplus H_0(\xi^s)$, we obtain, by using (6),

$$\hat{\xi}_n = \hat{\mathsf{E}}(\xi_n^s + \xi_n^r | H_0(\xi)) = \hat{\mathsf{E}}(\xi_n^s | H_0(\xi)) + \hat{\mathsf{E}}(\xi_n^r | H_0(\xi))$$

$$= \hat{\mathsf{E}}(\xi_n^s | H_0(\xi^r) \oplus H_0(\xi^s)) + \hat{\mathsf{E}}(\xi_n^r | H_0(\xi^r) \oplus H_0(\xi^s))$$

$$= \hat{\mathsf{E}}(\xi_n^s | H_0(\xi^s)) + \hat{\mathsf{E}}(\xi_n^r | H_0(\xi^r))$$

$$= \xi_n^s + \hat{\mathsf{E}}\left(\sum_{k=0}^{\infty} a_k \varepsilon_{n-k} | H_0(\xi^r) \right).$$

In (6), the sequence $\varepsilon = (\varepsilon_n)$ is an innovation sequence for $\xi^r = (\xi_n^r)$ and therefore $H_0(\xi^r) = H_0(\varepsilon)$. Therefore

$$\hat{\xi}_n = \xi_n^s + \hat{\mathsf{E}}\left(\sum_{k=0}^{\infty} a_k \varepsilon_{n-k} | H_0(\varepsilon) \right) = \xi_n^s + \sum_{k=n}^{\infty} a_k \varepsilon_{n-k} \tag{8}$$

and the mean-square error of predicting ξ_n by $\xi_0 = (\ldots, \xi_{-1}, \xi_0)$ is

$$\sigma_n^2 = \mathsf{E}\,|\xi_n - \hat{\xi}_n|^2 = \sum_{k=0}^{n-1} |a_k|^2. \tag{9}$$

We can draw two important conclusions.

(a) If ξ is *singular*, then for every $n \geq 1$ the error (in the extrapolation) σ_n^2 is zero; in other words, we can predict ξ_n without error from its "past" $\xi^0 = (\ldots, \xi_{-1}, \xi_0)$.

(b) If ξ is *regular*, then $\sigma_n^2 \leq \sigma_{n+1}^2$ and

$$\lim_{n \to \infty} \sigma_n^2 = \sum_{k=0}^{\infty} |a_k|^2. \tag{10}$$

Since

$$\sum_{k=0}^{\infty} |a_k|^2 = \mathsf{E}\,|\xi_n|^2,$$

it follows from (10) and (9) that

$$\hat{\xi}_n \xrightarrow{L^2} 0, \qquad n \to \infty;$$

i.e. as n increases, the prediction of ξ_n in terms of $\xi_0 = (\ldots, \xi_{-1}, \xi_0)$ becomes trivial (reducing simply to $\mathsf{E}\xi_n = 0$).

4. Let us suppose that ξ is a nondegenerate regular stationary sequence. According to Theorem 2, every such sequence admits a representation as a one-sided moving average

$$\xi_n = \sum_{k=0}^{\infty} a_k \varepsilon_{n-k}, \tag{11}$$

where $\sum_{k=0}^{\infty} |a_k|^2 < \infty$ and the orthonormal sequence $\varepsilon = (\varepsilon_n)$ has the important property that

$$H_n(\xi) = H_n(\varepsilon), \qquad n \in \mathbb{Z}. \tag{12}$$

The representation (11) means (see Subsection 3, §3) that ξ_n can be interpreted as the output signal of a physically realizable filter with impulse response $a = (a_k)$, $k \geq 0$, when the input is $\varepsilon = (\varepsilon_n)$.

Like any sequence of two-sided moving averages, a regular sequence has a spectral density $f(\lambda)$. But since a regular sequence admits a representation as a one-sided moving average it is possible to obtain additional information about properties of the spectral density.

In the first place, it is clear that

$$f(\lambda) = \frac{1}{2\pi} |\varphi(\lambda)|^2,$$

where

$$\varphi(\lambda) = \sum_{k=0}^{\infty} e^{-i\lambda k} a_k, \qquad \sum_{k=0}^{\infty} |a_k|^2 < \infty. \tag{13}$$

Put

$$\Phi(z) = \sum_{k=0}^{\infty} a_k z^k. \tag{14}$$

This function is analytic in the open domain $|z| < 1$ and since $\sum_{k=0}^{\infty} |a_k|^2 < \infty$ it belongs to the *Hardy class H^2*, the class of functions $g = g(z)$, analytic in $|z| < 1$, satisfying

$$\sup_{0 \le r < 1} \frac{1}{2\pi} \int_{-\pi}^{\pi} |g(re^{i\theta})|^2 \, d\theta < \infty. \tag{15}$$

In fact,

$$\frac{1}{2\pi} \int_{-\pi}^{\pi} |\Phi(re^{i\theta})|^2 \, d\theta = \sum_{k=0}^{\infty} |a_k|^2 r^{2k}$$

and

$$\sup_{0 \le r < 1} \sum |a_k|^2 r^{2k} \le \sum |a_k|^2 < \infty.$$

It is shown in the theory of functions of a complex variable that the boundary function $\Phi(e^{i\lambda})$, $-\pi \le \lambda < \pi$, of $\Phi \in H^2$, not identically zero, has the property that

$$\int_{-\pi}^{\pi} \ln |\Phi(e^{-i\lambda})| \, d\lambda > -\infty. \tag{16}$$

In our case

$$f(\lambda) = \frac{1}{2\pi} |\Phi(e^{-i\lambda})|^2,$$

where $\Phi \in H^2$. Therefore

$$\ln f(\lambda) = -\ln 2\pi + 2 \ln |\Phi(e^{-i\lambda})|,$$

and consequently the spectral density $f(\lambda)$ of a regular process satisfies

$$\int_{-\pi}^{\pi} \ln f(\lambda) \, d\lambda > -\infty. \tag{17}$$

On the other hand, let the spectral density $f(\lambda)$ satisfy (17). It again follows from the theory of functions of a complex variable that there is then a function $\Phi(z) = \sum_{k=0}^{\infty} a_k z^k$ in the Hardy class H^2 such that (almost everywhere with respect to Lebesgue measure)

$$f(\lambda) = \frac{1}{2\pi} |\Phi(e^{-i\lambda})|^2.$$

Therefore if we put $\varphi(\lambda) = \Phi(e^{-i\lambda})$ we obtain

$$f(\lambda) = \frac{1}{2\pi} |\varphi(\lambda)|^2,$$

where $\varphi(\lambda)$ is given by (13). Then it follows from the corollary to Theorem 3, §3, that ξ admits a representation as a one-sided moving average (11), where $\varepsilon = (\varepsilon_n)$ is an orthonormal sequence. From this and from the Remark on Theorem 2, it follows that ξ is regular.

Thus we have the following theorem.

Theorem 4 (Kolmogorov). *Let ξ be a nondegenerate regular stationary sequence. Then there is a spectral density $f(\lambda)$ such that*

$$\int_{-\pi}^{\pi} \ln f(\lambda) \, d\lambda > -\infty. \tag{18}$$

In particular, $f(\lambda) > 0$ (almost everywhere with respect to Lebesgue measure).

Conversely, if ξ is a stationary sequence with a spectral density satisfying (18), the sequence is regular.

5. PROBLEMS

1. Show that a stationary sequence with discrete spectrum (piecewise-constant spectral function $F(\lambda)$) is singular.

2. Let $\sigma_n^2 = \mathsf{E}|\xi_n - \hat{\xi}_n|^2$, $\hat{\xi}_n = \hat{\mathsf{E}}(\xi_n | H_0(\xi))$. Show that if $\sigma_n^2 = 0$ for some $n \geq 1$, the sequence is singular; if $\sigma_n^2 \to R(0)$ as $n \to \infty$, the sequence is regular.

3. Show that the stationary sequence $\xi = (\xi_n)$, $\xi_n = e^{in\varphi}$, where φ is a uniform random variable on $[0, 2\pi]$, is regular. Find the estimator $\hat{\xi}_n$ and the number σ_n^2, and show that the *nonlinear* estimator

$$\tilde{\xi}_n = \left(\frac{\xi_0}{\xi_{-1}} \right)^n$$

provides a correct estimate of ξ_n by the "past" $\xi^0 = (\dots, \xi_{-1}, \xi_0)$, i.e.

$$\mathsf{E}|\tilde{\xi}_n - \xi_n|^2 = 0, \qquad n \geq 1.$$

§6. Extrapolation, Interpolation and Filtering

1. Extrapolation. According to the preceding section, a singular sequence admits an error-free prediction (extrapolation) of ξ_n, $n \geq 1$, in terms of the "past," $\xi^0 = (\dots, \xi_{-1}, \xi_0)$. Consequently it is reasonable, when considering the problem of extrapolation for arbitrary stationary sequences, to begin with the case of regular sequences.

According to Theorem 2 of §5, every regular sequence $\xi = (\xi_n)$ admits a representation as a one-sided moving average,

$$\xi_n = \sum_{k=0}^{\infty} a_k \varepsilon_{n-k} \tag{1}$$

with $\sum_{k=0}^{\infty} |a_k|^2 < \infty$ and some innovation sequence $\varepsilon = (\varepsilon_n)$. It follows from §5 that the representation (1) solves the problem of finding the optimal (linear) estimator $\hat{\xi} = \hat{\mathsf{E}}(\xi_n | H_0(\xi))$ since, by (5.8),

$$\hat{\xi}_n = \sum_{k=n}^{\infty} a_k \varepsilon_{n-k} \tag{2}$$

and

$$\sigma_n^2 = \mathsf{E}|\xi_n - \hat{\xi}_n|^2 = \sum_{k=0}^{n-1} |a_k|^2. \tag{3}$$

However, this can be considered only as a theoretical solution, for the following reasons.

The sequences that we consider are ordinarily not given to us by means of their representations (1), but by their covariance functions $R(n)$ or the spectral densities $f(\lambda)$ (which exist for regular sequences). Hence a solution (2) can only be regarded as satisfactory if the coefficients a_k are given in terms of $R(n)$ or of $f(\lambda)$, and ε_k are given by their values $\cdots \xi_{k-1}, \xi_k$.

Without discussing the problem in general, we consider only the special case (of interest in applications) when the spectral density has the form

$$f(\lambda) = \frac{1}{2\pi} |\Phi(e^{-i\lambda})|^2, \tag{4}$$

where $\Phi(z) = \sum_{k=0}^{\infty} b_k z^k$ has radius of convergence $r > 1$ and has no zeros in $|z| \leq 1$.

Let

$$\xi_n = \int_{-\pi}^{\pi} e^{i\lambda n} Z(d\lambda) \tag{5}$$

be the spectral representation of $\xi = (\xi_n)$, $n \in \mathbb{Z}$.

Theorem 1. *If the spectral density of ξ has the density (4), then the optimal (linear) estimator $\hat{\xi}_n$ of ξ_n in terms of $\xi^0 = (\ldots, \xi_{-1}, \xi_0)$ is given by*

$$\hat{\xi}_n = \int_{-\pi}^{\pi} \hat{\varphi}_n(\lambda) Z(d\lambda), \tag{6}$$

where

$$\hat{\varphi}_n(\lambda) = e^{i\lambda n} \frac{\Phi_n(e^{-i\lambda})}{\Phi(e^{-i\lambda})} \tag{7}$$

and

$$\Phi_n(z) = \sum_{k=n}^{\infty} b_k z^k.$$

PROOF. According to the remark on Theorem 2 of §3, every variable $\xi_n \in H_0(\xi)$ admits a representation in the form

$$\hat{\xi}_n = \int_{-\pi}^{\pi} \tilde{\varphi}_n(\lambda) Z(d\lambda), \qquad \tilde{\varphi}_n \in H_0(F), \tag{8}$$

where $H_0(F)$ is the closed linear manifold spanned by the functions $e_n = e^{i\lambda n}$ for $n \leq 0$ $(F(\lambda) = \int_{-\pi}^{\lambda} f(v)\, dv)$.

Since

$$\mathsf{E}\,|\xi_n - \hat{\xi}_n|^2 = \mathsf{E}\left| \int_{-\pi}^{\pi} (e^{i\lambda n} - \tilde{\varphi}_n(\lambda)) Z(d\lambda) \right|^2$$

$$= \int_{-\pi}^{\pi} |e^{i\lambda n} - \tilde{\varphi}_n(\lambda)|^2 f(\lambda)\, d\lambda,$$

the proof that (6) is optimal reduces to proving that

$$\inf_{\tilde{\varphi}_n \in H_0(F)} \int_{-\pi}^{\pi} |e^{i\lambda n} - \tilde{\varphi}_n(\lambda)|^2 f(\lambda)\, d\lambda = \int_{-\pi}^{\pi} |e^{i\lambda n} - \hat{\varphi}_n(\lambda)|^2 f(\lambda)\, d\lambda. \tag{9}$$

It follows from Hilbert-space theory (§11, Chapter II) that the optimal function $\hat{\varphi}_n(\lambda)$ (in the sense of (9)) is determined by the two conditions

(1) $\quad \hat{\varphi}_n(\lambda) \in H_0(F)$, $\qquad\qquad\qquad\qquad\qquad\qquad\qquad$ (10)
(2) $\quad e^{i\lambda n} - \hat{\varphi}_n(\lambda) \perp H_0(F)$.

Since

$$e^{i\lambda n}\Phi_n(e^{-i\lambda}) = e^{i\lambda n}[b_n e^{-i\lambda n} + b_{n+1} e^{-i\lambda(n+1)} + \cdots] \in H_0(F)$$

and in a similar way $1/\Phi(e^{-i\lambda}) \in H_0(F)$, the function $\hat{\varphi}_n(\lambda)$ defined in (7) belongs to $H_0(F)$. Therefore in proving that $\hat{\varphi}_n(\lambda)$ is optimal it is sufficient to verify that, for every $m \geq 0$,

$$e^{i\lambda n} - \hat{\varphi}_n(\lambda) \perp e^{i\lambda m},$$

i.e.

$$I_{n,m} \equiv \int_{-\pi}^{\pi} [e^{i\lambda n} - \hat{\varphi}_n(\lambda)] e^{-i\lambda m} f(\lambda)\, d\lambda = 0, \qquad m \geq 0.$$

The following chain of equations shows that this is actually the case:

$$I_{n,m} = \frac{1}{2\pi} \int_{-\pi}^{\pi} e^{i\lambda(n-m)} \left[1 - \frac{\Phi_n(e^{-i\lambda})}{\Phi(e^{-i\lambda})} \right] |\Phi(e^{-i\lambda})|^2\, d\lambda$$

$$= \frac{1}{2\pi} \int_{-\pi}^{\pi} e^{i\lambda(n-m)} [\Phi(e^{-i\lambda}) - \Phi_n(e^{-i\lambda})] \overline{\Phi(e^{-i\lambda})}\, d\lambda$$

$$= \frac{1}{2\pi} \int_{-\pi}^{\pi} e^{i\lambda(n-m)} \left(\sum_{k=0}^{n-1} b_k e^{-i\lambda k} \right) \left(\sum_{l=0}^{\infty} \bar{b}_l e^{i\lambda l} \right) d\lambda$$

$$= \frac{1}{2\pi} \int_{-\pi}^{\pi} e^{-i\lambda m} \left(\sum_{k=0}^{n-1} b_k e^{i\lambda(n-k)} \right) \left(\sum_{l=0}^{\infty} \bar{b}_l e^{i\lambda l} \right) d\lambda = 0,$$

where the last equation follows because, for $m \geq 0$ and $r > 1$,

$$\int_{-\pi}^{\pi} e^{-i\lambda m} e^{i\lambda r} \, d\lambda = 0.$$

This completes the proof of the theorem.

Remark 1. Expanding $\hat{\varphi}_n(\lambda)$ in a Fourier series, we find that the predicted value $\hat{\xi}_n$ of ξ_n, $n \geq 1$, in terms of the past, $\xi^0 = (\ldots, \xi_{-1}, \xi_0)$, is given by the formula

$$\hat{\xi}_n = C_0 \xi_0 + C_{-1} \xi_{-1} + C_{-2} \xi_{-2} + \cdots.$$

Remark 2. A typical example of a spectral density represented in the form (4) is the *rational* function

$$f(\lambda) = \frac{1}{2\pi} \left| \frac{P(e^{-i\lambda})}{Q(e^{-i\lambda})} \right|^2,$$

where the polynomials $P(z) = a_0 + a_1 z + \cdots + a_p z^p$ and $Q(z) = 1 + b_1 z + \cdots + b_q z^q$ have no zeros in $\{z : |z| \leq 1\}$.

In fact, in this case it is enough to put $\Phi(z) = P(z)/Q(z)$. Then $\Phi(z) = \sum_{k=0}^{\infty} C_k z^k$ and the radius of convergence of this series is greater than one.

Let us illustrate Theorem 1 with two examples.

EXAMPLE 1. Let the spectral density be

$$f(\lambda) = \frac{1}{2\pi}(5 + 4 \cos \lambda).$$

The corresponding covariance function $R(n)$ has the shape of a triangle with

$$R(0) = 5, \qquad R(\pm 1) = 2, \qquad R(n) = 0 \qquad \text{for} \quad |n| \geq 2. \qquad (11)$$

Since this spectral density can be represented in the form

$$f(\lambda) = \frac{1}{2\pi} |2 + e^{-i\lambda}|^2,$$

we may apply Theorem 1. We find easily that

$$\hat{\varphi}_1(\lambda) = e^{i\lambda} \frac{e^{-i\lambda}}{2 + e^{-i\lambda}}, \qquad \hat{\varphi}_n(\lambda) = 0 \qquad \text{for} \quad n \geq 2. \qquad (12)$$

Therefore $\hat{\xi}_n = 0$ for all $n \geq 2$, i.e. the (linear) prediction of ξ_n in terms of $\xi^0 = (\ldots, \xi_{-1}, \xi_0)$ is trivial, which is not at all surprising if we observe that, by (11), the correlation between ξ_n and any of $\xi_0, \xi_{-1}, \ldots$ is zero for $n \geq 2$.

For $n = 1$ we find from (6) and (12) that

$$\hat{\xi}_1 = \int_{-\pi}^{\pi} e^{i\lambda} \frac{e^{-i\lambda}}{2 + e^{-i\lambda}} Z(d\lambda)$$

$$= \frac{1}{2} \int_{-\pi}^{\pi} \frac{1}{\left(1 + \dfrac{e^{-i\lambda}}{2}\right)} Z(d\lambda) = \sum_{k=0}^{\infty} \frac{(-1)^k}{2^{k+1}} \int_{-\pi}^{\pi} e^{-ik\lambda} Z(d\lambda)$$

$$= \sum_{k=0}^{\infty} \frac{(-1)^k \xi_k}{2^{k+1}} = \tfrac{1}{2}\xi_0 - \tfrac{1}{4}\xi_{-1} + \cdots.$$

EXAMPLE 2. Let the covariance function be

$$R(n) = a^n, \qquad |a| < 1.$$

Then (see Example 5 in §1)

$$f(\lambda) = \frac{1}{2\pi} \frac{1 - |a|^2}{|1 - ae^{-i\lambda}|^2},$$

i.e.

$$f(\lambda) = \frac{1}{2\pi} |\Phi(e^{-i\lambda})|^2,$$

where

$$\Phi(z) = \frac{(1 - |a|^2)^{1/2}}{1 - az} = (1 - |a|^2)^{1/2} \sum_{k=0}^{\infty} (az)^k,$$

from which $\hat{\varphi}_n(\lambda) = a^n$ and therefore

$$\hat{\xi}_n = \int_{-\pi}^{\pi} a^n Z(d\lambda) = a^n \xi_0.$$

In other words, in order to predict the value of ξ_n from the observations $\xi^0 = (\ldots, \xi_{-1}, \xi_0)$ it is sufficient to know only the last observation ξ_0.

Remark 3. It follows from the Wold expansion of the regular sequence $\xi = (\xi_n)$ with

$$\xi_n = \sum_{k=0}^{\infty} a_k \xi_{n-k} \tag{13}$$

that the spectral density $f(\lambda)$ admits the representation

$$f(\lambda) = \frac{1}{2\pi} |\Phi(e^{-i\lambda})|^2, \tag{14}$$

where

$$\Phi(z) = \sum_{k=0}^{\infty} a_k z^k. \tag{15}$$

It is evident that the converse also holds, that is, if $f(\lambda)$ admits the representation (14) with a function $\Phi(z)$ of the form (15), then the Wold expansion of ξ_n has the form (13). Therefore the problem of representing the spectral density in the form (14) and the problem of determining the coefficients a_k in the Wold expansion are equivalent.

The assumptions that $\Phi(z)$ in Theorem 1 has no zeros for $|z| \leq 1$ and that $r > 1$ are in fact not essential. In other words, if the spectral density of a regular sequence is represented in the form (14), then the optimal estimator $\hat{\xi}_n$ (in the mean square sense) for ξ_n in terms of $\xi^0 = (\dots, \xi_{-1}, \xi_0)$ is determined by formulas (6) and (7).

Remark 4. Theorem 1 (with the preceding remark) solves the prediction problem for regular sequences. Let us show that in fact the same answer remains valid for arbitrary stationary sequences. More precisely, let

$$\xi_n = \xi_n^s + \xi_n^r, \qquad \xi_n = \int_{-\pi}^{\pi} e^{i\lambda n} Z(d\lambda), \qquad F(\Delta) = \mathsf{E}\,|Z(\Delta)|^2,$$

and let $f^r(\lambda) = (1/2\pi)|\Phi(e^{-i\lambda})|^2$ be the spectral density of the regular sequence $\xi^r = (\xi_n^r)$. Then $\hat{\xi}_n$ is determined by (6) and (7).

In fact, let (see Subsection 3, §5)

$$\hat{\xi}_n = \int_{-\pi}^{\pi} \hat{\varphi}_n(\lambda) Z(d\lambda), \qquad \hat{\xi}_n^r = \int_{-\pi}^{\pi} \hat{\varphi}_n^r(\lambda) Z^r(d\lambda),$$

where $Z^r(\Delta)$ is the orthogonal stochastic measure in the representation of the regular sequence ξ^r. Then

$$\mathsf{E}\,|\xi_n - \hat{\xi}_n|^2 = \int_{-\pi}^{\pi} |e^{i\lambda n} - \hat{\varphi}_n(\lambda)|^2 F(d\lambda)$$

$$\geq \int_{-\pi}^{\pi} |e^{i\lambda n} - \hat{\varphi}_n(\lambda)|^2 f^r(\lambda)\,d\lambda \geq \int_{-\pi}^{\pi} |e^{i\lambda n} - \hat{\varphi}_n^r(\lambda)|^2 f^r(\lambda)\,d\lambda$$

$$= \mathsf{E}\,|\xi_n^r - \hat{\xi}_n^r|^2. \tag{16}$$

But $\xi_n - \hat{\xi}_n = \hat{\xi}_n^r - \xi^r$. Hence $\mathsf{E}\,|\xi_n - \hat{\xi}_n|^2 = \mathsf{E}\,|\xi_n^r - \hat{\xi}_n^r|^2$, and it follows from (16) that we may take $\hat{\varphi}_n(\lambda)$ to be $\hat{\varphi}_n^r(\lambda)$.

2. Interpolation. Suppose that $\xi = (\xi_n)$ is a regular sequence with spectral density $f(\lambda)$. The simplest interpolation problem is the problem of constructing the optimal (mean-square) linear estimator from the results of the measurements $\{\xi_n, n = \pm 1, \pm 2, \dots\}$ omitting ξ_0.

Let $H^0(\xi)$ be the closed linear manifold spanned by $\xi_n, n \neq 0$. Then according to the results of Theorem 2, §3, every random variable $\eta \in H^0(\xi)$ can be represented in the form

$$\eta = \int_{-\pi}^{\pi} \varphi(\lambda) Z(d\lambda),$$

where φ belongs to $H^0(F)$, the closed linear manifold spanned by the functions $e^{i\lambda n}$, $n \neq 0$. The estimator

$$\check{\xi}_0 = \int_{-\pi}^{\pi} \check{\varphi}(\lambda) Z(d\lambda) \tag{17}$$

will be optimal if and only if

$$\inf_{\eta \in H^0(\xi)} \mathsf{E} |\xi_0 - \eta|^2 = \inf_{\varphi \in H^0(F)} \int_{-\pi}^{\pi} |1 - \varphi(\lambda)|^2 F(d\lambda)$$

$$= \int_{-\pi}^{\pi} |1 - \check{\varphi}(\lambda)|^2 F(d\lambda) = \mathsf{E} |\xi_0 - \check{\xi}_0|^2.$$

It follows from the perpendicularity properties of the Hilbert space $H^0(F)$ that $\check{\varphi}(\lambda)$ is completely determined (compare (10)) by the two conditions

(1) $\check{\varphi}(\lambda) \in H^0(F)$, $\qquad\qquad\qquad\qquad\qquad\qquad$ (18)
(2) $1 - \check{\varphi}(\lambda) \perp H^0(F)$.

Theorem 2 (Kolmogorov). *Let $\xi = (\xi_n)$ be a regular sequence such that*

$$\int_{-\pi}^{\pi} \frac{d\lambda}{f(\lambda)} < \infty. \tag{19}$$

Then

$$\check{\varphi}(\lambda) = 1 - \frac{\alpha}{f(\lambda)}, \tag{20}$$

where

$$\alpha = \frac{2\pi}{\displaystyle\int_{-\pi}^{\pi} \frac{d\lambda}{f(\lambda)}}, \tag{21}$$

and the interpolation error $\delta^2 = \mathsf{E} |\xi_0 - \check{\xi}_0|^2$ is given by $\delta^2 = 2\pi \cdot \alpha$.

PROOF. We shall give the proof only under very stringent hypotheses on the spectral density, specifically that

$$0 < c \leq f(\lambda) \leq C < \infty. \tag{22}$$

It follows from (2) and (18) that

$$\int_{-\pi}^{\pi} [1 - \check{\varphi}(\lambda)] e^{in\lambda} f(\lambda) \, d\lambda = 0 \tag{23}$$

for every $n \neq 0$. By (22), the function $[1 - \check{\varphi}(\lambda)] f(\lambda)$ belongs to the Hilbert space $L^2([-\pi, \pi], \mathscr{B}[-\pi, \pi], \mu)$ with Lebesgue measure μ. In this space the functions $\{e^{in\lambda}/\sqrt{2\pi}, n = 0, \pm 1, \ldots\}$ form an orthonormal basis (Problem 7, §11, Chapter II). Hence it follows from (23) that $[1 - \check{\varphi}(\lambda)] f(\lambda)$ is a constant, which we denote by α. Thus the second condition in (18) leads to the conclusion that

$$\check{\varphi}(\lambda) = 1 - \frac{\alpha}{f(\lambda)}. \tag{24}$$

Starting from the first condition (18), we now determine α.

By (22), $\check{\varphi} \in L^2$ and the condition $\check{\varphi} \in H^0(F)$ is equivalent to the condition that $\check{\varphi}$ belongs to the closed (in the L^2 norm) linear manifold spanned by the functions $e^{i\lambda n}$, $n \neq 0$. Hence it is clear that the zeroth coefficient in the expansion of $\check{\varphi}(\lambda)$ must be zero. Therefore

$$0 = \int_{-\pi}^{\pi} \check{\varphi}(\lambda)\, d\lambda = 2\pi - \alpha \int_{-\pi}^{\pi} \frac{d\lambda}{f(\lambda)}$$

and hence α is determined by (21).

Finally,

$$\delta^2 = \mathsf{E}\,|\xi_0 - \check{\xi}_0|^2 = \int_{-\pi}^{\pi} |1 - \check{\varphi}(\lambda)|^2 f(\lambda)\, d\lambda$$

$$= |\alpha|^2 \int_{-\pi}^{\pi} \frac{f(\lambda)}{f^2(\lambda)}\, d\lambda = \frac{4\pi^2}{\displaystyle\int_{-\pi}^{\pi} \frac{d\lambda}{f(\lambda)}}.$$

This completes the proof (under condition (22)).

Corollary. *If*

$$\check{\varphi}(\lambda) = \sum_{0 < |k| \leq N} c_k e^{i\lambda k},$$

then

$$\check{\xi}_0 = \sum_{0 < |k| \leq N} c_k \int_{-\pi}^{\pi} e^{i\lambda k} Z(d\lambda) = \sum_{0 < |k| \leq N} c_k \xi_k.$$

EXAMPLE 3. Let $f(\lambda)$ be the spectral density in Example 2 above. Then an easy calculation shows that

$$\check{\xi}_0 = \int_{-\pi}^{\pi} \frac{a}{1 + |a|^2} [e^{i\lambda} + e^{-i\lambda}] Z(d\lambda) = \frac{a}{1 + |a|^2} [\xi_1 + \xi_{-1}],$$

and the interpolation error is

$$\delta^2 = \frac{1 - |\alpha|^2}{1 + |\alpha|^2}.$$

3. Filtering. Let $(\theta, \xi) = ((\theta_n), (\xi_n))$, $n \in \mathbb{Z}$, be a *partially observed sequence*, where $\theta = (\theta_n)$ and $\xi = (\xi_n)$ are respectively the unobserved and the observed components.

Each of the sequences θ and ξ will be supposed stationary (wide sense) with zero mean; let the spectral densities be

$$\theta_n = \int_{-\pi}^{\pi} e^{i\lambda n} Z_\theta(d\lambda), \quad \text{and} \quad \xi_n = \int_{-\pi}^{\pi} e^{i\lambda n} Z_\xi(d\lambda).$$

We write

$$F_\theta(\Delta) = \mathsf{E}\,|Z_\theta(\Delta)|^2, \qquad F_\xi(\Delta) = \mathsf{E}\,|Z_\xi(\Delta)|^2$$

and

$$F_{\theta\xi}(\Delta) = \mathsf{E}\,Z_\theta(\Delta)\bar{Z}_\xi(\Delta).$$

In addition, we suppose that θ and ξ are *connected in a stationary way*, i.e. that their covariance functions $\mathsf{cov}(\theta_n, \xi_m) = \mathsf{E}\theta_n\bar{\xi}_m$ depend only on the differences $n - m$. Let $R_{\theta\xi}(n) = \mathsf{E}\theta_n\bar{\xi}_0$; then

$$R_{\theta\xi}(n) = \int_{-\pi}^{\pi} e^{i\lambda n} F_{\theta\xi}(d\lambda).$$

The filtering problem that we shall consider is the construction of the optimal (mean-square) linear estimator $\hat{\theta}_n$ of θ_n in terms of some observation of the sequence ξ.

The problem is easily solved under the assumption that θ_n is to be constructed from *all* the values ξ_m, $m \in \mathbb{Z}$. In fact, since $\hat{\theta}_n = \hat{\mathsf{E}}(\theta_n | H(\xi))$ there is a function $\hat{\varphi}_n(\lambda)$ such that

$$\hat{\theta}_n = \int_{-\pi}^{\pi} \hat{\varphi}_n(\lambda) Z_\xi(d\lambda). \tag{25}$$

As in Subsections 1 and 2, the conditions to impose on the optimal $\hat{\varphi}_n(\lambda)$ are that

(1) $\hat{\varphi}_n(\lambda) \in H(F_\xi)$,
(2) $\theta_n - \hat{\theta}_n \perp H(\xi)$.

From the latter condition we find

$$\int_{-\pi}^{\pi} e^{i\lambda(n-m)} F_{\theta\xi}(d\lambda) - \int_{-\pi}^{\pi} e^{-i\lambda m} \hat{\varphi}_n(\lambda) F_\xi(d\lambda) = 0 \tag{26}$$

for every $m \in \mathbb{Z}$. Therefore if we suppose that $F_{\theta\xi}(\lambda)$ and $F_\xi(\lambda)$ have densities $f_{\theta\xi}(\lambda)$ and $f_\xi(\lambda)$, we find from (26) that

$$\int_{-\pi}^{\pi} e^{i\lambda(n-m)} [f_{\theta\xi}(\lambda) - e^{-i\lambda n} \hat{\varphi}_n(\lambda) f_\xi(\lambda)]\, d\lambda = 0.$$

If $f_\xi(\lambda) > 0$ (almost everywhere with respect to Lebesgue measure) we find immediately that

$$\hat{\varphi}_n(\lambda) = e^{i\lambda n}\hat{\varphi}(\lambda), \tag{27}$$

where

$$\hat{\varphi}(\lambda) = f_{\theta\xi}(\lambda) \cdot f_\xi^\oplus(\lambda)$$

and $f_\xi^\oplus(\lambda)$ is the "pseudotransform" of $f_\xi(\lambda)$, i.e.

$$f_\xi^\oplus(\lambda) = \begin{cases} f_\xi^{-1}(\lambda), & f_\xi(\lambda) > 0, \\ 0, & f_\xi(\lambda) = 0. \end{cases}$$

Then the filtering error is

$$\mathsf{E}|\theta_n - \hat{\theta}_n|^2 = \int_{-\pi}^{\pi} [f_\theta(\lambda) - f_{\theta\xi}^2(\lambda) f_\xi^\oplus(\lambda)] \, d\lambda. \tag{28}$$

As is easily verified, $\hat{\varphi} \in H(F_\xi)$, and consequently the estimator (25), with the function (27), is optimal.

EXAMPLE 4. *Detection of a signal in the presence of noise.* Let $\xi_n = \theta_n + \eta_n$, where the signal $\theta = (\theta_n)$ and the noise $\eta = (\eta_n)$ are uncorrelated sequences with spectral densities $f_\theta(\lambda)$ and $f_\eta(\lambda)$. Then

$$\hat{\theta}_n = \int_{-\pi}^{\pi} e^{i\lambda n} \hat{\varphi}(\lambda) Z_\xi(d\lambda),$$

where

$$\hat{\varphi}(\lambda) = f_\theta(\lambda)[f_\theta(\lambda) + f_\eta(\lambda)]^\oplus,$$

and the filtering error is

$$\mathsf{E}|\theta_n - \hat{\theta}_n|^2 = \int_{-\pi}^{\pi} [f_\theta(\lambda) f_\eta(\lambda)][f_\theta(\lambda) + f_\eta(\lambda)]^\oplus \, d\lambda.$$

The solution (25) obtained above can now be used to construct an optimal estimator $\tilde{\theta}_{n+m}$ of θ_{n+m} as a result of observing ξ_k, $k \le n$, where m is a given element of $\mathbb{Z}$. Let us suppose that $\xi = (\xi_n)$ is regular, with spectral density

$$f(\lambda) = \frac{1}{2\pi} |\Phi(e^{-i\lambda})|^2,$$

where $\Phi(z) = \sum_{k=0}^\infty a_k z^k$. By the Wold expansion,

$$\xi_n = \sum_{k=0}^\infty a_k \varepsilon_{n-k},$$

where $\varepsilon = (\varepsilon_k)$ is white noise with the spectral resolution

$$\varepsilon_n = \int_{-\pi}^{\pi} e^{i\lambda n} Z_\varepsilon(d\lambda).$$

Since

$$\tilde{\theta}_{n+m} = \hat{\mathsf{E}}[\theta_{n+m}|H_n(\xi)] = \hat{\mathsf{E}}[\hat{\mathsf{E}}[\theta_{n+m}|H(\xi)]|H_n(\xi)] = \hat{\mathsf{E}}[\hat{\theta}_{n+m}|H_n(\xi)]$$

and

$$\hat{\theta}_{n+m} = \int_{-\pi}^{\pi} e^{i\lambda(n+m)} \hat{\varphi}(\lambda) \Phi(e^{-i\lambda}) Z_\varepsilon(d\lambda) = \sum_{k \leq n+m} \hat{a}_{n+m-k} \varepsilon_k,$$

where

$$\hat{a}_k = \frac{1}{2\pi} \int_{-\pi}^{\pi} e^{i\lambda k} \hat{\varphi}(\lambda) \Phi(e^{-i\lambda}) \, d\lambda, \tag{29}$$

then

$$\tilde{\theta}_{n+m} = \hat{\mathsf{E}}\left[\sum_{k \leq n+m} \hat{a}_{n+m-k} \varepsilon_k \,\big|\, H_n(\xi) \right].$$

But $H_n(\xi) = H_n(\varepsilon)$ and therefore

$$\tilde{\theta}_{n+m} = \sum_{k \leq n} \hat{a}_{n+m-k} \varepsilon_k = \int_{-\pi}^{\pi} \left[\sum_{k \leq n} \hat{a}_{n+m-k} e^{i\lambda k} \right] Z_\varepsilon(d\lambda)$$

$$= \int_{-\pi}^{\pi} e^{i\lambda n} \left[\sum_{l=0}^{\infty} \hat{a}_{l+m} e^{-i\lambda l} \right] \Phi^{\oplus}(e^{-i\lambda}) Z_\xi(d\lambda),$$

where $\Phi^{\oplus}$ is the pseudotransform of Φ.

We have therefore established the following theorem.

Theorem 3. *If the sequence $\xi = (\xi_n)$ under observation is regular, then the optimal (mean-square) linear estimator $\tilde{\theta}_{n+m}$ of θ_{n+m} in terms of ξ_k, $k \leq n$, is given by*

$$\tilde{\theta}_{n+m} = \int_{-\pi}^{\pi} e^{i\lambda n} H_m(e^{-i\lambda}) Z_\xi(d\lambda), \tag{30}$$

where

$$H_m(e^{-i\lambda}) = \sum_{l=0}^{\infty} \hat{a}_{l+m} e^{-i\lambda l} \Phi^{\oplus}(e^{-i\lambda}) \tag{31}$$

and the coefficients a_k are defined by (29).

4. PROBLEMS

1. Let ξ be a nondegenerate regular sequence with spectral density (4). Show that $\Phi(z)$ has no zeros for $|z| \leq 1$.

2. Show that the conclusion of Theorem 1 remains valid even without the hypotheses that $\Phi(z)$ has radius of convergence $r > 1$ and that the zeros of $\Phi(z)$ all lie in $|z| > 1$.

3. Show that, for a regular process, the function $\Phi(z)$ introduced in (4) can be represented in the form

$$\Phi(z) = \sqrt{2\pi}\, \exp\left\{\tfrac{1}{2}c_0 + \sum_{k=1}^{\infty} c_k z^k\right\}, \qquad |z| < 1,$$

where

$$c_k = \frac{1}{2\pi} \int_{-\pi}^{\pi} e^{ik\lambda}\, \ln f(\lambda)\, d\lambda.$$

Deduce from this formula and (5.9) that the one-step prediction error $\sigma_1^2 = \mathsf{E}|\hat\xi_1 - \xi_1|^2$ is given by the Szegö–Kolmogorov formula

$$\sigma_1^2 = 2\pi \exp\left\{\frac{1}{2\pi} \int_{-\pi}^{\pi} \ln f(\lambda)\, d\lambda\right\}.$$

4. Prove Theorem 2 without using (22).

5. Let a signal θ and a noise η, not correlated with each other, have spectral densities

$$f_\theta(\lambda) = \frac{1}{2\pi} \cdot \frac{1}{|1 + b_1 e^{-i\lambda}|^2} \quad\text{and}\quad f_\eta(\lambda) = \frac{1}{2\pi} \cdot \frac{1}{|1 + b_2 e^{-i\lambda}|^2}.$$

Using Theorem 3, find an estimator $\hat\theta_{n+m}$ for θ_{n+m} in terms of ξ_k, $k \le n$, where $\xi_k = \theta_k + \eta_k$. Consider the same problem for the spectral densities

$$f_\theta(\lambda) = \frac{1}{2\pi}|2 + e^{-i\lambda}|^2 \quad\text{and}\quad f_\eta(\lambda) = \frac{1}{2\pi}.$$

§7. The Kalman–Bucy Filter and Its Generalizations

1. From a computational point of view, the solution presented above for the problem of filtering out an unobservable component θ by means of observations of ξ is not practical, since, because it is expressed in terms of the spectrum, it has to be carried out by spectral methods. In the method proposed by Kalman and Bucy, the synthesis of the optimal filter is carried out recursively; this makes it possible to do it with a digital computer. There are also other reasons for the wide use of the Kalman–Bucy filter, one being that it still "works" even without the assumption that the sequence (θ, ξ) is *stationary*.

We shall present not only the usual Kalman–Bucy method, but also a generalization in which the recurrent equations determined by (θ, ξ) have coefficients that depend on all the data observed in the past.

Thus, let us suppose that $(\theta, \xi) = ((\theta_n), (\xi_n))$ is a partially observed sequence, and let

$$\theta_n = (\theta_1(n), \ldots, \theta_k(n)) \quad\text{and}\quad \xi_n = (\xi_1(n), \ldots, \xi_l(n))$$

be governed by the recurrent equations

$$\theta_{n+1} = a_0(n, \xi) + a_1(n, \xi)\theta_n + b_1(n, \xi)\varepsilon_1(n+1) + b_2(n, \xi)\varepsilon_2(n+1),$$

$$\xi_{n+1} = A_0(n, \xi) + A_1(n, \xi)\theta_n + B_1(n, \xi)\varepsilon_1(n+1) + B_2(n, \xi)\varepsilon_2(n+1).$$

$$(1)$$

Here

$$\varepsilon_1(n) = (\varepsilon_{11}(n), \ldots, \varepsilon_{1k}(n)) \quad \text{and} \quad \varepsilon_2(n) = (\varepsilon_{21}(n), \ldots, \varepsilon_{2l}(n))$$

are independent Gaussian vectors with independent components, each of which is normally distributed with parameters 0 and 1; $a_0(n, \xi) = (a_{01}(n, \xi), \ldots, \alpha_{0k}(n, \xi))$ and $A_0(n, \xi) = (A_{01}(n, \xi), \ldots, A_{0l}(n, \xi))$ are vector functions, where the dependence on $\xi = \{\xi_0, \ldots, \xi_n\}$ is determined without looking ahead, i.e. for a given n the functions $a_0(n, \xi), \ldots, A_{0l}(n, \xi)$ depend only on $\xi_0, \ldots, \xi_n$; the matrix functions

$$b_1(n, \xi) = \|b_{ij}^{(1)}(n, \xi)\|, \qquad b_2(n, \xi) = \|b_{ij}^{(2)}(n, \xi)\|,$$
$$B_1(n, \xi) = \|B_{ij}^{(1)}(n, \xi)\|, \qquad B_2(n, \xi) = \|B_{ij}^{(2)}(n, \xi)\|,$$
$$a_1(n, \xi) = \|a_{ij}^{(1)}(n, \xi)\|, \qquad A_1(n, \xi) = \|A_{ij}^{(1)}(n, \xi)\|$$

have orders $k \times k$, $k \times l$, $l \times k$, $l \times l$, $k \times k$, $l \times k$, respectively, and also depend on ξ without looking ahead. We also suppose that the initial vector (θ_0, ξ_0) is independent of the sequences $\varepsilon_1 = (\varepsilon_1(n))$ and $\varepsilon_2 = (\varepsilon_2(n))$.

To simplify the presentation, we shall frequently not indicate the dependence of the coefficients on ξ.

So that the system (1) will have a solution with finite second moments, we assume that $E(\|\theta_0\|^2 + \|\xi_0\|^2) < \infty$

$$\left(\|x\|^2 = \sum_{i=1}^{k} x_i^2, x = (x_1, \ldots, x_k)\right), \qquad |a_{ij}^{(1)}(n, \xi)| \le C, \qquad |A_{ij}^{(1)}(n, \xi)| \le C,$$

and if $g(n, \xi)$ is any of the functions a_{0i}, A_{0j}, $b_{ij}^{(1)}$, $b_{ij}^{(2)}$, $B_{ij}^{(1)}$ or $B_{ij}^{(2)}$ then $E|g(n, \xi)|^2 < \infty$, $n = 0, 1, \ldots$. With these assumptions, (θ, ξ) has $E(\|\theta_n\|^2 + \|\xi_n\|^2) < \infty, n \ge 0$.

Now let $\mathscr{F}_n^\xi = \sigma\{\omega \colon \xi_0, \ldots, \xi_n\}$ be the smallest σ-algebra generated by $\xi_0, \ldots, \xi_n$ and

$$m_n = E(\theta_n | \mathscr{F}_n^\xi), \qquad \gamma_n = E[(\theta_n - m_n)(\theta_n - m_n)^* | \mathscr{F}_n^\xi].$$

According to Theorem 1, §8, Chapter II, $m_n = (m_1(n), \ldots, m_k(n))$ is an optimal estimator (in the mean square sense) for the vector $\theta_n = (\theta_1(n), \ldots, \theta_k(n))$, and $E\gamma_n = E[(\theta_n - m_n)(\theta_n - m_n)^*]$ is the matrix of errors of observation. To determine these matrices for arbitrary sequences (θ, ξ) governed by equations (1) is a very difficult problem. However, there is a further supplementary condition on (θ_0, ξ_0) that leads to a system of recurrent equations for m_n and γ_m that still contains the Kalman–Bucy filter. This is the condition that the conditional distribution $P(\theta_0 \le a | \xi_0|)$ is Gaussian,

$$P(\theta_0 \le a | \xi_0) = \frac{1}{\sqrt{2\pi\gamma_0}} \int_{-\infty}^{a} \exp\left\{-\frac{(x - m_0)^2}{2\gamma_0^2}\right\} dx, \qquad (2)$$

with parameters $m_0 = m_0(\xi_0)$, $\gamma_0 = \gamma_0(\xi_0)$.

To begin with, let us establish an important auxiliary result.

Lemma 1. *Under the assumptions made above about the coefficients of* (1), *together with* (2), *the sequence* (θ, ξ) *is conditionally Gaussian, i.e. the conditional distribution function*

$$P\{\theta_0 \leq a_0, \ldots, \eta_n \leq a_n | \mathscr{F}_n^\xi\}$$

is (P-a.s.) *the distribution function of an n-dimensional Gaussian vector whose mean and covariance matrix depend on* $(\xi_0, \ldots, \xi_n)$.

PROOF. We prove only the Gaussian character of $P(\theta_n \leq a | \mathscr{F}_n^\xi)$; this is enough to let us obtain equations for m_n and γ_n.

First we observe that (1) implies that the conditional distribution

$$P(\theta_{n+1} \leq a_1, \xi_{n+1} \leq x | \mathscr{F}_n^\xi, \theta_n = b)$$

is Gaussian with mean-value vector

$$\mathbb{A}_0 + \mathbb{A}_1 b = \begin{pmatrix} a_0 + a_1 b \\ A_0 + A_1 b \end{pmatrix}$$

and covariance matrix

$$\mathbb{B} = \begin{pmatrix} b \circ b & b \circ B \\ (b \circ B)^* & B \circ B \end{pmatrix},$$

where $b \circ b = b_1 b_1^* + b_2 b_2^*$, $b \circ B = b_1 B_1^* + b_2 B_2^*$, $B \circ B = B_1 B_1^* + B_2 B_2^*$. Let $\zeta_n = (\theta_n, \xi_n)$ and $t = (t_1, \ldots, t_{k+1})$. Then

$$E[\exp(it^*\zeta_{n+1}) | \mathscr{F}_n^\xi, \theta_n] = \exp\{it^*(\mathbb{A}_0(n, \xi) + \mathbb{A}_1(n, \xi)\theta_n) - \tfrac{1}{2}t^*\mathbb{B}(n, \xi)t\}. \tag{3}$$

Suppose now that the conclusion of the lemma holds for some $n \geq 0$. Then

$$E[\exp(it^*\mathbb{A}_1(n, \xi)\theta_n) | \mathscr{F}_n^\xi] = \exp(it^*\mathbb{A}_1(n, \xi)m_n - \tfrac{1}{2}t^*(\mathbb{A}_1(n, \xi)\gamma_n\mathbb{A}_1^*(n, \xi))t. \tag{4}$$

Let us show that (4) is also valid when n is replaced by $n + 1$.
From (3) and (4), we have

$$E[\exp(it^*\zeta_{n+1}) | \mathscr{F}_n^\xi] = \exp\{it^*(\mathbb{A}_0(n, \xi) + \mathbb{A}_1(n, \xi)m_n) \\ - \tfrac{1}{2}t^*\mathbb{B}(n, \xi)t - \tfrac{1}{2}t^*(\mathbb{A}_1(n, \xi)\gamma_n\mathbb{A}_1^*(n, \xi))t\}.$$

Hence the conditional distribution

$$P(\theta_{n+1} \leq a, \xi_{n+1} \leq x | \mathscr{F}_n^\xi) \tag{5}$$

is Gaussian.

As in the proof of the theorem on normal correlation (Theorem 2, §13, Chapter II) we can verify that there is a matrix C such that the vector

$$\eta = [\theta_{n+1} - E(\theta_{n+1} | \mathscr{F}_n^\xi)] - C[\xi_{n+1} - E(\xi_{n+1} | \mathscr{F}_n^\xi)]$$

has the property that (P-a.s.)

$$E[\eta(\xi_{n+1} - E(\xi_{n+1} | \mathscr{F}_n^\xi))^* | \mathscr{F}_n^\xi] = 0.$$

It follows that the conditionally-Gaussian vectors η and ξ_{n+1}, considered under the condition $\mathscr{F}_n^\xi$, are independent, i.e.

$$P(\eta \in A, \xi_{n+1} \in B | \mathscr{F}_n^\xi) = P(\eta \in A | \mathscr{F}_n^\xi) \cdot P(\xi_{n+1} \in B | \mathscr{F}_n^\xi)$$

for all $A \in \mathscr{B}(R^k)$, $B \in \mathscr{B}(R^l)$.

Therefore if $s = (s_1, \ldots, s_n)$ then

$$
\begin{aligned}
E[\exp(is^*\theta_{n+1}) | \mathscr{F}_n^\xi, \xi_{n+1}] \\
&= E\{\exp(is^*[E(\theta_{n+1} | \mathscr{F}_n^\xi) + \eta + C[\xi_{n+1} - E(\xi_{n+1} | \mathscr{F}_n^\xi)]]) | \mathscr{F}_n^\xi, \xi_{n+1}\} \\
&= \exp\{is^*[E(\theta_{n+1} | \mathscr{F}_n^\xi) + C[\xi_{n+1} - E(\xi_{n+1} | \mathscr{F}_n^\xi)]\} \\
&\quad \times E[\exp(is^*\eta) | \mathscr{F}_n^\xi, \xi_{n+1}] \\
&= \exp\{is^*[E(\theta_{n+1} | \mathscr{F}_n^\xi)] + C[\xi_{n+1} - E(\xi_{n+1} | \mathscr{F}_n^\xi)]\} \\
&\quad \times E(\exp(is^*\eta) | \mathscr{F}_n^\xi).
\end{aligned}
\tag{6}
$$

By (5), the conditional distribution $P(\eta \le y | \mathscr{F}_n^\xi)$ is Gaussian. With (6), this shows that the conditional distribution $P(\theta_{n+1} \le a | \mathscr{F}_{n+1}^\xi)$ is also Gaussian.

This completes the proof of the lemma.

Theorem 1. *Let (θ, ξ) be a partial observation of a sequence that satisfies the system (1) and condition (2). Then (m_n, γ_n) obey the following recursion relations:*

$$
\begin{aligned}
m_{n+1} &= [a_0 + a_1 m_n] + [b \circ B + a_1 \gamma_n A_1^*][B \circ B + A_1 \gamma_n A_1^*]^\oplus \\
&\quad \times [\xi_{n+1} - A_0 - A_1 m_n],
\end{aligned}
\tag{7}
$$

$$
\begin{aligned}
\gamma_{n+1} &= [a_1 \gamma_n a_1^* + b \circ b] - [b \circ B + a_1 \gamma_n A_1^*][B \circ B + A_1 \gamma_n A_1^*]^\oplus \\
&\quad \times [b \circ B + a_1 \gamma_n A_1^*]^*.
\end{aligned}
\tag{8}
$$

PROOF. From (1),

$$E(\theta_{n+1} | \mathscr{F}_n^\xi) = a_0 + a_1 m_n, \qquad E(\xi_{n+1} | \mathscr{F}_n^\xi) = A_0 + A_1 m_n \tag{9}$$

and

$$
\begin{aligned}
\theta_{n+1} - E(\theta_{n+1} | \mathscr{F}_n^\xi) &= a_1[\theta_n - m_n] + b_1 \varepsilon_1(n+1) + b_2 \varepsilon_2(n+1), \\
\xi_{n+1} - E(\xi_{n+1} | \mathscr{F}_n^\xi) &= A_1[\theta_n - m_n] + B_1 \varepsilon_1(n+1) + B_2 \varepsilon_2(n+1).
\end{aligned}
\tag{10}
$$

Let us write

$$
\begin{aligned}
d_{11} &= \operatorname{cov}(\theta_{n+1}, \theta_{n+1} | \mathscr{F}_n^\xi) \\
&= E\{[\theta_{n+1} - E(\theta_{n+1} | \mathscr{F}_n^\xi)][\theta_{n+1} - E(\theta_{n+1} | \mathscr{F}_n^\xi)]^* / \mathscr{F}_n^\xi\}, \\
d_{12} &= \operatorname{cov}(\theta_{n+1}, \xi_{n+1} | \mathscr{F}_n^\xi) \\
&= E\{[\theta_{n+1} - E[\theta_{n+1} | \mathscr{F}_n^\xi)][\xi_{n+1} - E(\xi_{n+1} | \mathscr{F}_n^\xi)]^* / \mathscr{F}_n^\xi\}, \\
d_{22} &= \operatorname{cov}(\xi_{n+1}, \xi_{n+1} | \mathscr{F}_n^\xi) \\
&= E\{[\xi_{n+1} - E(\xi_{n+1} | \mathscr{F}_n^\xi)][\xi_{n+1} - E(\xi_{n+1} | \mathscr{F}_n^\xi)]^* / \mathscr{F}_n^\xi\}.
\end{aligned}
$$

Then, by (10),

$$d_{11} = a_1\gamma_n a_1^* + b \circ b, \qquad d_{12} = a_1\gamma_n A_1^* + b \circ B, \qquad d_{22} = A_1\gamma_n A_1^* + B \circ B. \tag{11}$$

By the theorem on normal correlation (see Theorem 2 and Problem 4, §13, Chapter II),

$$m_{n+1} = \mathsf{E}(\theta_{n+1}|\mathscr{F}_n^\xi, \xi_{n+1}) = \mathsf{E}(\theta_{n+1}|\mathscr{F}_n^\xi) + d_{12}d_{22}^\oplus(\xi_{n+1} - \mathsf{E}(\xi_{n+1}|\mathscr{F}_n^\xi))$$

and

$$\gamma_{n+1} = \mathsf{cov}(\theta_{n-1}, \theta_{n+1}|\mathscr{F}_n^\xi, \xi_{n+1}) = d_{11} - d_{12}d_{22}^\oplus d_{12}^*.$$

If we then use the expressions from (9) for $\mathsf{E}(\theta_{n+1}|\mathscr{F}_n^\xi)$ and $\mathsf{E}(\xi_{n+1}|\mathscr{F}_n^\xi)$ and those for d_{11}, d_{12}, d_{22} from (11), we obtain the required recursion formulas (7) and (8).

This completes the proof of the theorem.

Corollary 1. *If the coefficients $a_0(n, \xi), \ldots, B_2(n, \xi)$ in (1) are independent of ξ the corresponding method is known as the* **Kalman–Bucy method,** *and equations (7) and (8) for m_n and γ_n describe the* **Kalman–Bucy filter.** *It is important to observe that in this case the conditional and unconditional error matrices γ_n agree, i.e.*

$$\gamma_n \equiv \mathsf{E}\gamma_n = \mathsf{E}[(\theta_n - m_n)(\theta_n - m_n)^*].$$

Corollary 2. *Suppose that a partially observed sequence (θ_n, ξ_n) has the property that θ_n satisfies the first equation (1), and that ξ_n satisfies the equation*

$$\begin{aligned}\xi_n = {} &\tilde{A}_0(n-1, \xi) + \tilde{A}_1(n-1, \xi)\theta_n \\ &+ \tilde{B}_1(n-1, \xi)\varepsilon_1(n) + \tilde{B}_2(n-1, \xi)\varepsilon_2(n).\end{aligned} \tag{12}$$

Then evidently

$$\begin{aligned}\xi_{n+1} = {} &\tilde{A}_0(n, \xi) + \tilde{A}_1(n, \xi)[a_0(n, \xi) + a_1(n, \xi)\theta_n \\ &+ b_1(n, \xi)\varepsilon_1(n+1) + b_2(n, \xi)\varepsilon_2(n+1)] + \tilde{B}_1(n, \xi)\varepsilon_1(n+1) \\ &+ \tilde{B}_2(n, \xi)\varepsilon_2(n+1),\end{aligned}$$

and with the notation

$$A_0 = \tilde{A}_0 + \tilde{A}_1 a_0, \qquad A_1 = \tilde{A}_1 a_1,$$
$$B_1 = \tilde{A}_1 b_1 + \tilde{B}_1, \qquad B_2 = \tilde{A}_1 b_2 + \tilde{B}_2,$$

we find that the case under consideration also depends on the model (1), and that m_n and γ_n satisfy (7) and (8).

2. We now consider a *linear* model (compare (1))

$$\begin{aligned}\theta_{n+1} &= a_0 + a_1\theta_n + a_2\xi_n + b_1\varepsilon_1(n+1) + b_2\varepsilon_2(n+1), \\ \xi_{n+1} &= A_0 + A_1\theta_n + A_2\xi_n + B_1\varepsilon_1(n+1) + B_2\varepsilon_2(n+1),\end{aligned} \tag{13}$$

where the coefficients $a_0, \ldots, B_n$ may depend on n (but not on ξ), and $\varepsilon_{ij}(n)$ are independent Gaussian random variables with $\mathsf{E}\varepsilon_{ij}(n) = 0$ and $\mathsf{E}\varepsilon_{ij}^2(n) = 1$.

Let (13) be solved for the initial values (θ_0, ξ_0) so that the conditional distribution $\mathsf{P}(\theta_0 \le a|\xi_0)$ is Gaussian with parameters $m_0 = \mathsf{E}(\theta_0, \xi_0)$ and $\gamma = \mathsf{cov}(\theta_0, \theta_0|\xi_0) = \mathsf{E}\gamma_0$. Then, by the theorem on normal correlation and (7) and (8), the optimal estimator $m_n = \mathsf{E}(\theta_n|\mathscr{F}_n^\xi)$ is a linear function of $\xi_0, \xi_1, \ldots, \xi_n$.

This remark makes it possible to prove the following important statement about the structure of the optimal linear filter without the assumption that it is Gaussian.

Theorem 2. *Let* $(\theta, \xi) = (\theta_n, \xi_n)_{n \ge 0}$ *be a partially observed sequence that satisfies* (13), *where* $\varepsilon_{ij}(n)$ *are uncorrelated random variables with* $\mathsf{E}\varepsilon_{ij}(n) = 0$, $\mathsf{E}\varepsilon_{ij}^2(n) = 1$, *and the components of the initial vector* (θ_0, ξ_0) *have finite second moments. Then the optimal linear estimator* $\hat{m}_n = \mathsf{E}(\theta_n|\xi_0, \ldots, \xi_n)$ *satisfies* (7) *with* $a_0(n, \xi) = a_0(n) + a_2(n)\xi_n$, $A_0(n, \xi) = A_0(n) + A_2(n)\xi_n$, *and the error matrix* $\hat{\gamma}_n = \mathsf{E}[(\theta_n - \theta_m)(\theta_n - m_n)^*]$ *satisfies* (8) *with initial values*

$$\hat{m}_0 = \mathsf{cov}(\theta_0, \xi_0)\mathsf{cov}^\oplus(\xi_0, \xi_0) \cdot \xi_0,$$
$$\hat{\gamma}_0 = \mathsf{cov}(\theta_0, \theta_0) - \mathsf{cov}(\theta_0, \xi_0)\mathsf{cov}^\oplus(\xi_0, \xi_0)\mathsf{cov}^*(\theta_0, \xi_0). \tag{14}$$

For the proof of this lemma, we need the following lemma, which reveals the role of the Gaussian case in determining optimal linear estimators.

Lemma 2. *Let* (α, β) *be a two-dimensional random vector with* $\mathsf{E}(\alpha^2 + \beta^2) < \infty$, $a(\tilde{\alpha}, \tilde{\beta})$ *a two-dimensional Gaussian vector with the same first and second moments as* (α, β), *i.e.*

$$\mathsf{E}\tilde{\alpha}^i = \mathsf{E}\alpha^i, \qquad \mathsf{E}\tilde{\beta}^i = \mathsf{E}\beta^i, \qquad i = 1, 2; \qquad \mathsf{E}\tilde{\alpha}\tilde{\beta} = \mathsf{E}\alpha\beta.$$

Let $\lambda(b)$ *be a linear function of* b *such that*

$$\lambda(b) = \mathsf{E}(\tilde{\alpha} \,|\, \tilde{\beta} = b).$$

Then $\lambda(\beta)$ *is the optimal (in the mean square sense) linear estimator of* α *in terms of* β, *i.e.*

$$\hat{\mathsf{E}}(\alpha|\beta) = \lambda(\beta).$$

Here $\mathsf{E}\lambda(\beta) = \mathsf{E}\alpha.$

PROOF. We first observe that the existence of a linear function $\lambda(b)$ coinciding with $\mathsf{E}(\tilde{\alpha}|\tilde{\beta} = b)$ follows from the theorem on normal correlation. Moreover, let $\bar{\lambda}(b)$ be any other linear estimator. Then

$$\mathsf{E}[\tilde{\alpha} - \bar{\lambda}(\tilde{\beta})]^2 \ge \mathsf{E}[\tilde{\alpha} - \lambda(\tilde{\beta})]^2$$

and since $\bar{\lambda}(b)$ and $\lambda(b)$ are linear and the hypotheses of the lemma are satisfied, we have

$$\mathsf{E}[\alpha - \bar{\lambda}(\beta)]^2 = \mathsf{E}[\tilde{\alpha} - \bar{\lambda}(\tilde{\beta})]^2 \geq \mathsf{E}[\tilde{\alpha} - \lambda(\tilde{\beta})]^2 = \mathsf{E}[\alpha - \lambda(\beta)]^2,$$

which shows that $\lambda(\beta)$ is optimal in the class of linear estimators. Finally,

$$\mathsf{E}\lambda(\beta) = \mathsf{E}\lambda(\tilde{\beta}) = \mathsf{E}[\mathsf{E}(\tilde{\alpha}|\bar{\beta})] = \mathsf{E}\tilde{\alpha} = \mathsf{E}\alpha.$$

This completes the proof of the lemma.

PROOF OF THEOREM 2. We consider, besides (13), the system

$$
\begin{aligned}
\tilde{\theta}_{n+1} &= a_0 + a_1\tilde{\theta}_n + a_2\tilde{\xi}_n + b_1\tilde{\varepsilon}_{11}(n+1) + b_2\tilde{\varepsilon}_{12}(n+1), \\
\tilde{\xi}_{n+1} &= A_0 + A_1\tilde{\theta}_n + A_2\tilde{\xi}_n + B_1\tilde{\varepsilon}_{21}(n+1) + B_2\tilde{\varepsilon}_{22}(n+1),
\end{aligned}
\tag{15}
$$

where $\tilde{\varepsilon}_{ij}(n)$ are independent Gaussian random variables with $\mathsf{E}\tilde{\varepsilon}_{ij}(n) = 0$ and $\mathsf{E}\tilde{\varepsilon}_{ij}^2(n) = 1$. Let $(\tilde{\theta}_0, \tilde{\xi}_0)$ also be a Gaussian vector which has the same first moment and covariance as (θ_0, ξ_0) and is independent of $\tilde{\varepsilon}_{ij}(n)$. Then since (15) is linear, the vector $(\tilde{\theta}_0, \ldots, \tilde{\theta}_n, \tilde{\xi}_0, \ldots, \tilde{\xi}_n)$ is Gaussian and therefore the conclusion of the theorem follows from Lemma 2 (more precisely, from its multidimensional analog) and the theorem on normal covariance.

This completes the proof of the theorem.

3. Let us consider some illustrations of Theorems 1 and 2.

EXAMPLE 1. Let $\theta = (\theta_n)$ and $\eta = (\eta_n)$ be two stationary (wide sense) uncorrelated random sequences with $\mathsf{E}\theta_n = \mathsf{E}\eta_n = 0$ and spectral densities

$$f_\theta(\lambda) = \frac{1}{2\pi|1 + b_1 e^{-i\lambda}|^2} \quad \text{and} \quad f_\eta(\lambda) = \frac{1}{2\pi} \cdot \frac{1}{|1 + b_2 e^{-i\lambda}|^2},$$

where $|b_1| < 1, |b_2| < 1$.

We are going to interpret θ as a useful signal and η as noise, and suppose that observation produces a sequence $\xi = (\xi_n)$ with

$$\xi_n = \theta_n + \eta_n.$$

According to Corollary 2 to Theorem 3 of §3 there are (mutually uncorrelated) white noises $\varepsilon_1 = (\varepsilon_1(n))$ and $\varepsilon_2 = (\varepsilon_2(n))$ such that

$$\theta_{n+1} + b_1\theta_n = \varepsilon_1(n+1), \qquad \eta_{n+1} + b_2\eta_n = \varepsilon_2(n+1).$$

Then

$$
\begin{aligned}
\xi_{n+1} = \theta_{n+1} + \eta_{n+1} &= -b_1\theta_n - b_2\eta_n + \varepsilon_1(n+1) + \varepsilon_2(n+1) \\
&= -b_2(\theta_n + \eta_n) - \theta_n(b_1 - b_2) + \varepsilon_1(n+1) + \varepsilon_2(n+1) \\
&= -b_2\xi_n - (b_1 - b_2)\theta_n + \varepsilon_1(n+1) + \varepsilon_2(n+1).
\end{aligned}
$$

Hence θ and ξ satisfy the recursion relations

$$\theta_{n+1} = -b_1\theta_n + \varepsilon_1(n+1),$$
$$\xi_{n+1} = -(b_1 - b_2)\theta_n - b_2\xi_n + \varepsilon_1(n+1) + \varepsilon_2(n+1), \tag{16}$$

and, according to Theorem 2, $m_n = \hat{\mathsf{E}}(\theta_n|\xi_0,\ldots,\xi_n)$ and $\gamma_n = \mathsf{E}(\theta_n - m_n)^2$ satisfy the following system of recursion equations for optimal linear filtering:

$$m_{n+1} = -b_1 m_n + \frac{b_1(b_1 - b_2)\gamma_n}{2 + (b_1 - b_2)^2\gamma_n}[\xi_{n+1} + (b_1 - b_2)m_n + b_2\xi_n],$$
$$\gamma_{n+1} = b_1^2\gamma_n + 1 - \frac{[1 + b_1(b_1 - b_2)\gamma_n]^2}{2 + (b_1 - b_2)^2\gamma_n}. \tag{17}$$

Let us find the initial conditions under which we should solve this system. Write $d_{11} = \mathsf{E}\theta_n^2$, $d_{12} = \mathsf{E}\theta_n\xi_n$, $d_{22} = \mathsf{E}\xi_n^2$. Then we find from (16) that

$$d_{11} = b_1^2 d_{11} + 1,$$
$$d_{12} = b_1(b_1 - b_2)d_{11} + b_1 b_2 d_{12} + 1,$$
$$d_{22} = (b_1 - b_2)^2 d_{11} + b_2^2 d_{22} + 2b_2(b_1 - b_2)d_{12} + 2,$$

from which

$$d_{11} = \frac{1}{1 - b_1^2}, \qquad d_{12} = \frac{1}{1 - b_1^2}, \qquad d_{22} = \frac{2 - b_1^2 - b_2^2}{(1 - b_1^2)(1 - b_2^2)},$$

which, by (14), leads to the following initial values:

$$m_0 = \frac{d_{12}}{d_{22}}\xi_0 = \frac{1 - b_2^2}{2 - b_1^2 - b_2^2}\xi_0,$$

$$\gamma_0 = d_{11} - \frac{d_{12}^2}{d_{22}} = \frac{1}{1 - b_1^2} - \frac{1 - b_2^2}{(1 - b_1^2)(2 - b_1^2 - b_2^2)} = \frac{1}{2 - b_1^2 - b_2^2}. \tag{18}$$

Thus the optimal (in the least squares sense) linear estimators m_n for the signal θ_n in terms of $\xi_0,\ldots,\xi_n$ and the mean-square error are determined by the system of recurrent equations (17), solved under the initial conditions (18). Observe that the equation for γ_n does not contain any random components, and consequently the number γ_n, which is needed for finding m_n, can be calculated in advance, before the filtering problem has been solved.

EXAMPLE 2. This example is instructive because it shows that the result of Theorem 2 can be applied to find the optimal linear filter in a case where the sequence (θ, ξ) is described by a (nonlinear) system which is different from (13).

Let $\varepsilon_1 = (\varepsilon_1(n))$ and $\varepsilon_2 = (\varepsilon_2(n))$ be two independent Gaussian sequences of independent random variables with $\mathsf{E}\varepsilon_i(n) = 0$ and $\mathsf{E}\varepsilon_i^2(n) = 1$, $n \geq 1$. Consider a pair of sequences $(\theta, \xi) = (\theta_n, \xi_n)$, $n \geq 0$, with

$$\theta_{n+1} = a\theta_n + (1 + \theta_n)\varepsilon_1(n + 1),$$
$$\xi_{n+1} = A\theta_n + \varepsilon_2(n + 1). \tag{19}$$

We shall suppose that θ_0 is independent of $(\varepsilon_1, \varepsilon_2)$ and that $\theta_0 \sim \mathcal{N}(m_0, \gamma_0)$.

The system (19) is *nonlinear*, and Theorem 2 is not immediately applicable. However, if we put

$$\tilde{\varepsilon}_1(n + 1) = \frac{1 + \theta_n}{\sqrt{\mathsf{E}(1 + \theta_n)^2}}\,\varepsilon_1(n + 1),$$

we can observe that $\mathsf{E}\tilde{\varepsilon}_1(n) = 0$, $\mathsf{E}\tilde{\varepsilon}_1(n)\tilde{\varepsilon}_1(m) = 0$, $n \neq m$, $\hat{\mathsf{E}}\tilde{\varepsilon}_1^2(n) = 1$. Hence we have reduced (19) to a linear system

$$\theta_{n+1} = a_1\theta_n + b_1\tilde{\varepsilon}_1(n + 1),$$
$$\xi_{n+1} = A_1\theta_n + \varepsilon_2(n + 1), \tag{20}$$

where $b_1 = \sqrt{\mathsf{E}(1 + \theta_n)^2}$, and $\{\tilde{\varepsilon}_1(n)\}$ is a sequence of uncorrelated random variables.

Now (20) is a linear system of the same type as (13), and consequently the optimal linear estimator $\hat{m}_n = \hat{\mathsf{E}}(\theta_n | \xi_0, \ldots, \xi_n)$ and its error $\hat{\gamma}_n$ can be determined from (7) and (8) via Theorem 2, applied in the following form in the present case:

$$m_{n+1} = a_1 m_n + \frac{a_1 A_1 \gamma_n}{1 + A_1^2 \gamma_n}\,[\xi_{n+1} - A_1 m_n],$$

$$\gamma_{n+1} = (a_1^2 \gamma_n + b_1^2) - \frac{(a_1 A_1 \gamma_n)^2}{1 + A_1^2 \gamma_n},$$

where $b_1 = \sqrt{\mathsf{E}(1 + \theta_n)^2}$ must be found from the first equation in (19).

EXAMPLE 3. *Estimators for parameters.* Let $\theta = (\theta_1, \ldots, \theta_k)$ be a Gaussian vector with $\mathsf{E}\theta = m$ and $\mathsf{cov}(\theta, \theta) = \gamma$. Suppose that (with known m and v) we want the optimal estimator of θ in terms of observations on an l-dimensional sequence $\xi = (\xi_n)$, $n \geq 0$, with

$$\xi_{n+1} = A_0(n, \xi) + A_1(n, \xi)\theta + B_1(n, \xi)\varepsilon_1(n + 1), \qquad \xi_0 = 0, \tag{21}$$

where ε_1 is as in (1).

Then from (7) and (8), with $m_n = \mathsf{E}(\theta | \mathscr{F}_n^\xi)$ and γ_n, we find that

$$m_{n+1} = m_n + \gamma_n A_1^*(n, \xi)[(B_1 B_1^*)(n, \xi) + A_1(n, \xi)\gamma_n A_1^*(n, \xi)]^\oplus$$
$$\times [\xi_{n+1} - A_0(n, \xi) - A_1(n, \xi)m_n],$$

$$\gamma_{n+1} = \gamma_n - \gamma_n A_1^*(n, \xi)[(B_1 B_1^*)(n, \xi) + A_1(n, \xi)\gamma_n A_1^*(n, \xi)]^\oplus A_1(n, \xi)\gamma_n. \tag{22}$$

If the matrices $B_1 B_1^*$ are nonsingular, the solution of (22) is given by

$$m_{n+1} = \left[E + \gamma \sum_{m=0}^{n} A_1^*(m, \xi)(B_1 B_1^*)^{-1}(m, \xi) A_1^*(m, \xi) \right]^{-1}$$

$$\times \left[m + \gamma \sum_{m=0}^{n} A_1^*(m, \xi)(B_1 B_1^*)^{-1}(m, \xi)(\xi_{m+1} - A_0(m, \xi)) \right],$$

$$\gamma_{n+1} = \left[E + \gamma \sum_{m=0}^{n} A_1^*(m, \xi)(B_1 B_1^*)^{-1}(m, \xi) A_1(m, \xi) \right]^{-1} \gamma, \qquad (23)$$

where E is a unit matrix.

4. Problems

1. Show that the vectors m_n and $\theta_n - m_n$ in (1) are uncorrelated:

$$E[m_n^*(\theta - m_n)] = 0.$$

2. In (1), let γ and the coefficients other than $a_0(n, \xi)$ and $A_0(n, \xi)$ be independent of "chance" (i.e. of ξ). Show that then the conditional covariance γ_n is independent of "chance": $\gamma_n = E\gamma_n$.

3. Show that the solution of (22) is given by (23).

4. Let $(\theta, \xi) = (\theta_n, \xi_n)$ be a Gaussian sequence satisfying the following special case of (1):

$$\theta_{n+1} = a\theta_n + b\varepsilon_1(n + 1), \qquad \xi_{n+1} = A\theta_n + B\varepsilon_2(n + 1).$$

Show that if $A \neq 0$, $b \neq 0$, $B \neq 0$, the limiting error of filtering, $\gamma = \lim_{n \to \infty} \gamma_n$, exists and is determined as the positive root of the equation

$$\gamma^2 + \left[\frac{B^2(1 - a^2)}{A^2} - b^2 \right] \gamma - \frac{b^2 B^2}{A^2} = 0.$$

CHAPTER VII

Sequences of Random Variables That Form Martingales

§1. Definitions of Martingales and Related Concepts

1. The study of the dependence of random variables arises in various ways in probability theory. In the theory of stationary (wide sense) random sequences, the basic indicator of dependence is the covariance function, and the inferences made in this theory are determined by the properties of that function. In the theory of Markov chains (§12 of Chapter I; Chapter VIII) the basic dependence is supplied by the transition function, which completely determines the development of the random variables involved in Markov dependence.

In the present chapter (see also §11, Chapter I), we single out a rather wide class of sequences of random variables (martingales and their generalizations) for which dependence can be studied by methods based on a discussion of the properties of conditional expectations.

2. Let $(\Omega, \mathscr{F}, \mathsf{P})$ be a given probability space, and let $(\mathscr{F}_n)$ be a family of σ-algebras $\mathscr{F}_n$, $n \geq 0$, such that $\mathscr{F}_0 \subseteq \mathscr{F}_1 \subseteq \cdots \subseteq \mathscr{F}$.

Let $X_0, X_1, \ldots$ be a sequence of random variables defined on $(\Omega, \mathscr{F}, \mathsf{P})$. If, for each $n \geq 0$, the variable X_n is $\mathscr{F}_n$-*measurable*, we say that the set $X = (X_n, \mathscr{F}_n)$, $n \geq 0$, or simply $X = (X_n, \mathscr{F}_n)$, is a *stochastic sequence*.

If a stochastic sequence $X = (X_n, \mathscr{F}_n)$ has the property that, for each $n \geq 1$, the variable X_n is $\mathscr{F}_{n-1}$-*measurable*, we write $X = (X_n, \mathscr{F}_{n-1})$, taking $F_{-1} = F_0$, and call X a *predictable sequence*. We call such a sequence *increasing* if $X_0 = 0$ and $X_n \leq X_{n+1}$ (P-a.s.).

Definition 1. A stochastic sequence $X = (X_n, \mathscr{F}_n)$ is a *martingale*, or a *submartingale*, if, for all $n \geq 0$,

$$\mathsf{E}|X_n| < \infty \tag{1}$$

and, respectively,

$$\mathsf{E}(X_{n+1}|\mathscr{F}_n) = X_n \quad \text{(P-a.s.)} \quad \text{(martingale)}$$

or   *≤ super martingale*   (2)

$$\mathsf{E}(X_{n+1}|\mathscr{F}_n) \geq X_n \quad \text{(P-a.s.)} \quad \text{(submartingale)}.$$

A stochastic sequence $X = (X_n, \mathscr{F}_n)$ is a *supermartingale* if the sequence $-X = (-X_n, \mathscr{F}_n)$ is a submartingale.

In the special case when $\mathscr{F}_n = \mathscr{F}_n^X$, where $\mathscr{F}_n^X = \sigma\{\omega\colon X_0, \ldots, X_n\}$, and the stochastic sequence $X = (X_n, \mathscr{F}_n)$ is a martingale (or submartingale), we say that the sequence $(X_n)_{n\geq 0}$ itself is a martingale (or submartingale).

It is easy to deduce from the properties of conditional expectations that (2) is equivalent to the property that, for every $n \geq 0$ and $A \in \mathscr{F}_n$,

$$\int_A X_{n+1}\, d\mathsf{P} = \int_A X_n\, d\mathsf{P}$$

or   (3)

$$\int_A X_{n+1}\, d\mathsf{P} \geq \int_A X_n\, d\mathsf{P}.$$

⇒ $E(X_1) = E(X_2) = \cdots$ if $A = \omega$.

EXAMPLE 1. If $(\xi_n)_{n\geq 0}$ is a sequence of independent random variables with $\mathsf{E}\xi_n = 0$ and $X_n = \xi_0 + \cdots + \xi_n$, $\mathscr{F}_n = \sigma\{\omega\colon \xi_0, \ldots, \xi_n\}$, the stochastic sequence $X = \{X_n, \mathscr{F}_n\}$ is a martingale.

EXAMPLE 2. If $(\xi_n)_{n\geq 0}$ is a sequence of independent random variables with $\mathsf{E}\xi_n = 1$, the stochastic sequence $(X_n, \mathscr{F}_n)$ with $X_n = \prod_{k=0}^n \xi_k$, $\mathscr{F}_n = \sigma\{\omega\colon \xi_0, \ldots, \xi_n\}$ is also a martingale.

EXAMPLE 3. Let ξ be a random variable with $\mathsf{E}|\xi| < \infty$ and

$$\mathscr{F}_0 \subseteq \mathscr{F}_1 \subseteq \cdots \subseteq \mathscr{F}.$$

Then the sequence $X = (X_n, \mathscr{F}_n)$ with $X_n = \mathsf{E}(\xi|\mathscr{F}_n)$ is a martingale.

EXAMPLE 4. If $(\xi_n)_{n\geq 0}$ is a sequence of nonnegative integrable random variables, the sequence (X_n) with $X_n = \xi_0 + \cdots + \xi_n$ is a submartingale.

EXAMPLE 5. If $X = (X_n, \mathscr{F}_n)$ is a martingale and $g(x)$ is convex downward with $\mathsf{E}|g(X_n)| < \infty$, $n \geq 0$, then the stochastic sequence $(g(X_n), \mathscr{F}_n)$ is a submartingale (as follows from Jensen's inequality).

If $X = (X_n, \mathscr{F}_n)$ is a submartingale and $g(x)$ is convex downward and nondecreasing, with $\mathsf{E}|g(X_n)| < \infty$ for all $n \geq 0$, then $(g(X_n), \mathscr{F}_n)$ is also a submartingale.

Assumption (1) in Definition 1 ensures the existence of the conditional expectations $\mathsf{E}(X_{n+1}|\mathscr{F}_n)$, $n \geq 0$. However, these expectations can also exist without the assumption that $\mathsf{E}|X_{n+1}| < \infty$. Recall that by §7 of Chapter

II, $E(X_{n+1}^+|\mathscr{F}_n)$ and $E(X_{n+1}^-|\mathscr{F}_n)$ are always defined. Let us write $A = B$ (P-a.s.) when $P(A \triangle B) = 0$. Then if

$$\{\omega: E(X_{n+1}^+|\mathscr{F}_n) < \infty\} \cup \{\omega: E(X_n^-|\mathscr{F}_n) < \infty\} = \Omega \quad \text{(P-a.s.)}$$

we say that $E(X_{n+1}|\mathscr{F}_n)$ is also defined and is given by

$$E(X_{n+1}|\mathscr{F}_n) = E(X_{n+1}^+|\mathscr{F}_n) - E(X_{n+1}^-|\mathscr{F}_n).$$

After this, the following definition is natural.

Definition 2. A stochastic sequence $X = (X_n, \mathscr{F}_n)$ is a *generalized martingale* (or *submartingale*) if the conditional expectations $E(X_{n+1}|\mathscr{F}_n)$ are defined for every $n \geq 0$ and (2) is satisfied.

Notice that it follows from this definition that $E(X_{n+1}^-|\mathscr{F}_n) < \infty$ for a generalized submartingale, and the $E(|X_{n+1}|\,|\mathscr{F}_n) < \infty$ (P-a.s.) for a generalized martingale.

3. In the following definition we introduce the concept of a Markov time, which plays a very important role in the subsequent theory.

Definition 3. A random variable $\tau = \tau(\omega)$ with values in the set $\{0, 1, \ldots, +\infty\}$ is a *Markov time* (with respect to $(\mathscr{F}_n)$) (or a *random variable independent of the future*) if, for each $n \geq 0$,

$$\{\tau = n\} \in \mathscr{F}_n. \tag{4}$$

When $P(\tau < \infty) = 1$, a Markov time τ is called a *stopping time*.

Let $X = (X_n, \mathscr{F}_n)$ be a stochastic sequence and let τ be a Markov time (with respect to $(\mathscr{F}_n)$). We write

$$X_\tau = \sum_{n=0}^{\infty} X_n I_{\{\tau = n\}}(\omega)$$

(hence $X_\tau = 0$ on the set $\{\omega: \tau = \infty\}$).
    Then for every $B \in \mathscr{B}(R)$,

$$\{\omega: X_\tau \in B\} = \sum_{n=0}^{\infty} \{X_n \in B, \tau = n\} \in \mathscr{F},$$

and consequently X_τ is a random variable.

EXAMPLE 6. Let $X = (X_n, \mathscr{F}_n)$ be a stochastic sequence and let $B \in \mathscr{B}(R)$. Then the time of first hitting the set B, that is,

$$\tau_B = \inf\{n \geq 0: X_n \in B\}$$

(with $\tau_B = +\infty$ if $\{\cdot\} = \varnothing$) is a Markov time, since

$$\{\tau_B = n\} = \{X_0 \notin B, \ldots, X_{n-1} \notin B, X_n \in B\} \in \mathscr{F}_n$$

for every $n \geq 0$.

EXAMPLE 7. Let $X = (X_n, \mathscr{F}_n)$ be a martingale (or submartingale) and τ a
Markov time (with respect to $(\mathscr{F}_n)$). Then the "stopped" process $X^\tau = (X_{n \wedge \tau}, \mathscr{F}_n)$ is also a martingale (or submartingale).

In fact, the equation

$$X_{n \wedge \tau} = \sum_{m=0}^{n-1} X_m I_{\{\tau = m\}} + X_n I_{\{\tau \geq n\}}$$

implies that the variables $X_{n \wedge \tau}$ are $\mathscr{F}_n$-measurable, are integrable, and satisfy

$$X_{(n+1) \wedge \tau} - X_{n \wedge \tau} = I_{\{\tau > n\}}(X_{n+1} - X_n),$$

whence

$$\mathsf{E}[X_{(n+1) \wedge \tau} - X_{n \wedge \tau} | \mathscr{F}_n] = I_{\{\tau > n\}} \mathsf{E}[X_{n+1} - X_n | \mathscr{F}_n] = 0 \quad (\text{or} \geq 0).$$

Every system $(\mathscr{F}_n)$ and Markov time τ corresponding to it generate a
collection of sets

$$\mathscr{F}_\tau = \{A \in \mathscr{F} : A \cap \{\tau = n\} \in \mathscr{F}_n \text{ for all } n \geq 0\}.$$

It is clear that $\Omega \in \mathscr{F}_\tau$ and $\mathscr{F}_\tau$ is closed under countable unions. Moreover, if
$A \in \mathscr{F}_\tau$, then $\bar{A} \cap \{\tau = n\} = \{\tau = n\} \setminus (A \cap \{\tau = n\}) \in \mathscr{F}_n$ and therefore $\bar{A} \in \mathscr{F}_\tau$.
Hence it follows that $\mathscr{F}_\tau$ is a σ-algebra.

If we think of $\mathscr{F}_n$ as a collection of events observed up to time n (inclusive),
then $\mathscr{F}_\tau$ can be thought of as a collection of events observed at the "random"
time τ.

It is easy to show (Problem 3) that the random variables τ and X_τ are
$\mathscr{F}_\tau$-measurable.

4. Definition 4. A stochastic sequence $X = (X_n, \mathscr{F}_n)$ is a *local martingale*
(or *submartingale*) if there is a (localizing) sequence $(\tau_k)_{k \geq 1}$ of Markov times
such that $\tau_k \leq \tau_{k+1}$ (P-a.s.), $\tau_k \uparrow \infty$ (P-a.s.) as $k \to \infty$, and every "stopped"
sequence $X^{\tau_k} = (X_{\tau_k \wedge n} \cdot I_{\{\tau_k > 0\}}, \mathscr{F}_n)$ is a martingale (or submartingale).

In Theorem 1 below, we show that in fact the class of local martingales
coincides with the class of generalized martingales. Moreover, every local
martingale can be obtained by a "martingale transformation" from a martingale and a predictable sequence.

Definition 5. Let $Y = (Y_n, \mathscr{F}_n)$ be a stochastic sequence and let $V = (V_n, \mathscr{F}_{n-1})$ be a predictable sequence ($\mathscr{F}_{-1} = \mathscr{F}_0$). The stochastic sequence $V \cdot Y = ((V \cdot Y)_n, \mathscr{F}_n)$ with

$$(V \cdot Y)_n = V_0 Y_0 + \sum_{i=1}^{n} V_i \Delta Y_i, \tag{5}$$

where $\Delta Y_i = Y_i - Y_{i-1}$, is called the *transform of Y by V*. If, in addition, Y is a martingale, we say that $V \cdot Y$ is a *martingale transform*.

Theorem 1. *Let $X = (X_n, \mathscr{F}_n)_{n \geq 0}$ be a stochastic sequence and let $X_0 = 0$ (P-a.s.). The following conditions are equivalent:*

(a) *X is a local martingale;*
(b) *X is a generalized martingale;*
(c) *X is a martingale transform, i.e. there are a predictable sequence $V = (V_n, \mathscr{F}_{n-1})$ with $V_0 = 0$ and a martingale $Y = (Y_n, \mathscr{F}_n)$ with $Y_0 = 0$ such that $X = V \cdot Y$.*

PROOF. (a) $\Rightarrow$ (b). Let X be a local martingale and let (τ_k) be a local sequence of Markov times for X. Then for every $m \geq 0$

$$\mathsf{E}[|X_{m \wedge \tau_k}| I_{\{\tau_k > 0\}}] < \infty, \tag{6}$$

and therefore

$$\mathsf{E}[|X_{(n+1) \wedge \tau_k}| I_{\{\tau_k > n\}}] = \mathsf{E}[|X_{n+1}| I_{\{\tau_k > n\}}] < \infty. \tag{7}$$

The random variable $I_{\{\tau_k > n\}}$ is $\mathscr{F}_n$-measurable. Hence it follows from (7) that

$$\mathsf{E}[|X_{n+1}| I_{\{\tau_k > n\}} | \mathscr{F}_n] = I_{\{\tau_k > n\}} \mathsf{E}[|X_{n+1}| \, | \mathscr{F}_n] < \infty \quad \text{(P-a.s.)}.$$

Here $I_{\{\tau_k > n\}} \to 1$ (P-a.s.), $k \to \infty$, and therefore

$$\mathsf{E}[|X_{n+1}| \, | \mathscr{F}_n] < \infty \quad \text{(P-a.s.)}. \tag{8}$$

Under this condition, $\mathsf{E}[X_{n+1} | \mathscr{F}_n]$ is defined, and it remains only to show that $\mathsf{E}[X_{n+1} | \mathscr{F}_n] = X_n$ (P-a.s.).

To do this, we need to show that

$$\int_A X_{n+1} \, d\mathsf{P} = \int_A X_n \, d\mathsf{P}$$

for $A \in \mathscr{F}_n$. By Problem 7, §7, Chapter II, we have $\mathsf{E}[|X_{n+1}| \mathscr{F}_n] < \infty$ (P-a.s.) if and only if the measure $\int_A |X_{n+1}| \, d\mathsf{P}$, $A \in \mathscr{F}_n$, is σ-finite. Therefore if we show that the measure $\int_A |X_n| \, d\mathsf{P}$, $A \in \mathscr{F}_n$, is also σ-finite, then in order to establish the equation in which we are interested it will be sufficient to establish it only for those sets $B \in \mathscr{F}_n$ for which $\int_B |X_{n+1}| \, d\mathsf{P} < \infty$.

Since X^{τ_k} is a martingale, $|X^{\tau_k}| = (|X_{\tau_k \wedge n}| \cdot I_{\{\tau_k > 0\}}, \mathscr{F}_n)$ is a submartingale and hence, if we recall that $\{\tau_k > n\} \in \mathscr{F}_n$, we obtain

$$\int_{B \cap \{\tau_k > n\}} |X_n| \, d\mathbf{P} = \int_{B \cap \{\tau_k > n\}} |X_{n \wedge \tau_k} I_{\{\tau_k > 0\}}| \, d\mathbf{P}$$

$$\leq \int_{B\{\tau_k > n\}} |X_{(n+1) \wedge \tau_k} I_{\{\tau_k > 0\}}| \, d\mathbf{P} = \int_{B\{\tau_k > n\}} |X_{n+1}| \, d\mathbf{P}.$$

Letting $k \to \infty$, we find that

$$\int_B |X_n| \, d\mathbf{P} \leq \int_B |X_{n+1}| \, d\mathbf{P}.$$

It follows that if $B \in \mathscr{F}_n$ is such that $\int_B |X_{n+1}| \, d\mathbf{P} < \infty$, then (by Lebesgue's dominated convergence theorem) we can take limits as $k \to \infty$ in the martingale equation

$$\int_{B \cap \{\tau_k > n\}} X_n \, d\mathbf{P} = \int_{B \cap \{\tau_k > n\}} X_{n+1} \, d\mathbf{P}.$$

Thus

$$\int_B X_n \, d\mathbf{P} = \int_B X_{n+1} \, d\mathbf{P}$$

for $B \in \mathscr{F}_n$ and such that $\int_B |X_{n+1}| \, d\mathbf{P} < \infty$. Hence it follows that this equation is valid for all $B \in \mathscr{F}_n$, and implies $\mathsf{E}(X_{n+1} | \mathscr{F}_n) = X_n$ (P-a.s.).

(b) $\Rightarrow$ (c). Let

$$\Delta X_n = X_n - X_{n-1}, X_0 = 0$$

and

$$V_0 = 0, V_n = \mathsf{E}[|\Delta X_n| \, | F_{n-1}], n \geq 1.$$

Put $W_n = V_n^{\oplus}, Y_0 = 0$, and

$$Y_n = \sum_{i=1}^n W_i \Delta X_i, \qquad n \geq 1.$$

It is clear that

$$\mathsf{E}[|\Delta Y_n| \, | \mathscr{F}_{n-1}] \leq 1 \quad \text{and} \quad \mathsf{E}[\Delta Y_n | \mathscr{F}_{n-1}] = 0.$$

Consequently $Y = (Y_n, \mathscr{F}_n)$ is a martingale. Moreover, $X_0 = V_0 \cdot Y_0 = 0$ and $\Delta(V \cdot Y)_n = \Delta X_n$. Therefore

$$X = V \cdot Y.$$

(c) $\Rightarrow$ (a). Let $X = V \cdot Y$ where V is a predictable sequence, Y is a martingale and $V_0 = Y_0 = 0$. Put

$$\tau_k = \inf\{n \geq 0 : |V_{n+1}| > k\},$$

and suppose that $\tau_k = \infty$ if the set $\{\cdot\} = \emptyset$. Since V_{n+1} is $\mathscr{F}_n$-measurable, the variables τ_k are Markov times for every $k \geq 1$.

Consider a "stopped" sequence $X^{\tau_k} = ((V \cdot Y)_{n \wedge \tau_k} I_{\{\tau_k > 0\}}, \mathscr{F}_n)$. On the set $\{\tau_k > 0\}$, the inequality $|V_{n \wedge \tau_k}| \leq k$ is in effect. Hence it follows that $\mathsf{E}|(V \cdot Y)_{n \wedge \tau_k} I_{\{\tau_k > 0\}}| < \infty$ for every $n \geq 1$. In addition, for $n \geq 1$,

$$\mathsf{E}\{[(V \cdot Y)_{(n+1) \wedge \tau_k} - (V \cdot Y)_{n \wedge \tau_k}]I_{\{\tau_k > 0\}} | \mathscr{F}_n\}$$
$$= I_{\{\tau_k > 0\}} \cdot V_{(n+1) \wedge \tau_k} \cdot \mathsf{E}\{Y_{(n+1) \wedge \tau_k} - Y_{n \wedge \tau_k} | \mathscr{F}_n\} = 0$$

since (see Example 7) $\mathsf{E}\{Y_{(n+1) \wedge \tau_k} - Y_{n \wedge \tau_k} | \mathscr{F}_n\} = 0$.

Thus for every $k \geq 1$ the stochastic sequences X^{τ_k} are martingales, $\tau_k \uparrow \infty$ (P-a.s.), and consequently X is a local martingale.

This completes the proof of the theorem.

5. EXAMPLE 8. Let $(\eta_n)_{n \geq 1}$ be a sequence of independent identically distributed Bernoulli random variables and let $\mathsf{P}(\eta_n = 1) = p$, $\mathsf{P}(\eta_n = -1) = q$, $p + q = 1$. We interpret the event $\{\eta_n = 1\}$ as success (gain) and $\{\eta_n = -1\}$ as failure (loss) of a player at the nth turn. Let us suppose that the player's stake at the nth turn is V_n. Then the player's total gain through the nth turn is

$$X_n = \sum_{i=1}^{n} V_i \eta_i = X_{n-1} + V_n \eta_n, \qquad X_0 = 0.$$

It is quite natural to suppose that the amount V_n at the nth turn may depend on the results of the preceding turns, i.e. on $V_1, \ldots, V_{n-1}$ and on $\eta_1, \ldots, \eta_{n-1}$. In other words, if we put $F_0 = \{\emptyset, \Omega\}$ and $F_n = \sigma\{\omega: \eta_1, \ldots, \eta_n\}$, then V_n is an $\mathscr{F}_{n-1}$-measurable random variable, i.e. the sequence $V = (V_n, \mathscr{F}_{n-1})$ that determines the player's "strategy" is predictable. Putting $Y_n = \eta_1 + \cdots + \eta_n$, we find that

$$X_n = \sum_{i=1}^{n} V_i \Delta Y_i,$$

i.e. the sequence $X = (X_n, \mathscr{F}_n)$ with $X_0 = 0$ is the transform of Y by V.

From the player's point of view, the game in question is *fair* (or *favorable*, or *unfavorable*) if, at every stage, the conditional expectation

$$\mathsf{E}(X_{n+1} - X_n | \mathscr{F}_n) = 0 \text{ (or } \geq 0 \text{ or } \leq 0).$$

Moreover, it is clear that the game is

> fair if $p = q = \frac{1}{2}$,
> favorable if $p > q$,
> unfavorable, if $p < q$.

Since $X = (X_n, \mathscr{F}_n)$ is a

> martingale if $p = q = \frac{1}{2}$,
> submartingale if $p > q$,
> supermartingale if $p < q$,

we can say that the assumption that the game is fair (or favorable, or unfavorable) corresponds to the assumption that the sequence X is a martingale (or submartingale, or supermartingale).

Let us now consider the special class of strategies $V = (V_n, \mathscr{F}_{n-1})_{n \geq 1}$ with $V_1 = 1$ and (for $n > 1$)

$$V_n = \begin{cases} 2^{n-1} & \text{if } \eta_1 = -1, \ldots, \eta_{n-1} = -1, \\ 0 & \text{otherwise.} \end{cases} \tag{9}$$

In such a strategy, a player, having started with a stake $V_1 = 1$, doubles the stake after a loss and drops out of the game immediately after a win.

If $\eta_1 = -1, \ldots, \eta_n = -1$, the total loss to the player after n turns will be

$$\sum_{i=1}^{n} 2^{i-1} = 2^n - 1.$$

Therefore if also $\eta_{n+1} = 1$, we have

$$X_{n+1} = X_n + V_{n+1} = -(2^n - 1) + 2^n = 1.$$

Let $\tau = \inf\{n \geq 1 : X_n = 1\}$. If $p = q = \frac{1}{2}$, i.e. the game in question is fair, then $P(\tau = n) = (\frac{1}{2})^n$, $P(\tau < \infty) = 1$, $P(X_\tau = 1) = 1$, and $EX_\tau = 1$. Therefore even for a fair game, by applying the strategy (9), a player can in a finite time (with probability unity) complete the game "successfully," increasing his capital by one unit ($EX_\tau = 1 > X_0 = 0$).

In gambling practice, this system (doubling the stakes after a loss and dropping out of the game after a win) is called a martingale. This is the origin of the mathematical term "martingale."

Remark. When $p = q = \frac{1}{2}$, the sequence $X = (X_n, \mathscr{F}_n)$ with $X_0 = 0$ is a martingale and therefore

$$EX_n = EX_0 = 0 \qquad \text{for every } n \geq 1.$$

We may therefore expect that this equation is preserved if the instant n is replaced by a random instant τ. It will appear later (Theorem 1, §2) that $EX_\tau = EX_0$ in "typical" situations. Violations of this equation (as in the game discussed above) arise in what we may describe as physically unrealizable situations, when either τ or $|X_n|$ takes values that are much too large. (Note that the game discussed above would be physically unrealizable, since it supposes an unbounded time for playing and an unbounded initial capital for the player.)

6. Definition 6. A stochastic sequence $\xi = (\xi_n, \mathscr{F}_n)$ is a *martingale-difference* if $E|\xi| < \infty$ for all $n \geq 0$ and

$$E(\xi_{n+1} | \mathscr{F}_n) = 0 \quad \text{(P-a.s.)}. \tag{10}$$

The connection between martingales and martingale-differences is clear from Definitions 1 and 6. Thus if $X = (X_n, \mathscr{F}_n)$ is a martingale, then $\xi = (\xi_n, \mathscr{F}_n)$ with $\xi_0 = X_0$ and $\xi_n = \Delta X_n$, $n \geq 1$, is a martingale-difference. In turn, if $\xi = (\xi_n, \mathscr{F}_n)$ is a martingale-difference, then $X = (X_n, \mathscr{F}_n)$ with $X_n = \xi_0 + \cdots + \xi_n$ is a martingale.

In agreement with this terminology, every sequence $\xi = (\xi_n)_{n \geq 0}$ of independent integrable random variables with $E\xi_n = 0$ is a martingale-difference (with $\mathscr{F}_n = \sigma\{\omega : \xi_0, \xi_1, \ldots, \xi_n\}$).

7. The following theorem elucidates the structure of submartingales (or supermartingales).

Theorem 2 (Doob). *Let $X = (X_n, \mathscr{F}_n)$ be a submartingale. Then there are a martingale $m = (m_n, \mathscr{F}_n)$ and a predictable increasing sequence $A = (A_n, \mathscr{F}_{n-1})$ such that, for every $n \geq 0$, Doob's decomposition*

$$X_n = m_n + A_n \quad \text{(P-a.s.)} \tag{11}$$

holds. A decomposition of this kind is unique.

PROOF. Let us put $m_0 = X_0$, $A_0 = 0$ and

$$m_n = m_0 + \sum_{j=0}^{n-1} [X_{j+1} - E(X_{j+1}|\mathscr{F}_j)], \tag{12}$$

$$A_n = \sum_{j=0}^{n-1} [E(X_{j+1}|\mathscr{F}_j) - X_j]. \tag{13}$$

It is evident that m and A, defined in this way, have the required properties. In addition, let $X_n = m'_n + A'_n$, where $m' = (m'_n, \mathscr{F}_n)$ is a martingale and $A' = (A'_n, F_n)$ is a predictable increasing sequence. Then

$$A'_{n+1} - A'_n = (A_{n+1} - A_n) + (m_{n+1} - m_n) - (m'_{n+1} - m'_n),$$

and if we take conditional expectations on both sides, we find that (P-a.s.) $A'_{n+1} - A'_n = A_{n+1} - A_n$. But $A_0 = A'_0 = 0$, and therefore $A_n = A'_n$ and $m_n = m'_n$ (P-a.s.) for all $n \geq 0$.

This completes the proof of the theorem.

It follows from (11) that the sequence $A = (A_n, F_{n-1})$ compensates $X = (X_n, F_n)$ so that it becomes a martingale. This observation is justified by the following definition.

Definition 7. A predictable increasing sequence $A = (A_n, \mathscr{F}_{n-1})$ appearing in the Doob decomposition (11) is called a *compensator* (of the submartingale X).

The Doob decomposition plays a key role in the study of square integrable martingales $M = (M_n, F_n)$ i.e. martingales for which $E M_n^2 < \infty$, $n \geq 0$; this depends on the observation that the stochastic sequence $M^2 = (M^2, \mathscr{F}_n)$ is a submartingale. According to Theorem 2 there are a martingale $m = (m_n, \mathscr{F}_n)$ and a predictable increasing sequence $\langle M \rangle = (\langle M \rangle_n, \mathscr{F}_{n-1})$ such that

$$M_n^2 = m_n + \langle M \rangle_n. \tag{14}$$

The sequence $\langle M \rangle$ is called the *quadratic variation* of M and, in many respects, determines its structure and properties.

It follows from (12) that

$$\langle M \rangle_n = \sum_{j=1}^{n} \mathsf{E}[(\Delta M_j)^2 | \mathscr{F}_{j-1}] \tag{15}$$

and, for all $l \le k$,

$$\mathsf{E}[(M_k - M_l)^2 | \mathscr{F}_l] = \mathsf{E}[M_k^2 - M_l^2 | \mathscr{F}_l] = \mathsf{E}[\langle M \rangle_k - \langle M \rangle_l | \mathscr{F}_l]. \tag{16}$$

In particular, if $M_0 = 0$ (P-a.s.) then

$$\mathsf{E} M_k^2 = \mathsf{E} \langle M \rangle_k. \tag{17}$$

It is useful to observe that if $M_0 = 0$ and $M_n = \xi_1 + \cdots + \xi_n$, where (ξ_n) is a sequence of independent random variables with $\mathsf{E}\xi_i = 0$ and $\mathsf{E}\xi_i^2 < \infty$, the quadratic variation

$$\langle M \rangle_n = \mathsf{E} M_n^2 = \mathsf{V}\xi_1 + \cdots + \mathsf{V}\xi_n \tag{18}$$

is not random, and indeed coincides with the variance.

If $X = (X_n, \mathscr{F}_n)$ and $Y = (Y_n, \mathscr{F}_n)$ are square integrable martingales, we put

$$\langle X, Y \rangle_n = \tfrac{1}{4}[\langle X + Y \rangle_n - \langle X - Y \rangle_n]. \tag{19}$$

It is easily verified that $(X_n Y_n - \langle X, Y \rangle_n, \mathscr{F}_n)$ is a martingale and therefore, for $l \le k$,

$$\mathsf{E}[(X_k - X_l)(Y_k - Y_l) | \mathscr{F}_l] = \mathsf{E}[\langle X, Y \rangle_k - \langle X, Y \rangle_l | \mathscr{F}_l]. \tag{20}$$

In the case when $X_n = \xi_1 + \cdots + \xi_n$, $Y_n = \eta_1 + \cdots + \eta_n$, where (ξ_n) and (η_n) are sequences of independent random variables with $\mathsf{E}\xi_i = \mathsf{E}\eta_i = 0$ and $\mathsf{E}\xi_i^2 < \infty$, $\mathsf{E}\eta_i^2 < \infty$, the variable $\langle X, Y \rangle_n$ is given by

$$\langle X, Y \rangle_n = \sum_{i=1}^{n} \mathrm{cov}(\xi_i, \eta_i).$$

The sequence $\langle X, Y \rangle = (\langle X, Y \rangle_n, \mathscr{F}_{n-1})$ is often called the *mutual variation* of the (square integrable) martingales X and Y.

8. Problems

1. Show that (2) and (3) are equivalent.

2. Let σ and τ be Markov times. Show that $\tau + \sigma$, $\tau \wedge \sigma$, and $\tau \vee \sigma$ are also Markov times; and if $\mathsf{P}(\sigma \le \tau) = 1$, then $\mathscr{F}_\sigma \subseteq \mathscr{F}_\tau$.

3. Show that τ and X_τ are $\mathscr{F}_\tau$-measurable.

4. Let $Y = (Y_n, \mathscr{F}_n)$ be a martingale (or submartingale), let $V = (V_n, \mathscr{F}_{n-1})$ be a predictable sequence, and let $(V \cdot Y)_n$ be integrable random variables, $n \geq 0$. Show that $V \cdot Y$ is a martingale (or submartingale).

5. Let $\mathscr{F}_1 \subseteq \mathscr{F}_2 \subseteq \cdots$ be a nondecreasing family of σ-algebras and ξ an integrable random variable. Show that $(X_n)_{n \geq 1}$ with $X_n = \mathsf{E}(\xi | \mathscr{F}_n)$ is a martingale.

6. Let $\mathscr{G}_1 \supseteq \mathscr{G}_2 \supseteq \cdots$ be a nonincreasing family of σ-algebras and let ξ be an integrable random variable. Show that $(X_n)_{n \geq 1}$ with $X_n = \mathsf{E}(\xi | \mathscr{G}_n)$ is a *bounded* martingale, i.e.

$$\mathsf{E}(X_n | X_{n+1}, X_{n+2}, \ldots) = X_{n+1} \quad \text{(P-a.s.)}$$

for every $n \geq 1$.

7. Let $\xi_1, \xi_2, \xi_3, \ldots$ be independent random variables, $\mathsf{P}(\xi_i = 0) = \mathsf{P}(\xi_i = 2) = \frac{1}{2}$ and $X_n = \prod_{i=1}^n \xi_i$. Show that there do not exist an integrable random variable ξ and a nondecreasing family $(\mathscr{F}_n)$ of σ-algebras such that $X_n = \mathsf{E}(\xi | \mathscr{F}_n)$. This example shows that not every martingale $(X_n)_{n \geq 1}$ can be represented in the form $(\mathsf{E}(\xi | \mathscr{F}_n))_{n \geq 1}$; compare Example 3, §11, Chapter I.)

8. Let $X = (X_n, \mathscr{F}_n), n \geq 0$, be a square integrable martingale with $\mathsf{E}X_n = 0$. Show that it has orthogonal increments, i.e.

$$E\Delta X_m \Delta X_n = 0, \qquad m \neq n,$$

where $\Delta X_k = X_k - X_{k-1}$ for $k \geq 1$ and $\Delta X_0 = X_0$.

(Consequently the square integrable martingales occupy a position in the class of stochastic sequences with zero mean and finite second moments, intermediate between sequences with independent increments and sequences with orthogonal increments.)

§2. Preservation of the Martingale Property Under Time Change at a Random Time

1. If $X = (X_n, \mathscr{F}_n)_{n \geq 0}$ is a martingale, we have

$$\mathsf{E}X_n = \mathsf{E}X_0 \tag{1}$$

for every $n \geq 1$. Is this property preserved if the time n is replaced by a Markov time τ? Example 8 of the preceding section shows that, in general, the answer is "no": there exist a martingale X and a Markov time τ (finite with probability 1) such that

$$\mathsf{E}X_\tau \neq \mathsf{E}X_0. \tag{2}$$

The following basic theorem describes the "typical" situation, in which, in particular, $\mathsf{E}X_\tau = \mathsf{E}X_0$.

Theorem 1 (Doob). *Let* $X = (X_n, \mathscr{F}_n)$ *be a martingale (or submartingale), and* τ_1 *and* τ_2, *stopping times for which*

$$\mathsf{E}\,|X_{\tau_i}| < \infty, \qquad i = 1, 2, \tag{3}$$

$$\lim_{n\to\infty} \int_{\{\tau_i > n\}} |X_n|\,d\mathsf{P} = 0, \qquad i = 1, 2. \tag{4}$$

Then

$$\mathsf{E}(X_{\tau_2}|\mathscr{F}_{\tau_1}) \underset{(\geq)}{=} X_{\tau_1} \quad (\{\tau_2 \geq \tau_1\}; \mathsf{P}\text{-}a.s.). \tag{5}$$

If also $\mathsf{P}(\tau_1 \leq \tau_2) = 1$, *then*

$$\mathsf{E}X_{\tau_2} \underset{(\geq)}{=} \mathsf{E}X_{\tau_1}. \tag{6}$$

(Here and in the formulas below, read the upper symbol for martingales and the lower symbol for submartingales.)

Proof. It is sufficient to show that, for every $A \in \mathscr{F}_{\tau_1}$,

$$\int_{A \cap \{\tau_2 \geq \tau_1\}} X_{\tau_2}\,d\mathsf{P} \underset{(\geq)}{=} \int_{A \cap \{\tau_2 \geq \tau_1\}} X_{\tau_1}\,d\mathsf{P}. \tag{7}$$

For this, in turn, it is sufficient to show that, for every $n \geq 0$,

$$\int_{A \cap \{\tau_2 \geq \tau_1\} \cap \{\tau_1 = n\}} X_{\tau_2}\,d\mathsf{P} \underset{(\geq)}{=} \int_{A \cap \{\tau_2 \geq \tau_1\} \cap \{\tau_1 = n\}} X_{\tau_1}\,d\mathsf{P},$$

or, what amounts to the same thing,

$$\int_{B \cap \{\tau_2 \geq n\}} X_{\tau_2}\,d\mathsf{P} \underset{(\geq)}{=} \int_{B \cap \{\tau_2 \geq n\}} X_n\,d\mathsf{P}, \tag{8}$$

where $B = A \cap \{\tau_1 = n\} \in \mathscr{F}_n$.
   We have

$$\int_{B \cap \{\tau_2 \geq n\}} X_n\,d\mathsf{P} = \int_{B \cap \{\tau_2 = n\}} X_n\,d\mathsf{P} + \int_{B \cap \{\tau_2 > n\}} X_n\,d\mathsf{P} \underset{(\leq)}{=} \int_{B \cap \{\tau_2 = n\}} X_n\,d\mathsf{P}$$

$$+ \int_{B \cap \{\tau_2 > n\}} \mathsf{E}(X_{n+1}|\mathscr{F}_n)\,d\mathsf{P} = \int_{B \cap \{\tau_2 = n\}} X_{\tau_2}\,d\mathsf{P} + \int_{B \cap \{\tau_2 \geq n+1\}} X_{n+1}\,d\mathsf{P}$$

$$\underset{(\leq)}{=} \int_{B \cap \{n \leq \tau_2 \leq n+1\}} X_{\tau_2}\,d\mathsf{P} + \int_{B \cap \{\tau_2 \geq n+2\}} X_{n+2}\,d\mathsf{P} \underset{(\leq)}{=} \cdots$$

$$\underset{(\leq)}{=} \int_{B \cap \{n \leq \tau_2 \leq m\}} X_{\tau_2}\,d\mathsf{P} + \int_{B \cap \{\tau_2 > m\}} X_m\,d\mathsf{P},$$

whence

$$\int_{B \cap \{n \leq \tau_2 \leq m\}} X_{\tau_2}\,d\mathsf{P} \underset{(\geq)}{=} \int_{B \cap \{n \leq \tau_2\}} X_n\,d\mathsf{P} - \int_{B \cap \{m < \tau_2\}} X_m\,d\mathsf{P}$$

and since $X_m = 2X_m^+ - |X_m|$, we have, by (4),

$$\int_{B \cap \{\tau_2 \geq n\}} X_{\tau_2}\, dP \underset{(\geq)}{=} \varlimsup_{m \to \infty}\left[\int_{B \cap \{n \leq \tau_2\}} X_n\, dP - \int_{B \cap \{m < \tau_2\}} X_m\, dP\right]$$

$$= \int_{B \cap \{n \leq \tau_2\}} X_n\, dP - \lim_{m \to \infty}\int_{B \cap \{m < \tau_2\}} X_m\, dP = \int_{B \cap \{\tau_2 \geq n\}} X_n\, dP,$$

which establishes (8), and hence (5). Finally, (6) follows from (5). This completes the proof of the theorem.

Corollary 1. *If there is a constant N such that* $P(\tau_1 \leq N) = 1$ *and* $P(\tau_2 \leq N) = 1$, *then (3) and (4) are satisfied. Hence if, in addition,* $P(\tau_1 \leq \tau_2) = 1$ *and* X *is a martingale, then*

$$\mathsf{E}X_0 = \mathsf{E}X_{\tau_1} = \mathsf{E}X_{\tau_2} = \mathsf{E}X_N. \qquad (9)$$

Corollary 2. *If the random variables* $\{X_n\}$ *are uniformly integrable (in particular, if* $|X_n| \leq C < \infty$, $n \geq 0$*), then (3) and (4) are satisfied.*

In fact, $P(\tau_i > n) \to 0$, $n \to \infty$, and hence (4) follows from Lemma 2, §6, Chapter II. In addition, since the family $\{X_n\}$ is uniformly integrable, we have (see II.6.(16))

$$\sup \mathsf{E}|X_N| < \infty. \qquad (10)$$

If τ is a stopping time and X is a submartingale, then by Corollary 1, applied to the bounded time $\tau_N = \tau \wedge N$,

$$\mathsf{E}X_0 \leq \mathsf{E}X_{\tau_N}.$$

Therefore

$$\mathsf{E}|X_{\tau_N}| = 2\mathsf{E}X_{\tau_N}^+ - \mathsf{E}X_{\tau_N} \leq 2\mathsf{E}X_{\tau_N}^+ - \mathsf{E}X_0. \qquad (11)$$

The sequence $X^+ = (X_n^+, \mathscr{F}_n)$ is a submartingale (Example 5, §1) and therefore

$$\mathsf{E}X_{\tau_N}^+ = \sum_{j=0}^{N} \int_{\{\tau_N = j\}} X_j^+\, dP + \int_{\{\tau > N\}} X_N^+\, dP \leq \sum_{j=0}^{N} \int_{\{\tau_N = j\}} X_N^+\, dP$$

$$+ \int_{\{\tau > N\}} X_N^+\, dP = \mathsf{E}X_N^+ \leq \mathsf{E}|X_N| \leq \sup_N \mathsf{E}|X_N|.$$

From this and (11) we have

$$\mathsf{E}|X_{\tau_N}| \leq 3\sup_N \mathsf{E}|X_N|,$$

and hence by Fatou's lemma

$$\mathsf{E}|X_\tau| \leq 3\sup_N \mathsf{E}|X_N|.$$

Therefore if we take $\tau = \tau_i$, $i = 1, 2$, and use (10), we obtain $E|X_{\tau_i}| < \infty$, $i = 1, 2$.

Remark. In Example 8 of the preceding section,

$$\int_{\{\tau > n\}} |X_n|\, dP = (2^n - 1)P\{\tau > n\} = (2^n - 1)\cdot 2^{-n} \to 1, \qquad n \to \infty,$$

and consequently (4) is violated (for $\tau_2 = \tau$).

2. The following proposition, which we shall deduce from Theorem 1, is often useful in applications.

Theorem 2. *Let $X = (X_n)$ be a martingale (or submartingale) and τ a stopping time (with respect to $(\mathscr{F}_n^X)$, where $\mathscr{F}_n^X = \sigma\{\omega: X_0, \ldots, X_n\}$). Suppose that*

$$E\tau < \infty,$$

and that for some $n \geq 0$ and some constant C

$$E\{|X_{n+1} - X_n| \,\big|\, \mathscr{F}_n^X\} \leq C \quad (\{\tau \geq n\}; P\text{-}a.s.).$$

Then

$$E|X_\tau| < \infty$$

and

$$EX_\tau \underset{(\geq)}{=} EX_0. \tag{12}$$

We first verify that hypotheses (3) and (4) of Theorem 1 are satisfied with $\tau_2 = \tau$.
Let

$$Y_0 = |X_0|, \qquad Y_j = |X_j - X_{j-1}|, \qquad j \geq 1.$$

Then $|X_\tau| \leq \sum_{j=0}^\tau Y_j$ and

$$E|X_\tau| \leq E\left(\sum_{j=0}^\tau Y_j\right) = \int_\Omega \left(\sum_{j=0}^\tau Y_j\right) dP = \sum_{n=0}^\infty \int_{\{\tau=n\}} \sum_{j=0}^n Y_j\, dP$$

$$= \sum_{n=0}^\infty \sum_{j=0}^n \int_{\{\tau=n\}} Y_j\, dP = \sum_{j=0}^\infty \sum_{n=j}^\infty \int_{\{\tau=n\}} Y_j\, dP = \sum_{j=0}^\infty \int_{\{\tau\geq j\}} Y_j\, dP.$$

The set $\{\tau \geq j\} = \Omega \setminus \{\tau < j\} \in \mathscr{F}_{j-1}^X, j \geq 1$. Therefore

$$\int_{\{\tau\geq j\}} Y_j\, dP = \int_{\{\tau\geq j\}} E[Y_j|X_0, \ldots, X_{j-1}]\, dP \leq CP\{\tau \geq j\}$$

for $j \geq 1$; and

$$\mathsf{E}|X_\tau| \leq \mathsf{E}\left(\sum_{j=0}^{\tau} Y_j\right) \leq \mathsf{E}|X_0| + C\sum_{j=1}^{\infty} \mathsf{P}\{\tau \geq j\} = \mathsf{E}|X_0| + C\mathsf{E}\tau < \infty.$$
(13)

Moreover, if $\tau > n$, then

$$\sum_{j=0}^{n} Y_j \leq \sum_{j=0}^{\tau} Y_j,$$

and therefore

$$\int_{\{\tau > n\}} |X_n|\,d\mathsf{P} \leq \int_{\{\tau > n\}} \sum_{j=0}^{\tau} Y_i\,d\mathsf{P}.$$

Hence since (by (13)) $\mathsf{E}\sum_{j=0}^{\tau} Y_j < \infty$ and $\{\tau > n\} \downarrow \emptyset, n \to \infty$, the dominated convergence theorem yields

$$\lim_{n\to\infty} \int_{\{\tau > n\}} |X_n|\,d\mathsf{P} \leq \lim_{n\to\infty} \int_{\{\tau > n\}} \left(\sum_{j=0}^{\tau} Y_j\right) d\mathsf{P} = 0.$$

Hence the hypotheses of Theorem 1 are satisfied, and (12) follows as required.

This completes the proof of the theorem.

3. Here we present some applications of the preceding theorems.

Theorem 3 (Wald's Identities). *Let $\xi_1, \xi_2, \ldots$ be independent identically distributed random variables with $\mathsf{E}|\xi_i| < \infty$ and τ a stopping time (with respect to $\mathscr{F}_n^\xi$), where $\mathscr{F}_n^\xi = \sigma\{\omega: \xi_1, \ldots, \xi_n\}, \tau \geq 1$), and $\mathsf{E}\tau < \infty$. Then*

$$\mathsf{E}(\xi_1 + \cdots + \xi_\tau) = \mathsf{E}\xi_1 \cdot \mathsf{E}\tau.$$
(14)

If also $\mathsf{E}\xi_i^2 < \infty$ then $, Var(S_\tau)$

$$\mathsf{E}\{(\xi_1 + \cdots + \xi_\tau) - \tau\mathsf{E}\xi_1\}^2 = \mathsf{V}\xi_1 \cdot \mathsf{E}\tau.$$
(15)

PROOF. It is clear that $X = (X_n, \mathscr{F}_n^\xi)_{n\geq 1}$ with $X_n = (\xi_1 + \cdots + \xi_n) - n\mathsf{E}\xi_1$ is a martingale with

$$\mathsf{E}[|X_{n+1} - X_n||X_1, \ldots, X_n] = \mathsf{E}[|\xi_{n+1} - \mathsf{E}\xi_1||\xi_1, \ldots, \xi_n]$$
$$= \mathsf{E}|\xi_{n+1} - \mathsf{E}\xi_1| \leq 2\mathsf{E}|\xi_1| < \infty.$$

Therefore $\mathsf{E}X_\tau = \mathsf{E}X_0 = 0$, by Theorem 2, and (14) is established.

Similar considerations applied to the martingale $Y = (Y_n, \mathscr{F}_n^\xi)$ with $Y_n = X_n^2 - n\mathsf{V}\xi_1$ lead to a proof of (15).

Corollary. *Let $\xi_1, \xi_2, \ldots$ be independent identically distributed random variables with*

$$\mathsf{P}(\xi_i = 1) = \mathsf{P}(\xi_i = -1) = \tfrac{1}{2}, S_n = \xi_1 + \cdots + \xi_n$$

and $\tau = \inf\{n \geq 1: S_n = 1\}$. Then $\mathsf{P}\{\tau < \infty\} = 1$ (see, for example, (I.9.20)) and therefore $\mathsf{P}(S_\tau = 1) = 1, \mathsf{E}S_\tau = 1$. Hence it follows from (14) that $\mathsf{E}\tau = \infty$.

Theorem 4 (Wald's Fundamental Identity). *Let $\xi_1, \xi_2, \ldots$, be a sequence of independent identically distributed random variables, $S_n = \xi_1 + \cdots + \xi_n$, and $n \geq 1$. Let $\varphi(t) = \mathsf{E}e^{t\xi_1}, t \in R$, and for some $t_0 \neq 0$ let $\varphi(t_0)$ exist and $\varphi(t_0) \geq 1$.*

If τ is a stopping time (with respect to $(\mathscr{F}_n^\xi), \mathscr{F}_n^\xi = \sigma\{\omega: \xi_1, \ldots, \xi_n\}, \tau \geq 1$), such that $|S_n| \leq C$ ($\{\tau \geq n\}$; P-a.s.) and $\mathsf{E}\tau < \infty$, then

$$\mathsf{E}\left[\frac{e^{t_0 S_\tau}}{(\varphi(t_0))^\tau}\right] = 1. \tag{16}$$

PROOF. Take

$$Y_n = e^{t_0 S_n}(\varphi(t_0))^{-n}.$$

Then $Y = (Y_n, \mathscr{F}_n^\xi)_{n \geq 1}$ is a martingale with $\mathsf{E}Y_n = 1$ and, on the set $\{\tau \geq n\}$,

$$\mathsf{E}\{|Y_{n+1} - Y_n| \,|\, Y_1, \ldots, Y_n\} = Y_n\mathsf{E}\left\{\left|\frac{e^{t_0\xi_{n+1}}}{\varphi(t_0)} - 1\right| \,\Big|\, \xi_1, \ldots, \xi_n\right\}$$

$$= Y_n \cdot \mathsf{E}\{|e^{t_0\xi_1}\varphi^{-1}(t_0) - 1|\} \leq B < \infty,$$

where B is a constant. Therefore Theorem 2 is applicable, and (16) follows since $\mathsf{E}Y_1 = 1$.

This completes the proof.

EXAMPLE 1. This example will let us illustrate the use of the preceding examples to find the probabilities of ruin and of mean duration in games (see §9, Chapter I).

Let $\xi_1, \xi_2, \ldots$ be a sequence of independent Bernoulli random variables with $\mathsf{P}(\xi_i = 1) = p, \mathsf{P}(\xi_i = -1) = q, p + q = 1, S = \xi_1 + \cdots + \xi_n$, and

$$\tau = \inf\{n \geq 1: S_n = B \text{ or } A\}, \tag{17}$$

where $(-A)$ and B are positive integers.

It follows from (I.9.20) that $\mathsf{P}(\tau < \infty) = 1$ and $\mathsf{E}\tau < \infty$. Then if $\alpha = \mathsf{P}(S_\tau = A), \beta = \mathsf{P}(S_\tau = B)$, we have $\alpha + \beta = 1$. If $p = q = \frac{1}{2}$, we obtain

$$0 = \mathsf{E}S_\tau = \alpha A + \beta B, \quad \text{from (14)},$$

whence

$$\alpha = \frac{B}{B + |A|}, \qquad \beta = \frac{|A|}{B + |A|}.$$

Applying (15), we obtain

$$\mathsf{E}_\tau = \mathsf{E}S_\tau^2 = \alpha A^2 + \beta B^2 = |AB|.$$

However, if $p \neq q$ we find, by considering the martingale $((q/p)^{S_n})_{n \geq 1}$, that

$$\mathsf{E}\left(\frac{q}{p}\right)^{S_\tau} = \mathsf{E}\left(\frac{q}{p}\right)^{S_1} = 1,$$

and therefore

$$\alpha\left(\frac{q}{p}\right)^A + \beta\left(\frac{q}{p}\right)^B = 1.$$

Together with the equation $\alpha + \beta = 1$ this yields

$$\alpha = \frac{\left(\dfrac{q}{p}\right)^B - 1}{\left(\dfrac{q}{p}\right)^B - \left(\dfrac{q}{p}\right)^{|A|}}, \qquad \beta = \frac{1 - \left(\dfrac{q}{p}\right)^{|A|}}{\left(\dfrac{q}{p}\right)^B - \left(\dfrac{q}{p}\right)^{|A|}}. \tag{18}$$

Finally, since $\mathsf{E}S_\tau = (p - q)\mathsf{E}\tau$, we find

$$\mathsf{E}\tau = \frac{\mathsf{E}S_\tau}{p - q} = \frac{\alpha A + \beta B}{p - q},$$

where α and β are defined by (18).

EXAMPLE 2. In the example considered above, let $p = q = \frac{1}{2}$. Let us show that for every λ in $0 < \lambda < \pi/(B + |A|)$ and every time τ defined in (17),

$$\mathsf{E}(\cos \lambda)^{-\tau} = \frac{\cos \lambda \cdot \dfrac{B + A}{2}}{\cos \lambda \cdot \dfrac{B + |A|}{2}}. \tag{19}$$

For this purpose we consider the martingale $X = (X_n, \mathscr{F}_n^\xi)_{n \geq 0}$ with

$$X_n = (\cos \lambda)^{-n} \cos \lambda\left(S_n - \frac{B + A}{2}\right) \tag{20}$$

and $S_0 = 0$. It is clear that

$$\mathsf{E}X_n = \mathsf{E}X_0 = \cos \lambda \frac{B + A}{2}. \tag{21}$$

Let us show that the family $\{X_{n \wedge \tau}\}$ is uniformly integrable. For this purpose we observe that, by Corollary 1 to Theorem 1 for $0 < \lambda < \pi/(B + |A|)$,

$$\mathsf{E}X_0 = \mathsf{E}X_{n \wedge \tau} = \mathsf{E}(\cos \lambda)^{-(n \wedge \tau)} \cos \lambda\left(S_{n \wedge \tau} - \frac{B + A}{2}\right)$$

$$\geq \mathsf{E}(\cos \lambda)^{-(n \wedge \tau)} \cos \lambda \frac{B - A}{2}.$$

Therefore, by (21),

$$\mathsf{E}(\cos \lambda)^{-(n \wedge \tau)} \le \frac{\cos \lambda \dfrac{B + A}{2}}{\cos \lambda \dfrac{B + |A|}{2}},$$

and consequently by Fatou's lemma,

$$\mathsf{E}(\cos \lambda)^{-\tau} \le \frac{\cos \lambda \dfrac{B + A}{2}}{\cos \lambda \dfrac{B + |A|}{2}}. \tag{22}$$

Consequently, by (20),

$$|X_{n \wedge \tau}| \le (\cos \lambda)^{-\tau}.$$

With (22), this establishes the uniform integrability of the family $\{X_{n \wedge \tau}\}$. Then, by Corollary 2 to Theorem 1,

$$\cos \lambda \frac{B + A}{2} = \mathsf{E}X_0 = \mathsf{E}X_\tau = \mathsf{E}(\cos \lambda)^{-\tau} \cos \lambda \frac{B - A}{2},$$

from which the required inequality (19) follows.

4. Problems

1. Show that Theorem 1 remains valid for submartingales if (4) is replaced by

$$\lim_{n \to \infty} \int_{\{\tau_i > n\}} X_n^+ \, d\mathsf{P} = 0, \qquad i = 1, 2.$$

2. Let $X = (X_n, \mathscr{F}_n)_{n \ge 0}$ be a square-integrable martingale, τ a stopping time and

$$\lim_{n \to \infty} \int_{\{\tau > n\}} X_n^2 \, d\mathsf{P} = 0,$$

$$\lim_{n \to \infty} \int_{\{\tau > n\}} |X_n| \, d\mathsf{P} = 0.$$

Show that then

$$\mathsf{E}X_\tau^2 = \mathsf{E}\langle X \rangle_\tau \left(= \mathsf{E} \sum_{j=0}^{\tau} (\Delta X_j)^2 \right),$$

where $\Delta X_0 = X_0, \Delta X_j = X_j - X_{j-1}, j \ge 1$.

3. Show that

$$\mathsf{E}|X_\tau| \le \lim_{n \to \infty} \mathsf{E}|X_n|$$

for every martingale or nonnegative submartingale $X = (X_n, \mathscr{F}_n)_{n \ge 0}$ and every stopping time τ.

4. Let $X = (X_n, \mathscr{F}_n)_{n \geq 0}$ be a submartingale such that $X_n \geq \mathsf{E}(\xi | \mathscr{F}_n)$ (P-a.s.), $n \geq 0$, where $\mathsf{E}|\xi| < \infty$. Show that if τ_1 and τ_2 are stopping times with $\mathsf{P}(\tau_1 \leq \tau_2) = 1$, then

$$X_{\tau_1} \geq \mathsf{E}(X_{\tau_2} | \mathscr{F}_{\tau_1}) \quad \text{(P-a.s.)}.$$

5. Let $\xi_1, \xi_2, \ldots$ be a sequence of independent random variables with $\mathsf{P}(\xi_i = 1) = \mathsf{P}(\xi_i = -1) = \frac{1}{2}$, a and b positive numbers, $b > a$,

$$X_n = a \sum_{k=1}^{n} I(\xi_k = +1) - b \sum_{k=1}^{n} I(\xi_k = -1)$$

and

$$\tau = \inf\{n \geq 1 : X_n \leq -r\}, \qquad r > 0.$$

Show that $\mathsf{E}e^{\lambda \tau} < \infty$ for $\lambda \leq \alpha_0$ and $\mathsf{E}e^{\lambda \tau} = \infty$ for $\lambda > \alpha_0$, where

$$\alpha_0 = \frac{b}{a+b} \ln \frac{2b}{a+b} + \frac{a}{a+b} \ln \frac{2a}{a+b}.$$

6. Let $\xi_1, \xi_2, \ldots$ be a sequence of independent random variables with $\mathsf{E}\xi_i = 0$, $\mathsf{V}\xi_i = \sigma_i^2$, $S_n = \xi_1 + \cdots + \xi_n$, $\mathscr{F}_n^{\xi} = \sigma\{\omega : \xi_1, \ldots, \xi_n\}$. Prove the following generalizations of Wald's identities (14) and (15): If $\mathsf{E} \sum_{i=1}^{\tau} \mathsf{E}|\xi_j| < \infty$ then $\mathsf{E}S_\tau = 0$; if $\mathsf{E} \sum_{j=1}^{\tau} \mathsf{E}\xi_j^2 < \infty$, then

$$\mathsf{E}S_\tau^2 = \mathsf{E} \sum_{j=1}^{\tau} \xi_j^2 = \mathsf{E} \sum_{j=1}^{\tau} \sigma_j^2. \tag{23}$$

§3. Fundamental Inequalities

1. Let $X = (X_n, \mathscr{F}_n)_{n \geq 0}$ be a stochastic sequence,

$$X_n^* = \max_{0 \leq j \leq n} |X_j|, \|X_n\|_p = (\mathsf{E}|X_n|^p)^{1/p}, \qquad p > 0,$$

Theorem 1 (Doob). *Let $X = (X_n, \mathscr{F}_n)$ be a nonnegative submartingale. Then, for every $\varepsilon > 0$ and all $n \geq 0$,*

$$\mathsf{P}\{X_n^* \geq \varepsilon\} \leq \frac{1}{\varepsilon} \int_{\{X_n^* \geq \varepsilon\}} X_n^* d\mathsf{P} \leq \frac{\mathsf{E}X_n}{\varepsilon}; \tag{1}$$

$$\|X_n\|_p \leq \|X_n^*\|_p \leq \frac{p}{p-1} \|X_n\|_p \qquad \text{if } p > 1; \tag{2}$$

$$\|X_n\|_p \leq \|X_n^*\|_p \leq \frac{e}{e-1} \{1 + \|X_n \ln^+ X_n\|_p\} \quad \text{if } p = 1. \tag{3}$$

PROOF. Put

$$\tau_n = \min\{j \leq n : X_j \geq \varepsilon\},$$

taking $\tau_n = n$ if $\max_{0 \le j \le n} X_j < \varepsilon$. Then, by (2.6),

$$\mathsf{E} X_n \ge \mathsf{E} X_{\tau_n}$$

$$= \int_{\{X_n^* \ge \varepsilon\}} X_{\tau_n} \, d\mathsf{P} + \int_{\{X_n^* < \varepsilon\}} X_{\tau_n} \, d\mathsf{P} \ge \varepsilon \int_{\{X_n^* \ge \varepsilon\}} d\mathsf{P} + \int_{\{X_n^* < \varepsilon\}} X_n \, d\mathsf{P}.$$

Therefore

$$\varepsilon \mathsf{P}\{X_n^* \ge \varepsilon\} \le \mathsf{E} X_n - \int_{\{X_n^* < \varepsilon\}} X_n \, d\mathsf{P} = \int_{\{X_n^* \ge \varepsilon\}} X_n \, d\mathsf{P} \le \mathsf{E} X_n,$$

which establishes (1).

The first inequalities in (2) and (3) are evident.

In proving the second inequality in (2), we first suppose that

$$\|X_n^*\|_p < \infty, \tag{4}$$

and use the equation

$$\mathsf{E} \xi^r = r \int_0^\infty t^{r-1} \mathsf{P}(\xi \ge t) \, dt, \tag{5}$$

which is satisfied for every nonnegative random variable ξ and for $r > 0$. Then we find from (1) and Fubini's theorem that when $p > 1$,

$$\mathsf{E}(X_n^*)^p = p \int_0^\infty t^{p-1} \mathsf{P}\{X_n^* \ge t\} \, dt \le p \int_0^\infty t^{p-2} \left(\int_{\{X_n^* \ge t\}} X_n \, d\mathsf{P} \right) dt$$

$$= p \int_0^\infty t^{p-2} \left[\int_\Omega X_n I\{X_n^* \ge t\} \right] dt = p \int_\Omega X_n \left[\int_0^{X_n^*} t^{p-2} \, dt \right] d\mathsf{P}$$

$$= \frac{p}{p-1} \mathsf{E}[X_n (X_n^*)^{p-1}]. \tag{6}$$

Hence by Hölder's inequality

$$\mathsf{E}(X_n^*)^p \le q \|X_n\|_p \cdot \|(X_n^*)^{p-1}\|_q = q \|X_n\|_p [\mathsf{E}(X_n^*)^p]^{1/q}, \tag{7}$$

where $q = p/(p-1)$.

If (4) is satisfied, the second inequality in (2) follows at once.

If (4) is not satisfied, we may proceed as follows. In (6), we consider $(X_n^* \wedge L)$ instead of X_n^*, where L is a constant. We obtain

$$\mathsf{E}(X_n^* \wedge L)^p \le q \mathsf{E}[X_n (X_n^* \wedge L)^{p-1}] \le q \|X_n\|_p [\mathsf{E}(X_n^* \wedge L)^p]^{1/q},$$

and it follows from the inequality $\mathsf{E}(X_n^* \wedge L)^p \le L^p < \infty$ that

$$\mathsf{E}(X_n^* \wedge L)^p \le q^p \mathsf{E} X_n^p = q^p \|X_n\|_p^p$$

and therefore

$$\mathsf{E}(X_n^*)^p = \lim_{L \to \infty} \mathsf{E}(X_n^* \wedge L)^p \le q^p \|X_n\|_p^p.$$

We can now prove the second inequality in (3).
Applying (1) again, we find that

$$\mathsf{E}X_n^* - 1 \leq \mathsf{E}(X_n^* - 1)^+ = \int_0^\infty \mathsf{P}\{X_n^* - 1 \geq t\}\, dt$$

$$\leq \int_0^\infty \frac{1}{1+t}\left[\int_{\{X_n^* \geq 1+t\}} X_n\, d\mathsf{P}\right] dt = \mathsf{E}X_n \int_0^{X_n^* - 1} \frac{dt}{1+t}$$

$$= \mathsf{E}X_n \ln X_n^*.$$

Since

$$a \ln b \leq a \ln^+ a + be^{-1} \qquad\qquad (8)$$

for all $a \geq 0$ and $b > 0$, we have

$$\mathsf{E}X_n^* - 1 \leq \mathsf{E}X_n \ln X_n^* \leq \mathsf{E}X_n \ln^+ X_n + e^{-1}\mathsf{E}X_n^*.$$

If $\mathsf{E}X_n^* < \infty$ we then obtain (3) immediately. If $\mathsf{E}X_n^* = \infty$, we again introduce $X_n^* \wedge L$ in place of X_n^*, and proceed as above.

This completes the proof of the theorem.

Corollary 1. *Let* $X = (X_n, \mathscr{F}_n)$ *be a square-integrable martingale. Then* $X^2 = (X_n^2, \mathscr{F}_n)$ *is a submartingale, and it follows from* (1) *that*

$$\mathsf{P}\left\{\max_{j \leq n} |X_j| \geq \varepsilon\right\} \leq \frac{\mathsf{E}X_n^2}{\varepsilon^2}. \qquad\qquad (9)$$

In particular, if $X_j = \xi_0 + \cdots + \xi_j$, *where* (ξ_i) *is a sequence of independent random variables with* $\mathsf{E}\xi_j = 0$ *and* $\mathsf{E}\xi_j^2 < \infty$, *inequality* (9) *becomes Kolmogorov's inequality* (§2, Chapter IV).

Corollary 2. *If* $X = (X_n, \mathscr{F}_n)$ *is a square-integrable martingale, we find from* (2) *that*

$$\mathsf{E}\left[\max_{j \leq n} X_j^2\right] \leq 4\mathsf{E}X_n^2. \qquad\qquad (10)$$

---

2. Let $X = (X_n, \mathscr{F}_n)$ be a nonnegative submartingale and let

$$X_n = M_n + A_n$$

be its Doob decomposition. Then since $\mathsf{E}M_n = 0$ it follows from (1) that

$$\mathsf{P}\{X_n^* \geq \varepsilon\} \leq \frac{\mathsf{E}A_n}{\varepsilon}.$$

Theorem 2 (below) will show that this inequality is valid not only for submartingales but also for the wider class of sequences that satisfy a dominance relation, in the following sense.

Definition. Let $(X_n, \mathscr{F}_n)$ be a nonnegative stochastic sequence and let $A = (A_n, \mathscr{F}_{n-1})$ be an increasing predictable sequence. We say that X is *dominated* by A if

$$\mathsf{E}X_\tau \leq \mathsf{E}A_\tau \qquad (11)$$

for every stopping time τ.

Theorem 2. *If* $X = (X_n, \mathscr{F}_n)$ *is a nonnegative stochastic sequence dominated by the increasing predictable sequence* $A = (A_n, \mathscr{F}_{n-1})$, *then we have, for every* $\varepsilon > 0, a > 0,$ *and stopping time* τ,

$$\mathsf{P}\{X_\tau^* \geq \varepsilon\} \leq \frac{\mathsf{E}A_\tau}{\varepsilon}, \qquad (12)$$

$$\mathsf{P}\{X_\tau^* \geq \varepsilon\} \leq \frac{1}{\varepsilon}\mathsf{E}(A_\tau \wedge a) + \mathsf{P}(A_\tau \geq a), \qquad (13)$$

and

$$\|X_\tau^*\|_p \leq \left(\frac{2-p}{1-p}\right)^{1/p}\|A_\tau\|_p, \qquad 0 < p < 1. \qquad (14)$$

PROOF. Put

$$\sigma_n = \min\{j \leq \tau \wedge n \colon X_j \geq \varepsilon\},$$

taking $\sigma = \tau \wedge n$ if $\{\cdot\} = \varnothing$. Then

$$\mathsf{E}A_\tau \geq \mathsf{E}A_{\sigma_n} \geq \mathsf{E}X_{\sigma_n} \geq \int_{\{X_{\tau \wedge n}^* > \varepsilon\}} X_{\sigma_n} d\mathsf{P} \geq \varepsilon \mathsf{P}\{X_{\tau \wedge n}^* > \varepsilon\},$$

whence

$$\mathsf{P}\{X_{\tau \wedge n}^* > \varepsilon\} \leq \frac{1}{\varepsilon}\mathsf{E}A_\tau,$$

Inequality (12) now follows from Fatou's lemma.

To prove (13) we introduce the time

$$\gamma = \inf\{j \colon A_{j+1} \geq a\},$$

taking $\gamma = \infty$ if $\{\cdot\} = \varnothing$. Then

$$\mathsf{P}\{X_\tau^* \geq \varepsilon\} = \mathsf{P}\{X_\tau^* \geq \varepsilon, A_\tau < a\} + \mathsf{P}\{X_\tau^* \geq \varepsilon, A_\tau \geq a\}$$

$$\leq \mathsf{P}\{I_{\{A_\tau < a\}} X_\tau^* \geq \varepsilon\} + \mathsf{P}\{A_\tau \geq a\}$$

$$\leq \mathsf{P}\{X_{\tau \wedge \gamma}^* \geq \varepsilon\} + \mathsf{P}\{A_\tau \geq a\} \leq \frac{1}{\varepsilon}\mathsf{E}A_{\tau \wedge \gamma} + \mathsf{P}\{A_\tau \geq a\}$$

$$\leq \varepsilon^{-1}\mathsf{E}(A_\tau \wedge a) + \mathsf{P}(A_\tau \geq a),$$

where we have used (12) and the inequality $I_{\{A_\tau < a\}} X_\tau^* \le X_{\tau \wedge \gamma}^*$. Finally, by (13),

$$\|X_\tau^*\|_p^p = E(X_\tau^*)^p = \int_0^\infty P\{(X_\tau^*)^p \ge t\}\, dt = \int_0^\infty P\{X_\tau^* \ge t^{1/p}\}\, dt$$

$$\le \int_0^\infty t^{-1/p} E[A_\tau \wedge t^{1/p}]\, dt + \int_0^\infty P\{A_\tau^p \ge t\}\, dt$$

$$= E \int_0^{A_\tau^p} dt + E \int_{A_\tau^p}^\infty (A_\tau t^{-1/p})\, dt + E A_\tau^p = \frac{2-p}{1-p} E A_\tau^p.$$

This completes the proof of the theorem.

Remark. Suppose that under the hypotheses of the theorem the increasing sequence $A = (A_n, \mathscr{F}_n)$ is not predictable, but for some $c > 0$

$$P\left(\sup_{k \ge 1} |\Delta A_k| \le c\right) = 1,$$

where $\Delta A_k = A_k - A_{k-1}$ for $k \ge 1$. Then (compare (13)) we have the inequality

$$P(X_\tau^* \ge \varepsilon) \le \frac{1}{\varepsilon} E(A_\tau \wedge (a + c)) + P(A_\tau \ge a).$$

(The proof is the same as for (13) with $\gamma = \inf\{j: A_{j+1} \ge a\}$ replaced by $\gamma = \inf\{j: A_j \ge a\}$, taking account of the inequality $A_\gamma \le a + c$.)

Corollary. *Let the sequences X^n and A^n satisfy, for each $n \ge 1$, the hypotheses of Theorem 2 or of the preceding Remark (with $P(\sup|\Delta A_k^n| \le c) = 1$), and for some sequence of stopping times $\{\tau_n\}$ let*

$$A_{\tau_n}^n \xrightarrow{P} 0, \qquad n \to \infty.$$

Then

$$(X^n)_{\tau_n}^* \xrightarrow{P} 0, \qquad n \to \infty.$$

3. In this subsection we present (without proofs, but with applications) a number of significant inequalities for martingales. These generalize the inequalities of Khinchin and of Marcinkiewicz and Zygmund for sums of independent random variables.

Khinchin's Inequalities. *Let $\xi_1, \xi_2, \ldots$ be independent identically distributed Bernoulli random variables with $P(\xi_i = 1) = P(\xi_i = -1) = \frac{1}{2}$ and let $(c_n)_{n \ge 1}$ be a sequence of numbers.*

Then for every p, $0 < p < \infty$, there are universal constants A_p and B_p (independent of (c_n)) such that

$$A_p \left(\sum_{j=1}^{n} c_j^2 \right)^{1/2} \leq \left\| \sum_{j=1}^{n} c_j \xi_j \right\|_p \leq B_p \left(\sum_{j=1}^{n} c_j^2 \right)^{1/2} \qquad (15)$$

for every $n \geq 1$.

The following result generalizes these inequalities (for $p \geq 1$):

Marcinkiewicz and Zygmund's Inequalities. *If ξ_1, $\xi_2, \ldots$ is a sequence of independent integrable random variables with $\mathsf{E}\xi_i = 0$, then for $p \geq 1$ there are universal constants A_p and B_p (independent of (ξ_n)) such that*

$$A_p \left\| \left(\sum_{i=1}^{n} \xi_j^2 \right)^{1/2} \right\|_p \leq \left\| \sum_{j=1}^{n} \xi_j \right\|_p \leq B_p \left\| \left(\sum_{j=1}^{n} \xi_j^2 \right)^{1/2} \right\|_p \qquad (16)$$

for every $n \geq 1$.

In (15) and (16) the sequences $X = (X_n)$ with $X_n = \sum_{j=1}^{n} c_j \xi_j$ and $X_n = \sum_{j=1}^{n} \xi_j$ are martingales. It is natural to ask whether the inequalities can be extended to arbitrary martingales.

The first result in this direction was obtained by Burkholder.

Burkholder's Inequalities. *If $X = (X_n, \mathscr{F}_n)$ is a martingale, then for every $p > 1$ there are universal constants A_p and B_p (independent of X) such that*

$$A_p \| \sqrt{[X]_n} \|_p \leq \| X_n \|_p \leq B_p \| \sqrt{[X]_n} \|_p, \qquad (17)$$

for every $n \geq 1$, where $[X]_n$ is the quadratic variation of X_n,

$$[X]_n = \sum_{j=1}^{n} (\Delta X_j)^2, \qquad X_0 = 0. \qquad (18)$$

The constants A_p and B_p can be taken to have the values

$$A_p = [18 p^{3/2}/(p-1)]^{-1}, \qquad B_p = 18 p^{3/2}/(p-1)^{1/2}.$$

It follows from (17), by using (2), that

$$A_p \| \sqrt{[X]_n} \|_p \leq \| X_n^* \|_p \leq B_p^* \| \sqrt{[X]_n} \|_p, \qquad (19)$$

where

$$A_p = [18 p^{3/2}/(p-1)]^{-1}, \qquad B_p^* = 18 p^{5/2}/(p-1)^{3/2}.$$

Burkholder's inequalities (17) hold for $p > 1$, whereas the Marcinkiewicz–Zygmund inequalities (16) also hold when $p = 1$. What can we say about the validity of (17) for $p = 1$? It turns out that a direct generalization to $p = 1$ is impossible, as the following example shows.

EXAMPLE. Let $\xi_1, \xi_2, \ldots$ be independent Bernoulli random variables with $\mathsf{P}(\xi_i = 1) = \mathsf{P}(\xi_i = -1) = \frac{1}{2}$ and let

$$X_n = \sum_{j=1}^{n \wedge \tau} \xi_j,$$

where

$$\tau = \inf\left\{ n \geq 1 : \sum_{i=1}^{n} \xi_j = 1 \right\}.$$

The sequence $X = (X_n, \mathscr{F}_n^\xi)$ is a martingale with

$$\|X_n\|_1 = \mathsf{E}\,|X_n| = 2\mathsf{E}X_n^+ \to 2, \qquad n \to \infty.$$

But

$$\|\sqrt{[X]_n}\|_1 = \mathsf{E}\sqrt{[X]_n} = \mathsf{E}\left(\sum_{j=1}^{\tau \wedge n} 1\right)^{1/2} = \mathsf{E}\sqrt{\tau \wedge n} \to \infty.$$

Consequently the first inequality in (17) fails.

It turns out that when $p = 1$ we must generalize not (17), but (19) (which is equivalent when $p > 1$).

Davis's Inequality. *If* $X = (X_n, \mathscr{F}_n)$ *is a martingale, there are universal constants* A *and* B, $0 < A < B < \infty$, *such that*

$$A\|\sqrt{[X]_n}\|_1 \leq \|X_n^*\|_1 \leq B\|\sqrt{[X]_n}\|_1, \qquad (20)$$

i.e.

$$A\mathsf{E}\sqrt{\sum_{j=1}^{n} (\Delta X_j)^2} \leq \mathsf{E}\left[\max_{1 \leq j \leq n} |X_n|\right] \leq B\mathsf{E}\sqrt{\sum_{j=1}^{n} (\Delta X_j)^2}.$$

Corollary 1. *Let* $\xi_1, \xi_2, \ldots$ *be independent identically distributed random variables;* $S_n = \xi_1 + \cdots + \xi_n$. *If* $\mathsf{E}\,|\xi_1| < \infty$ *and* $\mathsf{E}\xi_1 = 0$, *then according to Wald's inequality* (2.14) *we have*

$$\mathsf{E}S_\tau = 0 \qquad (21)$$

for every stopping time τ *(with respect to* $(\mathscr{F}_n^\xi)$) *for which* $\mathsf{E}\tau < \infty$.

It turns out that (21) is still valid under a weaker hypothesis than $\mathsf{E}\tau < \infty$ if we impose stronger conditions on the random variables. In fact, if

$$\mathsf{E}\,|\xi_1|^r < \infty,$$

where $1 < r \leq 2$, the condition $\mathsf{E}\tau^{1/r} < \infty$ is a sufficient condition for $\mathsf{E}S_\tau = 0$.

For the proof, we put $\tau_n = \tau \wedge n$, $Y = \sup_n |S_{\tau_n}|$, and let $m = [t^r]$ (integral part of t^r) for $t > 0$. By Corollary 1 to Theorem 1, §2, we have $\mathsf{E}S_{\tau_n} = 0$. Therefore a sufficient condition for $\mathsf{E}S_\tau = 0$ is (by the dominated convergence theorem) that $\mathsf{E}\sup_n |S_{\tau_n}| < \infty$.

Using (1) and (17), we obtain

$$P(Y \geq t) = P(\tau \geq t', Y \geq t) + P(\tau < t', Y \geq t)$$

$$\leq P(\tau \geq t') + P\left\{ \max_{1 \leq j \leq m} |S_{\tau_j}| \geq t \right\}$$

$$\leq P(\tau \geq t') + t^{-r}E|S_{\tau_m}|^r$$

$$\leq P(\tau \geq t') + t^{-r}B_r E\left(\sum_{j=1}^{\tau_m} \xi_j^2 \right)^{r/2}$$

$$\leq P(\tau \geq t') + t^{-r}B_r E \sum_{j=1}^{\tau_m} |\xi_j|^r.$$

Notice that (with $\mathscr{F}_0^\xi = \{\varnothing, \Omega\}$)

$$E \sum_{j=1}^{\tau_m} |\xi_j|^r = E \sum_{j=1}^{\infty} I(j \leq \tau_m)|\xi_j|^r$$

$$= \sum_{j=1}^{\infty} EE[I(j \leq \tau_m)|\xi_j|^r | \mathscr{F}_{j-1}^\xi]$$

$$= E \sum_{j=1}^{\infty} I(j \leq \tau_m)E[|\xi|^r | \mathscr{F}_{j-1}^\xi] = E \sum_{j=1}^{\tau_m} E|\xi_j|^r = \mu_r E\tau_m,$$

where $\mu_r = E|\xi_1|^r$. Consequently

$$P(Y \geq t) \leq P(\tau \geq t') + t^{-r}B_r \mu_r E\tau_m$$

$$= P(\tau \geq t') + B_r \mu_r t^{-r}\left[mP(\tau \geq t') + \int_{\{\tau < t'\}} \tau \, dP \right]$$

$$\leq (1 + B_r\mu_r)P(\tau \geq t') + B_r \mu_r t^{-r} \int_{\{\tau < t'\}} \tau \, dP$$

and therefore

$$EY \int_0^\infty P(Y \geq t) \, dt \leq (1 + B_r\mu_r)E\tau^{1/r} + B_r \mu_r \int_0^\infty t^{-r}\left[\int_{\{\tau < t'\}} \tau \, dP \right] dt$$

$$= (1 + B_r\mu_r)E\tau^{1/r} + B_r \mu_r \int_\Omega \tau \left[\int_{\tau^{1/r}}^\infty t^{-r} \, dt \right] dP$$

$$= \left(1 + B_r\mu_r + \frac{B_r\mu_r}{r-1} \right) E\tau^{1/r} < \infty.$$

Corollary 2. *Let $M = (M_n)$ be a martingale with $E|M_n|^{2r} < \infty$ for some $r \geq 1$ and such that (with $M_0 = 0$)*

$$\sum_{n=1}^{\infty} \frac{E|\Delta M_n|^{2r}}{n^{1+r}} < \infty. \tag{22}$$

Then (compare Theorem 2 of §3, Chapter IV) *we have the strong law of large numbers:*

$$\frac{M_n}{n} \to 0 \quad (\text{P-}a.s.), \qquad n \to \infty. \tag{23}$$

When $r = 1$ the proof follows the same lines as the proof of Theorem 2, §3, Chapter IV. In fact, let

$$m_n = \sum_{k=1}^{n} \frac{\Delta M_k}{k}.$$

Then

$$\frac{M_n}{n} = \frac{\sum_{k=1}^{n} \Delta M_k}{n} = \frac{1}{n} \sum_{k=1}^{n} k \Delta m_k$$

and, by Kronecker's lemma (§3, Chapter IV) a sufficient condition for the limit relation (P-a.s.)

$$\frac{1}{n} \sum_{k=1}^{n} k \Delta m_k \to 0, \qquad n \to \infty,$$

is that the limit $\lim_n m_n$ exists and is finite (P-a.s.) which in turn (Theorems 1 and 4, §10, Chapter II) is true if and only if

$$\mathsf{P}\left\{ \sup_{k \geq 1} |m_{n+k} - m_n| \geq \varepsilon \right\} \to 0, \qquad n \to \infty. \tag{24}$$

By (1),

$$\mathsf{P}\left\{ \sup_{k \geq 1} |m_{n+k} - m_n| \geq \varepsilon \right\} \leq \varepsilon^{-2} \sum_{k=n}^{\infty} \frac{\mathsf{E}(\Delta M_k)^2}{k^2}.$$

Hence the required result follows from (22) and (24).

Now let $r > 1$. Then the statement (23) is equivalent (Theorem 1, §10, Chapter II) to the statement that

$$\varepsilon^{2r} \mathsf{P}\left\{ \sup_{j \geq n} \frac{|M_j|}{j} \geq \varepsilon \right\} \to 0, \qquad n \to \infty \tag{25}$$

for every $\varepsilon > 0$. By inequality (29) of Problem 1,

$$\varepsilon^{2r} \mathsf{P}\left\{ \sup_{j \geq n} \frac{|M_j|}{j} \geq \varepsilon \right\} = \varepsilon^{2r} \lim_{m \to \infty} \mathsf{P}\left\{ \max_{n \leq j \leq m} \frac{|M_j|^{2r}}{j^{2r}} \geq \varepsilon^{2r} \right\}$$

$$\leq \frac{1}{n^{2r}} \mathsf{E}|M_n|^{2r} + \sum_{j \geq n+1} \frac{1}{j^{2r}} \mathsf{E}(|M_j|^{2r} - |M_{j-1}|^{2r}).$$

It follows from Kronecker's lemma and (22) that

$$\lim_{n \to \infty} \frac{1}{n^{2r}} \mathsf{E}|M_n|^{2r} = 0.$$

Hence to prove (25) we need only prove that

$$\sum_{j\geq 2}\frac{1}{j^{2r}}\mathsf{E}(|M_j|^{2r}-|M_{j-1}|^{2r})<\infty. \tag{26}$$

We have

$$I_N = \sum_{j=2}^{N}\frac{1}{j^{2r}}[\mathsf{E}|M_j|^{2r}-\mathsf{E}|M_{j-1}|^{2r}]$$

$$\leq \sum_{j=3}^{N}\left[\frac{1}{(j-1)^{2r}}-\frac{1}{j^{2r}}\right]\mathsf{E}|M_{j-1}|^{2r}+\frac{\mathsf{E}|M_N|^{2r}}{N^{2r}}.$$

By Burkholder's inequality (17) and Hölder's inequality,

$$\mathsf{E}|M_j|^{2r}\leq \mathsf{E}\left[\sum_{i=1}^{j}(\Delta M_i)^2\right]^r\leq \mathsf{E}j^{r-1}\sum_{i=1}^{j}|\Delta M_i|^{2r}.$$

Hence

$$I_N \leq \sum_{j=2}^{N-1}\left[\frac{1}{j^{2r}}-\frac{1}{(j+1)^{2r}}\right]j^{r-1}\sum_{i=1}^{j}\mathsf{E}|\Delta M_i|^{2r}$$

$$\leq C_1\sum_{j=2}^{N-1}\frac{1}{j^{r+2}}\sum_{i=1}^{j}\mathsf{E}|\Delta M_i|^{2r}\leq C_2\sum_{j=2}^{N}\frac{\mathsf{E}|\Delta M_i|^{2r}}{j^{r+1}}+C_3$$

(C_i are constants). By (22), this establishes (26).

The sequence of random variables $\{X_n\}_{n\geq 1}$ has a limit $\lim X_n$ (finite or infinite) with probability 1, if and only if the number of "oscillations between two arbitrary rational numbers a and b, $a < b$" is finite with probability 1. Theorem 3, below, provides an upper bound for the number of "oscillations" for submartingales. In the next section, this will be applied to prove the fundamental result on their convergence.

Let us choose two numbers a and b, $a < b$, and define the following *times* in terms of the stochastic sequence $X = (X_n, \mathscr{F}_n)$:

$$\tau_0 = 0,$$
$$\tau_1 = \min\{n > 0: X_n \leq a\},$$
$$\tau_2 = \min\{n > \tau_1: X_n \geq b\},$$
$$\dots$$
$$\tau_{2m-1} = \min\{n > \tau_{2m-2}: X_n \leq a\},$$
$$\tau_{2m} = \min\{n > \tau_{2m-1}: X_n \geq b\},$$

taking $\tau_k = \infty$ if the corresponding set $\{\cdot\}$ is empty.

In addition, for each $n \geq 1$ we define the random variables

$$\beta_n(a,b) = \begin{cases} 0, & \text{if } \tau_2 > n, \\ \max\{m: \tau_{2m}\leq n\} & \text{if } \tau_2 \leq n. \end{cases}$$

In words, $\beta_n(a, b)$ is the *number of upcrossings* of $[a, b]$ by the sequence $X_1, \ldots, X_n$.

Theorem 3 (Doob). *Let* $X = (X_n, \mathscr{F}_n)_{n \geq 1}$ *be a submartingale. Then, for every* $n \geq 1$,

$$\mathsf{E}\beta_n(a, b) \leq \frac{\mathsf{E}[X_n - a]^+}{b - a}. \tag{27}$$

PROOF. The number of intersections of $X = (X_n, \mathscr{F}_n)$ with $[a, b]$ is equal to the number of intersections of the nonnegative submartingale $X^+ = ((X_n - a)^+, \mathscr{F}_n)$ with $[0, b - a]$. Hence it is sufficient to suppose that X is nonnegative with $a = 0$, and show that

$$\mathsf{E}\beta_n(0, b) \leq \frac{\mathsf{E}X_n}{b}. \tag{28}$$

Put $X_0 = 0$, $\mathscr{F}_0 = \{\varnothing, \Omega\}$, and for $i = 1, 2, \ldots$, let

$$\varphi_i = \begin{cases} 1 & \text{if } \tau_m < i \leq \tau_{m+1} \text{ for some odd } m, \\ 0 & \text{if } \tau_m < i \leq \tau_{m+1} \text{ for some even } m. \end{cases}$$

It is easily seen that

$$b\beta_n(0, b) \leq \sum_{i=1}^{n} \varphi_i[X_i - X_{i-1}]$$

and

$$\{\varphi_i = 1\} = \bigcup_{\text{odd } m} [\{\tau_m < i\} \setminus \{\tau_{m+1} < i\}] \in \mathscr{F}_{i-1}.$$

Therefore

$$b\mathsf{E}\beta_n(0, b) \leq \mathsf{E} \sum_{i=1}^{n} \varphi_i[X_i - X_{i-1}] = \sum_{i=1}^{n} \int_{\{\varphi_i = 1\}} (X_i - X_{i-1}) \, d\mathsf{P}$$

$$= \sum_{i=1}^{n} \int_{\{\varphi_i = 1\}} \mathsf{E}(X_i - X_{i-1} | \mathscr{F}_{i-1}) \, d\mathsf{P}$$

$$= \sum_{i=1}^{n} \int_{\{\varphi_i = 1\}} [\mathsf{E}(X_i | \mathscr{F}_{i-1}) - X_{i-1}] \, d\mathsf{P}$$

$$\leq \sum_{i=1}^{n} \int_{\Omega} [\mathsf{E}(X_i | \mathscr{F}_{i-1}) - X_{i-1}] \, d\mathsf{P} = \mathsf{E}X_n,$$

which establishes (28).

4. PROBLEMS

1. Let $X = (X_n, \mathscr{F}_n)$ be a nonnegative submartingale and let $V = (V_n, \mathscr{F}_{n-1})$ be a predictable sequence such that $0 \leq V_{n+1} \leq V_n \leq C$ (P-a.s.), where C is a constant. Establish the following generalization of (1):

$$\varepsilon \mathsf{P}\left\{ \max_{i \leq j \leq n} V_j X_j \geq \varepsilon \right\} + \int_{\{\max_{1 \leq j \leq n} V_j X_j < \varepsilon\}} V_n X_n \, d\mathsf{P} \leq \sum_{j=1}^{n} \mathsf{E} V_j \Delta X_j. \tag{29}$$

2. Let $X = (X_n, \mathscr{F}_n)$ be a supermartingale. Show that

$$\mathsf{P}\left\{\max_{1 \le j \le n} |X_j| \ge \varepsilon\right\} \le \frac{C}{\varepsilon} \cdot \max_{1 \le j \le n} \mathsf{E}|X_j|,$$

where $C \le 3$ (the constant C can be taken to be 1 if X is a martingale or if X does not change sign).

3. Establish *Krickeberg's decomposition*: every martingale $X = (X_n, \mathscr{F}_n)$ with $\sup \mathsf{E}|X_n| < \infty$ can be represented as the difference of two nonnegative martingales.

4. Let $X = (X_n, \mathscr{F}_n)$ be a submartingale. Show that, for every $\varepsilon > 0$ and $n \ge 1$,

$$\varepsilon \mathsf{P}\left\{\min_{1 \le j \le n} X_j \le -\varepsilon\right\} \le \mathsf{E}(X_n - X_1) - \int_{\{\min_{1 \le j \le n} X_j \le -\varepsilon\}} X_n \, d\mathsf{P}$$

$$\le \mathsf{E} X_n^+ - \mathsf{E} X_1.$$

5. Let $\xi_1, \xi_2, \ldots$ be a sequence of independent random variables, $S_n = \xi_1 + \cdots + \xi_n$ and $S_{m,n} = \sum_{j=m+1}^{n} \xi_j$. Establish *Ottaviani's inequality*:

$$\mathsf{P}\left\{\max_{1 \le j \le n} |S_j| > 2\varepsilon\right\} \le \frac{\mathsf{P}\{|S_n| > \varepsilon\}}{\min_{1 \le j \le n} \mathsf{P}\{|S_{j,n}| \le \varepsilon\}}$$

and deduce that

$$\int_0^\infty \mathsf{P}\left\{\max_{1 \le j \le n} |S_j| > 2t\right\} dt \le 2\mathsf{E}|S_n| + 2\int_{2\mathsf{E}|S_n|}^\infty \mathsf{P}\{|S_n| > t\} \, dt. \tag{30}$$

6. Let $\xi_1, \xi_2, \ldots$ be a sequence of independent random variables with $\mathsf{E}\xi_i = 0$. Use (30) to show that in this case we can strengthen inequality (3) to

$$\mathsf{E} S_n^* \le 8\mathsf{E}|S_n|.$$

7. Verify formula (5).

8. Establish inequality (8).

9. Let the σ-algebra $\mathscr{F}_0, \ldots, \mathscr{F}_n$ be such that $\mathscr{F}_0 \subseteq \mathscr{F}_1 \subseteq \cdots \subseteq \mathscr{F}_n$ and let the events $A_k \in \mathscr{F}_k, k = 1, \ldots, n$. Use (13) to establish *Dvoretzky's inequality*: for each $\varepsilon > 0$,

$$\mathsf{P}\left[\bigcup_{k=1}^{n} A_k \middle| \mathscr{F}_0\right] \le \varepsilon + \mathsf{P}\left[\sum_{k=1}^{n} \mathsf{P}(A_k | \mathscr{F}_{k-1}) > \varepsilon \middle| \mathscr{F}_0\right] \quad \text{(P-a.s.)}.$$

10. Let $(X_n)_{n \ge 1}$ be a sequence of random variables with zero means, finite second moments, and orthogonal differences, $\mathsf{E}\Delta X_m \Delta X_n = 0$, $m \ne n$, where $\Delta X_k = X_k - X_{k-1}, k > 1$; $\Delta X_1 = X_2$ (compare Problem 8, §1). Prove (compare Doob's inequality (10)) the *Rademacher–Menshov inequality*

$$\mathsf{E}\left[\max_{j \le n} X_j^2\right] \le \left(\frac{\ln 4n}{\ln 2}\right)^2 \mathsf{E} X_n^2.$$

§4. General Theorems on the Convergence of Submartingales and Martingales

1. The following result, which is fundamental for all problems about the convergence of submartingales, can be thought of as an analog of the fact that in real analysis a bounded monotonic sequence of numbers has a (finite) limit.

Theorem 1 (Doob). *Let $X = (X_n, \mathscr{F}_n)$ be a submartingale with*

$$\sup_n \mathsf{E}\,|X_n| < \infty. \tag{1}$$

Then with probability 1, the limit $\lim X_n = X_\infty$ *exists and* $\mathsf{E}\,|X_\infty| < \infty$.

PROOF. Suppose that

$$\mathsf{P}(\overline{\lim}\, X_n > \underline{\lim}\, X_n) > 0. \tag{2}$$

Then since

$$\{\overline{\lim}\, X_n > \underline{\lim}\, X_n\} = \bigcup_{a < b} \{\overline{\lim}\, X_n > b > a > \underline{\lim}\, X_n\}$$

(here a and b are rational numbers), there are values a and b such that

$$\mathsf{P}\{\overline{\lim}\, X_n > b > a > \underline{\lim}\, X_n\} > 0. \tag{3}$$

Let $\beta_n(a, b)$ be the number of upcrossings of (a, b) by the sequence $X_1, \ldots, X_n$, and let $\beta_\infty(a, b) = \lim_n \beta_n(a, b)$. By (3.27),

$$\mathsf{E}\beta_n(a, b) \leq \frac{\mathsf{E}[X_n - a]^+}{b - a} \leq \frac{\mathsf{E}X_n^+ + |a|}{b - a}$$

and therefore

$$\mathsf{E}\beta_\infty(a, b) = \lim_n \mathsf{E}\beta_n(a, b) \leq \frac{\sup_n \mathsf{E}X_n^+ + |a|}{b - a} < \infty,$$

which follows from (1) and the remark that

$$\sup_n \mathsf{E}\,|X_n| < \infty \Leftrightarrow \sup_n \mathsf{E}X_n^+ < \infty$$

for submartingales (since $\mathsf{E}X_n^+ \leq \mathsf{E}\,|X_n| = 2\mathsf{E}X_n^+ - \mathsf{E}X_n \leq 2\mathsf{E}X_n^+ - \mathsf{E}X_1$). But the condition $\mathsf{E}\beta_\infty(a, b) < \infty$ contradicts assumption (3). Hence $\lim X_n = X_\infty$ exists with probability 1, and then by Fatou's lemma

$$\mathsf{E}\,|X_\infty| \leq \sup_n \mathsf{E}\,|X_n| < \infty.$$

This completes the proof of the theorem.

Corollary 1. *If X is a nonpositive submartingale, then with probability 1 the limit* $\lim X_n$ *exists and is finite.*

Corollary 2. *If* $X = (X_n, \mathscr{F}_n)_{n \geq 1}$ *is a nonpositive submartingale, the sequence* $\overline{X} = (X_n, \mathscr{F}_n)$ *with* $1 \leq n \leq \infty$, $X_\infty = \lim X_n$ *and* $\mathscr{F}_\infty = \sigma\{\bigcup \mathscr{F}_n\}$ *is a (nonpositive) submartingale.*

In fact, by Fatou's lemma

$$\mathsf{E} X_\infty = \mathsf{E} \lim X_n \geq \overline{\lim} \, \mathsf{E} X_n \geq \mathsf{E} X_1 > -\infty$$

and (P-a.s.)

$$\mathsf{E}(X_\infty | \mathscr{F}_m) = \mathsf{E}(\lim X_n | \mathscr{F}_m) \geq \overline{\lim} \, \mathsf{E}(X_n | \mathscr{F}_m) \geq X_m.$$

Corollary 3. *If* $X = (X_n, \mathscr{F}_n)$ *is a nonnegative martingale, then* $\lim X_n$ *exists with probability* 1.

In fact, in that case

$$\sup \mathsf{E} |X_n| = \sup \mathsf{E} X_n = \mathsf{E} X_1 < \infty,$$

and Theorem 1 is applicable.

2. Let $\xi_1, \xi_2, \ldots$ be a sequence of independent random variables with $\mathsf{P}(\xi_i = 0) = \mathsf{P}(\xi_i = 2) = \frac{1}{2}$. Then $X = (X_n, \mathscr{F}_n^\xi)$, with $X_n = \prod_{i=1}^n \xi_i$ and $\mathscr{F}_n^\xi = \sigma\{\omega: \xi_1, \ldots, \xi_n\}$ is a martingale with $\mathsf{E} X_n = 1$ and $X_n \to X_\infty \equiv 0$ (P-a.s.). At the same time, it is clear that $\mathsf{E} |X_n - X_\infty| = 1$ and therefore $X_n \overset{L^1}{\nrightarrow} X_\infty$. Therefore condition (1) does not in general guarantee the convergence of X_n to X_∞ in the L^1 sense.

Theorem 2 below shows that if hypothesis (1) is strengthened to uniform integrability of the family $\{X_n\}$ (from which (1) follows by Subsection 4, §6, Chapter II), then besides almost sure convergence we also have convergence in L^1.

Theorem 2. *Let* $X = \{X_n, \mathscr{F}_n\}$ *be a uniformly integrable submartingale (that is, the family* $\{X_n\}$ *is uniformly integrable). Then there is a random variable* X_∞ *with* $\mathsf{E} |X_\infty| < \infty$, *such that as* $n \to \infty$

$$X_n \to X_\infty \quad \text{(P-a.s.)}, \tag{4}$$

$$X_n \overset{L^1}{\to} X_\infty. \tag{5}$$

Moreover, the sequence $\overline{X} = (X_n, \mathscr{F}_n)$, $1 \leq n \leq \infty$, *with* $\mathscr{F}_\infty = \sigma(\bigcup \mathscr{F}_n)$, *is also a submartingale.*

PROOF. Statement (4) follows from Theorem 1, and (5) follows from (4) and Theorem 4, §6, Chapter II.

Moreover, if $A \in \mathscr{F}_n$ and $m \geq n$, then

$$\mathsf{E} I_A |X_m - X_\infty| \to 0, \qquad m \to \infty,$$

and therefore

$$\lim_{m \to \infty} \int_A X_m \, d\mathsf{P} = \int_A X_\infty \, d\mathsf{P}.$$

The sequence $\{\int_A X_m \, d\mathsf{P}\}_{m \geq n}$ is nondecreasing and therefore

$$\int_A X_n \, d\mathsf{P} \leq \int_A X_m \, d\mathsf{P} \leq \int_A X_\infty \, d\mathsf{P},$$

whence $X_n \leq \mathsf{E}(X_\infty | \mathscr{F}_n)$ (P-a.s.) for $n \geq 1$.

This completes the proof of the theorem.

Corollary. *If $X = (X_n, \mathscr{F}_n)$ is a submartingale and, for some $p > 1$,*

$$\sup_n \mathsf{E} |X_n|^p < \infty, \tag{6}$$

then there is an integrable random variable X_∞ for which (4) and (5) are satisfied.

For the proof, it is enough to observe that, by Lemma 3 of §6 of Chapter II, condition (6) guarantees the uniform integrability of the family $\{X_n\}$.

3. We now present a theorem on the continuity properties of conditional expectations; this was one of the very first results about the convergence of martingales.

Theorem 3 (P. Lévy). *Let $(\Omega, \mathscr{F}, \mathsf{P})$ be a probability space, and let $(\mathscr{F}_n)_{n \geq 1}$ be a nondecreasing family of σ-algebras, $\mathscr{F}_1 \subseteq \mathscr{F}_2 \subseteq \cdots \subseteq \mathscr{F}$. Let ξ be a random variable with $\mathsf{E}|\xi| < \infty$ and $\mathscr{F}_\infty = \sigma(\bigcup_n \mathscr{F}_n)$. Then, both P-a.s. and in the L^1 sense,*

$$\mathsf{E}(\xi | F_n) \to \mathsf{E}(\xi | F_\infty), \qquad n \to \infty. \tag{7}$$

PROOF. Let $X_n = \mathsf{E}(\xi | \mathscr{F}_n)$, $n \geq 1$. Then, with $a > 0$ and $b > 0$,

$$\int_{\{|X_i| \geq a\}} |X_i| \, d\mathsf{P} \leq \int_{\{|X_i| \geq a\}} \mathsf{E}(|\xi| \,|\, F_i) \, d\mathsf{P} = \int_{\{|X_i| \geq a\}} |\xi| \, d\mathsf{P}$$

$$\leq \int_{\{|X_i| \geq a\} \cap \{|\xi| \leq b\}} |\xi| \, d\mathsf{P} + \int_{\{|X_i| \geq a\} \cap \{|\xi| > b\}} |\xi| \, d\mathsf{P}$$

$$\leq b\mathsf{P}\{|X_i| \geq a\} + \int_{\{|\xi| > b\}} |\xi| \, d\mathsf{P}$$

$$\leq \frac{b}{a} \mathsf{E} |X_i| + \int_{\{|\xi| > b\}} |\xi| \, d\mathsf{P}$$

$$\leq \frac{b}{a} \mathsf{E} |\xi| + \int_{\{|\xi| > b\}} |\xi| \, d\mathsf{P}.$$

Letting $a \to \infty$ and then $b \to \infty$, we obtain

$$\lim_{a \to \infty} \sup_i \int_{\{|X_i| \geq a\}} |X_i| \, d\mathsf{P} = 0,$$

i.e. the family $\{X_n\}$ is uniformly integrable.

Therefore, by Theorem 2, there is a random variable X_∞ such that $X_n = \mathsf{E}(\xi|F_n) \to X_\infty$ ((P-a.s.) and in the L^1 sense). Hence we have only to show that

$$X_\infty = \mathsf{E}(\xi|\mathscr{F}_\infty) \quad \text{(P-a.s.)}.$$

Let $m \geq n$ and $A \in \mathscr{F}_n$. Then

$$\int_A X_m \, d\mathsf{P} = \int_A X_n \, d\mathsf{P} = \int_A \mathsf{E}(\xi|F_n) \, d\mathsf{P} = \int_A \xi \, d\mathsf{P}.$$

Since the family $\{X_n\}$ is uniformly integrable and since, by Theorem 5, §6, Chapter II, we have $\mathsf{E}I_A|X_m - X_\infty| \to 0$ as $m \to \infty$, it follows that

$$\int_A X_\infty \, d\mathsf{P} = \int_A \xi \, d\mathsf{P}. \qquad (8)$$

This equation is satisfied for all $A \in \mathscr{F}_n$ and therefore for all $A \in \bigcup_{n=1}^\infty \mathscr{F}_n$. Since $\mathsf{E}|X_\infty| < \infty$ and $\mathsf{E}|\xi| < \infty$, the left-hand and right-hand sides of (8) are σ-additive measures; possibly taking negative as well as positive values, but finite and agreeing on the algebra $\bigcup_{n=1}^\infty \mathscr{F}_n$. Because of the uniqueness of the extension of a σ-additive measure to an algebra over the smallest σ-algebra containing it (Carathéodory's theorem, §3, Chapter II, equation (8) remains valid for sets $A \in F_\infty = \sigma(\bigcup F_n)$. Thus,

$$\int_A X_\infty \, d\mathsf{P} = \int_A \xi \, d\mathsf{P} = \int_A \mathsf{E}(\xi|\mathscr{F}_\infty) \, d\mathsf{P}, \qquad A \in \mathscr{F}_\infty. \qquad (9)$$

Since X_∞ and $\mathsf{E}(\xi|\mathscr{F}_\infty)$ are $\mathscr{F}_\infty$-measurable, it follows from Property I of Subsection 2, §6, Chapter II, and from (9), that $X_\infty = \mathsf{E}(\xi|\mathscr{F}_\infty)$ (P-a.s.). This completes the proof of the theorem.

Corollary. *A stochastic sequence* $X = (X_n, \mathscr{F}_n)$ *is a uniformly integrable martingale if and only if there is a random variable ξ with* $\mathsf{E}|\xi| < \infty$ *such that* $X_n = \mathsf{E}(\xi|F_n)$ *for all $n \geq 1$. Here $X_n \to \mathsf{E}(\xi|F_\infty)$ (both P-a.s. and in the L^1 sense) as $n \to \infty$.*

In fact, if $X = (X_n, \mathscr{F}_n)$ is a uniformly integrable martingale, then by Theorem 2 there is an integrable random variable X_∞ such that $X_n \to X_\infty$ (P-a.s. and in the L^1 sense) and $X_n = \mathsf{E}(X_\infty|F_n)$. As the random variable ξ we may take the $\mathscr{F}_\infty$-measurable variable X_∞.

The converse follows from Theorem 3.

4. We now turn to some applications of these theorems.

EXAMPLE 1. *The "zero or one" law.* Let $\xi_1, \xi_2, \ldots$ be a sequence of independent random variables, $\mathscr{F}_n^\xi = \sigma\{\omega: \xi_1, \ldots, \xi_n\}$ and let $\mathbf{X}$ be the σ-algebra of the "tail" events. By Theorem 3, we have $\mathsf{E}(I_A|F_n^\xi) \to \mathsf{E}(I_A|F_\infty^\xi) = I_A$ (P-a.s.). But I_A and $(\xi_1, \ldots, \xi_n)$ are independent. Since $\mathsf{E}(I_A|F_n^\xi) = \mathsf{E}I_A$ and therefore $I_A = \mathsf{E}I_A$ (P-a.s.), we find that either $\mathsf{P}(A) = 0$ or $\mathsf{P}(A) = 1$.

EXAMPLE 2. Let $\xi_1, \xi_2, \ldots$ be a sequence of random variables. According to Theorem 2 of §10, Chapter II, the convergence of the series $\sum \xi_n$ implies its convergence in probability and in distribution. It turns out that if we also assume that $\xi_1, \xi_2, \ldots$ are *independent*, there is also a converse: *the convergence of $\sum \xi_n$ in distribution implies its convergence in probability and with probability 1.*

Thus for a series $\sum \xi_n$ whose terms are independent random variables, all three kinds of convergence (with probability 1, in probability, or in distribution) turn out to be equivalent (compare Problem 3 of §2, Chapter IV).

For the proof we must evidently show that if $S_n = \xi_1 + \cdots + \xi_n, n \geq 1$, then the convergence of S_n in distribution, as $n \to \infty$, implies its convergence with probability 1. A simple and elegant proof of this can be based on Theorem 1.

In fact, let $S_n \xrightarrow{d} S$. Then, for every real t, we have $\mathsf{E}e^{itS_n} \to \mathsf{E}e^{itS}$. There is clearly a $\delta > 0$ such that $|\mathsf{E}e^{itS}| > 0$ for all $|t| < \delta$. Take $|t_0| < \delta$; then there is also an $n_0 = n_0(t_0)$ such that $|\mathsf{E}e^{it_0 S_n}| \geq c > 0$ for all $n > n_0$, where c is a constant. For $n \geq n_0$, form the sequence $X = (X_n, \mathscr{F}_n)$ with

$$X_n = \frac{e^{it_0 S_n}}{\mathsf{E}e^{it_0 S_n}}, \qquad \mathscr{F}_n = \sigma\{\omega : \xi_1, \ldots \xi_n\}.$$

Since the variables $\xi_1, \xi_2, \ldots$ are assumed independent, the stochastic sequence $X = (X_n, \mathscr{F}_n)$ is a martingale and

$$\sup_{n \geq n_0} \mathsf{E}|X_n| \leq c^{-1} < \infty.$$

Hence it follows from Theorem 1 that, with probability 1, the limit $\lim_n X_n$ exists and is finite, and therefore the limit $\lim e^{it_0 S_n}$ exists with probability 1. Consequently we may say that there is a $\delta > 0$ such that for every t in the set $T = \{t : |t| < \delta\}$ the limit $\lim_n e^{itS_n}$ exists P-a.s.

Write $T \times \Omega = \{(t, \omega) : t \in T, \omega \in \Omega\}$, let $\overline{\mathscr{B}}(T)$ be the σ-algebra of Lebesgue sets on T, let λ denote Lebesgue measure on $(T, \overline{\mathscr{B}}(T))$, and let

$$C = \{(t, \omega) \in T \times \Omega : \lim e^{itS_n(\omega)} \text{ exists}\}.$$

It is clear that $C \in \overline{\mathscr{B}}(T) \otimes \mathscr{F}$.

According to what was established above, we have $\mathsf{P}(C_t) = 1$ for each $t \in T$, where $C_t = \{\omega \in \Omega : (t, \omega) \in C\}$ is the cross-section of C at t. Then, by Fubini's theorem (Theorem 8, §6, Chapter II)

$$\int_{T \times \Omega} I_c(t, \omega)\, d(\lambda \times \mathsf{P}) = \int_T \left(\int_\Omega I_c(t, \omega)\, d\mathsf{P} \right) d\lambda$$

$$= \int_T \mathsf{P}(C_t)\, d\lambda = \lambda(T) = 2\delta > 0.$$

On the other hand, again by Fubini's theorem,

$$\lambda(T) = \int_{T\times\Omega} I_c(t,\omega)\,d(\lambda\times\mathsf{P}) = \int_\Omega d\mathsf{P}\left(\int_T I_c(t,\omega)\,d\lambda\right) = \int_\Omega \lambda(C_\omega)\,d\mathsf{P},$$

where $C_\omega = \{t:(t,\omega)\in C\}$.

Hence it follows that there is a set $\tilde\Omega$ with $\mathsf{P}(\tilde\Omega)=1$ such that

$$\lambda(C_\omega) = \lambda(T) = 2\delta > 0$$

for all $\omega\in\tilde\Omega$.

Hence we can say that, for each $\omega\in\tilde\Omega$, the limit $\lim_n e^{itS_n(\omega)}$ exists for all $t\in C_\omega$; moreover, the Lebesgue measure of C_ω is positive. From this and Problem 8 it follows that $\lim_n S_n(\omega)$ exists and is finite for $\omega\in\tilde\Omega$; since $\mathsf{P}(\tilde\Omega)=1$, this also holds P-a.s.

The next two examples illustrate possible applications of the preceding results to convergence theorems in analysis.

EXAMPLE 3. If $f = f(x)$ satisfies a Lipschitz condition on $[0,1)$, it is absolutely continuous and, as is shown in courses in analysis, there is a (Lebesgue) integrable function $g = g(x)$ such that

$$f(x) - f(0) = \int_0^x g(y)\,dy. \tag{10}$$

(In this sense, $g(x)$ is a "derivative" of $f(x)$.)

Let us show how this result can be deduced from Theorem 1.

Let $\Omega = [0,1)$, $\mathscr{F} = \mathscr{B}([0,1))$, and let P denote Lebesgue measure. Put

$$\xi_n(x) = \sum_{k=1}^{2^n} \frac{k-1}{2^n} I\left\{\frac{k-1}{2^n} \le x < \frac{k}{2^n}\right\},$$

$\mathscr{F}_n = \sigma\{x:\xi_1,\dots,\xi_n\} = \sigma\{x:\xi_n\}$, and

$$X_n = \frac{f(\xi_n + 2^{-n}) - f(\xi_n)}{2^{-n}}.$$

Since for a given ξ_n the random variable ξ_{n+1} takes only the values ξ_n and $\xi_n + 2^{-(n+1)}$ with conditional probabilities equal to $\frac12$, we have

$$\mathsf{E}[X_{n+1}|\mathscr{F}_n] = \mathsf{E}[X_{n+1}|\xi_n] = 2^{n+1}\mathsf{E}[f(\xi_{n+1} + 2^{-(n+1)}) - f(\xi_{n+1})|\xi_n]$$

$$= 2^{n+1}\{\tfrac12[f(\xi_n + 2^{-(n+1)}) - f(\xi_n)] + \tfrac12[f(\xi_n + 2^{-n}) - f(\xi_n + 2^{-n+1})]\}$$

$$= 2^n\{f(\xi_n + 2^{-n}) - f(\xi_n)\} = X_n.$$

It follows that $X = (X_n, \mathscr{F}_n)$ is a martingale, and it is uniformly integrable since $|X_n| \le L$, where L is the Lipschitz constant: $|f(x) - f(y)| \le L|x-y|$. Observe that $\mathscr{F} = \mathscr{B}([0,1)) = \sigma(\bigcup \mathscr{F}_n)$. Therefore, by the corollary to

Theorem 3, there is an $\mathscr{F}$-measurable function $g = g(x)$ such that $X_n \to g$ (P-a.s.) and

$$X_n = \mathsf{E}[g \mid \mathscr{F}_n].\tag{11}$$

Consider the set $B = [0, k/2^n]$. Then by (11)

$$f\left(\frac{k}{2^n}\right) - f(0) = \int_0^{k/2^n} X_n dx = \int_0^{k/2^n} g(x)\,dx,$$

and since n and k are arbitrary, we obtain the required equation (10).

EXAMPLE 4. Let $\Omega = [0, 1)$, $\mathscr{F} = \mathscr{B}([0, 1))$ and let P denote Lebesgue measure. Consider the Haar system $\{H_n(x)\}_{n \geq 1}$, as defined in Example 3 of §11, Chapter II. Put $\mathscr{F}_n = \sigma\{x : H_1, \dots, H_n\}$ and observe that $\sigma(\bigcup \mathscr{F}_n) = \mathscr{F}$. From the properties of conditional expectations and the structure of the Haar functions, it is easy to deduce that

$$\mathsf{E}[f(x) \mid \mathscr{F}_n] = \sum_{k=1}^n a_k H_k(x) \quad \text{(P-a.s.)},\tag{12}$$

for every Borel function $f \in L$, where

$$a_k = (f, H_k) = \int_0^1 f(x) H_k(x)\,dx.$$

In other words, the conditional expectation $\mathsf{E}[f(x) \mid \mathscr{F}_n]$ is a partial sum of the Fourier series of $f(x)$ in the Haar system. Then if we apply Theorem 3 to the martingale we find that, as $n \to \infty$,

$$\sum_{k=1}^n (f, H_k) H_k(x) \to f(x) \quad \text{(P-a.s.)}$$

and

$$\int_0^1 \left| \sum_{k=1}^n (f, H_k) H_k(x) - f(x) \right| dx \to 0.$$

5. PROBLEMS

1. Let $\{\mathscr{G}_n\}$ be a nonincreasing family of σ-algebras, $\mathscr{G}_1 \supseteq \mathscr{G}_2 \supseteq \cdots \mathscr{G}_\infty = \bigcap \mathscr{G}_n$, and let η be an integrable random variable. Establish the following analog of Theorem 3: as $n \to \infty$,

$$\mathsf{E}(\eta \mid G_n) \to \mathsf{E}(\eta \mid G_\infty) \quad \text{(P-a.s. and in the } L^1 \text{ sense).}$$

2. Let $\xi_1, \xi_2, \dots$ be a sequence of independent identically distributed random variables with $\mathsf{E}|\xi_1| < \infty$ and $\mathsf{E}\xi_1 = m$; let $S_n = \xi_1 + \cdots + \xi_n$. Having shown (see Problem 2, §7, Chapter II) that

$$\mathsf{E}(\xi_1 \mid S_n, S_{n+1}, \dots) = \mathsf{E}(\xi_1 \mid S_n) = \frac{S_n}{n} \quad \text{(P-a.s.)},$$

deduce from Problem 1 a stronger form of the law of large numbers: as $n \to \infty$,

$$\frac{S_n}{n} \to m \quad \text{(P-a.s. and in the } L^1 \text{ sense).}$$

3. Establish the following result, which combines Lebesgue's dominated convergence theorem and P. Lévy's theorem. Let $\{\xi_n\}_{n \geq 1}$ be a sequence of random variables such that $\xi_n \to \xi$ (P-a.s.), $|\xi_n| \leq \eta$, $E\eta < \infty$ and $\{\mathscr{F}_m\}_{m \geq 1}$ is a nondecreasing family of σ-algebras, with $\mathscr{F}_\infty = \sigma(\bigcup \mathscr{F}_n)$. Then

$$\lim_{\substack{m \to \infty \\ n \to \infty}} E(\xi_n | \mathscr{F}_m) = E(\xi | \mathscr{F}_\infty) \quad \text{(P-a.s.)}.$$

4. Establish formula (12).

5. Let $\Omega = [0, 1]$, $\mathscr{F} = \mathscr{B}([0, 1))$, let P denote Lebesgue measure, and let $f = f(x) \in L^1$. Put

$$f_n(x) = 2^n \int_{k2^{-n}}^{(k+1)2^{-n}} f(y) \, dy, \qquad k2^{-n} \leq x < (k+1)2^{-n}.$$

Show that $f_n(x) \to f(x)$ (P-a.s.).

6. Let $\Omega = [0, 1)$, $\mathscr{F} = \mathscr{B}([0, 1))$, let P denote Lebesgue measure and let $f = f(x) \in L^1$. Continue this function periodically on $[0, 2)$ and put

$$f_n(x) = \sum_{i=1}^{2^n} 2^{-n} f(x + i2^{-n}).$$

Show that $f_n(x) \to f(x)$ (P-a.s.).

7. Prove that Theorem 1 remains valid for generalized submartingales $X = (X_n, \mathscr{F}_n)$, if $\inf_m \sup_{n \geq m} E(X_n^+ | \mathscr{F}_m) < \infty$ (P-a.s.).

8. Let a_n, $n \geq 1$, be a sequence of real numbers such that for all real numbers t with $|t| < \delta$, $\delta > 0$, the limit $\lim_n e^{ita_n}$ exists. Prove that then the limit $\lim a_n$ exists and is finite.

§5. Sets of Convergence of Submartingales and Martingales

1. Let $X = (X_n, \mathscr{F}_n)$ be a stochastic sequence. Let us denote by $\{X_n \to\}$, or $\{-\infty < \lim X_n < \infty\}$, the set of sample points for which $\lim X_n$ *exists* and is *finite*. Let us also write $A \subseteq B$ (P-a.s.) if $P(I_A \leq I_B) = 1$.

If X is a submartingale and $\sup E|X_n| < \infty$ (or, equivalently, if $\sup EX_n^+ < \infty$), then according to Theorem 1 of §4 we have

$$\{X_n \to\} = \Omega \quad \text{(P-a.s.)}.$$

Let us consider the structure of sets $\{X_n \to\}$ of convergence for submartingales when the hypothesis $\sup E|X_n| < \infty$ is not satisfied.

Let $a > 0$, and $\tau_a \mathrel{\overset{\bullet}{=}} \inf\{n \geq 1: X_n > a\}$ with $\tau_a = \infty$ if $\{\cdot\} = \varnothing$.

Definition. A stochastic sequence $X = (X_n, \mathscr{F}_n)$ belongs to *class* C^+ $(X \in C^+)$ if

$$E(\Delta X_{\tau_a})^+ I\{\tau_a < \infty\} < \infty \tag{1}$$

for every $a > 0$, where $\Delta X_n = X_n - X_{n-1}$, $X_0 = 0$.

It is evident that $X \in C^+$ if

$$\mathsf{E} \sup_n |\Delta X_n| < \infty \qquad (2)$$

or, all the more so, if

$$|\Delta X_n| \le C < \infty \quad \text{(P-a.s.)}, \qquad (3)$$

for all $n \ge 1$.

Theorem 1. *If the submartingale* $X \in C^+$ *then*

$$\{\sup X_n < \infty\} = \{X_n \to\} \quad \text{(P-a.s.)}. \qquad (4)$$

PROOF. The inclusion $\{X_n \to\} \subseteq \{\sup X_n < \infty\}$ is evident. To establish the inclusion in the opposite direction, we consider the stopped submartingale $X^{\tau_a} = (X_{\tau_a \wedge n}, \mathscr{F}_n)$. Then, by (1),

$$\begin{aligned}
\sup_n \mathsf{E} X^+_{\tau_a \wedge n} &\le a + \mathsf{E}[X^+_{\tau_a} \cdot I\{\tau_a < \infty\}] \\
&\le 2a + \mathsf{E}[(\Delta X_{\tau_a})^+ \cdot I\{\tau_a < \infty\}] < \infty,
\end{aligned} \qquad (5)$$

and therefore by Theorem 1 of §4,

$$\{\tau_a = \infty\} \subseteq \{X_n \to\} \quad \text{(P-a.s.)}.$$

But $\bigcup_{a>0} \{\tau_a = \infty\} = \{\sup X_n < \infty\}$; hence $\{\sup X_n < \infty\} \subseteq \{X_n \to\}$ (P-a.s.}.

This completes the proof of the theorem.

Corollary. *Let* X *be a martingale with* $\mathsf{E} \sup |\Delta X_n| < \infty$. *Then* (P-a.s.)

$$\{X_n \to\} \cup \{\varliminf X_n = -\infty, \varlimsup X_n = +\infty\} = \Omega. \qquad (6)$$

In fact, if we apply Theorem 1 to X and to $-X$, we find that (P-a.s.)

$$\{\varlimsup X_n < \infty\} = \{\sup X_n < \infty\} = \{X_n \to\},$$

$$\{\varliminf X_n > -\infty\} = \{\inf X_n > -\infty\} = \{X_n \to\}.$$

Therefore (P-a.s.)

$$\{\varlimsup X_n < \infty\} \cup \{\varliminf X_n > -\infty\} = \{X_n \to\},$$

which establishes (6).

Statement (6) means that, provided that $\mathsf{E} \sup |\Delta X_n| < \infty$, either almost all trajectories of the martingale M have finite limits, or else all behave very badly, in the sense that $\varlimsup X_n = +\infty$ and $\varliminf X_n = -\infty$.

2. If $\xi_1, \xi_2, , \ldots$ is a sequence of independent random variables with $\mathsf{E}\xi_i = 0$ and $|\xi_i| \le c < \infty$, then by Theorem 1 of §2, Chapter IV, the series $\sum \xi_i$ converges (P-a.s.) if and only if $\sum \mathsf{E}\xi_i^2 < \infty$. The sequence $X = (X_n, \mathscr{F}_n)$ with

$X_n = \xi_1 + \cdots + \xi_n$ and $\mathscr{F}_n = \sigma\{\omega: \xi_1, \ldots, \xi_n\}_n$ is a square-integrable martingale with $\langle X \rangle_n = \sum_{i=1}^{n} \mathsf{E}\xi_i^2$, and the proposition just stated can be interpreted as follows:

$$\{\langle X \rangle_\infty < \infty\} = \{X_n \to\} = \Omega \quad \text{(P-a.s.)},$$

where $\langle X \rangle_\infty = \lim_n \langle X \rangle_n$.

The following proposition generalizes this result to more general martingales and submartingales.

Theorem 2. *Let* $X = (X_n, \mathscr{F}_n)$ *be a submartingale and*

$$X_n = m_n + A_n$$

its Doob decomposition.

(a) *If X is a nonnegative submartingale, then* (P-a.s.)

$$\{A_\infty < \infty\} \subseteq \{X_n \to\} \subseteq \{\sup X_n < \infty\}. \tag{7}$$

(b) *If $X \in C^+$ then* (P-a.s.)

$$\{X_n \to\} = \{\sup X_n < \infty\} \subseteq \{A_\infty < \infty\}. \tag{8}$$

(c) *If X is a nonnegative submartingale and $X \in C^+$, then* (P-a.s.)

$$\{X_n \to\} = \{\sup X_n < \infty\} = \{A_\infty < \infty\}. \tag{9}$$

PROOF. (a) The second inclusion in (7) is obvious. To establish the first inclusion we introduce the *times*

$$\sigma_a = \inf\{n \geq 1: A_{n+1} > a\}, \qquad a > 0,$$

taking $\sigma_a = +\infty$ if $\{\cdot\} = \varnothing$. Then $A_{\sigma_a} \leq a$ and by Corollary 1 to Theorem 1 of §2, we have

$$\mathsf{E} X_{n \wedge \sigma_a} = \mathsf{E} A_{n \wedge \sigma_a} \leq a.$$

Let $Y_n^a = X_{n \wedge \sigma_a}$. Then $Y^a = (Y_n^a, \mathscr{F}_n)$ is a submartingale with $\sup \mathsf{E} Y_n^a \leq a < \infty$. Since the martingale is nonnegative, it follows from Theorem 1, §4, that (P-a.s.)

$$\{A_\infty \leq a\} = \{\sigma_a = \infty\} \subseteq \{X_n \to\}.$$

Therefore (P-a.s.)

$$\{A_\infty < \infty\} = \bigcup_{a>0} \{A_\infty \leq a\} \subseteq \{X_n \to\}.$$

(b) The first equation follows from Theorem 1. To prove the second, we notice that, in accordance with (5),

$$\mathsf{E} A_{\tau_a \wedge n} = \mathsf{E} X_{\tau_a \wedge n} \leq \mathsf{E} X_{\tau_a \wedge n}^+ \leq 2a + \mathsf{E}[(\Delta X_{\tau_a})^+ I\{\tau_a < \infty\}]$$

and therefore

$$\mathsf{E} A_{\tau_a} = \mathsf{E} \lim_n A_{\tau_a \wedge n} < \infty.$$

Hence $\{\tau_a = \infty\} \subseteq \{A_\infty < \infty\}$ and we obtain the required conclusion since $\bigcup_{a>0} \{\tau_a = \infty\} = \{\sup X_n < \infty\}$.

(c) This is an immediate consequence of (a) and (b).

This completes the proof of the theorem.

Remark. The hypothesis that X is nonnegative can be replaced by the hypothesis $\sup_n \mathsf{E} X_n^- < \infty$.

Corollary 1. *Let* $X_n = \xi_1 + \cdots + \xi_n$, *where* $\xi_i \geq 0$, $\mathsf{E}\xi_i < \infty$, ξ_i *are* $\mathscr{F}_i$-*measurable, and* $\mathscr{F}_0 = \{\varnothing, \Omega\}$. *Then* (**P**-*a.s.*)

$$\left\{ \sum_{n=1}^\infty \mathsf{E}(\xi_n | \mathscr{F}_{n-1}) < \infty \right\} \subseteq \{X_n \to\}, \tag{10}$$

and if, in addition, $\mathsf{E}\sup_n \xi_n < \infty$ *then* (**P**-*a.s.*)

$$\left\{ \sum_{n=1}^\infty \mathsf{E}(\xi_n | \mathscr{F}_{n-1}) < \infty \right\} = \{X_n \to\}. \tag{11}$$

Corollary 2 (Borel–Cantelli–Lévy Lemma). *If the events* $B_n \in \mathscr{F}_n$, *then if we put* $\xi_n = I_{B_n}$ *in* (11), *we find that*

$$\left\{ \sum_{n=1}^\infty \mathsf{P}(B_n | \mathscr{F}_{n-1}) < \infty \right\} = \left\{ \sum_{n=1}^\infty I_{B_n} < \infty \right\}. \tag{12}$$

3. Theorem 3. *Let* $M = (M_n, \mathscr{F}_n)_{n \geq 1}$ *be a square-integrable martingale. Then* (**P**-*a.s.*)

$$\{\langle M \rangle_\infty < \infty\} \subseteq \{M_n \to\}. \tag{13}$$

If also $\mathsf{E}\sup |\Delta M_n|^2 < \infty$, *then* (**P**-*a.s.*)

$$\{\langle M \rangle_\infty < \infty\} = \{M_n \to\}, \tag{14}$$

where

$$\langle M \rangle_\infty = \sum_{n=1}^\infty \mathsf{E}((\Delta M_n)^2 | \mathscr{F}_{n-1}) \tag{15}$$

with $M_0 = 0$, $\mathscr{F}_0 = \{\varnothing, \Omega\}$.

PROOF. Consider the two submartingales $M^2 = (M_n^2, \mathscr{F}_n)$ and $(M + 1)^2 = ((M + 1)^2, \mathscr{F}_n)$. Let their Doob decompositions be

$$M_n^2 = m_n' + A_n', \qquad (M_n + 1)^2 = m_n'' + A_n''.$$

Then A_n' and A_n'' are the same, since

$$A_n' = \sum_{k=1}^n \mathsf{E}(\Delta M_k^2 | \mathscr{F}_{k-1}) = \sum_{k=1}^n \mathsf{E}((\Delta M_k)^2 | \mathscr{F}_{k-1})$$

and

$$A_n'' = \sum_{k=1}^{n} \mathsf{E}(\Delta(M_k + 1)^2 | \mathscr{F}_{k-1}) = \sum_{k=1}^{n} \mathsf{E}(\Delta M_k^2 | \mathscr{F}_{k-1})$$

$$= \sum_{k=1}^{n} \mathsf{E}((\Delta M_k)^2 | \mathscr{F}_{k-1}).$$

Hence (7) implies that (P-a.s.)

$$\{\langle M \rangle_{\infty} < \infty\} = \{A_{\infty}' < \infty\} \subseteq \{M_n^2 \to\} \cap \{(M_n + 1)^2 \to\} = \{M_n \to\}.$$

Because of (9), equation (14) will be established if we show that the condition $\mathsf{E} \sup |\Delta M_n|^2 < \infty$ guarantees that M^2 belongs to C^+.

Let $\tau_a = \inf\{n \geq 1 : M_n^2 > a\}$, $a > 0$. Then, on the set $\{\tau_a < \infty\}$,

$$|\Delta M_{\tau_a}^2| = |M_{\tau_a}^2 - M_{\tau_a - 1}^2| \leq |M_{\tau_a} - M_{\tau_a - 1}|^2$$

$$+ 2|M_{\tau_a - 1}| \cdot |M_{\tau_a} - M_{\tau_a - 1}| \leq (\Delta M_{\tau_a})^2 + 2a^{1/2}|\Delta M_{\tau_a}|,$$

whence

$$\mathsf{E} |\Delta M_{\tau_a}^2| I\{\tau_a < \infty\} \leq \mathsf{E}(\Delta M_{\tau_a})^2 I\{\tau_a < \infty\} + 2a^{1/2}\sqrt{\mathsf{E}(\Delta M_{\tau_a})^2 I\{\tau_a < \infty\}}$$

$$\leq \mathsf{E} \sup |\Delta M_n|^2 + 2a^{1/2}\sqrt{\mathsf{E} \sup |\Delta M_n|^2} < \infty.$$

This completes the proof of the theorem.

As an illustration of this theorem, we present the following result, which can be considered as a distinctive version of the strong law of large numbers for square-integrable martingales (compare Theorem 2 of §3, Chapter IV and Corollary 2 of Subsection 3 of §3).

Theorem 4. *Let* $M = (M_n, \mathscr{F}_n)$ *be a square-integrable martingale and let* $A = (A_n, \mathscr{F}_{n-1})$ *be a predictable increasing sequence with* $A_1 \geq 1$, $A_\infty = \infty$ (P-*a.s.*).
If (P-*a.s.*)

$$\sum_{i=1}^{\infty} \frac{\mathsf{E}[(\Delta M_i)^2 | F_{i-1}]}{A_i^2} < \infty, \tag{16}$$

then

$$M_n/A_n \to 0, \qquad n \to \infty, \tag{17}$$

with probability 1.

In particular, if $\langle M \rangle = (M_n, \mathscr{F}_n)$ *is the quadratic variation of the square-integrable martingale,* $M = (M_n, \mathscr{F}_n)$ *and* $\langle M \rangle_\infty = \infty$ (P-*a.s.*), *then with probability 1*

$$\frac{M_n}{\langle M \rangle_n} \to 0, \qquad n \to \infty. \tag{18}$$

PROOF. Consider the square-integrable martingale $m = (m_n, \mathscr{F}_n)$ with

$$m_n = \sum_{i=1}^{n} \frac{\Delta M_i}{A_i}.$$

Then

$$\langle m \rangle_n = \sum_{i=1}^{n} \frac{\mathsf{E}[(\Delta M_i)^2 | \mathscr{F}_{i-1}]}{A_i^2}. \tag{19}$$

Since

$$\frac{M_n}{A_n} = \frac{\sum_{k=1}^{n} A_k \Delta m_k}{A_n},$$

we have, by Kronecker's lemma (§3, Chapter IV), $M_n/A_n \to 0$ (P-a.s.) if the limit $\lim_n m_n$ exists (finite) with probability 1. By (13),

$$\{\langle m \rangle_\infty < \infty\} \subseteq \{m_n \to\}. \tag{20}$$

Therefore it follows from (19) that (16) is a sufficient condition for (17).

If now $A_n = \langle M \rangle_n$, then (16) is automatically satisfied (see Problem 6) and consequently we have

$$\frac{M_n}{\langle M \rangle_n} \to 0 \quad \text{(P-a.s.)}.$$

This completes the proof of the theorem.

EXAMPLE. Consider a sequence $\xi_1, \xi_2, \ldots$ of independent random variables with $\mathsf{E}\xi_i = 0$, $\mathsf{V}\xi_i = V_i > 0$, and let the sequence $X = \{X_n\}_{n \geq 0}$ be defined recursively by

$$X_{n+1} = \theta X_n + \xi_{n+1}, \tag{21}$$

where X_0 is independent of $\xi_1, \xi_2, \ldots$ and θ is an unknown parameter, $-\infty < \theta < \infty$.

We interpret X_n as the result of an observation made at time n and ask for an estimator of the unknown parameter θ. As an estimator of θ in terms of $X_0, X_1, \ldots, X_n$, we take

$$\hat{\theta}_n = \frac{\displaystyle\sum_{k=0}^{n-1} \frac{X_k X_{k+1}}{V_{k+1}}}{\displaystyle\sum_{k=0}^{n-1} \frac{X_k^2}{V_{k+1}}}, \tag{22}$$

taking this to be 0 if the denominator is 0. (The number θ is the *least-squares* estimator.)

It is clear from (21) and (22) that

$$\hat{\theta} = \theta + \frac{M_n}{A_n},$$

where

$$M_n = \sum_{k=0}^{n-1} \frac{X_k \xi_{k+1}}{V_{k+1}}, \qquad A_n = \langle M \rangle_n = \sum_{k=0}^{n-1} \frac{X_k^2}{V_{k+1}}.$$

Therefore if the true value of the unknown parameter is θ, then

$$P(\hat{\theta}_n \to \theta) = 1, \tag{23}$$

when (P-a.s.)

$$\frac{M_n}{A_n} \to 0, \qquad n \to \infty. \tag{24}$$

(An estimator θ_n with property (23) is said to be *strongly consistent*; compare the notion of consistency in §7, Chapter I.) Let us show that the conditions

$$\sup_n \frac{V_{n+1}}{V_n} < \infty, \qquad \sum_{n=1}^{\infty} E\left(\frac{\xi_n^2}{V_n} \wedge 1\right) = \infty \tag{25}$$

are sufficient for (24), and therefore sufficient for (23).

We have

$$\sum_{n=1}^{\infty} \left(\frac{\xi_n^2}{V_n} \wedge 1\right) \le \sum_{n=1}^{\infty} \frac{\xi_n^2}{V_n} = \sum_{n=1}^{\infty} \frac{(X_n - \theta X_{n-1})^2}{V_n}$$

$$\le 2\left[\sum_{n=1}^{\infty} \frac{X_n^2}{V_n} + \theta^2 \sum_{n=1}^{\infty} \frac{X_{n-1}^2}{V_n}\right] \le 2\left[\sup \frac{V_{n+1}}{V_n} + \theta^2\right] \langle M \rangle_\infty.$$

Therefore

$$\left\{\sum_{n=1}^{\infty} \left(\frac{\xi_n^2}{V_n} \wedge 1\right) = \infty\right\} \subseteq \{\langle M \rangle_\infty = \infty\}.$$

By the three-series theorem (Theorem 3 of §2, Chapter IV) the divergence of $\sum_{n=1}^{\infty} E((\xi_n^2/V_n) \wedge 1)$ guarantees the divergence (P-a.s.) of $\sum_{n=1}^{\infty} ((\xi^2/V_n) \wedge 1)$. Therefore $P\{\langle M \rangle_\infty = \infty\} = 1$. Moreover, if

$$m_n = \sum_{i=1}^{n} \frac{\Delta M_i}{\langle M \rangle_i},$$

then

$$\langle m \rangle_n = \sum_{i=1}^{n} \frac{\Delta \langle M \rangle_i}{\langle M \rangle_i^2}$$

and (see Problem 6) $P(m_\infty < \infty) = 1$. Hence (24) follows directly from Theorem 4.

(In Subsection 5 of the next section we continue the discussion of this example for *Gaussian* variables $\xi_1, \xi_2, \ldots$.)

Theorem 5. *Let* $X = (X_n, \mathscr{F}_n)$ *be a submartingale, and let*

$$X_n = m_n + A_n$$

be its Doob decomposition. If $|\Delta X_n| \leq C$, *then* (P-a.s.)

$$\{\langle m \rangle_\infty + A_\infty < \infty\} = \{X_n \to\}, \tag{26}$$

or equivalently,

$$\left\{\sum_{n=1}^{\infty} \mathsf{E}[\Delta X_n + (\Delta X_n)^2 | \mathscr{F}_{n-1}] < \infty\right\} = \{X_n \to\}. \tag{27}$$

PROOF. Since

$$A_n = \sum_{k=1}^{n} \mathsf{E}(\Delta X_k | \mathscr{F}_{k-1}), \tag{28}$$

and

$$m_n = \sum_{k=1}^{n} [\Delta X_k - \mathsf{E}(\Delta X_k | \mathscr{F}_{k-1})], \tag{29}$$

it follows from the assumption that $|\Delta X_k| \leq C$ that the martingale $m = (m_n, \mathscr{F}_n)$ is square-integrable with $|\Delta m_n| \leq 2C$. Then by (13)

$$\{\langle m \rangle_\infty + A_\infty < \infty\} \subseteq \{X_n \to\} \tag{30}$$

and according to (8)

$$\{X_n \to\} \subseteq \{A_\infty < \infty\}.$$

Therefore, by (14) and (20),

$$\{X_n \to\} = \{X_n \to\} \cap \{A_\infty < \infty\} = \{X_n \to\} \cap \{A_\infty < \infty\} \cap \{m_n \to\}$$

$$= \{X_n \to\} \cap \{A_\infty < \infty\} \cap \{\langle m \rangle_\infty < \infty\}$$

$$= \{X_n \to\} \cap \{A_\infty + \langle m \rangle_\infty < \infty\} = \{A_\infty + \langle m \rangle_\infty < \infty\}.$$

Finally, the equivalence of (26) and (27) follows because, by (29),

$$\langle m \rangle_n = \sum \{\mathsf{E}[(\Delta X_k)^2 | \mathscr{F}_{k-1}] - [\mathsf{E}(\Delta X_k | \mathscr{F}_{k-1})]^2\},$$

and the convergence of the series $\sum_{k=1}^{\infty} \mathsf{E}(\Delta X_k | \mathscr{F}_{k-1})$ of nonnegative terms implies the convergence of $\sum_{k=1}^{\infty} [\mathsf{E}(\Delta X_k | \mathscr{F}_{k-1})]^2$. This completes the proof.

4. Kolmogorov's three-series theorem (Theorem 3 of §2, Chapter IV) gives a necessary and sufficient condition for the convergence, with probability 1, of a series $\sum \xi_n$ of independent random variables. The following theorems, whose proofs are based on Theorems 2 and 3, describe sets of convergence of $\sum \xi_n$ without the assumption that the random variables $\xi_1, \xi_2, \ldots$ are independent.

Theorem 6. *Let* $\xi = (\xi_n, \mathscr{F}_n)$, $n \geq 1$, *be a stochastic sequence, let* $\mathscr{F}_0 = \{\varnothing, \Omega\}$, *and let c be a positive constant. Then the series* $\sum \xi_n$ *converges on the set A of sample points for which the three series*

$$\sum P(|\xi_n| \geq c \,|\, \mathscr{F}_{n-1}), \qquad \sum E(\xi_n^c \,|\, \mathscr{F}_{n-1}), \qquad \sum V(\xi_n^c \,|\, \mathscr{F}_{n-1})$$

converge, where $\xi_n^c = \xi_n I(|\xi_n| \leq c)$.

PROOF. Let $X_n = \sum_{k=1}^{n} \xi_k$. Since the series $\sum P(|\xi_n| \geq c \,|\, \mathscr{F}_{n-1})$ converges, by Corollary 2 of Theorem 2, and by the convergence of the series $\sum E(\xi_n^c \,|\, \mathscr{F}_{n-1})$, we have

$$A \cap \{X_n \to\} = A \cap \left\{ \sum_{k=1}^{n} \xi_k I(|\xi_k| \leq c) \to \right\}$$

$$= A \cap \left\{ \sum_{k=1}^{n} [\xi_k I(|\xi_k| \leq c) - E(\xi_k I(|\xi_k| \leq c) \,|\, \mathscr{F}_{k-1})] \to \right\}.$$

$$(31)$$

Let $\eta_k = \xi_k I(|\xi_k| \leq c) - E(\xi_k I(|\xi_k| \leq c) \,|\, \mathscr{F}_{k-1})$ and let $Y_n = \sum_{k=1}^{n} \eta_k$. Then $Y = (Y_n, \mathscr{F}_n)$ is a square-integrable martingale with $|\eta_k| \leq 2c$. By Theorem 3, we have

$$A \subseteq \{ \sum V(\xi_n^c \,|\, \mathscr{F}_{n-1}) < \infty \} = \{ \langle Y \rangle_\infty < \infty \} = \{ Y_n \to \}. \qquad (32)$$

Then it follows from (31) that

$$A \cap \{X_n \to\} = A,$$

and therefore $A \subseteq \{X_n \to\}$; this completes the proof.

5. PROBLEMS

1. Show that if a submartingale $X = (X_n, \mathscr{F}_n)$ satisfies $E \sup_n |X_n| < \infty$, then it belongs to class C^+.

2. Show that Theorems 1 and 2 remain valid for generalized submartingales.

3. Show that generalized submartingales satisfy (P-a.s.) the inclusion

$$\left\{ \inf_m \sup_{n \geq m} E(X_n^+ \,|\, \mathscr{F}_m) < \infty \right\} \subseteq \{X_n \to\}.$$

4. Show that the corollary to Theorem 1 remains valid for generalized martingales.

5. Show that every generalized submartingale of class C^+ is a local submartingale.

6. Let $a_n > 0$, $n \geq 1$, and let $b_n = \sum_{k=1}^{n} a_k$. Show that

$$\sum_{n=1}^{\infty} \frac{a_n}{b_n^2} < \infty.$$

§6. Absolute Continuity and Singularity of Probability Distributions

1. Let $(\Omega, \mathscr{F})$ be a measurable space on which there is defined a family $(\mathscr{F}_n)_{n \geq 1}$ of σ-algebras such that $\mathscr{F}_1 \subseteq \mathscr{F}_2 \subseteq \cdots \subseteq \mathscr{F}$ and

$$\mathscr{F} = \sigma\left(\bigcup_{n=1}^{\infty} \mathscr{F}_n\right). \tag{1}$$

Let us suppose that two probability measures P and $\tilde{\mathsf{P}}$ are given on $(\Omega, \mathscr{F})$. Let us write

$$\mathsf{P}_n = \mathsf{P} | \mathscr{F}_n, \qquad \tilde{\mathsf{P}}_n = \tilde{\mathsf{P}} | \mathscr{F}_n$$

for the restrictions of these measures to $\mathscr{F}_n$, i.e. let P_n and $\tilde{\mathsf{P}}_n$ be measures on $(\Omega, \mathscr{F}_n)$ and for $B \in \mathscr{F}_n$ let

$$\mathsf{P}_n(B) = \mathsf{P}(B), \qquad \tilde{\mathsf{P}}_n(B) = \tilde{\mathsf{P}}(B).$$

Definition 1. The probability measure $\tilde{\mathsf{P}}$ is *absolutely continuous* with respect to P (notation, $\tilde{\mathsf{P}} \ll \mathsf{P}$) if $\tilde{\mathsf{P}}(A) = 0$ whenever $\mathsf{P}(A) = 0$, $A \in \mathscr{F}$.

When $\tilde{\mathsf{P}} \ll \mathsf{P}$ and $\mathsf{P} \ll \tilde{\mathsf{P}}$ the measures $\tilde{\mathsf{P}}$ and P are *equivalent* (notation, $\tilde{\mathsf{P}} \sim \mathsf{P}$).

The measures $\tilde{\mathsf{P}}$ and P are *singular* (or *orthogonal*) if there is a set $A \in \mathscr{F}$ such that $\tilde{\mathsf{P}}(A) = 1$ and $\mathsf{P}(\bar{A}) = 1$ (notation, $\tilde{\mathsf{P}} \perp \mathsf{P}$).

Definition 2. We say that $\tilde{\mathsf{P}}$ is *locally absolutely continuous* with respect to P (notation, $\tilde{\mathsf{P}} \overset{\text{loc}}{\ll} \mathsf{P}$) if

$$\tilde{\mathsf{P}}_n \ll \mathsf{P}_n \tag{2}$$

for every $n \geq 1$.

The fundamental question that we shall consider in this section is the determination of conditions under which local absolute continuity $\tilde{\mathsf{P}} \overset{\text{loc}}{\ll} \mathsf{P}$ implies one of the properties $\tilde{\mathsf{P}} \ll \mathsf{P}, \tilde{\mathsf{P}} \sim \mathsf{P}, \tilde{\mathsf{P}} \perp \mathsf{P}$. It will become clear that martingale theory is the mathematical apparatus that lets us give definitive answers to these questions.

Let us then suppose that $\tilde{\mathsf{P}} \overset{\text{loc}}{\ll} \mathsf{P}$. We write

$$z_n = \frac{d\tilde{\mathsf{P}}_n}{d\mathsf{P}_n}$$

the Radon–Nikodým derivative of $\tilde{\mathsf{P}}_n$ with respect to P_n. It is clear that z_n is $\mathscr{F}_n$-measurable; and if $A \in \mathscr{F}_n$ then

$$\int_A z_{n+1}\, d\mathsf{P} = \int_A \frac{d\tilde{\mathsf{P}}_{n+1}}{d\mathsf{P}_{n+1}}\, d\mathsf{P} = \tilde{\mathsf{P}}_{n+1}(A) = \tilde{\mathsf{P}}_n(A)$$

$$= \int_A \frac{d\tilde{\mathsf{P}}_n}{d\mathsf{P}_n}\, d\mathsf{P} = \int_A z_n\, d\mathsf{P}.$$

It follows that, *with respect to* P, *the stochastic sequence* $Z = (z_n, \mathscr{F}_n)_{n \geq 1}$ *is a martingale.*

Write

$$z_\infty = \overline{\lim}\, z_n.$$

Since $\mathsf{E} z_n = 1$, it follows from Theorem 1, §4, that $\lim z_n$ exists P-a.s. and. therefore $\mathsf{P}(z_\infty = \lim z_n) = 1$. (In the course of the proof of Theorem 1 it will be established that $\lim z_n$ exists also for $\tilde{\mathsf{P}}$, so that $\tilde{\mathsf{P}}(z_\infty = \lim z_n) = 1$.)

The key to problems on absolute continuity and singularity is *Lebesgue's decomposition:*

Theorem 1. *Let* $\tilde{\mathsf{P}} \overset{loc}{\ll} \mathsf{P}$. *Then for every* $A \in \mathscr{F}$,

$$\tilde{\mathsf{P}}(A) = \int_A z_\infty \, d\mathsf{P} + \tilde{\mathsf{P}}\{A \cap (z_\infty = \infty)\}, \tag{3}$$

and the measures $\mu(A) = \tilde{\mathsf{P}}\{A \cap (z_\infty = \infty)\}$ *and* $\mathsf{P}(A)$, $A \in \mathscr{F}$, *are singular.*

PROOF. Let us notice first that the classical *Lebesgue decomposition* shows that if P and $\tilde{\mathsf{P}}$ are two measures, there are unique measures λ and μ such that $\tilde{\mathsf{P}} = \lambda + \mu$, where $\lambda \ll \mathsf{P}$ and $\mu \perp \mathsf{P}$. Conclusion (3) can be thought of as a specialization of this decomposition under the assumption that $\tilde{\mathsf{P}}_n \ll \mathsf{P}_n$, $n \geq 1$.

Let us introduce the probability measures

$$\mathsf{Q} = \tfrac{1}{2}(\mathsf{P} + \tilde{\mathsf{P}}), \qquad \mathsf{Q}_n = \tfrac{1}{2}(\mathsf{P}_n + \tilde{\mathsf{P}}_n), \qquad n \geq 1,$$

and the notation

$$\tilde{\mathfrak{z}} = \frac{d\tilde{\mathsf{P}}}{d\mathsf{Q}}, \qquad \mathfrak{z} = \frac{d\mathsf{P}}{d\mathsf{Q}}, \qquad \tilde{\mathfrak{z}}_n = \frac{d\tilde{\mathsf{P}}_n}{d\mathsf{Q}_n}, \qquad \mathfrak{z}_n = \frac{d\mathsf{P}_n}{d\mathsf{Q}_n}.$$

Since $\tilde{\mathsf{P}}(\tilde{\mathfrak{z}} = 0) = \mathsf{P}(\mathfrak{z} = 0) = 0$, we have $\mathsf{Q}(\tilde{\mathfrak{z}} = 0, \mathfrak{z} = 0) = 0$. Consequently the product $\tilde{\mathfrak{z}} \cdot \mathfrak{z}^{-1}$ can be defined consistently on the set $\Omega \backslash \{\tilde{\mathfrak{z}} = 0, \mathfrak{z} = 0\}$; we define it to be zero on the set $\{\tilde{\mathfrak{z}} = 0, \mathfrak{z} = 0\}$.

Since $\tilde{\mathsf{P}}_n \ll \mathsf{P}_n \ll \mathsf{Q}_n$, we have (see (II.7.36))

$$\frac{d\tilde{\mathsf{P}}_n}{d\mathsf{Q}_n} = \frac{d\tilde{\mathsf{P}}_n}{d\mathsf{P}_n} \cdot \frac{d\mathsf{P}_n}{d\mathsf{Q}_n} \quad (\mathsf{Q}\text{-a.s.}) \tag{4}$$

i.e.

$$\tilde{\mathfrak{z}}_n = z_n \mathfrak{z}_n \quad (\mathsf{Q}\text{-a.s.}) \tag{5}$$

whence

$$z_n = \tilde{\mathfrak{z}}_n \cdot \mathfrak{z}_n^{-1} \quad (\mathsf{Q}\text{-a.s.})$$

where, as before, we take $\tilde{\mathfrak{z}}_n \cdot \mathfrak{z}_n^{-1} = 0$ on the set $\{\tilde{\mathfrak{z}}_n = 0, \mathfrak{z}_n = 0\}$, which is of Q-measure zero.

Each of the sequences $(\tilde{\mathfrak{z}}_n, \mathscr{F}_n)$ and $(\mathfrak{z}_n, \mathscr{F}_n)$ is (with respect to $\mathbf{Q}$) a uniformly integrable martingale and consequently the limits $\lim \tilde{\mathfrak{z}}_n$ and $\lim \mathfrak{z}_n$ exist. Moreover ($\mathbf{Q}$-a.s.)

$$\lim \tilde{\mathfrak{z}}_n = \tilde{\mathfrak{z}}, \qquad \lim \mathfrak{z}_n = \mathfrak{z}. \tag{6}$$

From this and the equations $z_n = \tilde{\mathfrak{z}}_n \mathfrak{z}_n^{-1}$ ($\mathbf{Q}$-a.s.) and $\mathbf{Q}(\tilde{\mathfrak{z}} = 0, \mathfrak{z} = 0) = 0$, it follows that ($\mathbf{Q}$-a.s.) the limit $\lim z_n = z_\infty$ exists and is equal to $\tilde{\mathfrak{z}} \cdot \mathfrak{z}^{-1}$.

It is clear that $\mathbf{P} \ll \mathbf{Q}$ and $\tilde{\mathbf{P}} \ll \mathbf{Q}$. Therefore $\lim z_n$ exists both with respect to $\mathbf{P}$ and with respect to $\tilde{\mathbf{P}}$.

Now let

$$\lambda(A) = \int_A z_\infty \, d\mathbf{P}, \qquad \mu(A) = \tilde{\mathbf{P}}\{A \cap (z_\infty = \infty)\}.$$

To establish (3), we must show that

$$\tilde{\mathbf{P}}(A) = \lambda(A) + \mu(A), \qquad \lambda \ll \mathbf{P}, \quad \mu \perp \mathbf{P}.$$

We have

$$\tilde{\mathbf{P}}(A) = \int_A \tilde{\mathfrak{z}} \, d\mathbf{Q} = \int_A \tilde{\mathfrak{z}} \mathfrak{z} \mathfrak{z}^{\oplus} \, d\mathbf{Q} + \int_A \tilde{\mathfrak{z}}[1 - \mathfrak{z} \mathfrak{z}^{\oplus}] \, d\mathbf{Q}$$

$$= \int_A \mathfrak{z} \mathfrak{z}^{\oplus} \, d\mathbf{P} + \int_A [1 - \mathfrak{z} \mathfrak{z}^{\oplus}] \, d\tilde{\mathbf{P}} = \int_A z_\infty \, d\mathbf{P} + \tilde{\mathbf{P}}\{A \cap (\mathfrak{z} = 0)\}, \tag{7}$$

where the last equation follows from

$$\mathbf{P}\left\{\overset{\oplus}{\mathfrak{z}} = \mathfrak{z}^{-1}\right\} = 1, \qquad \tilde{\mathbf{P}}\{z_\infty = \tilde{\mathfrak{z}} \cdot \mathfrak{z}^{-1}\} = 1.$$

Furthermore,

$$\tilde{\mathbf{P}}\{A \cap (\mathfrak{z} = 0)\} = \tilde{\mathbf{P}}\{A \cap (\mathfrak{z} = 0) \cap (\tilde{\mathfrak{z}} > 0)\}$$
$$= \tilde{\mathbf{P}}\{A \cap (\tilde{\mathfrak{z}} \cdot \mathfrak{z}^{-1} = \infty)\} = \tilde{\mathbf{P}}\{A \cap (z_\infty = \infty)\},$$

which, together with (7), establishes (3).

It is clear from the construction of λ that $\lambda \ll \mathbf{P}$ and that $\mathbf{P}(z_\infty < \infty) = 1$. But we also have

$$\mu(z_\infty < \infty) = \tilde{\mathbf{P}}\{(z_\infty < \infty) \cap (z_\infty = \infty)\} = 0.$$

Consequently the theorem is proved.

The Lebesgue decomposition (3) implies the following useful tests for absolute continuity or singularity for locally absolutely continuous probability measures.

Theorem 2. *Let* $\tilde{\mathsf{P}} \overset{\text{loc}}{\ll} \mathsf{P}$, *i.e.* $\tilde{\mathsf{P}}_n \ll \mathsf{P}_n$, $n \geq 1$. *Then*

$$\tilde{\mathsf{P}} \ll \mathsf{P} \Leftrightarrow \mathsf{E} z_\infty = 1 \Leftrightarrow \tilde{\mathsf{P}}(z_\infty < \infty) = 1, \tag{8}$$

$$\tilde{\mathsf{P}} \perp \mathsf{P} \Leftrightarrow \mathsf{E} z_\infty = 0 \Leftrightarrow \tilde{\mathsf{P}}(z_\infty = \infty) = 1, \tag{9}$$

where E *denotes averaging with respect to* P.

PROOF. Putting $A = \Omega$ in (3), we find that

$$\mathsf{E} z_\infty = 1 \Leftrightarrow \tilde{\mathsf{P}}(z_\infty = \infty) = 0, \tag{10}$$

$$\mathsf{E} z_\infty = 0 \Leftrightarrow \tilde{\mathsf{P}}(z_\infty = \infty) = 1. \tag{11}$$

If $\tilde{\mathsf{P}}(z_\infty = \infty) = 0$, it again follows from (3) that $\tilde{\mathsf{P}} \ll \mathsf{P}$.

Conversely, let $\tilde{\mathsf{P}} \ll \mathsf{P}$. Then since $\mathsf{P}(z_\infty = \infty) = 0$, we have $\tilde{\mathsf{P}}(z_\infty = \infty) = 0$.

In addition, if $\tilde{\mathsf{P}} \perp \mathsf{P}$ there is a set $B \in \mathscr{F}$ with $\tilde{\mathsf{P}}(B) = 1$ and $\mathsf{P}(B) = 0$. Then $\tilde{\mathsf{P}}(B \cap (z_\infty = \infty)) = 1$ by (3), and therefore $\tilde{\mathsf{P}}(z_\infty = \infty) = 1$. If, on the other hand, $\tilde{\mathsf{P}}(z_\infty = \infty) = 1$ the property $\tilde{\mathsf{P}} \perp \mathsf{P}$ is evident, since $\mathsf{P}(z_\infty = \infty) = 0$.

This completes the proof of the theorem.

2. It is clear from Theorem 2 that the tests for absolute continuity or singularity can be expressed either in terms of P (verify the equation $\mathsf{E} z_\infty = 1$ or $\mathsf{E} z_\infty = 0$), or in terms of $\tilde{\mathsf{P}}$ (verify that $\tilde{\mathsf{P}}(z_\infty < \infty) = 1$ or that $\tilde{\mathsf{P}}(z_\infty = \infty) = 1$.

By Theorem 5 of §6, Chapter II, the condition $\mathsf{E} z_\infty = 1$ is equivalent to the uniform integrability (with respect to P) of the family $\{z_n\}_{n \geq 1}$. This allows us to give simple *sufficient conditions for the absolute continuity* $\tilde{\mathsf{P}} \ll \mathsf{P}$. For example, if

$$\sup_n \mathsf{E}[z_n \ln^+ z_n] < \infty \tag{12}$$

or if

$$\sup_n \mathsf{E} z_n^{1+\varepsilon} < \infty, \qquad \varepsilon > 0, \tag{13}$$

then, by Lemma 3 of §6, Chapter II, the family of random variables $\{z_n\}_{n \geq 1}$ is uniformly integrable and therefore $\tilde{\mathsf{P}} \ll \mathsf{P}$.

In many cases it is preferable to verify the property of absolute continuity or of singularity by using a test in terms of $\tilde{\mathsf{P}}$, since then the question is reduced to the investigation of the probability of the "tail" event $\{z_\infty < \infty\}$, where one can use propositions like the "zero-one" law.

Let us show, by way of illustration, that the "Kakutani dichotomy" can be deduced from Theorem 2.

Let $(\Omega, \mathscr{F}, \mathsf{P})$ be a probability space, let $(R^\infty, \mathscr{B}_\infty)$ be a measurable space of sequences $x = (x_1, x_2, \ldots)$ of numbers with $\mathscr{B}_\infty = \mathscr{B}(R^\infty)$, and let $\mathscr{B}_n = \sigma\{x : \{x_1, \ldots, x_n\}\}$. Let $\xi = (\xi_1, \xi_2, \ldots)$ and $\tilde{\xi} = (\tilde{\xi}_1, \tilde{\xi}_2, \ldots)$ be sequences of independent random variables.

Let P and $\tilde{P}$ be the probability distributions on $(R^\infty, \mathscr{B}_\infty)$ for ξ and $\tilde{\xi}$, respectively, i.e.

$$P(B) = \mathsf{P}\{\xi \in B\}, \qquad \tilde{P}(B) = \mathsf{P}\{\tilde{\xi} \in B\}, \qquad B \in \mathscr{B}_\infty.$$

Also let

$$P_n = P \,|\, \mathscr{B}_n, \qquad \tilde{P}_n = \tilde{P} \,|\, \mathscr{B}_n$$

be the restrictions of P and $\tilde{P}$ to $\mathscr{B}_n$ and let

$$P_{\xi_n}(A) = \mathsf{P}(\xi_n \in A), \qquad P_{\tilde{\xi}_n}(A) = \mathsf{P}(\tilde{\xi}_n \in A), \qquad A \in \mathscr{B}(R^1).$$

Theorem 3 (Kakutani Dichotomy). *Let $\xi = (\xi_1, \xi_2, \ldots)$ and $\tilde{\xi} = (\tilde{\xi}_1, \tilde{\xi}_2, \ldots)$ be sequences of independent random variables for which*

$$P_{\tilde{\xi}_n} \ll P_{\xi_n}, \qquad n \geq 1. \tag{14}$$

Then either $\tilde{P} \ll P$ or $\tilde{P} \perp P$.

PROOF. Condition (14) is evidently equivalent to $\tilde{P}_n \ll P_n, n \geq 1$, i.e. $\tilde{P} \overset{\text{loc}}{\ll} P$. It is clear that

$$z_n = \frac{d\tilde{P}_n}{dP_n} = q_1(x_1) \cdots q_n(x_n),$$

where

$$q_i(x_i) = \frac{dP_{\tilde{\xi}_i}}{dP_{\xi_i}}(x_i). \tag{15}$$

Consequently

$$\{x : z_\infty < \infty\} = \{x : \ln z_\infty < \infty\} = \left\{ x : \sum_{i=1}^\infty \ln q_i(x_i) < \infty \right\}.$$

The event $\{x : \sum_{i=1}^\infty \ln q_i(x_i) < \infty\}$ is a tail event. Therefore, by the Kolmogorov zero-one law (Theorem 1 of §1, Chapter IV) the probability $\tilde{P}\{x : z_\infty < \infty\}$ has only two values (0 or 1), and therefore by Theorem 2 either $\tilde{P} \perp P$ or $\tilde{P} \ll P$.

This completes the proof of the theorem.

3. The following theorem provides, in "predictable" terms, a test for absolute continuity or singularity.

Theorem 4. *Let $\tilde{P} \overset{\text{loc}}{\ll} P$ and let*

$$\alpha_n = z_n z_{n-1}^\oplus, \qquad n \geq 1,$$

with $z_0 = 1$. Then (with $\mathscr{F}_0 = \{\varnothing, \Omega\}$)

$$\tilde{P} \ll P \Leftrightarrow \tilde{P}\left\{ \sum_{n=1}^\infty [1 - \mathsf{E}(\sqrt{\alpha_n} \,|\, \mathscr{F}_{n-1})] < \infty \right\} = 1, \tag{16}$$

$$\tilde{P} \perp P \Leftrightarrow \tilde{P}\left\{ \sum_{n=1}^\infty [1 - \mathsf{E}(\sqrt{\alpha_n} \,|\, \mathscr{F}_{n-1})] = \infty \right\} = 1. \tag{17}$$

PROOF. Since

$$\tilde{P}_n\{z_n = 0\} = \int_{[z_n = 0]} z_n\, dP = 0,$$

we have (P-a.s.)

$$z_n = \prod_{k=1}^{n} \alpha_k = \exp\left\{\sum_{k=1}^{n} \ln \alpha_k\right\}. \tag{18}$$

Putting $A = \{z_\infty = 0\}$ in (3), we find that $\tilde{P}\{z_\infty = 0\} = 0$. Therefore, by (18), we have ($\tilde{P}$-a.s.)

$$\{z_\infty < \infty\} = \{0 < z_\infty < \infty\} = \{0 < \lim z_n < \infty\}$$

$$= \left\{-\infty < \lim \sum_{k=1}^{n} \ln \alpha_k < \infty\right\}. \tag{19}$$

Let us introduce the function

$$u(x) = \begin{cases} x, & |x| \le 1, \\ \text{sign } x, & |x| > 1. \end{cases}$$

Then

$$\left\{-\infty < \lim \sum_{k=1}^{n} \ln \alpha_k < \infty\right\} = \left\{-\infty < \lim \sum_{k=1}^{n} u(\ln \alpha_k) < \infty\right\}. \tag{20}$$

Let $\tilde{E}$ denote averaging with respect to $\tilde{P}$ and let η be an $\mathscr{F}_n$-measurable integrable random variable. It follows from the properties of conditional expectations (Problem 4) that

$$z_{n-1}\tilde{E}(\eta|\mathscr{F}_{n-1}) = E(\eta z_n|\mathscr{F}_{n-1}) \quad \text{(P- and } \tilde{P}\text{-a.s.)}, \tag{21}$$

$$\tilde{E}(\eta|\mathscr{F}_{n-1}) = z_{n-1}^{\oplus} E(\eta z_n|\mathscr{F}_{n-1}) \quad (\tilde{P}\text{-a.s.)}. \tag{22}$$

Recalling that $\alpha_n = z_{n-1}^{\oplus} z_n$, we obtain the following useful formula from (22):

$$\tilde{E}(\eta|\mathscr{F}_{n-1}) = E(\alpha_n \eta|\mathscr{F}_{n-1}) \quad (\tilde{P}\text{-a.s.)}. \tag{23}$$

From this it follows, in particular, that

$$E(\alpha_n|\mathscr{F}_{n-1}) = 1 \quad (\tilde{P}\text{-a.s.)}. \tag{24}$$

By (23),

$$\tilde{E}[u(\ln \alpha_n)|\mathscr{F}_{n-1}] = E[\alpha_n u(\ln \alpha_n)|\mathscr{F}_{n-1}] \quad (\tilde{P}\text{-a.s.)}.$$

Since $xu(\ln x) \ge x - 1$ for $x \ge 0$, we have, by (24),

$$\tilde{E}[u(\ln \alpha_n)|\mathscr{F}_{n-1}] \ge 0 \quad (\tilde{P}\text{-a.s.)}.$$

It follows that the stochastic sequence $X = (X_n, \mathscr{F}_n)$ with

$$X_n = \sum_{k=1}^{n} u(\ln \alpha_k)$$

is a submartingale with respect to $\tilde{\mathsf{P}}$; and $|\Delta X_n| = |u(\ln \alpha_n)| \le 1$.

Then, by Theorem 5 of §5, we have ($\tilde{\mathsf{P}}$-a.s.)

$$\left\{ -\infty < \lim \sum_{k=1}^{n} u(\ln \alpha_k) < \infty \right\} = \left\{ \sum_{k=1}^{\infty} \tilde{\mathsf{E}}[u(\ln \alpha_k) + u^2(\ln \alpha_k)|\mathscr{F}_{k-1}] < \infty \right\}.$$

(25)

Hence we find, by combining (19), (20), (22) and (25), that (P-a.s.)

$$\{z_\infty < \infty\} = \left\{ \sum_{k=1}^{\infty} \tilde{\mathsf{E}}[u(\ln \alpha_k) + u^2(\ln \alpha_k)|\mathscr{F}_{k-1}] < \infty \right\}$$

$$= \left\{ \sum_{k=1}^{\infty} \mathsf{E}[\alpha_k u(\ln \alpha_k) + \alpha_k u^2(\ln \alpha_k)|\mathscr{F}_{k-1}] < \infty \right\}$$

and consequently, by Theorem 2,

$$\tilde{\mathsf{P}} \ll \mathsf{P} \Leftrightarrow \tilde{\mathsf{P}}\left\{ \sum_{k=1}^{\infty} \mathsf{E}[\alpha_k u(\ln \alpha_k) + \alpha_k u^2(\ln \alpha_k)|\mathscr{F}_{k-1}] < \infty \right\} = 1, \quad (26)$$

$$\tilde{\mathsf{P}} \perp \mathsf{P} \Leftrightarrow \tilde{\mathsf{P}}\left\{ \sum_{k=1}^{\infty} \mathsf{E}[\alpha_k u(\ln \alpha_k) + \alpha_k u^2(\ln \alpha_k)|\mathscr{F}_{k-1}] = \infty \right\} = 1. \quad (27)$$

We now observe that by (24),

$$\mathsf{E}[(1 - \sqrt{\alpha_n})^2|\mathscr{F}_{n-1}] = 2\mathsf{E}[1 - \sqrt{\alpha_n}|\mathscr{F}_{n-1}] \quad (\tilde{\mathsf{P}}\text{-a.s.})$$

and for $x \ge 0$ there are constants A and B $(0 < A < B < \infty)$ such that

$$A(1 - \sqrt{x})^2 \le xu(\ln x) + xu^2(\ln x) + 1 - x \le B(1 - \sqrt{x})^2. \quad (28)$$

Hence (16) and (17) follow from (26), (27) and (24), (28).

This completes the proof of the theorem.

Corollary 1. *If, for all $n \ge 1$, the σ-algebras $\sigma(\alpha_n)$ and $\mathscr{F}_{n-1}$ are independent with respect to P(or $\tilde{\mathsf{P}}$), and $\tilde{\mathsf{P}} \overset{\text{loc}}{\ll} \mathsf{P}$, then we have the dichotomy:* either $\tilde{\mathsf{P}} \ll \mathsf{P}$ or $\tilde{\mathsf{P}} \perp \mathsf{P}$. Correspondingly,

$$\tilde{\mathsf{P}} \ll \mathsf{P} \Leftrightarrow \sum_{n=1}^{\infty} [1 - \mathsf{E}\sqrt{\alpha_n}] < \infty,$$

$$\tilde{\mathsf{P}} \perp \mathsf{P} \Leftrightarrow \sum_{n=1}^{\infty} [1 - \mathsf{E}\sqrt{\alpha_n}] = \infty.$$

In particular, in the Kakutani situation (see Theorem 3) $\alpha_n = q_n$ and

$$\tilde{P} \ll P \Leftrightarrow \sum_{n=1}^{\infty} [1 - E\sqrt{q_n(x_n)}] < \infty,$$

$$\tilde{P} \perp P \Leftrightarrow \sum_{n=1}^{\infty} [1 - E\sqrt{q_n(x_n)}] = \infty.$$

Corollary 2. *Let* $\tilde{P} \overset{loc}{\ll} P$. *Then*

$$\tilde{P}\left\{ \sum_{n=1}^{\infty} E(\alpha_n \ln \alpha_n | \mathscr{F}_{n-1}) < \infty \right\} = 1 \Rightarrow \tilde{P} \ll P.$$

For the proof, it is enough to notice that

$$x \ln x + \tfrac{3}{2}(1 - x) \geq 1 - x^{1/2}, \tag{29}$$

for all $x \geq 0$, and apply (16) and (24).

Corollary 3. *Since the series* $\sum_{n=1}^{\infty}[1 - E(\sqrt{\alpha_n}|\mathscr{F}_{n-1})]$, *which has nonnegative* ($\tilde{P}$-a.s.) *terms, converges or diverges with the series* $\sum |\ln E(\sqrt{\alpha_n}|\mathscr{F}_{n-1})|$, *conclusions* (16) *and* (17) *of Theorem 4 can be put in the form*

$$\tilde{P} \ll P \Leftrightarrow \tilde{P}\left\{ \sum_{n=1}^{\infty} |\ln E(\sqrt{\alpha_n}|\mathscr{F}_{n-1})| < \infty \right\} = 1, \tag{30}$$

$$\tilde{P} \perp P \Leftrightarrow \tilde{P}\left\{ \sum_{n=1}^{\infty} |\ln E(\sqrt{\alpha_n}|\mathscr{F}_{n-1})| = \infty \right\} = 1. \tag{31}$$

Corollary 4. *Let there exist constants A and B such that* $0 \leq A < 1, B \geq 0$ *and*

$$P\{1 - A \leq \alpha_n \leq 1 + B\} = 1, \qquad n \geq 1.$$

Then if $\tilde{P} \overset{loc}{\ll} P$ *we have*

$$\tilde{P} \ll P \Leftrightarrow \tilde{P}\left\{ \sum_{n=1}^{\infty} E[(1 - \alpha_n)^2 | \mathscr{F}_{n-1}] < \infty \right\} = 1,$$

$$\tilde{P} \perp P \Leftrightarrow \tilde{P}\left\{ \sum_{n=1}^{\infty} E[(1 - \alpha_n)^2 | \mathscr{F}_{n-1}] = \infty \right\} = 1.$$

For the proof it is enough to notice that when $x \in [1 - A, 1 + B]$, where $0 \leq A < 1, B \geq 0$, there are constants c and C $(0 < c < C < \infty)$ such that

$$c(1 - x)^2 \leq (1 - \sqrt{x})^2 \leq C(1 - x)^2. \tag{32}$$

4. With the notation of Subsection 2, let us suppose that $\xi = (\xi_1, \xi_2, \ldots)$ and $\tilde{\xi} = (\tilde{\xi}_1, \tilde{\xi}_2, \ldots)$ are Gaussian sequences, $\tilde{P}_n \sim P_n$, $n \geq 1$. Let us show that, for such sequences, the "Hájek–Feldman dichotomy," *either* $\tilde{P} \sim P$ *or* $\tilde{P} \perp P$, follows from the "predictable" test given above.

By the theorem on normal correlation (Theorem 2 of §13, Chapter II) the conditional expectations $M(x_n|\mathscr{B}_{n-1})$ and $\tilde{M}(x_n|\mathscr{B}_{n-1})$, where M and $\tilde{M}$

are averages with respect to P and $\tilde{P}$, respectively, are linear functions of $x_1, \ldots, x_{n-1}$. We denote these linear functions by $a_{n-1}(x)$ and $\tilde{a}_{n-1}(x)$ and put

$$b_{n-1} = (M[x_n - a_{n-1}(x)]^2)^{1/2},$$
$$\tilde{b}_{n-1} = (\tilde{M}[x_n - \tilde{a}_{n-1}(x)]^2)^{1/2}.$$

Again by the theorem on normal correlation, there are sequences $\varepsilon = (\varepsilon_1, \varepsilon_2, \ldots)$ and $\tilde{\varepsilon} = (\tilde{\varepsilon}_1, \tilde{\varepsilon}_2, \ldots)$ of independent Gaussian random variables with zero means and unit variances, such that

$$x_n = a_{n-1}(x) + b_{n-1}\varepsilon_n, \quad (P\text{-a.s.}),$$
$$x_n = \tilde{a}_{n-1}(x) + \tilde{b}_{n-1}\tilde{\varepsilon}_n \quad (\tilde{P}\text{-a.s.}). \tag{33}$$

Notice that if $b_{n-1} = 0$, or $\tilde{b}_{n-1} = 0$, it is generally necessary to extend the probability space in order to construct ε_n or $\tilde{\varepsilon}_n$. However, if $b_{n-1} = 0$ the extended vector $(x_1, \ldots, x_n)$ will be contained (P-a.s.) in the linear manifold $x_n = a_{n-1}(x)$, and since by hypothesis $\tilde{P}_n \sim P_n$, we have $b_{n-1} = 0$, $a_{n-1} = \tilde{a}_{n-1}(x)$, and $\alpha_n(x) = 1$ (P- or $\tilde{P}$-a.s.). Hence we may suppose without loss of generality that $b_n^2 > 0$, $\tilde{b}_n^2 > 0$ for all $n \geq 1$, since otherwise the contribution of the corresponding terms of the sum $\sum_{n=1}^{\infty}[1 - M\sqrt{\alpha_n}|B_{n-1}]$ (see (16) and (17)) is zero.

Using the Gaussian hypothesis, we find from (33) that, for $n \geq 1$,

$$\alpha_n = d_{n-1}^{-1} \exp\left\{-\frac{(x_n - a_{n-1}(x))^2}{2b_{n-1}^2} + \frac{(x_n - \tilde{a}_{n-1}(x))^2}{2\tilde{b}_{n-1}^2}\right\}, \tag{34}$$

where $d_n = |\tilde{b}_n \cdot \tilde{b}_n^{-1}|$ and

$$a_0(x) = \mathsf{E}\xi_1, \qquad \tilde{a}_0(x) = \mathsf{E}\tilde{\xi}_1,$$
$$b_0^2 = \mathsf{V}\xi_1, \qquad \tilde{b}_0^2 = \mathsf{V}\tilde{\xi}_1.$$

From (34),

$$\ln M(\alpha_n^{1/2}|\mathscr{B}_{n-1}) = \tfrac{1}{2}\ln\frac{2d_{n-1}}{1+d_{n-1}^2} - \frac{d_{n-1}^2}{1+d_{n-1}^2}\left(\frac{a_{n-1}(x) - \tilde{a}_{n-1}(x)}{b_{n-1}}\right)^2.$$

Since $\ln[2d_{n-1}/(1 + d_{n-1}^2)] \leq 0$, statement (30) can be written in the form

$$\tilde{P} \ll P \Leftrightarrow \tilde{P}\left\{\sum_{n=1}^{\infty}\left[\tfrac{1}{2}\ln\frac{1+d_{n-1}^2}{2d_{n-1}} + \frac{d_{n-1}^2}{1+d_{n-1}^2}\cdot\left(\frac{a_{n-1}(x) - \tilde{a}_{n-1}(x)}{b_{n-1}}\right)^2\right] < \infty\right\}$$
$$= 1. \tag{35}$$

The series

$$\sum_{n=1}^{\infty}\ln\frac{1+d_{n-1}^2}{2d_{n-1}} \quad \text{and} \quad \sum_{n=1}^{\infty}(d_{n-1}^2 - 1)$$

converge or diverge together; hence it follows from (35) that

$$\tilde{P} \ll P \Leftrightarrow \tilde{P}\left\{ \sum_{n=0}^{\infty} \left[\left(\frac{\tilde{b}_n^2}{b_n^2} - 1 \right)^2 + \frac{\Delta_n^2(x)}{b_n^2} \right] < \infty \right\} = 1, \tag{36}$$

where $\Delta_n(x) = a_n(x) - \tilde{a}_n(x)$.

Since $a_n(x)$ and $\tilde{a}_n(x)$ are linear, the sequence of random variables $\{\Delta_n(x)/b_n\}_{n \geq 0}$ is a Gaussian system (with respect to both $\tilde{P}$ and P). As follows from a lemma that will be proved below, such sequences satisfy an analog of the zero-one law:

$$\tilde{P}\left\{ \sum \left(\frac{\Delta_n(x)}{b_n} \right)^2 < \infty \right\} = 1 \Leftrightarrow \sum \tilde{M}\left(\frac{\Delta_n(x)}{b_n} \right)^2 < \infty. \tag{37}$$

Hence it follows from (36) that

$$\tilde{P} \ll P \Leftrightarrow \sum_{n=0}^{\infty} \left[\tilde{M}\left(\frac{\Delta_n(x)}{b_n} \right)^2 + \left(\frac{\tilde{b}_n^2}{b_n^2} - 1 \right)^2 \right] < \infty$$

and in a similar way

$$\tilde{P} \perp P \Leftrightarrow \sum_{n=0}^{\infty} \left[\tilde{M}\left(\frac{\Delta_n(x)}{b_n} \right)^2 + \left(\frac{\tilde{b}_n^2}{b_n^2} - 1 \right)^2 \right] = \infty.$$

Then it is clear that if $\tilde{P}$ and P are not singular measures, we have $\tilde{P} \ll P$. But by hypothesis, $\tilde{P}_n \sim P_n$, $n \geq 1$; hence by symmetry we have $P \ll \tilde{P}$. Therefore we have the following theorem.

Theorem 5 (Hájek–Feldman Dichotomy). *Let $\xi = (\xi_1, \xi_2, \ldots)$ and $\tilde{\xi} = (\tilde{\xi}_1, \tilde{\xi}_2, \ldots)$ be Gaussian sequences whose finite-dimensional distributions are equivalent: $\tilde{P}_n \sim P_n, n \geq 1$. Then either $\tilde{P} \sim P$ or $\tilde{P} \perp P$. Moreover,*

$$\begin{aligned} \tilde{P} \sim P &\Leftrightarrow \sum_{n=0}^{\infty} \left[\tilde{M}\left(\frac{\Delta_n(x)}{b_n} \right)^2 + \left(\frac{\tilde{b}_n^2}{b_n^2} - 1 \right)^2 \right] < \infty, \\ \tilde{P} \perp P &\Leftrightarrow \sum_{n=0}^{\infty} \left[\tilde{M}\left(\frac{\Delta_n(x)}{b_n} \right)^2 + \left(\frac{\tilde{b}_n^2}{b_n^2} - 1 \right)^2 \right] = \infty. \end{aligned} \tag{38}$$

Let us now prove the zero-one law for Gaussian sequences that we need for the proof of Theorem 5.

Lemma. *Let $\beta = (\beta_n)_{n \geq 1}$ be a Gaussian sequence defined on $(\Omega, \mathscr{F}; P)$. Then*

$$P\left\{ \sum_{n=1}^{\infty} \beta_n^2 < \infty \right\} = 1 \Leftrightarrow \sum_{n=1}^{\infty} E\beta_n^2 < \infty. \tag{39}$$

PROOF. The implication $\Leftarrow$ follows from Fubini's theorem. To establish the opposite proposition, we first suppose that $E\beta_n = 0, n \geq 1$. Here it is enough to show that

$$E \sum_{n=1}^{\infty} \beta_n^2 \leq \left[E \exp\left(- \sum_{n=1}^{\infty} \beta_n^2 \right) \right]^{-2}, \tag{40}$$

since then the condition $\mathsf{P}\{\sum \beta_n^2 < \infty\} = 1$ will imply that the right-hand side of (40) is finite.

Select an $n \geq 1$. Then it follows from §§11 and 13, Chapter II, that there are independent Gaussian random variables $\beta_{k,n}$, $k = 1, \ldots, r \leq n$, with $\mathsf{E}\beta_{k,n} = 0$, such that

$$\sum_{k=1}^{n} \beta_k^2 = \sum_{k=1}^{r} \beta_{k,n}^2.$$

If we write $\mathsf{E}\beta_{k,n}^2 = \lambda_{k,n}$, we see easily that

$$\mathsf{E} \sum_{k=1}^{r} \beta_{k,n}^2 = \sum_{k=1}^{r} \lambda_{k,n} \tag{41}$$

and

$$\mathsf{E} \exp\left(- \sum_{k=1}^{r} \beta_{k,n}^2\right) = \prod_{k=1}^{r} (1 + 2\lambda_{k,n})^{-1/2}. \tag{42}$$

Comparing the right-hand sides of (41) and (42), we obtain

$$\mathsf{E} \sum_{k=1}^{n} \beta_k^2 = \mathsf{E} \sum_{k=1}^{r} \beta_{k,n}^2 \leq \left[\mathsf{E} \exp\left(- \sum_{k=1}^{r} \beta_{k,n}^2\right)\right]^{-2} = \left[\mathsf{E} \exp\left(- \sum_{k=1}^{n} \beta_k^2\right)\right]^{-2},$$

from which, by letting $n \to \infty$, we obtain the required inequality (40).

Now suppose that $\mathsf{E}\beta_n \not\equiv 0$.

Let us consider again the sequence $\tilde{\beta} = (\tilde{\beta}_n)_{n \geq 1}$ with the same distribution as $\beta = (\beta_n)_{n \geq 1}$ but independent of it (if necessary, extending the original probability space). If $\mathsf{P}\{\sum_{n=1}^{\infty} \beta_n^2 < \infty\} = 1$, then $\mathsf{P}\{\sum_{n=1}^{\infty} (\beta_n - \tilde{\beta}_n)^2 < \infty\} = 1$, and by what we have proved,

$$2 \sum_{n=1}^{\infty} \mathsf{E}(\beta_n - \mathsf{E}\beta_n)^2 = \sum_{n=1}^{\infty} \mathsf{E}(\beta_n - \tilde{\beta}_n)^2 < \infty.$$

Since

$$(\mathsf{E}\beta_n)^2 \leq 2\beta_n^2 + 2(\beta_n - \mathsf{E}\beta_n)^2,$$

we have $\sum_{n=1}^{\infty} (\mathsf{E}\beta_n)^2 < \infty$ and therefore

$$\sum_{n=1}^{\infty} \mathsf{E}\beta_n^2 = \sum_{n=1}^{\infty} (\mathsf{E}\beta_n)^2 + \sum_{n=1}^{\infty} \mathsf{E}(\beta_n - M\beta_n)^2 < \infty.$$

This completes the proof of the lemma.

5. We continue the discussion of the example in Subsection 3 of the preceding section, assuming that $\xi_0, \xi_1, \ldots$ are independent Gaussian random variables with $\mathsf{E}\xi_i = 0$, $\mathsf{V}\xi_i = V_i > 0$.

Again we let

$$X_{n+1} = \theta X_n + \xi_{n+1}$$

for $n \geq 1$, where $X_0 = \xi_0$, and the unknown parameter θ that is to be estimated has values in R. Let $\hat{\theta}_n$ be the least-squares estimator (see (5.22)).

Theorem 6. *A necessary and sufficient condition for the estimator $\hat{\theta}_n$, $n \geq 1$, to be strongly consistent is that*

$$\sum_{n=0}^{\infty} \frac{V_n}{V_{n+1}} = \infty. \tag{43}$$

PROOF. *Sufficiency.* Let P_θ denote the probability distribution on $(R^\infty, \mathscr{B}_\infty)$ corresponding to the sequence $(X_0, X_1, \ldots)$ when the true value of the unknown parameter is θ. Let E_θ denote an average with respect to P_θ.

We have already seen that

$$\hat{\theta}_n = \theta + \frac{M_n}{\langle M \rangle_n},$$

where

$$\langle M \rangle_n = \sum_{k=0}^{n-1} \frac{X_k^2}{V_{k+1}}.$$

According to the lemma from the preceding subsection,

$$P_\theta(\langle M \rangle_\infty = \infty) = 1 \Leftrightarrow E_\theta \langle M \rangle_\infty = \infty,$$

i.e. $\langle M \rangle_\infty = \infty$ (P_θ-a.s.) if and only if

$$\sum_{k=0}^{\infty} \frac{E_\theta X_k^2}{V_{k+1}} = \infty. \tag{44}$$

But

$$E_\theta X_k^2 = \sum_{i=0}^{k} \theta^{2i} V_{k-i}$$

and

$$\sum_{k=0}^{\infty} \frac{E_\theta X_k^2}{V_{k+1}} = \sum_{k=0}^{\infty} \frac{1}{V_{k+1}} \left(\sum_{i=0}^{k} \theta^{2i} V_{k-i} \right)$$

$$= \sum_{k=0}^{\infty} \theta^{2k} \sum_{i=k}^{\infty} \frac{V_{i-k}}{V_{i+1}} = \sum_{i=0}^{\infty} \frac{V_i}{V_{i+1}} + \sum_{k=1}^{\infty} \theta^{2k} \left(\sum_{i=k}^{\infty} \frac{V_{i-k}}{V_{i+1}} \right). \tag{45}$$

Hence (44) follows from (43) and therefore, by Theorem 4, the estimator $\hat{\theta}_n$, $n \geq 1$, is strongly consistent for every θ.

Necessity. For all $\theta \in R$, let $P_\theta(\hat{\theta}_n \to \theta) = 1$. It follows that if $\theta_1 \neq \theta_2$, the measures P_{θ_1} and P_{θ_2} are singular ($P_{\theta_1} \perp P_{\theta_2}$). In fact, since the sequence $(X_0, X_1, \ldots)$ is Gaussian, by Theorem 5 of §5 the measures P_{θ_1} and P_{θ_2} are either singular or equivalent. But they cannot be equivalent, since if $P_{\theta_1} \sim P_{\theta_2}$, but $P_{\theta_1}(\hat\theta_n \to \theta_1) = 1$, then also $P_{\theta_2}(\hat\theta_n \to \theta_1) = 1$. However, by hypothesis, $P_{\theta_2}(\hat\theta_n \to \theta_2) = 1$ and $\theta_2 \neq \theta_1$. Therefore $P_{\theta_1} \perp P_{\theta_2}$ for $\theta_1 \neq \theta_2$.

According to (5.38),

$$P_{\theta_1} \perp P_{\theta_2} \Leftrightarrow (\theta_1 - \theta_2)^2 \sum_{k=0}^{\infty} E_{\theta_1}\left[\frac{X_k^2}{V_{k+1}}\right] = \infty$$

for $\theta_1 \neq \theta_2$. Taking $\theta_1 = 0$ and $\theta_2 \neq 0$, we obtain from (45) that

$$P_0 \perp P_{\theta_2} \Leftrightarrow \sum_{i=0}^{\infty} \frac{V_i}{V_{i+1}} = \infty,$$

which establishes the necessity of (43).

This completes the proof of the theorem.

6. Problems

1. Prove (6).

2. Let $\tilde P_n \sim P_n, n \geq 1$. Show that

$$\tilde P \sim P \Leftrightarrow \tilde P\{z_\infty < \infty\} = P\{z_\infty > 0\} = 1,$$

$$\tilde P \perp P \Leftrightarrow \tilde P\{z_\infty = \infty\} = 1 \quad \text{or} \quad P\{z_\infty = 0\} = 1.$$

3. Let $\tilde P_n \ll P_n, n \geq 1$, let τ be a stopping time (with respect to $(\mathscr{F}_n)$), and let $\tilde P_\tau = \tilde P | \mathscr{F}_\tau$ and $P_\tau = P | \mathscr{F}_\tau$ be the restrictions of $\tilde P$ and P to the σ-algebra $\mathscr{F}_\tau$. Show that $\tilde P_\tau \ll P_\tau$ if and only if $\{\tau = \infty\} = \{z_\infty < \infty\}$ ($\tilde P$-a.s.). (In particular, if $\tilde P\{\tau < \infty\} = 1$ then $\tilde P_\tau \ll P_\tau$.)

4. Prove (21) and (22).

5. Verify (28), (29) and (32).

6. Prove (34).

7. In Subsection 2 let the sequences $\xi = (\xi_1, \xi_2, \ldots)$ and $\tilde\xi = (\tilde\xi_1, \tilde\xi_2, \ldots)$ consist of independent identically distributed random variables. Show that if $P_{\xi_1} \ll P_{\tilde\xi_1}$, then $\tilde P \ll P$ if and only if the measures $P_{\tilde\xi_1}$ and P_{ξ_1} coincide. If, however, $P_{\tilde\xi_1} \ll P_{\xi_1}$ and $P_{\tilde\xi_1} \neq P_{\xi_1}$, then $\tilde P \perp P$.

§7. Asymptotics of the Probability of the Outcome of a Random Walk with Curvilinear Boundary

1. Let $\xi_1, \xi_2, \ldots$ be a sequence of independent identically distributed random variables. Let $S_n = \xi_1 + \cdots + \xi_n$, let $g = g(n)$ be a "boundary," $n \geq 1$, and let

$$\tau = \inf\{n \geq 1 : S_n < g(n)\}$$

be the first time at which the random walk (S_n) is found below the boundary $g = g(n)$. (As usual, $\tau = \infty$ if $\{\cdot\} = \varnothing$.)

It is difficult to discover the exact form of the distribution of the time τ. In the present section we find the asymptotic form of the probability $P(\tau > n)$ as $n \to \infty$, for a wide class of boundaries $g = g(n)$ and assuming that the ξ_i are normally distributed. The method of proof is based on the idea of an absolutely continuous change of measure together with a number of the properties of martingales and Markov times that were presented earlier.

Theorem 1. *Let* $\xi_1, \xi_2, \ldots$ *be independent identically distributed random variables, with* $\xi_i \sim \mathcal{N}(0, 1)$. *Suppose that* $g = g(n)$ *is such that* $g(1) < 0$ *and, for* $n \geq 2$,

$$0 \leq \Delta g(n + 1) \leq \Delta g(n), \tag{1}$$

where $\Delta g(n) = g(n) - g(n - 1)$ *and*

$$\ln n = o\left(\sum_{k=2}^{n} [\Delta g(k)]^2 \right), \qquad n \to \infty. \tag{2}$$

Then

$$P(\tau > n) = \exp\left\{ -\frac{1}{2} \sum_{k=2}^{n} [\Delta g(k)]^2(1 + o(1)) \right\}, \qquad n \to \infty. \tag{3}$$

Before starting the proof, let us observe that (1) and (2) are satisfied if, for example,

$$g(n) = an^v + b, \qquad \tfrac{1}{2} < v \leq 1, \quad a + b < 0,$$

or (for sufficiently large n)

$$g(n) = n^v L(n), \qquad \tfrac{1}{2} \leq v \leq 1,$$

where $L(n)$ is a slowly varying function (for example, $L(n) = C(\ln n)^\beta$ with arbitrary β for $\tfrac{1}{2} < v < 1$ or with $\beta > 0$ for $v = \tfrac{1}{2}$).

2. We shall need the following two auxiliary propositions for the proof of Theorem 1.

Let us suppose that $\xi_1, \xi_2, \ldots$ is a sequence of independent identically distributed random variables, $\xi_i \sim \mathcal{N}(0, 1)$. Let $\mathscr{F}_0 = \{\varnothing, \Omega\}$, $\mathscr{F}_n = \sigma\{\omega : \xi_1, \ldots, \xi_n\}$, and let $\alpha = (a_n, \mathscr{F}_{n-1})$ be a predictable sequence with $P(|\alpha_n| \leq C) = 1$, $n \geq 1$, where C is a constant. Form the sequence $z = (z_n, \mathscr{F}_n)$ with

$$z_n = \exp\left\{ \sum_{k=1}^{n} \alpha_k \xi_k - \frac{1}{2} \sum_{k=1}^{n} \alpha_k^2 \right\}, \qquad n \geq 1. \tag{4}$$

It is easily verified that (with respect to P) the sequence $z = (z_n, \mathscr{F}_n)$ is a martingale with $Ez_n = 1, n \geq 1$.

Choose a value $n \geq 1$ and introduce a probability measure $\tilde{P}_n$ on the measurable space $(\Omega, \mathscr{F}_n)$ by putting

$$\tilde{P}_n(A) = EI(A)z_n, \qquad A \in \mathscr{F}_n. \tag{5}$$

Lemma 1. *With respect to $\tilde{\mathsf{P}}_n$, the random variables $\tilde{\xi}_k = \xi_k - \alpha_k, 1 \leq k \leq n$, are independent and normally distributed, $\tilde{\xi}_k \sim \mathcal{N}(0, 1)$.*

PROOF. Let $\tilde{\mathsf{E}}_n$ denote averaging with respect to $\tilde{\mathsf{P}}_n$. Then for $\lambda_k \in R, 1 \leq k \leq n$,

$$\tilde{\mathsf{E}}_n \exp\left\{ i \sum_{k=1}^{n} \lambda_k \tilde{\xi}_k \right\} = \mathsf{E} \exp\left\{ i \sum_{k=1}^{n} \lambda_k \tilde{\xi}_k \right\} z_n$$

$$= \mathsf{E}\left[\exp\left\{ i \sum_{k=1}^{n-1} \lambda_k \tilde{\xi}_k \right\} z_{n-1} \cdot \mathsf{E}\left\{ \exp\left(i\lambda_n(\xi_n - \alpha_n) + \alpha_n \xi_n - \frac{\alpha_n^2}{2} \right) \bigg| \mathscr{F}_{n-1} \right\} \right]$$

$$= \mathsf{E}\left[\exp\left\{ i \sum_{k=1}^{n-1} \lambda_k \tilde{\xi}_k \right\} z_{n-1} \right] \exp\{ -\tfrac{1}{2}\lambda_n^2 \} = \cdots = \exp\left\{ -\frac{1}{2} \sum_{k=1}^{n} \lambda_k^2 \right\}.$$

Now the desired conclusion follows from Theorem 4 of §12, Chapter II.

Lemma 2. *Let $X = (X_n, \mathscr{F}_n)_{n \geq 1}$ be a square-integrable martingale with mean zero and*

$$\sigma = \inf\{n \geq 1 : X_n \leq -b\},$$

where b is a constant, $b > 0$. Suppose that

$$\mathsf{P}(X_1 < -b) > 0.$$

Then there is a constant $C > 0$ such that, for all $n \geq 1$,

$$\mathsf{P}(\sigma > n) \geq \frac{C}{\mathsf{E}X_n^2}. \tag{6}$$

PROOF. By Corollary 1 to Theorem VII.2.1 we have $\mathsf{E}X_{\sigma \wedge n} = 0$, whence

$$-\mathsf{E}I(\sigma \leq n)X_\sigma = \mathsf{E}I(\sigma > n)X_n. \tag{7}$$

On the set $\{\sigma \leq n\}$

$$-X_\sigma \geq b > 0.$$

Therefore, for $n \geq 1$,

$$-\mathsf{E}I(\sigma \leq n)X_\sigma \geq b\mathsf{P}(\sigma \leq n) \geq b\mathsf{P}(\sigma = 1) = b\mathsf{P}(X_1 < -b) > 0. \tag{8}$$

On the other hand, by the Cauchy–Schwarz inequality,

$$\mathsf{E}I(\sigma > n)X_n \leq [\mathsf{P}(\sigma > n) \cdot \mathsf{E}X_n^2]^{1/2}, \tag{9}$$

which, with (7) and (8), leads to the required inequality with

$$C = (b\mathsf{P}(X_1 < -b))^2.$$

PROOF OF THEOREM 1. It is enough to show that

$$\lim_{n \to \infty} \ln \mathsf{P}(\tau > n) \bigg/ \sum_{k=2}^{n} [\Delta g(k)]^2 \geq -\tfrac{1}{2} \tag{10}$$

and

$$\varlimsup_{n\to\infty} \ln P(\tau > n) \Big/ \sum_{k=2}^{n} [\Delta g(k)]^2 \leq -\tfrac{1}{2}. \tag{11}$$

For this purpose we consider the (nonrandom) sequence $(\alpha_n)_{n\geq 1}$ with

$$\alpha_1 = 0, \quad \alpha_n = \Delta g(n), \quad n \geq 2,$$

and the probability measure $(\tilde{P}_n)_{n\geq 1}$ defined by (5). Then by Hölder's inequality

$$\tilde{P}_n(\tau > n) = EI(\tau > n) z_n \leq (P(\tau > n))^{1/q}(Ez_n^p)^{1/p}, \tag{12}$$

where $p > 1$ and $q = p/(p - 1)$.

The last factor is easily calculated explicitly:

$$(Ez_n^p)^{1/p} = \exp\left\{\frac{p-1}{2} \sum_{k=2}^{n} [\Delta g(k)]^2\right\}. \tag{13}$$

Now let us estimate the probability $\tilde{P}_n(\tau > n)$ that appears on the left-hand side of (12). We have

$$\tilde{P}_n(\tau > n) = \tilde{P}_n(S_k \geq g(k), 1 \leq k \leq n) = \tilde{P}_n(\tilde{S}_k \geq g(1), 1 \leq k \leq n),$$

where $\tilde{S}_k = \sum_{i=1}^{k} \tilde{\xi}_i, \tilde{\xi}_i = \xi_i - \alpha_i$. By Lemma 1, the variables are independent and normally distributed, $\tilde{\xi}_i \sim \mathcal{N}(0, 1)$, with respect to the measure $\tilde{P}_n$. Then by Lemma 2 (applied to $b = -g(1)$, $P = \tilde{P}_n$, $X_n = \tilde{S}_n$) we find that

$$\tilde{P}(\tau > n) \geq \frac{c}{n}, \tag{14}$$

where c is a constant.

Then it follows from (12)–(14) that, for every $p > 1$,

$$P(\tau > n) \geq C_p \exp\left\{-\frac{p}{2} \sum_{k=2}^{n} [\Delta g(k)]^2 - \frac{p}{p-1} \ln n\right\}, \tag{15}$$

where C_p is a constant. Then (15) implies the lower bound (10) by the hypotheses of the theorem, since $p > 1$ is arbitrary.

To obtain the upper bound (11), we first observe that since $z_n > 0$ (P- and $\tilde{P}$-a.s.), we have by (5)

$$P(\tau > n) = \tilde{E}_n I(\tau > n) z_n^{-1}, \tag{16}$$

where $\tilde{E}_n$ denotes an average with respect to $\tilde{P}_n$.

In the case under consideration, $\alpha_1 = 0$, $\alpha_n = \Delta g(n)$, $n \geq 2$, and therefore for $n \geq 2$

$$z_n^{-1} = \exp\left\{-\sum_{k=2}^{n} \Delta g(k) \cdot \xi_k + \frac{1}{2} \sum_{k=2}^{n} [\Delta g(k)]^2\right\}.$$

By the formula for summation by parts (see the proof of Lemma 2 of §3, Chapter IV)

$$\sum_{k=2}^{n} \Delta g(k) \cdot \xi_k = \Delta g(n) \cdot S_n - \sum_{k=2}^{n} S_{k-1}\Delta(\Delta g(k)).$$

Hence if we recall that by hypothesis $\Delta g(k) \geq 0$ and $\Delta(\Delta g(k)) \leq 0$, we find that, on the set $\{\tau > n\} = \{S_k \geq g(k), 1 \leq k \leq n\}$,

$$\sum_{k=2}^{n} \Delta g(k) \cdot \xi_k \geq \Delta g(n) \cdot g(n) - \sum_{k=3}^{n} g(k-1)\Delta(\Delta g(k)) - \xi_1 \Delta g(2)$$

$$= \sum_{k=2}^{n} [\Delta g(k)]^2 + g(1)\Delta g(2) - \xi_1 \Delta g(2).$$

Thus, by (16),

$$\mathsf{P}(\tau > n) \leq \exp\left\{-\frac{1}{2}\sum_{k=2}^{n}[\Delta g(k)]^2 - g(1)\Delta g(2)\right\}\tilde{\mathsf{E}}_n I(\tau > n)e^{-1\Delta g(2)}$$

$$\leq \exp\left\{-\frac{1}{2}\sum_{k=2}^{n}[\Delta g(k)]^2\right\}\tilde{\mathsf{E}}_n I(\tau > n)e^{-\xi_1\Delta g(2)},$$

where

$$\tilde{\mathsf{E}}_n I(\tau > n)e^{-\xi_1\Delta g(2)} \leq \mathsf{E}z_n e^{-\xi_1\Delta g(2)} = \mathsf{E}e^{-\xi_1\Delta g(2)} < \infty.$$

Therefore

$$\mathsf{P}(\tau > n) \leq C \exp\left\{-\frac{1}{2}\sum_{k=2}^{n}[\Delta g(k)]^2\right\},$$

where C is a positive constant; this establishes the upper bound (11).

This completes the proof of the theorem.

3. The idea of an absolutely continuous change of measure can be used to study similar problems, including the case of a two-sided boundary. We present (without proof) a result in this direction.

Theorem 2. Let $\xi_1, \xi_2, \ldots$ be independent identically distributed random variables with $\xi_i \sim \mathcal{N}(0, 1)$. Suppose that $f = f(n)$ is a positive function such that

$$f(n) \to \infty, \qquad n \to \infty,$$

and

$$\sum_{k=2}^{n} [\Delta f(k)]^2 = o\left(\sum_{k=1}^{n} f^{-2}(k)\right), \qquad n \to \infty.$$

Then if

$$\sigma = \inf\{n \geq 1 : |S_n| \geq f(n)\},$$

we have

$$P(\sigma > n) = \exp\left\{ -\frac{\pi^2}{8} \sum_{k=1}^{n} f^{-2}(k)(1 + o(1)) \right\}, \qquad n \to \infty, \qquad (17)$$

4. PROBLEMS

1. Show that the sequence defined in (4) is a martingale.

2. Establish (13).

3. Prove (17).

§8. Central Limit Theorem for Sums of Dependent Random Variables

1. Let us suppose that stochastic sequences are given on the probability space $(\Omega, \mathscr{F}, P)$:

$$\xi_n = (\xi_{nk}, \mathscr{F}_k^n), \qquad 0 \le k \le n, \quad n \ge 1,$$

with $\xi_{n0} = 0$, $\mathscr{F}_0^n = \{\varnothing, \Omega\}$, $\mathscr{F}_k^n \subseteq \mathscr{F}_{k+1}^n \subseteq \mathscr{F}$. Let

$$X_t^n = \sum_{k=0}^{[nt]} \xi_{nk}, \qquad 0 \le t \le 1,$$

and make the convention $\mathscr{F}_{-1}^n = \{\varnothing, \Omega\}$.

Theorem 1. *For a given t, $0 < t \le 1$, let the following conditions be satisfied: for each $\varepsilon \in (0, 1)$, as $n \to \infty$,*

(A) $\displaystyle\sum_{k=1}^{[nt]} P(|\xi_{nk}| > \varepsilon | \mathscr{F}_{k-1}^n) \xrightarrow{P} 0,$

(B) $\displaystyle\sum_{k=1}^{[nt]} E[\xi_{nk} I(|\xi_{nk}| \le 1) | \mathscr{F}_{k-1}^n] \xrightarrow{P} 0,$

(C) $\displaystyle\sum_{k=1}^{[nt]} V[\xi_{nk} I(|\xi_{nk}| \le \varepsilon) | \mathscr{F}_{k-1}^n] \xrightarrow{P} \sigma_t^2 \ge 0.$

Then

$$X_t^n \xrightarrow{d} \mathcal{N}(0, \sigma_t^2).$$

Let us begin by discussing the hypotheses of the theorem.

The difference from the hypotheses in §4 of Chapter III is that there we considered *independent* random variables, whereas here we consider arbitrary dependent variables, and moreover without assuming that $E|\xi_{nk}|$ is finite. It will be shown in Theorem 2 that hypothesis (A) is equivalent to

(A*) $$\max_{1 \le k \le [nt]} |\xi_{nk}| \xrightarrow{P} 0.$$

Therefore (compare Theorem 1 of §4, Chapter III) our Theorem 1 is a statement about the validity of the central limit theorem under the assumption that the variables that are added have the property of being *uniformly asymptotically infinitesimal* (see, however, Theorem 5 below).

Hypotheses (A) and (B) guarantee that X_t^n can be represented in the form $X_t^n = Y_t^n + Z_t^n$ with $Z_t^n \xrightarrow{P} 0$ and $Y_t^n = \sum_{k=0}^{[nt]} \eta_{nk}$, where the sequence $\eta^n = (\eta_{nk}, \mathscr{F}_k^n)$ is a martingale-difference, and $E(\eta_{nk}|\mathscr{F}_{k-1}^n) = 0$ with $|\eta_{nk}| \le c$, uniformly for $1 \le k \le n$ and $n \ge 1$. Consequently, in the cases under consideration, the proof reduces to proving the central limit theorem for martingale-differences.

In the case when the variables $\xi_{n1}, \ldots, \xi_{nn}$ are *independent*, conditions (A), (B) and (C), with $t = 1$, and $\sigma^2 = \sigma_1^2$, become

(a) $\displaystyle\sum_{k=1}^{n} P(|\xi_{nk}| > \varepsilon) \to 0,$

(b) $\displaystyle\sum_{k=1}^{n} E[\xi_{nk} I(|\xi_{nk}| \le 1)] \to 0,$

(c) $\displaystyle\sum_{k=1}^{n} V[\xi_{nk} I(|\xi_{nk}| \le \varepsilon)] \to \sigma^2.$

These are well known; see the book by Gnedenko and Kolmogorov [G5]. Hence we have the following corollary to Theorem 1.

Corollary. *If* $\xi_{n1}, \ldots, \xi_{nn}$ *are independent random variables, $n \ge 1$, then*

$$(a), (b), (c) \Rightarrow X_1^n \xrightarrow{d} \mathcal{N}(0, \sigma^2).$$

Remark 1. In hypothesis (C), the case $\sigma_t^2 = 0$ is *not excluded*. Hence, in particular, Theorem 1 yields a convergence condition for degenerate distributions ($X_t^n \xrightarrow{d} 0$).

Remark 2. The method used to prove Theorem 1 lets us state and prove the following more general proposition.

Let $0 < t_1 < t_2 < \cdots < t_j \le 1$, $\sigma_{t_1}^2 \le \sigma_{t_2}^2 \le \cdots \le \sigma_{t_j}^2$, $\sigma_0^2 = 0$, and let $\varepsilon_1, \ldots, \varepsilon_j$ be independent Gaussian random variables with zero means and $E\varepsilon_k^2 = \sigma_{t_k}^2 - \sigma_{t_{k-1}}^2$. Form the (Gaussian) vectors $(W_{t_1}, \ldots, W_{t_j})$ with $W_{t_k} = \varepsilon_1 + \cdots + \varepsilon_k$.

Let conditions (A), (B) and (C) be satisfied for $t = t_1, \ldots, t_j$. Then the joint distribution $(P_{t_1, \ldots, t_j}^n)$ of the random variables $(X_{t_1}^n, \ldots, X_{t_j}^n)$ converges weakly to the Gaussian distribution $P(t_1, \ldots, t_j)$ of the variables $(W_{t_1}, \ldots, W_{t_j})$:

$$P^n_{t_1, \ldots, t_j} \xrightarrow{w} P_{t_1, \ldots, t_j}.$$

2. Theorem 2.
(1) *Condition* (A) *is equivalent to* (A*).
(2) *Assuming* (A) *or* (A*), *condition* (C) *is equivalent to*

$$(C^*) \sum_{k=0}^{[nt]} [\xi_{nk} - E(\xi_{nk} I(|\xi_{nk}| \leq 1) | \mathscr{F}^n_{k-1})]^2 \xrightarrow{P} \sigma^2_t.$$

Theorem 3. *For each $n \geq 1$ let the sequence*

$$\xi^n = (\xi_{nk}, \mathscr{F}^n_k), \qquad 1 \leq k \leq n,$$

be a square-integrable martingale-difference:

$$E\xi^2_{nk} < \infty, \qquad E(\xi_{nk} | \mathscr{F}^n_{k-1}) = 0.$$

Suppose that the Lindeberg condition is satisfied: for $\varepsilon > 0$,

$$(L) \sum_{k=0}^{[nt]} E[\xi^2_{nk} I(|\xi_{nk}| > \varepsilon) | \mathscr{F}^n_{k-1}] \xrightarrow{P} 0.$$

Then (C) *is equivalent to*

$$\langle X^n \rangle_t \xrightarrow{P} \sigma^2_t, \tag{1}$$

where (quadratic variation)

$$\langle X^n \rangle_t = \sum_{k=0}^{[nt]} E(\xi^2_{nk} | \mathscr{F}^n_{k-1}), \tag{2}$$

and (C*) *is equivalent to*

$$[X^n]_t \xrightarrow{P} \sigma^2_t, \tag{3}$$

where (quadratic variation)

$$[X^n]_t = \sum_{k=0}^{[nt]} \xi^2_{nk}. \tag{4}$$

The next theorem is a corollary of Theorems 1–3.

Theorem 4. *Let the square-integrable martingale-differences $\xi^n = (\xi_{nk}, \mathscr{F}^n_k)$, $n \geq 1$, satisfy (for a given t, $0 < t \leq 1$) the Lindeberg condition* (L). *Then*

$$\sum_{k=0}^{[nt]} E(\xi^2_{nk} | \mathscr{F}^n_{k-1}) \xrightarrow{P} \sigma^2_t \Rightarrow X^n_t \xrightarrow{d} \mathcal{N}(0, \sigma^2_t), \tag{5}$$

$$\sum_{k=0}^{[nt]} \xi^2_{nk} \xrightarrow{P} \sigma^2_t \Rightarrow X^n_t \xrightarrow{d} \mathcal{N}(0, \sigma^2_t). \tag{6}$$

3. Proof of Theorem 1. Let us represent X_t^n in the form

$$X_t^n = \sum_{k=0}^{[nt]} \xi_{nk} I(|\xi_{nk}| \leq 1) + \sum_{k=0}^{[nt]} \xi_{nk} I(|\xi_{nk}| > 1)$$

$$= \sum_{k=0}^{[nt]} E[\xi_{nk} I(|\xi_{nk}| \leq 1) \big| \mathscr{F}_{k-1}^n] + \sum_{k=0}^{[nt]} \xi_{nk} I(|\xi_{nk}| > 1)$$

$$+ \sum_{k=0}^{[nt]} \{\xi_{nk} I(|\xi_{nk}| \leq 1) - E[\xi_{nk} I(|\xi_{nk}| \leq 1) \big| \mathscr{F}_{k-1}^n]\}. \tag{7}$$

We define

$$B_t^n = \sum_{k=0}^{[nt]} E[\xi_{nk} I(|\xi_{nk}| \leq 1) \big| \mathscr{F}_{k-1}^n],$$

$$\mu_k^n(\Gamma) = I(\xi_{nk} \in \Gamma), \tag{8}$$

$$\nu_k^n(\Gamma) = P(\xi_{nk} \in \Gamma \mid \mathscr{F}_{k-1}^n),$$

where Γ is a set from the smallest σ-algebra $\sigma(R \setminus \{0\})$ and $P(\xi_{nk} \in \Gamma \mid \mathscr{F}_{k-1}^n)$ is the regular conditional distribution of ξ_{nk} with respect to $\mathscr{F}_{k-1}^n$.

Then (7) can be rewritten in the following form:

$$X_t^n = B_t^n + \sum_{k=0}^{[nt]} \int_{|x|>1} x \, d\mu_k^n + \sum_{k=0}^{[nt]} \int_{|x|\leq 1} x \, d(\mu_k^n - \nu_k^n), \tag{9}$$

which is known as the *canonical* decomposition of $(X_t^n, \mathscr{F}_t^n)$. (The integrals are to be understood as Lebesgue–Stieltjes integrals, defined for every sample point.)

According to (B) we have $B_t^n \xrightarrow{P} 0$. Let us show that (A) implies

$$\sum_{k=0}^{[nt]} \int_{|x|>1} |x| \, d\mu_k^n \xrightarrow{P} 0. \tag{10}$$

We have

$$\sum_{k=0}^{[nt]} \int_{|x|>1} |x| \, d\mu_k^n = \sum_{k=0}^{[nt]} |\xi_{nk}| I(|\xi_{nk}| > 1). \tag{11}$$

For every $\delta \in (0, 1)$,

$$\left\{ \sum_{k=0}^{[nt]} |\xi_{nk}| I(|\xi_{nk}| > 1) > \delta \right\} \leq \left\{ \sum_{k=0}^{[nt]} I(|\xi_{nk}| > 1) > \delta \right\}. \tag{12}$$

It is clear that

$$\sum_{k=0}^{[nt]} I(|\xi_{nk}| > 1) = \sum_{k=0}^{[nt]} \int_{|x|>1} d\mu_k^n (\equiv U_{[nt]}^n).$$

By (A),

$$V^n_{[nt]} \equiv \sum_{k=0}^{[nt]} \int_{|x|>1} dv^n_k \xrightarrow{P} 0, \tag{13}$$

and V^n_k is $\mathscr{F}^n_{k-1}$-measurable.

Then by the corollary to Theorem 2 of §3, Chapter VII,

$$V^n_{[nt]} \xrightarrow{P} 0 \Rightarrow U^n_{[nt]} \xrightarrow{P} 0. \tag{14}$$

(By the same corollary and the inequality $\Delta U^n_{[nt]} \leq 1$, we also have the converse implication

$$U^n_{[nt]} \xrightarrow{P} 0 \Rightarrow V^n_{[nt]} \xrightarrow{P} 0, \tag{15}$$

which will be needed in the proof of Theorem 2.)

The required proposition (10) now follows from (11)–(14).

Thus

$$X^n_t = Y^n_t + Z^n_t, \tag{16}$$

where

$$Y^n_t = \sum_{k=0}^{[nt]} \int_{|x| \leq 1} x \, d(\mu^n_k - v^n_k), \tag{17}$$

and

$$Z^n_t = B^n_t + \sum_{k=0}^{[nt]} \int_{|x|>1} x \, d\mu^n_k \xrightarrow{P} 0. \tag{18}$$

It then follows by Problem 1 that to establish that

$$X^n_t \xrightarrow{d} \mathscr{N}(0, \sigma^2_t)$$

we need only show that

$$Y^n_t \xrightarrow{d} \mathscr{N}(0, \sigma^2_t). \tag{19}$$

Let us represent Y^n_t in the form

$$Y^n_t = Y^n_{[nt]}(\varepsilon) + \Delta^n_{[nt]}(\varepsilon), \qquad \varepsilon \in (0, 1],$$

where

$$\gamma^n_{[nt]}(\varepsilon) = \sum_{k=0}^{[nt]} \int_{\varepsilon < |x| \leq 1} x \, d(\mu^n_k - v^n_k), \tag{20}$$

$$\Delta^n_{[nt]}(\varepsilon) = \sum_{k=0}^{[nt]} \int_{|x| \leq \varepsilon} x \, d(\mu^n_k - v^n_k). \tag{21}$$

As in the proof of (14), it is easily verified that, because of (A), we have $\gamma^n_{[nt]}(\varepsilon) \xrightarrow{P} 0, n \to \infty$.

The sequence $\Delta^n(\varepsilon) = (\Delta_k^n(\varepsilon), \mathscr{F}_k^n)$, $1 \leq k \leq n$, is a square-integrable martingale with quadratic variation

$$\langle \Delta^n(\varepsilon) \rangle_k = \sum_{i=0}^{k} \left[\int_{|x| \leq \varepsilon} x^2 \, dv_i^n - \left(\int_{|x| \leq \varepsilon} x \, dv_i^n \right)^2 \right]$$

$$= \sum_{i=0}^{k} \mathsf{V}[\xi_{ni} I(|\xi_{ni}| \leq \varepsilon) \, | \, \mathscr{F}_{i-1}^n].$$

Because of (C),

$$\langle \Delta^n(\varepsilon) \rangle_{[nt]} \xrightarrow{\mathsf{P}} \sigma_t^2.$$

Hence, for every $\varepsilon \in (0, 1]$,

$$\max\{\gamma_{[nt]}^n(\varepsilon), |\langle \Delta^n(\varepsilon) \rangle_{[nt]} - \sigma_t^2|\} \xrightarrow{\mathsf{P}} 0.$$

By Problem 2 there is then a sequence of numbers $\varepsilon_n \downarrow 0$ such that

$$\gamma_{[nt]}^n(\varepsilon_n) \xrightarrow{\mathsf{P}} 0, \qquad \langle \Delta^n(\varepsilon_n) \rangle_{[nt]} \xrightarrow{\mathsf{P}} \sigma_t^2.$$

Therefore, again by Problem 1, it is enough to prove only that

$$M_{[nt]}^n \xrightarrow{d} \mathcal{N}(0, \sigma_t^2), \tag{22}$$

where

$$M_k^n \equiv \Delta_k^n(\varepsilon_n) = \sum_{i=0}^{k} \int_{|x| \leq \varepsilon_n} x(\mu_i^n - v_i^n). \tag{23}$$

For $\Gamma \in \sigma(R \setminus \{0\})$, let

$$\tilde{\mu}_k^n(\Gamma) = I(\Delta M_k^n \in \Gamma), \qquad \tilde{v}_k^n(\Gamma) = \mathsf{P}(\Delta M_k^n \in \Gamma \, | \, \mathscr{F}_{k-1}^n)$$

be a regular conditional probability, $\Delta M_k^n = M_k^n - M_{k-1}^n$, $k \geq 1$, $M_0^n = 0$. Then the square-integrable martingale $M^n = (M_k^n, \mathscr{F}_k^n)$, $1 \leq k \leq n$, can evidently be written in the form

$$M_k^n = \sum_{i=1}^{k} \Delta M_i^n = \sum_{i=1}^{k} \int_{|x| \leq 2\varepsilon_n} x \, d\tilde{\mu}_k^n.$$

(Notice that $|\Delta M_i^n| \leq 2\varepsilon_n$ by (23).)

To establish (22) we have to show that, for every real λ,

$$\mathsf{E} \exp\{i\lambda M_{[nt]}^n\} \to \exp(-\tfrac{1}{2}\lambda^2 \sigma_t^2). \tag{24}$$

Put

$$G_k^n = \sum_{j=1}^{k} \int_{|x| \leq 2\varepsilon_n} (e^{i\lambda x} - 1) \, d\tilde{v}_j^n$$

and

$$\mathscr{E}_k^n(G^n) = \prod_{j=1}^{k} (1 + \Delta G_k^n).$$

Observe that

$$1 + \Delta G_k^n = 1 + \int_{|x| \le 2\varepsilon_n} (e^{i\lambda x} - 1)\, d\tilde{v}_k^n = \int_{|x| \le 2\varepsilon_a} e^{i\lambda x}\, d\tilde{v}_k^n$$

$$= \mathsf{E}[\exp(i\lambda \Delta M_k^n)|\mathscr{F}_{k-1}^n]$$

and consequently

$$\mathscr{E}_k^n(G^n) = \prod_{j=1}^{k} (1 + \Delta G_k^n).$$

On the basis of a lemma that will be proved in Subsection 4, (24) will follow if for every real λ

$$|\mathscr{E}_{[nt]}^n(G^n)| = \left| \prod_{j=1}^{[nt]} \mathsf{E}[\exp(i\lambda \Delta M_j^n)|\mathscr{F}_{j-1}^n] \right| \ge C(\lambda) > 0 \qquad (25)$$

and

$$\mathscr{E}_{[nt]}^n(G^n) \xrightarrow{\mathsf{P}} \exp(-\tfrac{1}{2}\lambda^2 \sigma_t^2). \qquad (26)$$

To see this we represent $\mathscr{E}_k^n(G^n)$ in the form

$$\mathscr{E}_k^n(G^n) = \exp(G_k^n) \cdot \prod_{j=1}^{k} (1 + \Delta G_j^n) \exp(-\Delta G_j^n).$$

(Compare the function $E_t(A)$ defined by (76) in §6, Chapter II.)
Since

$$\int_{|x| \le 2\varepsilon_n} x\, d\tilde{v}_j^n = \mathsf{E}(\Delta M_j^n|\mathscr{F}_{j-1}^n) = 0,$$

we have

$$G_k^n = \sum_{j=1}^{k} \int_{|x| \le 2\varepsilon_n} (e^{i\lambda x} - 1 - i\lambda x)\, d\tilde{v}_j^n. \qquad (27)$$

Therefore

$$|\Delta G_k^n| \le \int_{|x| \le 2\varepsilon_n} |e^{i\lambda x} - 1 - i\lambda x|\, d\tilde{v}_k^n \le \tfrac{1}{2}\lambda^2 \int_{|x| \le 2\varepsilon_n} x^2\, d\tilde{v}_k^n$$

$$\le \tfrac{1}{2}\lambda^2 (2\varepsilon_n)^2 \to 0 \qquad (28)$$

and

$$\sum_{j=1}^{k} |\Delta G_j^n| \le \tfrac{1}{2}\lambda^2 \sum_{j=1}^{k} \int_{|x| \le 2\varepsilon_n} x^2\, d\tilde{v}_j^n = \tfrac{1}{2}\lambda^2 \langle M^n \rangle_k. \qquad (29)$$

By (C),

$$\langle M^n \rangle_{[nt]} \xrightarrow{\mathsf{P}} \sigma_t^2. \qquad (30)$$

Suppose first that $\langle M^n \rangle_k \leq a$ (P-a.s.), $k \leq [nt]$, where $a \geq \sigma_t^2 + 1$. Then by (28), (29) and Problem 3,

$$\prod_{k=1}^{[nt]} (1 + \Delta G_k^n) \exp(-\Delta G_k^n) \xrightarrow{\text{P}} 1, \qquad n \to \infty,$$

and therefore to establish (26) we have only to show that

$$G_{[nt]}^n \to -\tfrac{1}{2}\lambda^2 \sigma_t^2, \tag{31}$$

i.e., after (27), (29) and (30), that

$$\sum_{k=1}^{[nt]} \int_{|x| \leq 2\varepsilon_n} (e^{i\lambda x} - 1 - i\lambda x + \tfrac{1}{2}\lambda^2 x^2) \, d\tilde{v}_k^n \xrightarrow{\text{P}} 0. \tag{32}$$

But

$$|e^{i\lambda x} - 1 - i\lambda x + \tfrac{1}{2}\lambda^2 x^2| \leq \tfrac{1}{6}|\lambda x|^3$$

and therefore

$$\sum_{k=1}^{[nt]} \int_{|x| \leq 2\varepsilon_n} |e^{i\lambda x} - 1 - i\lambda x + \tfrac{1}{2}\lambda^2 x^2| \, d\tilde{v}_k^n \leq \tfrac{1}{6}|\lambda|^3 (2\varepsilon_n) \sum_{k=1}^{[nt]} \int_{|x| \leq 2\varepsilon_n} x^2 \, d\tilde{v}_k^n$$

$$= \tfrac{1}{3}\varepsilon_n |\lambda|^3 \langle M_n \rangle_{[nt]} \leq \tfrac{1}{3}\varepsilon_n |\lambda|^3 a \to 0, \qquad n \to \infty.$$

Therefore if $\langle M^n \rangle_{[nt]} \leq a$ (P-a.s.), (31) is established and consequently (26) is established also.

Let us now verify (25). Since $|e^{i\lambda x} - 1 - i\lambda x| \leq \tfrac{1}{2}(\lambda x)^2$, we find from (28) that, for sufficiently large n,

$$|\mathscr{E}_k^n(G^n)| = |\prod_{j=1}^{k}(1 + \Delta G_i^n)| \geq \prod_{j=1}^{k}(1 - \tfrac{1}{2}\lambda^2 \Delta \langle M^n \rangle_j)$$

$$= \exp\left\{ \sum_{j=1}^{k} \ln(1 - \tfrac{1}{2}\lambda^2 \Delta \langle M^n \rangle_j) \right\}.$$

But

$$\ln(1 - \tfrac{1}{2}\lambda^2 \Delta \langle M^n \rangle_j) \geq -\frac{\tfrac{1}{2}\lambda^2 \Delta \langle M^n \rangle_j}{1 - \tfrac{1}{2}\lambda^2 \Delta \langle M^n \rangle_j}$$

and $\Delta \langle M^n \rangle_j \leq (2\varepsilon_n)^2 \downarrow 0$, $n \to \infty$. Therefore there is an $n_0 = n_0(\lambda)$ such that for all $n \geq n_0(\lambda)$,

$$|\mathscr{E}_k^n(G^n)| \geq \exp\{-\lambda^2 \langle M^n \rangle_k\}$$

and therefore

$$|\mathscr{E}_{[nt]}^n(G^n)| \geq \exp\{-\lambda^2 \langle M^n \rangle_{[nt]} \geq e^{-\lambda^2 a}.$$

Hence the theorem is proved under the assumption that $\langle M^n \rangle_{[nt]} \leq a$ (P-a.s.). To remove this assumption, we proceed as follows.

Let

$$\tau^n = \min\{k \le [nt]: \langle M^n \rangle_k \ge \sigma_t^2 + 1\},$$

taking $\tau^n = \infty$ if $\langle M^n \rangle_{[nt]} \le \sigma_t^2 + 1$.

Then for $\overline{M}_k^n = M_{k \wedge \tau^n}^n$ we have

$$\langle \overline{M}^n \rangle_{[nt]} = \langle M^n \rangle_{[nt] \wedge \tau^n} \le 1 + \sigma_t^2 + 2\varepsilon_n^2 \le 1 + \sigma_t^2 + 2\varepsilon_1^2 \; (=a),$$

and by what has been proved,

$$\mathsf{E} \exp\{i\lambda \overline{M}_{[nt]}^n\} \to \exp(-\tfrac{1}{2}\lambda^2 \sigma_t^2).$$

But

$$\lim_n |\mathsf{E}\{\exp(i\lambda M_{[nt]}^n) - \exp(i\lambda \overline{M}_{[nt]}^n)\}| \le 2 \lim_n \mathsf{P}(\tau^n < \infty) = 0.$$

Consequently

$$\lim_n \mathsf{E} \exp(i\lambda M_{[nt]}^n) = \lim_n \mathsf{E}\{\exp(i\lambda M_{[nt]}^n) - \exp(i\lambda \overline{M}_{[nt]}^n)\}$$
$$+ \lim_n \mathsf{E} \exp(i\lambda \overline{M}_{[nt]}^n) = \exp(-\tfrac{1}{2}\lambda^2 \sigma_t^2).$$

This completes the proof of Theorem 1.

Remark. To prove the statement made in Remark 2 to Theorem 1, we need (using the Cramér–Wold method [B3]) to show that for all real numbers $\lambda_1, \ldots, \lambda_j$

$$\mathsf{E} \exp i\left[\lambda_1 M_{[nt_1]}^n + \sum_{k=2}^{j} \lambda_k(M_{[nt_k]}^n - M_{[nt_{k-1}]}^n) \right]$$
$$\to \exp(-\tfrac{1}{2}\lambda_1^2 \sigma_{t_1}^2) - \sum_{k=2}^{j} \tfrac{1}{2}\lambda_k^2(\sigma_{t_k}^2 - \sigma_{t_{k-1}}^2).$$

The proof of this is similar to the proof of (24), replacing $(M_k^n, \mathscr{F}_k^n)$ by the square-integrable martingales $(\hat{M}_k^n, \mathscr{F}_k^n)$,

$$\hat{M}_k^n = \sum_{i=1}^{k} v_i \Delta M_i^n,$$

where $v_i = \lambda_1$ for $i \le [nt_1]$ and $v_i = \lambda_j$ for $[nt_{j-1}] < i \le [nt_j]$.

4. In this subsection we prove a simple lemma which lets us reduce the verification of (24) to the verification of (25) and (26).

Let $\eta^n = (\eta_{nk}, \mathscr{F}_k^n)$, $1 \le k \le n$, $n \ge 1$, be stochastic sequences, let

$$Y^n = \sum_{k=1}^{n} \eta_{nk},$$

let

$$\mathscr{E}^n(\lambda) = \prod_{k=1}^{n} \mathsf{E}[\exp(i\lambda \eta_{nk})| \mathscr{F}_{k-1}^n], \qquad \lambda \in R,$$

and let Y be a random variable with

$$\mathscr{E}(\lambda) = \mathsf{E}e^{i\lambda Y}, \qquad \lambda \in R.$$

Lemma. *If (for a given λ) $|\mathscr{E}^n(\lambda)| \geq c(\lambda) > 0$, $n \geq 1$, a sufficient condition for the limit relation*

$$\mathsf{E}e^{i\lambda Y^n} \to \mathsf{E}e^{i\lambda Y} \tag{33}$$

is that

$$\mathscr{E}^n(\lambda) \xrightarrow{\text{P}} \mathscr{E}(\lambda). \tag{34}$$

PROOF. Let

$$m^n(\lambda) = \frac{e^{i\lambda Y^n}}{\mathscr{E}^n(\lambda)}.$$

Then $|m^n(\lambda)| \leq c^{-1}(\lambda) < \infty$, and it is easily verified that

$$\mathsf{E}m^n(\lambda) = 1.$$

Hence by (34) and the Lebesgue dominated convergence theorem,

$$|\mathsf{E}e^{i\lambda Y^n} - \mathsf{E}e^{i\lambda Y}| = |\mathsf{E}(e^{i\lambda Y^n} - \mathscr{E}(\lambda))|$$

$$= |\mathsf{E}(m^n(\lambda)[\mathscr{E}^n(\lambda) - \mathscr{E}(\lambda)])| \leq c^{-1}(\lambda)\mathsf{E}|\mathscr{E}^n(\lambda) - \mathscr{E}(\lambda)| \to 0, \qquad n \to \infty.$$

Remark. It follows, from (33) and the hypothesis that $\mathscr{E}^n(\lambda) \geq c(\lambda) > 0$, that $\mathscr{E}(\lambda) \neq 0$. In fact, the conclusion of the lemma remains valid without the assumption that $|\mathscr{E}^n(\lambda)| \geq c(\lambda) > 0$, if restated in the form: if $\mathscr{E}^n(\lambda) \xrightarrow{\text{P}} \mathscr{E}(\lambda)$ and $\mathscr{E}(\lambda) \neq 0$, then (33) holds (Problem 5).

5. PROOF OF THEOREM 2. (1) Let $\varepsilon > 0$, $\delta \in (0, \varepsilon)$, and for simplicity let $t = 1$. Since

$$\max_{1 \leq k \leq n} |\xi_{nk}| \leq \varepsilon + \sum_{k=1}^{n} |\xi_{nk}| I(|\xi_{nk}| > \varepsilon)$$

and

$$\left\{ \sum_{k=1}^{n} |\xi_{nk}| I(|\xi_{nk}| > \varepsilon) > \delta \right\} \subseteq \left\{ \sum_{k=1}^{n} I(|\xi_{nk}| > \varepsilon) > \delta \right\},$$

we have

$$\mathsf{P}\left\{ \max_{1 \leq k \leq n} |\xi_{nk}| > \varepsilon + \delta \right\} \leq \mathsf{P}\left\{ \sum_{k=1}^{n} I(|\xi_{nk}| > \varepsilon) > \delta \right\}$$

$$= \mathsf{P}\left\{ \sum_{k=1}^{n} \int_{|x| > \varepsilon} d\mu_k^n > \delta \right\}.$$

If (A) is satisfied, i.e.

$$\mathsf{P}\left\{ \sum_{k=1}^{n} \int_{|x| > \varepsilon} dv_k^n > \delta \right\} \to 0$$

then (compare (14)) we also have

$$P\left\{\sum_{k=1}^{n}\int_{|x|>\varepsilon}d\mu_k^n > \delta\right\} \to 0.$$

Therefore (A) $\Rightarrow$ (A*).
    Conversely, let

$$\sigma_n = \min\{k \le n: |\xi_{nk}| \ge \varepsilon/2\},$$

supposing that $\sigma_n = \infty$ if $\max_{1 \le k \le n}|\xi_{nk}| < \varepsilon/2$. By (A*), $\lim_n P(\sigma_n < \infty) = 0$.
    Now observe that, for every $\delta \in (0, 1)$, the sets

$$\left\{\sum_{k=1}^{n \wedge \sigma_n} I(|\xi_{nk}| \ge \varepsilon/2) > \delta\right\} \quad \text{and} \quad \left\{\max_{1 \le k \le n \wedge \sigma_n} |\xi_{nk}| \ge \tfrac{1}{2}\varepsilon\right\}$$

coincide, and by (A*)

$$\sum_{k=1}^{n \wedge \sigma_n} I(|\xi_{nk}| \ge \varepsilon/2) = \sum_{k=1}^{n \wedge \sigma_n}\int_{|x| \ge \varepsilon/2}d\mu_k^n \xrightarrow{P} 0.$$

Therefore by (15)

$$\sum_{k=1}^{n \wedge \sigma_n}\int_{|x| \ge \varepsilon}dv_k^n \le \sum_{k=1}^{n \wedge \sigma_n}\int_{|x| \ge \varepsilon/2}dv_k^n \xrightarrow{P} 0,$$

which, together with the property $\lim_n P(\sigma_n < \infty) = 0$, prove that (A*)
$\Rightarrow$ (A).
    (2) Again suppose that $t = 1$. Choose an $\varepsilon \in (0, 1]$ and consider the square-integrable martingales

$$\Delta^n(\delta) = (\Delta_k^n(\delta), \mathscr{F}_k^n) \qquad (1 \le k \le n),$$

with $\delta \in (0, \varepsilon]$. For the given $\varepsilon \in (0, 1]$, we have, according to (C),

$$\langle \Delta^n(\varepsilon)\rangle_n \xrightarrow{P} \sigma_1^2.$$

It is then easily deduced from (A) that for every $\delta \in (0, \varepsilon]$

$$\langle \Delta^n(\delta)\rangle_n \xrightarrow{P} \sigma_1^2. \tag{35}$$

Let us show that it follows from (C*), (A) and (A*) that, for every $\delta \in (0, \varepsilon]$,

$$[\Delta^n(\delta)]_n \xrightarrow{P} \sigma_1^2, \tag{36}$$

where

$$[\Delta^n(\delta)]_n = \sum_{k=1}^{n}[\xi_{nk}I(|\xi_{nk}| \le \delta) - \int_{|x| \le \delta}x \, dv_k^n]^2.$$

In fact, it is easily verified that by (A)

$$[\Delta^n(\delta)]_n - [\Delta^n(1)]_n \xrightarrow{P} 0. \tag{37}$$

But

$$\left| \sum_{k=1}^{n} \left[\xi_{nk} - \int_{|x| \leq 1} x \, dv_k^n \right]^2 - \sum_{k=1}^{n} \left[\xi_{nk} I(|\xi_{nk}| \leq 1) - \int_{|x| \leq 1} x \, dv_k^n \right]^2 \right|$$

$$\leq \sum_{k=1}^{n} I(|\xi_{nk}| > 1) \left[(\xi_{nk})^2 + 2|\xi_{nk}| \left| \int_{|x| \leq 1} x \, d(\mu_k^n - v_k^n) \right| \right]$$

$$\leq 5 \sum_{k=1}^{n} I(|\xi_{nk}| > 1) |\xi_{nk}|^2$$

$$\leq 5 \max_{1 \leq k \leq n} |\xi_{nk}|^2 \sum_{k=1}^{n} \int_{|x| > 1} d\mu_k^n \to 0. \tag{38}$$

Hence (36) follows from (37) and (38).

Consequently to establish the equivalence of (C) and (C*) it is enough to establish that when (C) is satisfied (for a given $\varepsilon \in (0, 1]$), then (C*) is also satisfied for every $a > 0$:

$$\lim_{\delta \to 0} \overline{\lim_{n}} \, \mathsf{P}\{|[\Delta^n(\sigma)]_n - \langle \Delta^n(\delta) \rangle_n| > a\} = 0. \tag{39}$$

Let

$$m_k^n(\delta) = [\Delta^n(\delta)]_k - \langle \Delta^n(\delta) \rangle_k, \qquad 1 \leq k \leq n.$$

The sequence $m^n(\delta) = (m_k^n(\delta), \mathscr{F}_k^n)$ is a square-integrable martingale, and $(m^n(\delta))^2$ is dominated (in the sense of the definition of §3 on p. 467) by the sequences $[m^n(\delta)]$ and $\langle m^n(\delta) \rangle)$.

It is clear that

$$[m^n(\delta)]_n = \sum_{k=1}^{n} (\Delta m_k^n(\delta))^2 \leq \max_{1 \leq k \leq n} |\Delta m_k^n(\delta)| \{ [\Delta^n(\delta)]_n + \langle \Delta^n(\delta) \rangle_n \}$$

$$\leq 3\delta^2 \{ [\Delta^n(\delta)]_n + \langle \Delta^n(\delta) \rangle_n \}. \tag{40}$$

Since $[\Delta^n(\delta)]$ and $\langle \Delta^n(\delta) \rangle$ dominate each other, it follows from (40) that $(m^n(\delta))^2$ is dominated by the sequences $6\delta^2 [\Delta^n(\delta)]$ and $6\delta^2 \langle \Delta^n(\delta) \rangle$.

Hence if (C) is satisfied, then for sufficiently small δ (for example, for $\delta < \frac{1}{6} b(\sigma_1^2 + 1)$)

$$\overline{\lim_{n}} \, \mathsf{P}(6\delta^2 \langle \Delta^n(\delta) \rangle_n > b) = 0,$$

and hence, by the corollary to Theorem 2 of §3, we have (39). If also (C*) is satisfied, then for the same values of δ,

$$\overline{\lim_{n}} \, \mathsf{P}(6\delta^2 [\Delta^n(\delta)]_k > b) = 0. \tag{41}$$

Since $|\Delta[\Delta^n(\delta)]_k| \leq (2\delta)^2$, the validity of (39) follows from (41) and another appeal to Theorem 2 of §3.

This completes the proof of Theorem 2.

6. Proof of Theorem 3. On account of the Lindeberg condition (L), the equivalence of (C) and (1), and of (C*) and (3), can be established by direct calculation (Problem 6).

7. Proof of Theorem 4. Condition (A) follows from the Lindeberg condition (L). As for condition (B), it is sufficient to observe that when ξ^n is a martingale-difference, the variables B_t^n that appear in the canonical decomposition (9) can be represented in the form

$$B_t^n = -\sum_{k=0}^{[nt]} \int_{|x|>1} x \, dv_n^k.$$

Therefore $B_t^n \xrightarrow{P} 0$ by the Lindeberg condition (L).

8. The fundamental theorem of the present section, namely Theorem 1, was proved under the hypothesis that the terms that are summed are uniformly asymptotically infinitesimal. It is natural to ask for conditions for the central limit theorem without such a hypothesis. For independent random variables, examples of such theorems are given by Theorem 1 (assuming finite second moments) or Theorem 5 (assuming finite first moments) from §4, Chapter III.

We quote (without proof) an analog of the first of these theorems, applicable only to sequences $\xi^n = (\xi_{nk}, \mathcal{F}_k^n)$ that are square-integrable martingale differences.

Let $\mathcal{F}_{nk}(x) = P(\xi_{nk} \le x \mid \mathcal{F}_{k-1}^n)$ be a regular distribution function of ξ_{nk} with respect to $\mathcal{F}_{k-1}^n$, and let $\Delta_{nk} = E(\xi_{nk}^2 \mid \mathcal{F}_{k-1}^n)$.

Theorem 5. *If a square-integrable martingale-difference* $\xi_n = (\xi_{nk}, \mathcal{F}_k^n)$, $0 \le k \le n, n \ge 1, \xi_{n0} = 0$, *satisfies the condition*

$$\sum_{k=0}^{[nt]} \Delta_{nk} \xrightarrow{P} \sigma_t^2, \qquad 0 \le \sigma_t^2 < \infty,$$

and for every $\varepsilon > 0$

$$\sum_{k=0}^{[nt]} \int_{|x|>\varepsilon} \left| |x| |\mathcal{F}_{nk}(x) - \Phi\left(\frac{x}{\sqrt{\Delta_{nk}}}\right) \right| dx \xrightarrow{P} 0,$$

then

$$X_t^n \xrightarrow{d} \mathcal{N}(0, \sigma_t^2).$$

9. Problems

1. Let $\xi_n = \eta_n + \zeta_n, n \ge 1$, where $\eta_n \xrightarrow{d} \eta$ and $\zeta_n \xrightarrow{d} 0$. Prove that $\xi_n \xrightarrow{d} \eta$.

2. Let $(\xi_n(\varepsilon)), n \ge 1, \varepsilon > 0$, be a family of random variables such that $\xi_n(\varepsilon) \xrightarrow{P} 0$ for each $\varepsilon > 0$ as $n \to \infty$. Using, for example, Problem 11 of §10, Chapter II, prove that there is a sequence $\varepsilon_n \downarrow 0$ such that $\xi_n(\varepsilon_n) \xrightarrow{P} 0$.

3. Let (α_k^n), $1 \le k \le n$, $n \ge 1$, be a complex-valued random variable such that (P-a.s.)

$$\sum_{k=1}^{n} |\alpha_k^n| \le C, \qquad |\alpha_k^n| \le a_n \downarrow 0.$$

Show that then (P-a.s.)

$$\lim_n \prod_{k=1}^{n} (1 + \alpha_k^n) \exp(-\alpha_k^n) = 1.$$

4. Prove the statement made in Remark 2 to Theorem 1.

5. Prove the statement made in Remark 1 to the lemma.

6. Prove Theorem 3.

7. Prove Theorem 5.

CHAPTER VIII

Sequences of Random Variables That Form Markov Chains

§1. Definitions and Basic Properties

1. In Chapter I (§12), for finite probability spaces, we took the basic idea to be that of *Markov dependence* between random variables. We also presented a variety of examples and considered the simplest regularities that are possessed by random variables that are connected by a Markov chain.

In the present chapter we give a general definition of a stochastic sequence of random variables that are connected by Markov dependence, and devote our main attention to the asymptotic properties of Markov chains with countable state spaces.

2. Let $(\Omega, \mathscr{F}, \mathsf{P})$ be a probability space with a distinguished nondecreasing family $(\mathscr{F}_n)$ of σ-algebras, $\mathscr{F}_0 \subseteq \mathscr{F}_1 \subseteq \cdots \subseteq \mathscr{F}$.

Definition. A stochastic sequence $X = (X_n, \mathscr{F}_n)$ is called a *Markov chain* (with respect to the measure P) if

$$\mathsf{P}\{X_n \in B \mid \mathscr{F}_m\} = \mathsf{P}\{X_n \in B \mid X_m\} \quad (\text{P-a.s.}) \tag{1}$$

for all $n \geq m \geq 0$ and all $B \in \mathscr{B}(R)$.

Property (1), the *Markov property*, can be stated in a number of ways. For example, it is equivalent to saying that

$$\mathsf{E}[g(X_n) \mid \mathscr{F}_m] = \mathsf{E}[g(X_n) \mid X_m] \quad (\text{P-a.s.}) \tag{2}$$

for every bounded Borel function $g = g(x)$.

Property (1) is also equivalent to the statement that, for a given "present" X_m, the "future" F and the "past" P are independent, i.e.

$$P(FP|X_m) = P(F|X_m)P(P|X_m), \tag{3}$$

where $F \in \sigma\{\omega: X_i, i \geq m\}$, and $B \in \mathscr{F}_n, n \leq m$.

In the special case when

$$\mathscr{F}_n = \mathscr{F}_n^X = \sigma\{\omega: X_0, \dots, X_n\}$$

and the stochastic sequence $X = (X_n, \mathscr{F}_n^X)$ is a Markov chain, we say that *the sequence $\{X_n\}$ itself is a Markov chain*. It is useful to notice that if $X = \{X_n, \mathscr{F}_n\}$ is a Markov chain, then (X_n) is also a Markov chain.

Remark. It was assumed in the definition that the variables X_m are real-valued. In a similar way, we can also define Markov chains for the case when X_n takes values in some measurable space $(E, \mathscr{E})$. In this case, if all singletons are measurable, the space is called a *phase space*, and we say that $X = (X_n, \mathscr{F}_n)$ is a Markov chain with values in the phase space $(E, \mathscr{E})$. When E is finite or countably infinite (and $\mathscr{E}$ is the σ-algebra of all its subsets) we say that the Markov chain is *discrete*. In turn, a discrete chain with a finite phase space is called a *finite chain*.

The theory of finite Markov chains, as presented in §12, Chapter I, shows that a fundamental role is played by the one-step transition probabilities $P(X_{n+1} \in B|X_n)$. By Theorem 3, §7, Chapter II, there are functions $P_{n+1}(x; B)$, the *regular conditional probabilities*, which (for given x) are measures on $(R, \mathscr{B}(R))$, and (for given B) are measurable functions of x, such that

$$P(X_{n+1} \in B|X_n) = P_{n+1}(X_n; B) \quad \text{(P-a.s.).} \tag{4}$$

The functions $P_n = P_n(x, B)$, $n \geq 0$, are called *transition functions*, and in the case when they coincide ($P_1 = P_2 = \cdots$), the corresponding Markov chain is said to be *homogeneous* (in time).

From now on we shall consider only homogeneous Markov chains, and the transition function $P_1 = P_1(x, B)$ will be denoted simply by $P = P(x, B)$.

Besides the transition function, an important probabilistic property of a Markov chain is the *initial distribution* $\pi = \pi(B)$, that is, the probability distribution defined by $\pi(B) = P(X_0 \in B)$.

The set of pairs (π, P), where π is an initial distribution and P is a transition function, completely determines the probabilistic properties of X, since every finite-dimensional distribution can be expressed (Problem 2) in terms of π and P: for every $n \geq 0$ and $A \in \mathscr{B}(R^{n+1})$

$$P\{(X_0, \dots, X_n) \in A\}$$

$$= \int_R \pi(dx_0) \int_R P(x_0; dx_1) \cdots \int_R I_A(x_0, \dots, x_n)P(x_{n-1}; dx_n). \tag{5}$$

We deduce, by a standard limiting process, that for any $\mathscr{B}(R^{n+1})$-measurable function $g(x_0, \ldots, x_n)$, either of constant sign or bounded,

$$\mathsf{E}g(X_0, \ldots, X_n)$$
$$= \int_R \pi(dx_0) \int_R P(x_0; dx_1) \cdots \int_R g(x_0, \ldots, x_n)P(x_{n-1}; dx_n). \quad (6)$$

3. Let $P^{(n)} = P^{(n)}(x; B)$ denote a regular variant of the *n-step transition probability*:

$$\mathsf{P}(X_n \in B | X_0) = P^{(n)}(X_0; B) \quad \text{(P-a.s.)}. \quad (7)$$

It follows at once from the Markov property that for all k and l, $(k, l \geq 1)$,

$$P^{(k+l)}(X_0; B) = \int_R P^{(k)}(X_0; dy)P^{(l)}(y; B) \quad \text{(P-a.s.)}. \quad (8)$$

It does *not* follow, of course, that for *all* $x \in R$

$$P^{(k+l)}(x; B) = \int_R P^{(k)}(x; dy)P^{(l)}(y; B). \quad (9)$$

It turns out, however, that regular variants of the transition probabilities *can be chosen* so that (9) will be satisfied for *all* $x \in R$ (see the discussion in the historical and bibliographical notes, p. 559).

Equation (9) is the *Kolmogorov–Chapman* equation (compare (I.12.13)) and is the starting point for the study of the probabilistic properties of Markov chains.

4. It follows from our discussion that with every Markov chain $X = (X_n, \mathscr{F}_n)$, defined on $(\Omega, \mathscr{F}, \mathsf{P})$ there is associated a set (π, P). It is natural to ask what properties a set (π, P) must have in order for $\pi = \pi(B)$ to be a probability distribution on $(R, \mathscr{B}(R))$ and for $P = P(x; B)$ to be a function that is measurable in x for given B, and a probability measure on B for every x, so that π will be the initial distribution, and P the transition function, for some Markov chain. As we shall now show, no additional hypotheses are required.

In fact, let us take $(\Omega, \mathscr{F})$ to be the measurable space $(R^\infty, \mathscr{B}(R^\infty))$. On the sets $A \in \mathscr{B}(R^{n+1})$ we define a probability measure by the right-hand side of formula (5). It follows from §9, Chapter II, that a probability measure P exists on $(R^\infty, \mathscr{B}(R^\infty))$ for which

$$\mathsf{P}\{\omega: (x_0, \ldots, x_n) \in A\}$$
$$= \int_R \pi(dx_0) \int_R P(x_0; dx_1) \cdots \int_R I_A(x_0, \ldots, x_n)P(x_{n-1}; dx_n). \quad (10)$$

Let us show that if we put $X_n(\omega) = x_n$ for $\omega = (x_0, x_1, \ldots)$, the sequence $X = (X_n)_{n \geq 0}$ will constitute a Markov chain (with respect to the measure P just constructed).

In fact, if $B \in \mathscr{B}(R)$ and $C \in \mathscr{B}(R^{n+1})$, then

$$P\{X_{n+1} \in B, (X_0, \ldots, X_n) \in C\}$$

$$= \int_R \pi(dx_0) \int_R P(x_0; dx_1) \cdots \int_R I_B(x_{n+1}) I_C(x_0, \ldots, x_n) P(x_n; dx_{n+1})$$

$$= \int_R \pi(dx_0) \int_R P(x_0; dx_1) \cdots \int_R P(x_n; B) I_C(x_0, \ldots, x_n) P(x_{n-1}; dx_n)$$

$$= \int_{\{\omega: (X_0, \ldots, X_n) \in C\}} P(X_n; B) \, dP,$$

whence (P-a.s.)

$$P\{X_{n+1} \in B \mid X_0, \ldots, X_n\} = P(X_n; B). \tag{11}$$

Similarly we can verify that (P-a.s.)

$$P\{X_{n+1} \in B \mid X_n\} = P(X_n; B). \tag{12}$$

Equation (1) now follows from (11) and (12). It can be shown in the same way that for every $k \geq 1$ and $n \geq 0$,

$$P\{X_{n+k} \in B \mid X_0, \ldots, X_n\} = P\{X_{n+k} \in B \mid X_n\} \quad \text{(P-a.s.)}.$$

This implies the homogeneity of Markov chains.

The Markov chain $X = (X_n)$ that we have constructed is known as the Markov chain generated by (π, P). To emphasize that the measure P on $(R^\infty, \mathscr{B}(R^\infty))$ has precisely the initial distribution π, it is often denoted by P_π.

If π is concentrated at the single point x, we write P_x instead of P_π, and the corresponding Markov chain is called the chain *generated by the point x* (since $P_x(X_0 = x) = 1$).

Consequently, each transition function $P = P(x, B)$ is in fact connected with the *whole family of probability measures* $\{P_x, x \in R\}$, and therefore with the whole family of Markov chains that arise when the sequence $(X_n)_{n \geq 0}$ is considered with respect to the measures P_x, $x \in R$. From now on, we shall use the phrase "Markov chain with given transition function" to mean the family of Markov chains in the sense just described.

We observe that the measures P_π and P_x constructed from the transition function $P = P(x, B)$ are *consistent* in the sense that, when $A \in \mathscr{B}(R^\infty)$,

$$P_\pi\{(X_0, X_1, \ldots) \in A \mid X_0 = x\} = P_x\{(X_0, X_1, \ldots) \in A\} \quad (\pi\text{-a.s.}) \tag{13}$$

and

$$P_\pi\{(X_0, X_1, \ldots) \in A\} = \int_R P_x\{(X_0, X_1, \ldots) \in A\} \pi(dx). \tag{14}$$

5. Let us suppose that $(\Omega, \mathcal{F}) = (R^{\infty}, \mathcal{B}(R^{\infty}))$ and that we are considering a sequence $X = (X_n)$ that is defined coordinate-wise, that is, $X_n(\omega) = x_n$ for $\omega = (x_0, x_1, \ldots)$. Also let $\mathcal{F}_n = \sigma\{\omega : X_0, \ldots, X_n\}$, $n \geq 0$.

Let us define the *shifting operators* θ_n, $n \geq 0$, on Ω by the equation

$$\theta_n(x_0, x_1, \ldots) = (x_n, x_{n+1}, \ldots),$$

and let us define, for every random variable $\eta = \eta(\omega)$, the random variables $\theta_n \eta$ by putting

$$(\theta_n \eta)(\omega) = \eta(\theta_n \omega).$$

In this notation, the Markov property of homogeneous chains can (Problem 1) be given the following form: For every $\mathcal{F}$-measurable $\eta = \eta(\omega)$, every $n \geq 0$, and $B \in \mathcal{B}(R)$,

$$P\{\theta_n \eta \in B | \mathcal{F}_n\} = P_{X_n}\{\eta \in B\} \quad \text{(P-a.s.).} \tag{15}$$

This form of the Markov property allows us to give the following important generalization: (15) remains valid if we replace n by stopping times τ.

Theorem. *Let* $X = (X_n)$ *be a homogeneous Markov chain defined on* $(R^{\infty}, \mathcal{B}(R^{\infty}), P)$ *and let* τ *be a stopping time. Then the following strong Markov property is valid:*

$$P\{\theta_\tau \eta \in B | \mathcal{F}_\tau\} = P_{X_\tau}\{\eta \in B\} \quad \text{(P-a.s.).} \tag{16}$$

PROOF. If $A \in \mathcal{F}_\tau$ then

$$P\{\theta_\tau \eta \in B, A\} = \sum_{n=0}^{\infty} P\{\theta_\tau \eta \in B, A, \tau = n\}$$

$$= \sum_{n=0}^{\infty} P\{\theta_n \eta \in B, A, \tau = n\}. \tag{17}$$

The events $A \cap \{\tau = n\} \in \mathcal{F}_n$, and therefore

$$P\{\theta_n \eta \in B, A \cap \{\tau = n\}\} = \int_{A \cap \{\tau = n\}} P\{\theta_n \eta \in B | \mathcal{F}_n\} \, dP$$

$$= \int_{A \cap \{\tau = n\}} P_{X_n}\{\eta \in B\} \, dP = \int_{A \cap \{\tau = n\}} P_{X_\tau}\{\eta \in B\} \, dP,$$

which, with (17), establishes (16).

Corollary. *If σ is a stopping time such that $P(\sigma \geq \tau) = 1$ and σ is $\mathcal{F}_\tau$-measurable, then*

$$P\{X_\sigma \in B, \sigma < \infty | \mathcal{F}_\tau\} = P_{X_\tau}(B) \quad (\{\sigma < \infty\}; \text{P-a.s.).} \tag{18}$$

6. As we said above, we are going to consider only discrete Markov chains (with phase space $E = \{\ldots, i, j, k, \ldots\}$). To simplify the notation, we shall now denote the transition functions $P(i; \{j\})$ by p_{ij} and call them transition probabilities; an n-step transition probability from i to j will be denoted by $p_{ij}^{(n)}$.

Let $E = \{1, 2, \ldots\}$. The principal questions that we study in §§2–4 are intended to clarify the conditions under which:

(A) The *limits* $\pi_j = \lim p_{i,j}^{(n)}$ *exist and are independent of* i;
(B) The limits $(\pi_1, \pi_2, \ldots)$ form a *probability distribution*, that is, $\pi_i \geq 0$, $\pi_i = 1$;
(C) The chain is *ergodic*, that is, the limits $(\pi_1, \pi_2, \ldots)$ have the properties $\pi_i > 0$, $\sum_{i=1}^{\infty} \pi_i = 1$;
(D) There is one and only one *stationary probability distribution* $\mathbb{Q} = (q_1, q_2, \ldots)$, that is, one such that $q_i \geq 0$, $\sum_{i=1}^{\infty} q_i = 1$, and $q_j = \sum_i q_i p_{ij}$, $j \in E$.

In the course of answering these questions we shall develop a classification of the states of a Markov chain as they depend on the arithmetic and asymptotic properties of $p_{ij}^{(n)}$ and $p_{ii}^{(n)}$.

7. PROBLEMS

1. Prove the equivalence of definitions (1), (2), (3) and (15) of the Markov property.

2. Prove formula (5).

3. Prove equation (18).

4. Let $(X_n)_{n \geq 0}$ be a Markov chain. Show that the reversed sequence $(\ldots, X_n, X_{n-1}, \ldots, X_0)$ is also a Markov chain.

§2. Classification of the States of a Markov Chain in Terms of Arithmetic Properties of the Transition Probabilities $p_{ij}^{(n)}$

1. We say that a state $i \in E = \{1, 2, \ldots\}$ is *inessential* if, with positive probability, it is possible to escape from it after a finite number of steps, without ever returning to it; that is, there exist m and j such that $p_{ij}^{(m)} > 0$, but $p_{ji}^{(n)} = 0$ for all n and j.

Let us delete all the inessential states from E. Then the remaining set of *essential* states has the property that a wandering particle that encounters it can never leave it (Figure 36). As will become clear later, it is essential states that are the most interesting.

Let us now consider the set of essential states. We say that state j is *accessible* from the point i ($i \to j$) if there is an $m \geq 0$ such that $p_{ij}^{(m)} > 0$

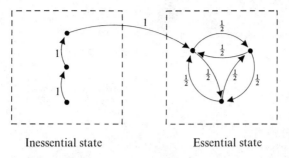

Inessential state   Essential state

Figure 36

$(p_{ij}^{(0)} = 1$ if $i = j$, and 0 if $i \neq j$). States i and j *communicate* $(i \leftrightarrow j)$ if j is accessible from i and i is accessible from j.

By the definition, the relation "$\leftrightarrow$" is symmetric and reflexive. It is easy to verify that it is also transitive $(i \leftrightarrow j, j \leftrightarrow k \Rightarrow i \leftrightarrow k)$. Consequently the set of essential states separates into a finite or countable number of disjoint sets $E_1, E_2, \ldots$, each of which consists of communicating sets but with the property that passage between different sets is impossible.

By way of abbreviation, we call the sets $E_1, E_2, \ldots$ *classes* or *indecomposable classes* (of essential communicating sets), and we call a Markov chain *indecomposable* if its states form a single indecomposable class.

As an illustration we consider the chain with matrix

$$
\mathbb{P} = \left|
\begin{array}{cc:ccc}
\frac{1}{3} & \frac{2}{3} & 0 & 0 & 0 \\
\frac{1}{4} & \frac{3}{4} & 0 & 0 & 0 \\
\hdashline
0 & 0 & 0 & 1 & 0 \\
0 & 0 & \frac{1}{2} & 0 & \frac{1}{2} \\
0 & 0 & 0 & 1 & 0
\end{array}
\right| = \begin{pmatrix} \mathbb{P}_1 & 0 \\ 0 & \mathbb{P}_2 \end{pmatrix}.
$$

The graph of this chain, with set of states $E = \{1, 2, 3, 4, 5\}$ has the form

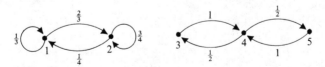

It is clear that this chain has two indecomposable classes $E_1 = \{1, 2\}$, $E_2 = \{3, 4, 5\}$, and the investigation of their properties reduces to the investigation of the two separate chains whose states are the sets E_1 and E_2, and whose transition matrices are $\mathbb{P}_1$ and $\mathbb{P}_2$.

Now let us consider any indecomposable class E, for example the one sketched in Figure 37.

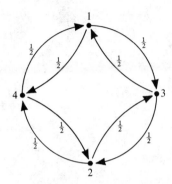

Figure 37. Example of a Markov chain with period $d = 2$.

Observe that in this case a return to each state is possible only after an even number of steps; a transition to an adjacent state, after an odd number; the transition matrix has block structure,

$$\mathbb{P} = \begin{pmatrix} 0 & 0 & \vdots & \frac{1}{2} & \frac{1}{2} \\ 0 & 0 & \vdots & \frac{1}{2} & \frac{1}{2} \\ \cdots & \cdots & \vdots & \cdots & \cdots \\ \frac{1}{2} & \frac{1}{2} & \vdots & 0 & 0 \\ \frac{1}{2} & \frac{1}{2} & \vdots & 0 & 0 \end{pmatrix}.$$

Therefore it is clear that the class $E = \{1, 2, 3, 4\}$ separates into two subclasses $C_0 = \{1, 2\}$ and $C_1 = \{3, 4\}$ with the following *cyclic* property: after one step from C_0 the particle necessarily enters C_1, and from C_1 it returns to C_0.

This example suggests a classification of indecomposable classes into *cyclic subclasses*.

2. Let us say that state j has period $d = d(j)$ if the following two conditions are satisfied:

(1) $p_{jj}^{(n)} > 0$ only for values of n of the form dm;
(2) d is the largest number satisfying (1).

In other words, d is the *greatest common divisor* of the numbers n for which $p_{jj}^{(n)} > 0$. (If $p_{jj}^{(n)} = 0$ for all $n \geq 1$, we put $d(j) = 0$.)

Let us show that all states of a single indecomposable class E have the same period d, which is therefore naturally called the *period* of the class, $d = d(E)$.

Let i and $j \in E$. Then there are numbers k and l such that $p_{ij}^{(k)} > 0$ and $p_{ji}^{(l)} > 0$. Consequently $p_{ii}^{(k+l)} \geq p_{ij}^{(k)} p_{ji}^{(l)} > 0$, and therefore $k + l$ is divisible by $d(i)$. Suppose that $n > 0$ and n is not divisible by $d(i)$. Then $n + k + l$ is also not divisible by $d(i)$ and consequently $p_{ii}^{(n+k+l)} = 0$. But

$$p_{ii}^{(n+k+l)} \geq p_{ij}^{(k)} p_{jj}^{(n)} p_{ji}^{(l)}$$

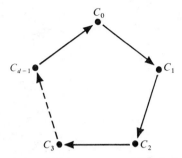

Figure 38. Motion among cyclic subclasses.

and therefore $p_{jj}^{(n)} = 0$. It follows that if $p_{jj}^{(n)} > 0$ we have n divisible by $d(i)$, and therefore $d(i) \leq d(j)$. By symmetry, $d(j) \leq d(i)$. Consequently $d(i) = d(j)$.

If $d(j) = 1$ ($d(E) = 1$), the state j (or class E) is said to be *aperiodic*.

Let $d = d(E)$ be the period of an indecomposable class E. The transitions within such a class may be quite freakish, but (as in the preceding example) there is a cyclic character to the transitions from one group of states to another. To show this, let us select a state i_0 and introduce (for $d \geq 1$) the following subclasses:

$$C_0 = \{j \in E: p_{i_0 j}^{(n)} > 0 \Rightarrow n \equiv 0 (\mathrm{mod}\ d)\};$$

$$C_1 = \{j \in E: p_{i_0 j}^{(n)} > 0 \Rightarrow n \equiv 1 (\mathrm{mod}\ d)\};$$

$$\dots\dots\dots\dots\dots\dots\dots\dots\dots\dots\dots\dots\dots\dots\dots$$

$$C_{d-1} = \{j \in E: p_{i_0 j}^{(n)} > 0 \Rightarrow n \equiv d - 1 (\mathrm{mod}\ d)\}.$$

Clearly $E = C_0 + C_1 + \cdots + C_{d-1}$. Let us show that the motion from subclass to subclass is as indicated in Figure 38.

In fact, let state $i \in C_p$ and $p_{ij} > 0$. Let us show that necessarily $j \in C_{p+1(\mathrm{mod}\ d)}$. Let n be such that $p_{i_0 i}^{(n)} > 0$. Then $n = ad + p$ and therefore $n \equiv p(\mathrm{mod}\ d)$ and $n + 1 \equiv p + 1(\mathrm{mod}\ d)$. Hence $p_{i_0 j}^{(n+1)} > 0$ and $f \in C_{p+1(\mathrm{mod}\ d)}$.

Let us observe that it now follows that the transition matrix $\mathbb{P}$ of an indecomposable chain has the following block structure:

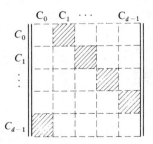

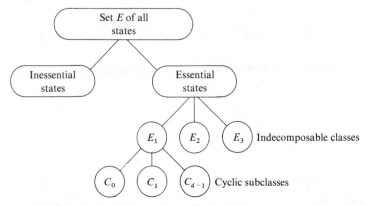

Figure 39. Classification of states of a Markov chain in terms of arithmetic properties of the probabilities p_{ij}^n.

Consider a subclass C_p. If we suppose that a particle is in the set C_0 at the initial time, then at time $s = p + dt, t = 0, 1, \dots$, it will be in the subclass C_p. Consequently, with each subclass C_p we can connect a new Markov chain with transition matrix $(p_{ij}^d)_{i, j \in C_p}$, which is indecomposable and aperiodic. Hence if we take account of the classification that we have outlined (see the summary in Figure 39) we infer that in studying problems on limits of probabilities $p_{ij}^{(n)}$ we can restrict our attention to *aperiodic indecomposable chains.*

3. PROBLEMS

1. Show that the relation "↔" is transitive.

2. For Example 1, §5, show that when $0 < p < 1$, all states belong to a single class with period $d = 2$.

3. Show that the Markov chains discussed in Examples 4 and 5 of §5 are aperiodic.

§3. Classification of the States of a Markov Chain in Terms of Asymptotic Properties of the Probabilities $p_{ii}^{(n)}$

1. Let $\mathbb{P} = \|p_{ij}\|$ be the transition matrix of a Markov chain,

$$f_{ii}^{(k)} = \mathsf{P}_i\{X_k = i, X_l \neq i, 1 \le l \le k - 1\} \tag{1}$$

and for $i \neq j$

$$f_{ij}^{(k)} = \mathsf{P}_i\{X_k = j, X_l \neq j, 1 \le l \le k - 1\}. \tag{2}$$

For $X_0 = i$, these are respectively the *probability of first return to state i at time k*, and the *probability of first arrival at state j at time k*.

Using the strong Markov property (1.16), we can show as in (I.12.38) that

$$p_{ij}^{(n)} = \sum_{k=1}^{n} f_{ij}^{(k)} p_{ij}^{(n-k)}. \tag{3}$$

For each $i \in E$ we introduce

$$f_{ii} = \sum_{n=1}^{\infty} f_{ii}^{(n)}, \tag{4}$$

which is the probability that a particle that leaves state i will sooner or later return to that state. In other words, $f_{ii} = P_i\{\sigma_i < \infty\}$, where $\sigma_i = \inf\{n \geq 1: X_n = i\}$ with $\sigma_i = \infty$ when $\{\cdot\} = \varnothing$.

We say that a state i is *recurrent* if

$$f_{ii} = 1,$$

and *nonrecurrent* if

$$f_{ii} < 1.$$

Every recurrent state can, in turn, be classified according to whether the *average time of return* is finite or infinite.

Let us say that a recurrent state i is *positive* if

$$\mu_i^{-1} \equiv \left(\sum_{n=1}^{\infty} n f_{ii}^{(n)} \right)^{-1} > 0,$$

and *null* if

$$\mu_i^{-1} \equiv \left(\sum_{n=1}^{\infty} n f_{ii}^{(n)} \right)^{-1} = 0.$$

Thus we obtain the classification of the states of the chain, as displayed in Figure 40.

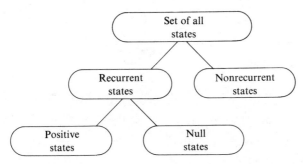

Figure 40. Classification of the states of a Markov chain in terms of the asymptotic properties of the probabilities $p_{ii}^{(n)}$.

2. Since the calculation of the functions $f_{ii}^{(n)}$ can be quite complicated, it is useful to have the following tests for whether a state i is recurrent or not.

Lemma 1

(a) *The state i is recurrent if and only if*

$$\sum_{n=1}^{\infty} p_{ii}^{(n)} = \infty. \tag{5}$$

(b) *If state j is recurrent and $i \leftrightarrow j$ then state i is also recurrent.*

PROOF. (a) By (3),

$$p_{ii}^{(n)} = \sum_{k=1}^{n} f_{ii}^{(k)} p_{ii}^{(n-k)},$$

and therefore (with $p_{ii}^{(0)} = 1$)

$$\sum_{n=1}^{\infty} p_{ii}^{(n)} = \sum_{n=1}^{\infty} \sum_{k=1}^{n} f_{ii}^{(k)} p_{ii}^{(n-k)} = \sum_{k=1}^{\infty} f_{ii}^{(k)} \sum_{n=k}^{\infty} p_{ii}^{(n-k)}$$

$$= f_{ii} \sum_{n=0}^{\infty} p_{ii}^{(n)} = f_{ii} \left(1 + \sum_{n=1}^{\infty} p_{ii}^{(n)} \right).$$

Therefore if $\sum_{n=1}^{\infty} p_{ii}^{(n)} < \infty$, we have $f_{ii} < 1$ and therefore state i is non-recurrent. Furthermore, let $\sum_{n=1}^{\infty} p_{ii}^{(n)} = \infty$. Then

$$\sum_{n=1}^{N} p_{ii}^{(n)} = \sum_{n=1}^{N} \sum_{k=1}^{n} f_{ii}^{(k)} p_{ii}^{(n-k)} = \sum_{k=1}^{N} f_{ii}^{(k)} \sum_{n=k}^{N} p_{ii}^{(n-k)} \leq \sum_{k=1}^{N} f_{ii}^{(k)} \sum_{l=0}^{N} p_{ii}^{(l)},$$

and therefore

$$f_{ii} = \sum_{k=1}^{\infty} f_{ii}^{(k)} \geq \sum_{k=1}^{N} f_{ii}^{(k)} \geq \frac{\sum_{n=1}^{N} p_{ii}^{(n)}}{\sum_{l=0}^{N} p_{ii}^{(l)}} \to 1, \qquad N \to \infty.$$

Thus if $\sum_{n=1}^{\infty} p_{ii}^{(n)} = \infty$ then $f_{ii} = 1$, that is, the state i is recurrent.

(b) Let $p_{ij}^{(s)} > 0$ and $p_{ji}^{(t)} > 0$. Then

$$p_{ii}^{(n+s+t)} \geq p_{ij}^{(s)} p_{ji}^{(n)} p_{ji}^{(t)},$$

and if $\sum_{n=1}^{\infty} p_{jj}^{(n)} = \infty$, then also $\sum_{n=1}^{\infty} p_{ii}^{(n)} = \infty$, that is, the state i is recurrent.

3. From (5) it is easy to deduce a first result on the asymptotic behavior of $p_{ij}^{(n)}$.

Lemma 2. *If state j is nonrecurrent then*

$$\sum_{n=1}^{\infty} p_{ij}^{(n)} < \infty \tag{6}$$

for every i, and therefore

$$p_{ij}^{(n)} \to 0, \qquad n \to \infty. \tag{7}$$

PROOF. By (3) and Lemma 1,

$$\sum_{n=1}^{\infty} p_{ij}^{(n)} = \sum_{n=1}^{\infty} \sum_{k=1}^{n} f_{ij}^{(k)} p_{jj}^{(n-k)} = \sum_{k=1}^{\infty} f_{ij}^{(k)} \sum_{n=0}^{\infty} p_{jj}^{(n)}$$

$$= f_{ij} \sum_{n=0}^{\infty} p_{jj}^{(n)} \le \sum_{n=0}^{\infty} p_{jj}^{(n)} < \infty.$$

Here we used the inequality $f_{ij} = \sum_{k=1}^{\infty} f_{ij}^{(k)} \le 1$, which holds because the series represents the probability that a particle starting at i eventually arrives at j. This establishes (6) and therefore (7).

Let us now consider recurrent states.

Lemma 3. *Let j be a recurrent state with $d(j) = 1$.*

(a) *If i communicates with j, then*

$$p_{ij}^{(n)} \to \frac{1}{\mu_j}, \qquad n \to \infty. \tag{8}$$

If in addition j is a positive state then

$$p_{ij}^{(n)} \to \frac{1}{\mu_j} > 0, \qquad n \to \infty. \tag{9}$$

If, however, j is a null state, then

$$p_{ij}^{(n)} \to 0, \qquad n \to \infty. \tag{10}$$

(b) *If i and j belong to different classes of communicating states, then*

$$p_{ij}^{(n)} \to \frac{f_{ij}}{\mu_j}, \qquad n \to \infty. \tag{11}$$

The proof of the lemma depends on the following theorem from analysis. Let $f_1, f_2, \ldots$ be a sequence of nonnegative numbers with $\sum_{i=1}^{\infty} f_i = 1$, such that the greatest common divisor of the indices j for which $f_j > 0$ is 1. Let $u_0 = 1$, $u_n = \sum_{k=1}^{n} f_k u_{n-k}$, $n = 1, 2, \ldots$, and let $\mu = \sum_{n=1}^{\infty} n f_n$. Then $u_n \to 1/\mu$ as $n \to \infty$. (For a proof, see [F1], §10 of Chapter XIII.)

Taking account of (3), we apply this to $u_n = p_{jj}^{(n)}$, $f_k = f_{jj}^{(k)}$. Then we immediately find that

$$p_{jj}^{(n)} \to \frac{1}{\mu_j},$$

where $\mu_j = \sum_{n=1}^{\infty} n f_{jj}^{(n)}$.

Taking $p_{jj}^{(s)} = 0$ for $s < 0$, we can rewrite (3) in the form

$$p_{ij}^{(n)} = \sum_{k=1}^{\infty} f_{ij}^{(k)} p_{jj}^{(n-k)}. \tag{12}$$

By what has been proved, we have $p_{jj}^{(n-k)} \to \mu_j^{-1}$, $n \to \infty$, for each given k. Therefore if we suppose that

$$\lim_{n} \sum_{k=1}^{\infty} f_{ij}^{(k)} p_{jj}^{(n-k)} = \sum_{k=1}^{\infty} f_{ij}^{(k)} \lim_{n} p_{jj}^{(n-k)}, \tag{13}$$

we immediately obtain

$$p_{ij}^{(n)} \to \frac{1}{\mu_j} \left(\sum_{k=1}^{\infty} f_{ij}^{(k)} \right) = \frac{1}{\mu_j} f_{ij}, \tag{14}$$

which establishes (11).

Recall that f_{ij} is the probability that a particle starting from state i arrives, sooner or later, at state j. State j is recurrent, and if i communicates with j, it is natural to suppose that $f_{ij} = 1$. Let us show that this is indeed the case.

Let f'_{ij} be the probability that a particle, starting from state i, visits state j infinitely often. Clearly $f_{ij} \geq f'_{ij}$. Therefore if we show that, for a recurrent state j and a state i that communicates with it, the probability $f'_{ij} = 1$, we will have established that $f_{ij} = 1$.

According to part (b) of Lemma 1, the state i is also recurrent, and therefore

$$f_{ii} = \sum f_{ii}^{(n)} = 1. \tag{15}$$

Let

$$\sigma_i = \inf\{n \geq 1 : X_n = i\}$$

be the first time (for times $n \geq 1$) at which the particle reaches state i; take $\sigma_i = \infty$ if no such time exists.

Then

$$1 = f_{ii} = \sum_{n=1}^{\infty} f_{ii}^{(n)} = \sum_{n=1}^{\infty} \mathsf{P}_i(\sigma_i = n) = \mathsf{P}_i(\sigma_i < \infty), \tag{16}$$

and consequently to say that state i is recurrent means that a particle starting at i will eventually return to the same state (at a random time σ_i). But after returning to this state the "life" of the particle starts over, so to speak (because of the strong Markov property). Hence it appears that if state i is recurrent the particle must return to it infinitely often:

$$\mathsf{P}_i\{X_n = i \text{ for infinitely many } n\} = 1. \tag{17}$$

Let us now give a formal proof.

Let i be a state (recurrent or nonrecurrent). Let us show that the probability of return to that state at least r times is $(f_{ii})^r$.

For $r = 1$ this follows from the definition of f_{ii}. Suppose that the proposition has been proved for $r = m - 1$. Then by using the strong Markov property and (16), we have

P_i (number of returns to i is greater than or equal to m)

$$= \sum_{k=1}^{\infty} \mathsf{P}_i \left(\begin{matrix} \sigma_i = k, \text{ and the number of returns to } i \text{ after time } k \\ \text{is at least } m - 1 \end{matrix} \right)$$

$$= \sum_{k=1}^{\infty} \mathsf{P}_i(\sigma_i = k) \mathsf{P}_i \left(\begin{matrix} \text{at least } m - 1 \text{ values} \\ \text{of } X_{\sigma_i+1}, X_{\sigma_i+2}, \dots \text{ equal } i \end{matrix} \middle| \sigma_i = k \right)$$

$$= \sum_{k=1}^{\infty} \mathsf{P}_i(\sigma_i = k) \mathsf{P}_i(\text{at least } m - 1 \text{ values of } X_1, X_2, \dots \text{ equal } i)$$

$$= \sum_{k=1}^{\infty} f_{ii}^{(k)} (f_{ii})^{m-1} = f_{ii}^m.$$

Hence it follows in particular that formula (17) holds for a recurrent state i. If the state is nonrecurrent, then

$$\mathsf{P}_i\{X_n = i \text{ for infinitely many } n\} = 0. \tag{18}$$

We now turn to the proof that $f'_{ij} = 1$. Since the state i is recurrent, we have by (17) and the strong Markov property

$$1 = \sum_{k=1}^{\infty} \mathsf{P}_i(\sigma_j = k) + \mathsf{P}_i(\sigma_j = \infty)$$

$$= \sum_{k=1}^{\infty} \mathsf{P}_i \left(\sigma_j = k, \begin{matrix} \text{the number of returns to } i \\ \text{after time } k \text{ is infinite} \end{matrix} \right) + \mathsf{P}_i(\sigma_j = \infty)$$

$$= \sum_{k=1}^{\infty} \mathsf{P}_i \left(\sigma_j = k, \begin{matrix} \text{infinitely many values of} \\ X_{\sigma_i+1}, X_{\sigma_j+2}, \dots \text{ equal } i \end{matrix} \right) + \mathsf{P}_i(\sigma_j = \infty)$$

$$= \sum_{k=1}^{\infty} \mathsf{P}_i(\sigma_j = k) \cdot \mathsf{P}_i \left(\begin{matrix} \text{infinitely many} \\ \text{values of } X_{\sigma_j+1}, X_{\sigma_j-2}, \\ \dots, \text{ equal } i \end{matrix} \middle| \begin{matrix} \sigma_j = k \\ X_{\sigma_j} = j \end{matrix} \right) + \mathsf{P}_i(\sigma_j = \infty)$$

$$= \sum_{k=1}^{\infty} f_{ij}^{(k)} \cdot \mathsf{P}_j \left(\begin{matrix} \text{infinitely many values} \\ \text{of } X_1, X_2, \dots \text{ equal } i \end{matrix} \right) + (1 - f_{ij})$$

$$= \sum_{k=1}^{\infty} f_{ij}^{(k)} f'_{ij} + (1 - f_{ij}) = f'_{ij} f_{ij} + (1 - f_{ij}).$$

Thus

$$1 = f'_{ij} f_{ij} + 1 - f_{ij}$$

and therefore

$$f_{ij} = f'_{ij} \cdot f_{ij}.$$

Since $i \leftrightarrow j$, we have $f_{ij} > 0$, and consequently $f'_{ij} = 1$ and $f_{ij} = 1$.

Therefore if we assume (13), it follows from (14) and the equation $f_{ij} = 1$ that, for communicating states i and j,

$$p_{ij}^{(n)} \to \frac{1}{\mu_j}, \qquad n \to \infty.$$

As for (13), its validity follows from the theorem on dominated convergence together with the remark that

$$p_{jj}^{(n-k)} \to \frac{1}{\mu_j}, \quad n \to \infty, \qquad \sum_{k=1}^{\infty} f_{ij}^{(k)} = f_{ij} \le 1.$$

This completes the proof of the lemma.

Next we consider periodic states.

Lemma 4. *Let j be a recurrent state and let $d(j) > 1$.*

(a) *If i and j belong to the same class (of states), and if i belongs to the cyclic subclass C_r and j to C_{r+a}, then*

$$p_{ij}^{(nd+a)} \to \frac{d}{\mu_j}. \tag{19}$$

(b) *With an arbitrary i,*

$$p_{ij}^{(nd+a)} \to \left[\sum_{r=0}^{\infty} f_{ij}^{(rd+a)} \right] \cdot \frac{d}{\mu_j}, \qquad a = 0, 1, \ldots, d-1. \tag{20}$$

PROOF. (a) First let $a = 0$. With respect to the transition matrix $\mathbb{P}^d$ the state j is recurrent and aperiodic. Consequently, by (8),

$$p_{ij}^{(nd)} \to \frac{1}{\sum_{k=1}^{\infty} k f_{jj}^{(kd)}} = \frac{d}{\sum_{k=1}^{\infty} kd f_{jj}^{(kd)}} = \frac{d}{\mu_j}.$$

Suppose that (19) has been proved for $a = r$. Then

$$p_{ij}^{(nd+r+1)} = \sum_{k=1}^{\infty} p_{ik} p_{kj}^{(nd+r)} \to \sum_{k=1}^{\infty} p_{ik} \cdot \frac{d}{\mu_j} = \frac{d}{\mu_j}.$$

(b) Clearly

$$p_{ij}^{(nd+a)} = \sum_{k=1}^{nd+a} f_{ij}^{(k)} p_{jj}^{(nd+a+k)}, \qquad a = 0, 1, \ldots, d-1.$$

State j has period d, and therefore $p_{jj}^{(nd+a-k)} = 0$, except when $k - a$ has the form $r \cdot d$. Therefore

$$p_{ij}^{(nd+a)} = \sum_{r=0}^{n} f_{ij}^{(rd+a)} p_{jj}^{((n-r)d)}$$

and the required result (20) follows from (19).

This completes the proof of the lemma.

Lemmas 2–4 imply, in particular, the following result about limits of $p_{ij}^{(n)}$.

Theorem 1. *Let a Markov chain be indecomposable (that is, its states form a single class of essential communicating states) and aperiodic.*
    Then:

(a) *If all states are either null or nonrecurrent, then, for all i and j,*

$$p_{ij}^{(n)} \to 0, \qquad n \to \infty; \tag{21}$$

(b) *if all states j are positive, then, for all i,*

$$p_{ij}^{(n)} \to \frac{1}{\mu_j} > 0, \qquad n \to \infty; \tag{22}$$

4. Let us discuss the conclusion of this theorem in the case of a Markov chain with a finite number of states, $E = \{1, 2, \ldots, r\}$. Let us suppose that the chain is indecomposable and aperiodic. It turns out that then it is automatically increasing and positive:

$$\begin{pmatrix} \text{indecomposability} \\ d = 1 \end{pmatrix} \Rightarrow \begin{pmatrix} \text{indecomposability} \\ \text{recurrence} \\ \text{positivity} \\ d = 1 \end{pmatrix} \tag{23}$$

For the proof, we suppose that all states are nonrecurrent. Then by (21) and the finiteness of the set of states of the chain,

$$1 = \lim_n \sum_{j=1}^r p_{ij}^{(n)} = \sum_{j=1}^r \lim_n p_{ij}^{(n)} = 0. \tag{24}$$

The resulting contradiction shows that not all states can be nonrecurrent. Let i_0 be a recurrent state and j an arbitrary state. Since $i_0 \leftrightarrow j$, Lemma 1 shows that j is also recurrent.

Thus all states of an aperiodic indecomposable chain are recurrent.

Let us now show that all recurrent states are positive.

If we suppose that they are all null states, we again obtain a contradiction with (24). Consequently there is at least one positive state, say i_0. Let i be any other state. Since $i \leftrightarrow i_0$, there are s and t such that $p_{i_0 i}^{(s)} > 0$ and $p_{i i_0}^{(t)} > 0$, and therefore

$$p_{ii}^{(n+s+t)} \geq p_{i i_0}^{(s)} p_{i_0 i_0}^{(n)} p_{i_0 i}^{(t)} \to p_{i i_0}^{(s)} \frac{1}{\mu_{i_0}} \cdot p_{i_0 i}^{(t)} > 0. \tag{25}$$

Hence there is a positive ε such that $p_{ii}^{(n)} \geq \varepsilon > 0$ for all sufficiently large n. But $p_{ii}^{(n)} \to 1/\mu_i$ and therefore $\mu_i > 0$. Consequently (23) is established.

Let $\pi_j = 1/\mu_j$. Then $\pi_j > 0$ by (22) and since

$$1 = \lim_n \sum_{j=1}^r p_{ij}^{(n)} = \sum_{j=1}^r \pi_j,$$

the (aperiodic indecomposable) chain is ergodic. Clearly, for all ergodic finite chains,

$$\text{there is an } n_0 \text{ such that } \min_{i,j} p_{ij}^{(n)} > 0 \text{ for all } n \geq n_0. \tag{26}$$

It was shown in §12 of Chapter I that the converse is also valid: (26) implies ergodicity.

Consequently we have the following implications:

$$\begin{pmatrix} \text{indecomposability} \\ d = 1 \end{pmatrix} \Leftrightarrow \begin{pmatrix} \text{indecomposability} \\ \text{recurrence} \\ \text{positivity} \\ d = 1 \end{pmatrix} \Rightarrow \text{ergodicity} \Leftrightarrow (26).$$

However, we can prove more.

Theorem 2. *For a finite Markov chain*

$$\begin{pmatrix} \text{indecomposability} \\ d = 1 \end{pmatrix} \Leftrightarrow \begin{pmatrix} \text{indecomposability} \\ \text{recurrence} \\ \text{positivity} \\ d = 1 \end{pmatrix} \Leftrightarrow (\text{ergodicity}) \Leftrightarrow (26).$$

PROOF. We have only to establish

$$(\text{ergodicity}) \Rightarrow \begin{pmatrix} \text{indecomposability} \\ \text{recurrence} \\ \text{positivity} \\ d = 1 \end{pmatrix}.$$

Indecomposability follows from (26). As for aperiodicity, increasingness, and positivity, they are valid in more general situations (the existence of a limiting distribution is sufficient), as will be shown in Theorem 2, §4.

5. PROBLEMS

1. Consider an indecomposable chain with states $0, 1, 2, \ldots$. A necessary and sufficient condition for it to be nonrecurrent is that the system of equations $u_j = \sum_i u_i p_{ij}$, $j = 0, 1, \ldots$, has a bounded solution such that $u_i \neq c, i = 0, 1, \ldots$.

2. A sufficient condition for an indecomposable chain with states $0, 1, \ldots$ to be recurrent is that there is a sequence $(u_0, u_1, \ldots)$ with $u_i \to \infty, i \to \infty$, such that $u_j \geq \sum_i u_i p_{ij}$ for all $j \neq 0$.

3. A necessary and sufficient condition for an indecomposable chain with states $0, 1, \ldots$ to be recurrent and positive is that the system of equations $u_j = \sum_i u_i p_{ij}, j = 0, 1, \ldots$, has a solution, not identically zero, such that $\sum_i |u_i| < \infty$.

4. Consider a Markov chain with states $0, 1, \ldots$ and transition probabilities

$$p_{00} = r_0, \qquad p_{01} = p_0 > 0,$$

$$p_{ij} = \begin{cases} p_i > 0, & j = i + 1, \\ r_i \geq 0, & j = i, \\ q_i > 0, & j = i - 1, \\ 0 & \text{otherwise.} \end{cases}$$

Let $\rho_0 = 1$, $\rho_m = (q_1 \ldots q_m)/(p_1 \ldots p_m)$. Prove the following propositions.

$$\text{Chain is recurrent} \Leftrightarrow \sum \rho_m = \infty,$$

$$\text{Chain is nonrecurrent} \Leftrightarrow \sum \rho_m < \infty,$$

$$\text{Chain is positive} \Leftrightarrow \sum \frac{1}{p_m \rho_m} < \infty,$$

$$\text{Chain is null} \Leftrightarrow \sum \rho_m = \infty, \sum \frac{1}{p_m \rho_m} = \infty.$$

5. Show that $f_{ik} \geq f_{ij} f_{jk}$ and $\sup_n p_{ij}^{(n)} \leq f_{ij} \leq \sum_{n=1}^{\infty} p_{ij}^{(n)}$.

6. Show that for every Markov chain with countably many states, the limit of $p_{ij}^{(n)}$ always exists in the *Cesàro sense*:

$$\lim_n \frac{1}{n} \sum_{k=1}^{n} p_{ij}^{(k)} = \frac{f_{ij}}{\mu_j}.$$

7. Consider a Markov chain $\xi_0, \xi_1, \ldots$ with $\xi_{k+1} = (\xi_k^+) + \eta_{k+1}$, where $\eta_1, \eta_2, \ldots$ is a sequence of independent identically distributed random variables with $P(\eta_k = j) = p_j$, $j = 0, 1, \ldots$. Write the transition matrix and show that if $p_0 > 0$, $p_0 + p_1 < 1$, the chain is recurrent if and only if $\sum_k k p_k \leq 1$.

§4. On the Existence of Limits and of Stationary Distributions

1. We begin with some necessary conditions for the existence of stationary distributions.

Theorem 1. *Let a Markov chain with countably many states* $E = \{1, 2, \ldots\}$ *and transition matrix* $\mathbb{P} = \|p_{ij}\|$ *be such that the limits*

$$\lim_n p_{ij}^{(n)} = \pi_j,$$

exist for all i and j and do not depend on i.

Then

(a) $\sum_i \pi_i \leq 1$, $\quad \sum_i \pi_i p_{ij} = \pi_j$;

(b) *either all* $\pi_j = 0$ *or* $\sum_j \pi_j = 1$;

(c) *if all* $\pi_j = 0$, *there is no stationary distribution; if* $\sum_i \pi_j = 1$, *then* $\Pi = (\pi_1, \pi_2, \ldots)$ *is the unique stationary distribution.*

PROOF. By Fatou's lemma,

$$\sum_j \pi_j = \sum_j \lim_n p_{ij}^{(n)} \leq \varliminf_n \sum_j p_{ij}^{(n)} = 1.$$

Moreover,

$$\sum_i \pi_i p_{ij} = \sum_i \left(\lim_n p_{ki}^{(n)}\right) p_{ij} \leq \varliminf_n \sum_i p_{ki}^{(n)} p_{ij} = \varliminf_n p_{kj}^{(n+1)} = \pi_j,$$

that is, for each j,

$$\sum_i \pi_i p_{ij} \leq \pi_j.$$

Suppose that

$$\sum_i \pi_i p_{ij_0} < \pi_{j_0}$$

for some j_0. Then

$$\sum_j \pi_j > \sum_j \left(\sum_i \pi_i p_{ij}\right) = \sum_i \pi_i \sum_j p_{ij} = \sum_i \pi_i.$$

This contradiction shows that

$$\sum_i \pi_i p_{ij} = \pi_j \tag{1}$$

for all j.

It follows from (1) that

$$\sum_i \pi_i p_{ij}^{(n)} = \pi_j.$$

Therefore

$$\pi_j = \lim_n \sum_i \pi_i p_{ij}^{(n)} = \sum_i \pi_i \lim_n p_{ij}^{(n)} = \left(\sum_i \pi_i\right)\pi_j,$$

that is, for all j,

$$\pi_j\left(1 - \sum_i \pi_i\right) = 0,$$

from which (b) follows.

Now let $\mathbb{Q} = (q_1, q_2, \ldots)$ be a stationary distribution. Since $\sum_i q_i p_{ij}^{(n)} = q_j$ and therefore $\sum_i q_i \pi_j = q_j$, that is, $\pi_j = q_j$ for all j, this stationary distribution must coincide with $\Pi = (\pi_1, \pi_2, \ldots)$. Therefore if all $\pi_j = 0$, there is no stationary distribution. If, however, $\sum_j \pi_j = 1$, then $\Pi = (\pi_1, \pi_2, \ldots)$ is the unique stationary distribution.

This completes the proof of the theorem.

Let us state and prove a fundamental result on the existence of a unique stationary distribution.

Theorem 2. *For Markov chains with countably many states, there is a unique stationary distribution if and only if the set of states contains precisely one positive recurrent class (of essential communicating states).*

PROOF. Let N be the number of positive recurrent classes.

Suppose $N = 0$. Then all states are either nonrecurrent or are recurrent null states, and by (3.10) and (3.20), $\lim_n p_{ij}^{(n)} = 0$ for all i and j. Consequently, by Theorem 1, there is no stationary distribution.

Let $N = 1$ and let C be the unique positive recurrent class. If $d(C) = 1$ we have, by (3.8),

$$p_{ij}^{(n)} \to \frac{1}{\mu_j} > 0, \qquad i, j \in C.$$

If $j \notin C$, then j is nonrecurrent, and $p_{ij}^{(n)} \to 0$ for all i as $n \to \infty$, by (3.7).

Put

$$q_j = \begin{cases} \dfrac{1}{\mu_j} > 0, & j \in C, \\[2mm] 0, & j \notin C. \end{cases}$$

Then, by Theorem 1, the set $\mathbb{Q} = (q_1, q_2, \ldots)$ is the unique stationary distribution.

Now let $d = d(C) > 1$. Let $C_0, \ldots, C_{d-1}$ be the cyclic subclasses. With respect to $\mathbb{P}^d$, each subclass C_k is a recurrent aperiodic class. Then if i and $j \in C_k$ we have

$$p_{ij}^{(nd)} \to \frac{d}{\mu_j} > 0$$

by (3.19). Therefore on each set C_k, the set d/μ_j, $j \in C_k$, forms (with respect to $\mathbb{P}^d$) the unique stationary distribution. Hence it follows, in particular, that $\sum_{j \in C_k} (d/\mu_j) = 1$, that is, $\sum_{j \in C_k} (1/\mu_j) = 1/d$.

Let us put

$$q_j = \begin{cases} \dfrac{1}{\mu_j}, & j \in C = C_0 + \cdots + C_{d-1}, \\[2mm] 0, & j \notin C, \end{cases}$$

and show that, for the original chain, the set $\mathbb{Q} = (q_1, q_2, \ldots)$ is the unique stationary distribution.

In fact, for $i \in C$,

$$p_{ii}^{(nd)} = \sum_{j \in C} p_{ij}^{(nd-1)} p_{ji}.$$

Then by Fatou's lemma,

$$\frac{d}{\mu_i} = \lim_n p_{ii}^{(nd)} \geq \sum_{j \in C} \varliminf_n p_{ij}^{(nd-1)} p_{ji} = \sum_{j \in C} \frac{1}{\mu_j} p_{ji}$$

and therefore

$$\frac{1}{\mu_i} \geq \sum_{j \in C} \frac{1}{\mu_j} p_{ji}.$$

But

$$\sum_{i \in C} \frac{1}{\mu_i} = \sum_{k=0}^{d-1} \left(\sum_{i \in C_k} \frac{1}{\mu_i} \right) = \sum_{k=0}^{d-1} \frac{1}{d} = 1.$$

As in Theorem 1, it can now be shown that in fact

$$\frac{1}{\mu_i} = \sum_{j \in C} \frac{1}{\mu_j} p_{ji}.$$

This shows that the set $\mathbb{Q} = (q_1, q_2, \ldots)$ is a stationary distribution, which is unique by Theorem 1.

Now let there be $N \geq 2$ positive recurrent classes. Denote them by $C^1, \ldots, C^N$, and let $\mathbb{Q}^i = (q_1^i, q_2^i, \ldots)$ be the stationary distribution corresponding to the class C^i and constructed according to the formula

$$q_j^i = \begin{cases} \dfrac{1}{\mu_j} > 0, & j \in C^i, \\[2mm] 0, & j \notin C^i. \end{cases}$$

Then, for all nonnegative numbers $a_1, \ldots, a_N$ such that $a_1 + \cdots + a_N = 1$, the set $a_1 \mathbb{Q}^1 + \cdots + a_N \mathbb{Q}^N$ will also form a stationary distribution, since

$$(a_1 \mathbb{Q}^1 + \cdots + a_N \mathbb{Q}^N)\mathbb{P} = a_1 \mathbb{Q}^1 \mathbb{P} + \cdots + a_N \mathbb{Q}^N \mathbb{P} = a_1 \mathbb{Q}^1 + \cdots + a_N \mathbb{Q}^N.$$

Hence it follows that when $N \geq 2$ there is a continuum of stationary distributions. Therefore there is a unique stationary distribution only in the case $N = 1$.

This completes the proof of the theorem.

2. The following theorem answers the question of when there is a limit distribution for a Markov chain with a countable set of states E.

Theorem 3. *A necessary and sufficient condition for the existence of a limit distribution is that there is, in the set E of states of the chain, exactly one aperiodic positive recurrent class C such that $f_{ij} = 1$ for all $j \in C$ and $i \in E$.*

PROOF. *Necessity.* Let $q_j = \lim p_{ij}^{(n)}$ and let $\mathbb{Q} = (q_1, q_2, \ldots)$ be a distribution $(q_i \geq 0, \sum_i q_i = 1)$. Then by Theorem 1 this limit distribution is the unique stationary distribution, and therefore by Theorem 2 there is one and only one recurrent positive class C. Let us show that this class has period $d = 1$. Suppose the contrary, that is, let $d > 1$. Let $C_0, C_1, \ldots, C_{d-1}$ be the cyclic subclasses. If $i \in C_0$ and $j \in C_1$, then by (19), $p_{ij}^{(nd+1)} \to d/\mu_j$ and $p_{ij}^{(nd)} = 0$ for all n. But $d/\mu_j > 0$, and therefore $p_{ij}^{(n)}$ does not have a limit as $n \to \infty$; this contradicts the hypothesis that $\lim_n p_{ij}^{(n)}$ exists. Now let $j \in C$ and $i \in E$. Then, by (3.11), $p_{ij}^{(n)} \to f_{ij}/\mu_j$. Consequently $\pi_j = f_{ij}/\mu_j$. But π_j is independent of i. Therefore $f_{ij} = f_{ji} = 1$.

Sufficiency. By (3.11), (3.10) and (3.7),

$$
p_{ij}^{(n)} \to
\begin{cases}
\dfrac{f_{ij}}{\mu_j}, & j \in C, \quad i \in E, \\[2mm]
0, & j \notin C, \quad i \in E.
\end{cases}
$$

Therefore if $f_{ij} = 1$ for all $j \in C$ and $i \in E$, then $q_j = \lim_n p_{ij}^{(n)}$ is independent of i. Class C is positive and therefore $q_j > 0$ for $j \in C$. Then, by Theorem 1, we have $\sum_j q_j = 1$ and the set $\mathbb{Q} = (q_1, q_2, \ldots)$ is a limit distribution.

3. Let us summarize the results obtained above on the existence of a limit distribution, the uniqueness of a stationary distribution and ergodicity, for the case of finite chains.

Theorem 4. *We have the following implications for finite Markov chains:*

$$
\begin{array}{ccc}
(ergodicity) & \overset{\{1\}}{\Leftrightarrow} & \begin{pmatrix} chain\ indecomposable, \\ recurrent,\ positive, \\ with\ d = 1 \end{pmatrix} \\[4mm]
\Downarrow & & \Downarrow \\[4mm]
\begin{pmatrix} limit\ distribution \\ exists \end{pmatrix} & \overset{\{2\}}{\Leftrightarrow} & \begin{pmatrix} there\ exists\ exactly\ one \\ recurrent\ positive\ class \\ with\ d = 1 \end{pmatrix} \\[4mm]
\Downarrow & & \Downarrow \\[4mm]
\begin{pmatrix} unique\ stationary \\ distribution \end{pmatrix} & \overset{\{3\}}{\Leftrightarrow} & \begin{pmatrix} there\ exists\ exactly\ one \\ recurrent\ positive\ class \end{pmatrix}
\end{array}
$$

PROOF. The "vertical" implications are evident. {1} is established in Theorem 2, §3; {2} in Theorem 3; {3} in Theorem 2.

4. PROBLEMS

1. Show that, in Example 1 of §5, neither stationary nor a limit distribution occurs.

2. Discuss the question of stationarity and limit distribution for the Markov chain with transition matrix

$$
\mathbb{P} \begin{pmatrix} \frac{1}{2} & 0 & \frac{1}{2} & 0 \\ 0 & 0 & 0 & 1 \\ \frac{1}{4} & \frac{1}{2} & \frac{1}{4} & 0 \\ 0 & \frac{1}{2} & \frac{1}{2} & 0 \end{pmatrix}.
$$

3. Let $\mathbb{P} = \|p_{ij}\|$ be a finite doubly stochastic matrix, that is, $\sum_{i=1}^{m} p_{ij} = 1, j = 1, \ldots, m$. Show that the stationary distribution of the corresponding Markov chain is the vector $\mathbb{Q} = (1/m, \ldots, 1/m)$.

§5. Examples

1. We present a number of examples to illustrate the concepts introduced above, and the results on the classification and limit behavior of transition probabilities.

EXAMPLE 1. A *simple random walk* is a Markov chain such that a particle remains in each state with a certain probability, and goes to the next state with a certain probability.

The simple random walk corresponding to the graph

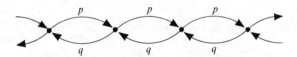

describes the motion of a particle among the states $E = \{0, \pm 1, \ldots\}$ with transitions one unit to the right with probability p and to the left with probability q. It is clear that the transition probabilities are

$$
p_{ij} = \begin{cases} p, & j = i + 1, \\ q, & j = i - 1, p + q = 1, \\ 0 & \text{otherwise.} \end{cases}
$$

If $p = 0$, the particle moves deterministically to the left; if $p = 1$, to the right. These cases are of little interest since all states are inessential. We therefore assume that $0 < p < 1$.

With this assumption, the states of the chain form a single class (of essential communicating states). A particle can return to each state after $2, 4, 6, \ldots$ steps. Hence the chain has period $d = 2$.

Since, for each $i \in E$,

$$p_{ii}^{(2n)} = C_{2n}^n (pq)^n = \frac{(2n)!}{(n!)^2} (pq)^n,$$

then by Stirling's formula (which says $n! \sim \sqrt{2\pi n}\, n^n e^{-n}$) we have

$$p_{ii}^{(2n)} \sim \frac{(4pq)^n}{\sqrt{\pi n}}.$$

Therefore $\sum_n p_{ii}^{(2n)} = \infty$ if $p = q$, and $\sum_n p_{ii}^{(2n)} < \infty$ if $p \neq q$. In other words, the chain is recurrent if $p = q$, but if $p \neq q$ it is nonrecurrent. It was shown in §10, Chapter I, that $f_{ii}^{(2n)} \sim 1/(2\sqrt{\pi}n^{3/2})$, $n \to \infty$, if $p = q = \frac{1}{2}$. Therefore $\mu_i = \sum_n (2n) f_{ii}^{(2n)} = \infty$, that is, all recurrent states are null states. Hence by Theorem 1 of §3, $p_{ij}^{(n)} \to 0$ as $n \to \infty$ for all i and j.

There are no stationary, limit, or ergodic distributions.

EXAMPLE 2. Consider a simple random walk with $E = \{0, 1, 2, \ldots\}$, where 0 is an absorbing barrier:

State 0 forms a unique positive recurrent class with $d = 1$. All other states are nonrecurrent. Therefore, by Theorem 2 of §4, there is a unique stationary distribution

$$\Pi = (\pi_0, \pi_1, \pi_2, \ldots)$$

with $\pi_0 = 1$ and $\pi_i = 0$, $i \geq 1$.

Let us now consider the question of limit distributions. Clearly $p_{00}^{(n)} = 1$, $p_{ij}^{(n)} \to 0$, $j \geq 1$, $i \geq 0$. Let us now show that for $i \geq 1$ the numbers $\alpha(i) = \lim_n p_{i0}^{(n)}$ are given by the formulas

$$\alpha(i) = \begin{cases} \left(\dfrac{q}{p}\right)^i, & p > q, \\[2mm] 1, & p \leq q. \end{cases} \tag{1}$$

We begin by observing that since state 0 is absorbing we have $p_{i0}^{(n)} = \sum_{k \leq n} f_{i0}^{(k)}$ and consequently $\alpha(i) = f_{i0}$, that is, the probability $\alpha(i)$ is the probability that a particle starting from state i sooner or later reaches the null state. By the method of §12, Chapter I (see also §2 of Chapter VII) we can obtain the recursion relation

$$\alpha(i) = p\alpha(i+1) + q\alpha(i-1), \tag{2}$$

with $\alpha(0) = 1$. The general solution of this equation has the form

$$\alpha(i) = a + b(q/p)^i, \tag{3}$$

and the condition $\alpha(0) = 1$ imposes the condition $a + b = 1$.

If we suppose that $q > p$, then since $\alpha(i)$ is bounded we see at once that $b = 0$, and therefore $\alpha(i) = 1$. This is quite natural, since when $q > p$ the particle tends to move toward the null state.

If, on the other hand, $p > q$ the opposite is true: the particle tends to move to the right, and so it is natural to expect that

$$\alpha(i) \to 0, \qquad i \to \infty, \tag{4}$$

and consequently $a = 0$ and

$$\alpha(i) = \left(\frac{q}{p}\right)^i. \tag{5}$$

To establish this equation, we shall not start from (4), but proceed differently.

In addition to the absorbing barrier at 0 we introduce an absorbing barrier at the integral point N. Let us denote by $\alpha_N(i)$ the probability that a particle that starts at i reaches the zero state before reaching N. Then $\alpha_N(i)$ satisfies (2) with the boundary conditions

$$\alpha_N(0) = 1, \qquad \alpha_N(N) = 0,$$

and, as we have already shown in §9, Chapter I,

$$\alpha_N(i) = \frac{\left(\dfrac{q}{p}\right)^i - \left(\dfrac{q}{p}\right)^N}{1 - \left(\dfrac{q}{p}\right)^N}, \qquad 0 \le i \le N. \tag{6}$$

Hence

$$\lim_N \alpha_N(i) = \left(\frac{q}{p}\right)^i$$

and consequently to prove (5) we have only to show that

$$\alpha(i) = \lim_N \alpha_N(i). \tag{7}$$

This is intuitively clear. A formal proof can be given as follows.

Let us suppose that the particle starts from a given state i. Then

$$\alpha(i) = \mathbf{P}_i(A), \tag{8}$$

where A is the event in which there is an N such that a particle starting from i reaches the zero state before reaching state N. If

$$A_N = \{\text{particle reaches } 0 \text{ before } N\},$$

then $A = \bigcup_{N=i+1}^{\infty} A_N$. It is clear that $A_N \subseteq A_{N+1}$ and

$$\mathsf{P}_i\left(\bigcup_{N=i+1}^{\infty} A_N\right) = \lim_{N \to \infty} \mathsf{P}_i(A_N). \qquad (9)$$

But $\alpha_N(i) = \mathsf{P}_i(A_N)$, so that (7) follows directly from (8) and (9).

Thus if $p > q$ the limit $\lim p_{i0}^{(1)}$ depends on i, and consequently there is no limit distribution in this case. If, however, $p \le q$, then in all cases $\lim p_{i0}^{(n)} = 1$ and $\lim p_{ij}^{(n)} = 0, j \ge 1$. Therefore in this case the limit distribution has the form $\Pi = (1, 0, 0, \ldots)$.

EXAMPLE 3. Consider a simple random walk with absorbing barriers at 0 and N:

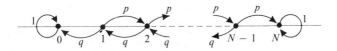

Here there are two positive recurrent classes $\{0\}$ and $\{N\}$. All other states $\{1, \ldots, N-1\}$ are nonrecurrent. It follows from Theorem 1, §3, that there are infinitely many stationary distributions $\Pi = (\pi_0, \pi_1, \ldots, \pi_N)$ with $\pi_0 = a$, $\pi_N = b$, $\pi_1 = \cdots = \pi_{N-1} = 0$, where $a \ge 0$, $b \ge 0$, $a + b = 1$. From Theorem 4, §4 it also follows that there is no limit distribution. This is also a consequence of the equations (Subsection 2, §9, Chapter I)

$$\lim_{n \to \infty} p_{i0}^{(n)} = \begin{cases} \dfrac{\left(\dfrac{q}{p}\right)^i - \left(\dfrac{q}{p}\right)^N}{1 - \left(\dfrac{q}{p}\right)^N}, & p \ne q, \\[3ex] 1 - \dfrac{i}{N}, & p = q, \end{cases} \qquad (10)$$

$$\lim_n p_{iN}^{(n)} = 1 - \lim_n p_{i0}^{(n)} \quad \text{and} \quad \lim_n p_{ij}^{(n)} = 0, 1 \le j \le N - 1.$$

EXAMPLE 4. Consider a simple random walk with $E = \{0, 1, \ldots\}$ and a *reflecting barrier* at 0:

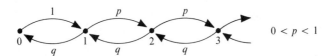

$0 < p < 1$

It is easy to see that the chain is periodic with period $d = 2$. Suppose that $p > q$ (the moving particle tends to move to the right). Let $i > 1$; to determine the probability f_{i1} we may use formula (1), from which it follows that

$$f_{i1} = \left(\frac{q}{p}\right)^{i-1} < 1, \qquad i > 1.$$

All states of this chain communicate with each other. Therefore if state i is recurrent, state 1 will also be recurrent. But (see the proof of Lemma 3 in §3) in that case f_{i1} must be 1. Consequently when $p > q$ all the states of the chain are nonrecurrent. Therefore $p_{ij}^{(n)} \to 0$, $n \to \infty$ for i and $j \in E$, and there is neither a limit distribution nor a stationary distribution.

Now let $p \leq q$. Then, by (1), $f_{i1} = 1$ for $i > 1$ and $f_{11} = q + pf_{21} = 1$. Hence the chain is recurrent.

Consider the system of equations determining the stationary distribution $\Pi = (\pi_0, \pi_1, \dots)$:

$$\pi_0 = \pi_1 q,$$
$$\pi_1 = \pi_0 + \pi_2 q,$$
$$\pi_2 = \pi_1 p + \pi_3 q,$$

that is,

$$\pi_1 = \pi_1 q + \pi_2 q,$$
$$\pi_2 = \pi_2 q + \pi_3 q,$$
$$\cdots \cdots \cdots \cdots$$

whence

$$\pi_j = \left(\frac{p}{q}\right)\pi_{j-1}, \qquad j = 2, 3, \dots.$$

If $p = q$ we have $\pi_1 = \pi_2 = \dots$, and consequently

$$\pi_0 = \pi_1 = \pi_2 = \cdots = 0.$$

In other words, if $p = q$, there is no stationary distribution, and therefore no limit distribution. From this and Theorem 3, §4, it follows, in particular, that in this case all states of the chain are null states.

It remains to consider the case $p < q$. From the condition $\sum_{j=0}^{\infty} \pi_j = 1$ we find that

$$\pi_1\left[q + 1 + \left(\frac{p}{q}\right) + \left(\frac{p}{q}\right)^2 + \cdots\right] = 1,$$

that is

$$\pi_1 = \frac{q - p}{2q}$$

and

$$\pi_j = \frac{q-p}{2q} \cdot \left(\frac{p}{q}\right)^{j-1}; \qquad j \geq 2.$$

Therefore the distribution Π is the unique stationary distribution. Hence when $p < q$ the chain is recurrent and positive (Theorem 2, §4). The distribution Π is also a limit distribution and is ergodic.

EXAMPLE 5. Again consider a simple random walk with *reflecting barriers at* 0 *and* N:

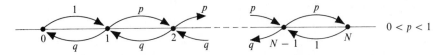

All the states of the chain are periodic with period $d = 2$, recurrent, and positive. According to Theorem 4 of §4, the chain is ergodic. Solving the system $\pi_j = \sum_{i=0}^{N} \pi_i p_{ij}$ subject to $\sum_{i=0}^{N} \pi_i = 1$, we obtain the ergodic distribution

$$\pi_i = \frac{\left(\frac{p}{q}\right)^{i-1}}{1 + \sum_{j=1}^{N-1}\left(\frac{p}{q}\right)^{j-1}}, \qquad 2 \leq j \leq N-1,$$

and

$$\pi_0 = \pi_1 q, \qquad \pi_N = \pi_{N-1} p.$$

2. EXAMPLE 6. It follows from Example 1 that the simple random walk considered there on the integral points of the line is recurrent if $p = q$, but nonrecurrent if $p \neq q$. Now let us consider simple random walks in the plane and in space, from the point of view of recurrence or nonrecurrence.

For the plane, we suppose that a particle in any state (i, j) moves up, down, to the right or to the left with probability $\frac{1}{4}$ (Figure 41).

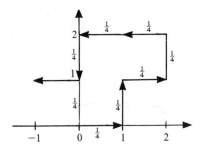

Figure 41. A walk in the plane.

For definiteness, consider the state $(0, 0)$. Then the probability $P_k = p^{(k)}_{(0,0),(0,0)}$ of going from $(0, 0)$ to $(0, 0)$ in k steps is given by

$$P_{2n+1} = 0, \qquad n = 0, 1, 2, \ldots,$$

$$P_{2n} = \sum_{\{(i,j):i+j=n,\,0 \le i \le n\}} \frac{(2n)!}{i!i!j!j!} (\tfrac{1}{4})^{2n}, \quad n = 1, 2, \ldots.$$

Multiplying numerators and denominators by $(n!)^2$, we obtain

$$P_{2n} = (\tfrac{1}{4})^{2n} C^n_{2n} \sum_{i=0}^{n} C^i_n C^{n-i}_n = (\tfrac{1}{4})^{2n} (C^n_{2n})^2,$$

since

$$\sum_{i=0}^{n} C^i_n C^{n-i}_n = C^n_{2n}.$$

Applying Stirling's formula, we find that

$$P_{2n} \sim \frac{1}{\pi n},$$

and therefore $\sum P_{2n} = \infty$. Consequently the state $(0, 0)$ (likewise any other) is *recurrent*.

It turns out, however, that in *three or more dimensions* the symmetric random walk is *nonrecurrent*. Let us prove this for walks on the integral points (i, j, k) in space.

Let us suppose that a particle moves from (i, j, k) by one unit along a coordinate direction, with probability $\tfrac{1}{6}$ for each.

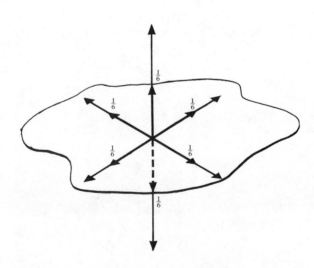

Then if P_k is the probability of going from $(0, 0, 0)$ to $(0, 0, 0)$ in k steps, we have

$$P_{2n+1} = 0, \qquad n = 0, 1, \ldots,$$

$$P_{2n} = \sum_{\{(i, j):0 \le i+j \le n,\, 0 \le i \le n,\, 0 \le j \le n\}} \frac{(2n)!}{(i!)^2 (j!)^2 ((n-i-j)!)^2} (\tfrac{1}{6})^{2n}$$

$$= \frac{1}{2^{2n}} C_{2n}^n \sum_{\{(i, j):0 \le i+j \le n,\, 0 \le i \le n,\, 0 \le j \le n\}} \left[\frac{n!}{i! j! (n-i-j)!} \right]^2 (\tfrac{1}{3})^{2n}$$

$$\le C_n \frac{1}{2^{2n}} C_{2n}^n \frac{1}{3^n} \sum_{\{(i, j):0 \le i+j \le n,\, 0 \le i \le n,\, 0 \le j \le n\}} \frac{n!}{i! j! (n-i-j)!} (\tfrac{1}{3})^n$$

$$= C_n \frac{1}{2^{2n}} C_{2n}^n \frac{1}{3^n}, \qquad n = 1, 2, \ldots, \tag{11}$$

where

$$C_n = \max_{\{(i, j):0 \le i+j \le n,\, 0 \le i \le n,\, 0 \le j \le n\}} \left[\frac{n!}{i! j! (n-i-j)!} \right]. \tag{12}$$

Let us show that when n is large, the max in (12) is attained for $i \sim n/3$, $j \sim n/3$. Let i_0 and j_0 be the values at which the max is attained. Then the following inequalities are evident:

$$\frac{n!}{j_0! (i_0 - 1)! (n - j_0 - i_0 + 1)!} \le \frac{n!}{j_0! i_0! (n - j_0 - i_0)!},$$

$$\frac{n!}{j_0! (i_0 + 1)! (n - j_0 - i_0 - 1)!} \le \frac{n!}{(j_0 - 1)! i_0! (n - j_0 - i_0 + 1)!}$$

$$\le \frac{n!}{(j_0 + 1)! i_0! (n - j_0 - i_0 - 1)!},$$

whence

$$n - i_0 - 1 \le 2j_0 \le n - i_0 + 1,$$

$$n - j_0 - 1 \le 2i_0 \le n - j_0 + 1,$$

and therefore we have, for large n, $i_0 \sim n/3$, $j_0 \sim n/3$, and

$$C_n \sim \frac{n!}{\left[\left(\frac{n}{3} \right)! \right]^3}.$$

By Stirling's formula,

$$C_n \frac{1}{2^{2n}} C_{2n}^n \frac{1}{3^n} \sim \frac{3\sqrt{3}}{2\pi^{3/2} n^{3/2}},$$

and since

$$\sum_{n=1}^{\infty} \frac{3\sqrt{3}}{2\pi^{3/2}n^{3/2}} < \infty,$$

we have $\sum_n P_{2n} < \infty$. Consequently the state $(0, 0, 0)$, and likewise any other state, is nonrecurrent. A similar result holds for dimensions greater than 3.

Thus we have the following result (Pólya):

Theorem. *For R^1 and R^2, the symmetric random walk is recurrent; for R^n, $n \geq 3$, it is nonrecurrent.*

3. PROBLEMS

1. Derive the recursion relation (1).

2. Establish (4).

3. Show that in Example 5 all states are aperiodic, recurrent, and positive.

4. Classify the states of a Markov chain with transition matrix

$$\mathbb{P} = \begin{pmatrix} p & q & 0 & 0 \\ 0 & 0 & p & q \\ p & q & 0 & 0 \\ 0 & 0 & p & q \end{pmatrix},$$

where $p + q = 1$, $p \geq 0$, $q \geq 0$.

Historical and Bibliographical Notes

Introduction

The history of probability theory up to the time of Laplace is described by Todhunter [T1]. The period from Laplace to the end of the nineteenth century is covered by Gnedenko and Sheinin in [K10]. Maistrov [M1] discusses the history of probability theory from the beginning to the thirties of the present century. There is a brief survey in Gnedenko [G4]. For the origin of much of the terminology of the subject see Aleksandrova [A3].

For the basic concepts see Kolmogorov [K8], Gnedenko [G4], Borovkov [B4], Gnedenko and Khinchin [G6], A. M. and I. M. Yaglom [Y1], Prohorov and Rozanov [P5], Feller [F1, F2], Neyman [N3], Loève [L7], and Doob [D3]. We also mention [M3] which contains a large number of problems on probability theory.

In putting this text together, the author has consulted a wide range of sources. We mention particularly the books by Breiman [B5], Ash [A4, A5], and Ash and Gardner [A6], which (in the author's opinion) contain an excellent selection and presentation of material.

For current work in the field see, for example, *Annals of Probability* (formerly *Annals of Mathematical Statistics*) and *Theory of Probability and its Applications* (translation of *Teoriya Veroyatnostei i ee Primeneniya*).

Mathematical Reviews and *Zentralblatt für Mathematik* contain abstracts of current papers on probability and mathematical statistics from all over the world.

For tables for use in computations, see [A1].

Chapter I

§1. Concerning the construction of probabilistic models see Kolmogorov [K7] and Gnedenko [G4]. For further material on problems of distributing objects among boxes see, e.g., Kolchin, Sevastyanov and Chistyakov [K3].

§2. For other probabilistic models (in particular, the one-dimensional Ising model) that are used in statistical physics, see Isihara [I2].

§3. Bayes's formula and theorem form the basis for the "Bayesian approach" to mathematical statistics. See, for example, De Groot [D1] and Zacks [Z1].

§4. A variety of problems about random variables and their probabilistic description can be found in Meshalkin [M3].

§5. A combinatorial proof of the law of large numbers (originating with James Bernoulli) is given in, for example, Feller [F1]. For the empirical meaning of the law of large numbers see Kolmogorov [K7].

§6. For sharper forms of the local and integrated theorems, and of Poisson's theorem, see Borovkov [B4] and Prohorov [P3].

§7. The examples of Bernoulli schemes illustrate some of the basic concepts and methods of mathematical statistics. For more detailed discussions see, for example, Cramér [C5] and van der Waerden [W1].

§8. Conditional probability and conditional expectation with respect to a partition will help the reader understand the concepts of conditional probability and conditional expectation with respect to σ-algebras, which will be introduced later.

§9. The ruin problem was considered in essentially the present form by Laplace. See Gnedenko and Sheinin [K10]. Feller [F1] contains extensive material from the same circle of ideas.

§10. Our presentation essentially follows Feller [F1]. The method for proving (10) and (11) is taken from Doherty [D2].

§11. Martingale theory is throughly covered in Doob [D3]. A different proof of the ballot theorem is given, for instance, in Feller [F1].

§12. There is extensive material on Markov chains in the books by Feller [F1], Dynkin [D4], Kemeny and Snell [K2], Sarymsakov [S1], and Sirazhdinov [S8]. The theory of branching processes is discussed by Sevastyanov [S3].

Chapter II

§1. Kolmogorov's axioms are presented in his book [K8].

§2. Further material on algebras and σ-algebras can be found in, for example, Kolmogorov and Fomin [K8], Neveu [N1], Breiman [B5], and Ash [A5].

§3. For a proof of Carathéodory's theorem see Loève [I7] or Halmos [H1].

§§4–5. More material on measurable functions is available in Halmos [H1].

§6. See also Kolmogorov and Fomin [K8], Halmos [H1], and Ash and Gardner [A6]. The Radon–Nikodým theorem is proved in these books. The inequality

$$P(|\xi| \geq \varepsilon) \leq \frac{E\xi^2}{\varepsilon^2}$$

is sometimes called Chebyshev's inequality, and the inequality

$$P(|\xi| \geq \varepsilon) \leq \frac{E|\xi|^r}{\varepsilon^r}, \qquad r > 0,$$

is called *Markov's inequality*.

For Pratt's lemma see [P2].

§7. The definitions of conditional probability and conditional expectation with respect to a σ-algebra were given by Kolmogorov [K8]. For additional material see Breiman [B5] and Ash [A5]. The result quoted in the Corollary to Theorem 5 can be found in [M5].

§8. See also Borovkov [B4], Ash [A5], Cramér [C5], and Gnedenko [G4].

§9. Kolmogorov's theorem on the existence of a process with given finite-dimensional distribution is in his book [K8]. For Ionescu–Tulcea's theorem see also Neveu [N1] and Ash [A5]. The proof in the text follows [A5].

§§10–11. See also Kolmogorov and Fomin [K9], Ash [A5], Doob [D3], and Loève [L7].

§12. The theory of characteristic functions is presented in many books. See, for example, Gnedenko [G4], Gnedenko and Kolmogorov [G5], Ramachandran [R1], Lukacs [L8], and Lukacs and Laha [L9]. Our presentation of the connection between moments and semi-invariants follows Leonov and Shiryayev [L4].

§13. See also Ibragimov and Rozanov [I1], Breiman [B5], and Liptser and Shiryayev [L5].

Chapter III

§1. Detailed investigations of problems on weak convergence of probability measures are given in Gnedenko and Kolmogorov [G5] and Billingsley [B3].

§2. Prohorov's theorem appears in his paper [P4].

§3. The monograph [G5] by Gnedenko and Kolmogorov studies the limit theorems of probability theory by the method of characteristic functions. See also Billingsley [B3]. Problem 2 includes both Bernoulli's law of large numbers and Poisson's law of large numbers (which assumes that $\xi_1, \xi_2, \ldots$ are independent and take only two values (1 and 0), but in general are differently distributed: $P(\xi_i = 1) = p_i$, $P(\xi_i = 0) = 1 - p_i$, $i \geq 1$).

§4. Concerning "nonclassical" conditions for the validity of the central limit theorem, see Zolotarev [Z2, Z3] and Rotar [R3]. The statement and proof of Theorem 1 were given by Rotar. The lemma in Subsection 6 is also due to him.

§5. Here the presentation follows Gnedenko and Kolmogorov [G5] and Ash [A5].

§6. The proof follows Sazonov [S2].

§7. See also Valkeila [V1].

Chapter IV

§1. Kolmogorov's zero-or-one law appears in his book [K8]. For the Hewitt–Savage zero-or-one law see also Borovkov [B4], Breiman [B5], and Ash [A5].

§§2–4. Here the fundamental results were obtained by Kolmogorov and Khinchin (see [K8] and the references given there). See also Petrov [P1] and Stout [S9]. For probabilistic methods in number theory see Kubilius [K11].

Chapter V

§§1–3. Our exposition of the theory of (strict sense) stationary random processes is based on Breiman [B5], Sinai [S7], and Lamperti [I2]. The simple proof of the maximal ergodic theorem was given by Garsia [G1].

Chapter VI

§1. The books by Rozanov [R4], and Gihman and Skorohod [G2, G3] are devoted to the theory of (wide sense) stationary random processes. Example 6 was frequently presented in Kolmogorov's lectures.

§2. For orthogonal stochastic measures and stochastic integrals see also Doob [D3], Gihman and Skorohod [G3], Rozanov [R4], and Ash and Gardner [A6].

§3. The spectral representation (2) was obtained by Cramér and Loève (see, for example, [I7]). The same representation (in different language) is contained in Kolmogorov [K5]. Also see Doob [D3], Rozanov [R4], and Ash and Gardner [A6].

§4. There is a detailed exposition of problems of statistical estimation of the covariance function and spectral density in Hannan [H2, H3].

§§5–6. See also Rozanov [R4], Lamperti [L2], and Gihman and Skorohod [G2, G3].

§7. The presentation follows Lipster and Shiryayev [L5].

Chapter VII

§1. Most of the fundamental results of the theory of martingales were obtained by Doob [D3]. Theorem 1 is taken from Meyer [M4]. Also see Meyer and Dellacherie [M5], Lipster and Shiryayev [15], and Gihman and Skorohod [G3].

§2. Theorem 1 is often called the theorem "on transformation under a system of optional stopping" (Doob [D3]). For the identities (14) and (15) and Wald's fundamental identity see Wald [W2].

§3. Chow and Teicher [C3] contains an illuminating study of the results presented here, including proofs of the inequalities of Khinchin, Marcinkiewicz and Zygmund, Burkholder, and Davis. Theorem 2 was given by Lenglart [L3].

§4. See Doob [D3].

§5. Here we follow Kabanov, Liptser and Shiryayev [K1], Engelbert and Shiryayev [E1], and Neveu [N2]. Theorem 4 and the example were given by Liptser.

§6. This approach to problems of absolute continuity and singularity, and the results given here, can be found in Kabanov, Liptser and Shiryayev [K1]. Theorem 6 was obtained by Kabanov.

§7. Theorems 1 and 2 were given by Novikov [N4]. Lemma 1 is a discrete analog of Girsonov's lemma (see [K1]).

§8. The exposition follows Liptser and Shiryayev [L6].

Chapter VIII

§1. For the basic definitions see Dynkin [D4], Ventzel [V2], Doob [D3], and Gihman and Skorohod [G3]. The existence of regular transition probabilities such that the Kolmogorov–Chapman equation (9) is satisfied for all $x \in R$ is proved in [N1] (corollary to Proposition V.2.1) and in [G3] (Volume I, Chapter II, §4). Kuznetsov (see Abstracts of the Twelfth European Meeting of Statisticians, Varna, 1979) has established the validity (which is far from trivial) of a similar result for Markov processes with continuous times and values in universal measurable spaces.

§§2–5. Here the presentation follows Kolmogorov [K4], Borovkov [B4], and Ash [A4].

References†

[A1]   M. Abramovitz and I. A. Stegun, editors. *Handbook of Mathematical Functions with Formulas, Graphs and Mathematical Tables*. National Bureau of Standards, Washington, D.C., 1964.

[A2]   P. S. Aleksandrov. *Einführung in die Mengenlehre und die Theorie der reellen Funktionen*. DVW, Berlin, 1956.

[A3]   N. V. Aleksandrova. *Mathematical Terms* [*Matematicheskie terminy*]. Vysshaia Shkola, Moscow, 1978.

[A4]   R. B. Ash. *Basic Probability Theory*. Wiley, New York, 1970.

[A5]   R. B. Ash. *Real Analysis and Probability*. Academic Press, New York, 1972.

[A6]   R. B. Ash and M. F. Gardner. *Topics in Stochastic Processes*. Academic Press, New York, 1975.

[B1]   S. N. Bernshtein. Chebyshev's work on the theory of probability (in Russian), in *The Scientific Legacy of P. L. Chebyshev* [*Nauchnoe nasledie P. L. Chebysheva*], pp. 43–68, Akademiya Nauk SSSR, Moscow–Leningrad, 1945.

[B2]   S. N. Bernshtein. *Theory of Probability* [*Teoriya veroyatnosteĭ*], 4th ed. Gostehizdat, Moscow, 1946.

[B3]   P. Billingsley. *Convergence of Probability Measures*. Wiley, New York, 1968.

[B4]   A. A. Borovkov. *Wahrscheinlichkeitstheorie: eine Einführung*. Birkhäuser, Basel–Stuttgart, 1976.

[B5]   L. Breiman. *Probability*. Addison-Wesley, Reading, MA, 1968.

[C1]   P. L. Chebyshev. *Theory of Probability: Lectures Given in 1879 and 1880* [*Teoriya veroyatnosteĭ: Lektsii akad. P. L. Chebysheva chitannye v 1879, 1880 gg.*]. Edited by A. N. Krylov from notes by A. N. Lyapunov. Moscow–Leningrad, 1936.

[C2]   Y. S. Chow, H. Robbins, and D. Siegmund. *Great Expectations: The Theory of Optimal Stopping*. Houghton-Mifflin, Boston, 1971.

† Translator's note: References to translations into Russian have been replaced by references to the original works. Russian references have been replaced by their translations whenever I could locate translations; otherwise they are reproduced (with translated titles). Names of journals are abbreviated according to the forms used in *Mathematical Reviews* (1982 version).

[C3]   Y. S. Chow and H. Teicher. *Probability Theory: Independence, Interchanga-bility, Martingales.* Springer-Verlag, New York, 1978.

[C4]   Kai-Lai Chung. *Markov Chains with Stationary Transition Probabilities.* Springer-Verlag, New York, 1967.

[C5]   H. Cramér, *Mathematical Methods of Statistics.* Princeton University Press, Princeton, NJ, 1957.

[D1]   M. H. De Groot. *Optimal Statistical Decisions.* McGraw-Hill, New York, 1970.

[D2]   M. Doherty. An amusing proof in fluctuation theory. *Lecture Notes in Mathe-matics,* no. 452, 101–104, Springer-Verlag, Berlin, 1975.

[D3]   J. L. Doob. *Stochastic Processes.* Wiley, New York, 1953.

[D4]   E. B. Dynkin. *Markov Processes.* Plenum, New York, 1963.

[E1]   H. J. Engelbert and A. N. Shiryayev. On the sets of convergence and generalized submartingales. *Stochastics* **2** (1979), 155–166.

[F1]   W. Feller. *An Introduction to Probability Theory and Its Applications,* vol. 1, 3rd ed. Wiley, New York, 1968.

[F2]   W. Feller. *An Introduction to Probability Theory and Its Applications,* vol. 2, 2nd ed. Wiley, New York, 1966.

[G1]   A. Garcia. A simple proof of E. Hopf's maximal ergodic theorem. *J. Math. Mech.* **14** (1965), 381–382.

[G2]   I. I. Gihman [Gikhman] and A. V. Skorohod [Skorokhod]. *Introduction to the Theory of Random Processes.* Saunders, Philadelphia, 1969.

[G3]   I. I. Gihman and A. V. Skorohod. *Theory of Stochastic Processes,* 3 vols. Springer-Verlag, New York–Berlin, 1974–1979.

[G4]   B. V. Gnedenko. *Lehrbuch der Wahrscheinlichkeitstheorie.* Akademische Verlagsgesellschaft, Berlin, 1967.

[G5]   B. V. Gnedenko and A. N. Kolmogorov. *Limit Distributions for Sums of Independent Variables.* Addison-Wesley, Cambridge, MA, 1954.

[G6]   B. V. Gnedenko and A. Ya. Khinchin. *Elementary Introduction to the Theory of Probability.* Freeman, San Francisco, 1961.

[H1]   P. R. Halmos. *Measure Theory.* Van Nostrand, New York, 1950.

[H2]   E. J. Hannan. *Time Series Analysis.* Methuen, London, 1960.

[H3]   E. J. Hannan. *Multiple Time Series.* New York, Wiley, 1970.

[I1]   I. A. Ibragimov and Yu. V. Linnik. *Independent and Stationary Sequences of Random Variables.* Walters-Noordhoff, Groningen, 1971.

[I2]   I. A. Ibragimov and Yu. A. Rozanov. *Gaussian Random Processes.* Springer-Verlag, New York, 1978.

[I3]   A. Isihara. *Statistical Physics.* Academic Press, New York, 1971.

[K1]   Yu. M. Kabanov, R. Sh. Liptser, and A. N. Shiryayev. On the question of the absolute continuity and singularity of probability measures. *Math. USSR-Sb.* **33** (1977), 203–221.

[K2]   J. Kemeny and L. J. Snell. *Finite Markov Chains.* Van Nostrand, Princeton, 1960.

[K3]   V. F. Kolchin, B. A. Sevastyanov, and V. P. Chistyakov. *Random Allocations.* Halsted, New York, 1978.

[K4]   A. N. Kolmogorov, Markov chains with countably many states. *Byull. Moskov. Univ.* **1** (1937), 1–16 (in Russian).

[K5]   A. N. Kolmogorov. Stationary sequences in Hilbert space. *Byull. Moskov. Univ. Mat.* **2** (1941), 1–40 (in Russian).

[K6]   A. N. Kolmogorov, The contribution of Russian science to the development of probability theory. *Uchen. Zap. Moskov. Univ.* 1947, no. 91, 56ff. (in Russian).

[K7]   A. N. Kolmogorov, Probability theory (in Russian), in *Mathematics: Its Contents, Methods, and Value* [*Matematika, ee soderzhanie, metody i znachenie*]. Akad. Nauk SSSR, vol. 2, 1956.

[K8]   A. N. Kolmogorov. *Foundations of the Theory of Probability*. Chelsea, New York, 1956.

[K9]   A. N. Kolmogorov and S. V. Fomin. *Elements of the Theory of Functions and Functional Analysis*. Graylock, Rochester, NY, 1957.

[K10] A. N. Kolmogorov and A. P. Yushkevich, editors. *Mathematics of the Nineteenth Century* [*Matematika XIX veka*]. Nauka, Moscow, 1978.

[K11] J. Kubilius. *Probabilistic Methods in the Theory of Numbers*. American Mathematical Society, Providence, 1964.

[L1]   J. Lamperti. *Probability*. Benjamin, New York, 1966.

[L2]   J. Lamperti. *Stochastic Processes*. Springer-Verlag, New York, 1977.

[L3]   E. Lenglart. Relation de domination entre deux processus. *Ann. Inst. H. Poincaré*. Sect. B (N.S.) **13** (1977), 171–179.

[L4]   V. P. Leonov and A. N. Shiryayev. On a method of calculation of semi-invariants. *Theory Probab. Appl.* **4** (1959), 319–329.

[L5]   R. S. Liptser and A. N. Shiryayev. *Statistics of Random Processes*. Springer-Verlag, New York, 1977.

[L6]   R. Sh. Liptser and A. N. Shiryayev. A functional central limit theorem for semimartingales. *Theory Probab. Appl.* **25** (1980), 667–688.

[L7]   M. Loève. *Probability Theory*. Springer-Verlag, New York, 1977–78.

[L8]   E. Lukacs. *Characteristic Functions*. Hafner, New York, 1960.

[L9]   E. Lukacs and R. G. Laha. *Applications of Characteristic Functions*. Hafner, New York, 1964.

[M1]   D. E. Maistrov. *Probability Theory: A Historical Sketch*. Academic Press, New York, 1974.

[M2]   A. A. Markov. *Calculus of Probabilities* [*Ischislenie veroyatnosteĭ*], 3rd ed. St. Petersburg, 1913.

[M3]   L. D. Meshalkin. *Collection of Problems on Probability Theory* [*Sbornik zadach po teorii veroyatnosteĭ*]. Moscow University Press, 1963.

[M4]   P.-A. Meyer, Martingales and stochastic integrals, I. *Lecture Notes in Mathematics*, no. 284. Springer-Verlag, Berlin–New York, 1972.

[M5]   P.-A. Meyer and C. Dellacherie. Probabilities and potential. *North-Holland Mathematical Studies*, no. 29. Hermann, Paris; North-Holland, Amsterdam, 1978.

[N1]   J. Neveu. *Mathematical Foundations of the Calculus of Probability*. Holden-Day, San Francisco, 1965.

[N2]   J. Neveu. *Discrete Parameter Martingales*. North-Holland, Amsterdam, 1975.

[N3]   J. Neyman. *First Course in Probability and Statistics*. Holt, New York, 1950.

[N4]   A. A. Novikov. On estimates and the asymptotic behavior of the probability of nonintersection of moving boundaries by sums of independent random variables. *Math. USSR-Izv.* **17** (1980), 129–145.

[P1]   V. V. Petrov. *Sums of Independent Random Variables*. Springer-Verlag, Berlin–New York, 1975.

[P2]   J. W. Pratt. On interchanging limits and integrals. *Ann. Math. Stat.* **31** (1960), 74–77.

[P3]   Yu. V. Prohorov [Prokhorov]. Asymptotic behavior of the binomial distribution. *Uspekhi Mat. Nauk* **8**, no. 3(55) (1953), 135–142 (in Russian).

[P4]   Yu. V. Prohorov. Convergence of random processes and limit theorems in probability theory. *Theory Probab. Appl.* **1** (1956), 157–214.

[P5]   Yu. V. Prohorov and Yu. A. Rozanov. *Probability Theory*. Springer-Verlag, Berlin–New York, 1969.

[R1]   B. Ramachandran. *Advanced Theory of Characteristic Functions.* Statistical Publishing Society, Calcutta, 1967.

[R2]   A. Rényi. *Probability Theory,* North-Holland, Amsterdam, 1970.

[R3]   V. I. Rotar. An extension of the Lindeberg–Feller theorem. *Math. Notes* **18** (1975), 660–663.

[R4]   Yu. A. Rozanov. *Stationary Random Processes* [*Statsionarnye sluchainye protsessy*]. Fizmatgiz, Moscow, 1963.

[S1]   T. A. Sarymsakov. *Foundations of the Theory of Markov Processes* [*Osnovy teorii protsessov Markova*]. GITTL, Moscow, 1954.

[S2]   V. V. Sazonov. Normal approximation: Some recent advances. *Lecture Notes in Mathematics,* no. 879. Springer-Verlag, Berlin–New York, 1981.

[S3]   B. A. Sevyastyanov [Sewastjanow]. *Verzweigungsprozesse.* Oldenbourg, Munich–Vienna, 1975.

[S4]   A. N. Shiryayev. *Random Processes* [*Sluchainye processy*]. Moscow State University Press, 1972.

[S5]   A. N. Shiryayev. *Probability, Statistics, Random Processes* [*Veroyatnost, statistika, sluchainye protsessy*], vols. I and II. Moscow State University Press, 1973, 1974.

[S6]   A. N. Shiryayev. *Statistical Sequential Analysis* [*Statisticheskii posledovatelnyi analiz*]. Nauka, Moscow, 1976.

[S7]   Ya. G. Sinaĭ. *Introduction to Ergodic Theory* [*Vvedenie v ergodicheskuyu teoriyu*]. Erevan University Press, 1973.

[S8]   S. H. Sirazhdinov. *Limit Theorems for Stationary Markov Chains* [*Predelnye teoremy dlya odnorodnyh tsepeĭ Markova*]. Akad. Nauk Uzbek. SSR, Tashkent, 1955.

[S9]   W. F. Stout. *Almost Sure Convergence.* Academic Press, New York, 1974.

[T1]   I. Todhunter. *A History of the Mathematical Theory of Probability from the Time of Pascal to that of Laplace.* Macmillan, London, 1865.

[V1]   E. Valkeila. A general Poisson approximation theorem. *Stochastics* **7** (1982), 159–171.

[V2]   A. D. Ventzel. *Course in the Theory of Random Processes* [*Kurs teorii sluchainyh protsessov*]. Nauka, Moscow, 1975.

[W1]   B. L. van der Waerden. *Mathematical Statistics.* Springer-Verlag, Berlin–New York, 1969.

[W2]   A. Wald. *Sequential Analysis.* Wiley, New York, 1947.

[Y1]   A. M. and I. M. Yaglom. *Wahrscheinlichkeit und Information.* DVW, Berlin, 1960; *Probabilité et Information.* Dunod, Paris, 1969.

[Z1]   S. Zacks. *The Theory of Statistical Inference.* Wiley, New York, 1971.

[Z2]   V. M. Zolotarev. A generalization of the Lindeberg–Feller theorem. *Theory Probab. Appl.* **12** (1967), 606–618.

[Z3]   V. M. Zolotarev. Théorèmes limites pour les sommes de variables aléatoires indépendantes qui ne sont pas infinitésimales. *C.R. Acad. Sci. Paris.* Ser. A–B **264** (1967), A799–A800.

Index of Symbols

Index